I belong to:

S. HODSON.

I belong to:

# The World of Food

# The World of Food

## Eva Medved

**Prentice Hall**    Needham, Massachusetts    Englewood Cliffs, New Jersey

## CREDITS

Program Manager: **Marita A. Sullivan**
Art Director: **L. Christopher Valente**
Contributing Writer: **Barbara A. Marchilonis**
Production Editor: **Dorothy R. Spence**
Design: **Sheaff Design, Inc.**
Design Production: **Richard Dalton**
Design Production Assistant: **Linda Dana Willis**
Preparation Services Manager: **Martha E. Ballentine**
Senior Buyer: **Annie Puciloski**
Cover Design: **Martucci Studio**

ISBN: 0-13-965690-1
10 9 8 7 6 5 4 3 2

Prentice-Hall of Australia, Pty, Ltd., Sydney
Prentice-Hall Canada Inc., Toronto
Prentice-Hall Hispanoamericana, S.A., Mexico
Prentice-Hall of India Private Ltd., New Delhi
Prentice-Hall International (UK) Limited, London
Prentice-Hall of Japan, Inc., Tokyo
Prentice-Hall of Southeast Asia Pte. Ltd., Singapore
Editora Prentice-Hall Do Brasil Ltda., Rio de Janeiro

**A Simon & Schuster Company**

## REVIEWERS

**M. Sue Blass**
Chairman, Home Economics Department
Valhalla High School
El Cajon, CA 92019

**Jenna Carnes**
Consumer-Homemaking Teacher
Chillicothe High School
Chillicothe, OH 45601

**Sharon Halvorsen**
Teacher of Home Economics
Holmdel High School
Holmdel, NJ 07712

**R. Penniston Hayes**
Teacher of Home Economics
Foods and Nutrition
Bloomfield High School
Bloomfield, NJ 07003

**M. Elizabeth Juriga**
Teacher of Foods and Nutrition
(Home Economics)
Rancocas Valley Regional High School
Mt. Holly, NJ 08060

**Rony B. Lohse**
Department Head, Vocational Home Economics
Bellbrook High School
Bellbrook, OH 45305

**Linda McNamara**
Home Economics Teacher/Coordinator
Bloomfield High School
Bloomfield, NJ 07003

**Carol D. Otis**
Home Economics Teacher
Benjamin Franklin Middle School
Teaneck, NJ 07666

**Janis Holt Richards**
Home Economics Teacher/Coordinator
Roselle Park High School
Roselle Park, NJ 07204

**Barbara E. Stacy**
Vocational Home Economics
Poland Seminary High School
Poland, OH 44514

# Contents

## Unit 3

# Food Management

# Food Around the World

# UNIT 6

# Looking Ahead

# Features

## Careers

## International

## Nutrition

## Technology

# Unit 1

# Food and Your World

1  Decisions About Food
2  Technology and Choices

# 1 Decisions About Food

## As you read, think about:

- why you need food.
- why the range of food choices has increased.
- how to prevent food-borne illnesses.
- why foods are cooked.
- how foods are packaged.
- how your emotions, habits, culture, and family affect your choice of food.
- why foods are processed.
- how to conserve food and energy resources.

**Vocabulary**
nutrients
enrichment
fortification
food-borne
  illness
toxins
food poisoning
nutrient density
physiological
hunger
appetite
processing
synthetic foods

Did you know that you are what you eat? Your body consists of an orderly arrangement of cells, tissues, and organs. Components of your body continuously need replacement. This process of replacement is carried on by using nutrients and the energy from nutrients. **Nutrients** are the chemical building blocks the body needs for nourishment. Your body cells are very energetic and sensitive, and they require a wide variety of nutrients to sustain the activities that promote growth and maintain health. The food you eat continuously replenishes the energy you burn and makes it possible for you to renew the worn-out components of your body.

# The Expanding World of Food

The world of food—the choices for human nourishment—has been expanding ever since people learned to raise crops and livestock instead of relying merely on what they could gather or hunt. As later generations learned to increase and vary their food productivity,

the diet familiar to us today slowly took shape. More recently, advances in technology have made possible both imitation and substitute foods, which have some advantages over the natural foods they replace.

## Substitute and Imitation Foods

As technology has progressed, a number of products have been created to replace natural foods for improved flavor or usability, longer storage life, reduced cost, or to substitute for a natural food that is unavailable. You are probably familiar with margarine as a substitute for butter, and hydrogenated shortening for lard. Imitation cream, ice cream, and whipping cream tend to be less expensive than their natural counterparts, but they often contain coconut oil, a more saturated fat than the butter fat it replaces, with no reduction in kilocalories.

Some manufactured foods may be less nutritious substitutes for the natural foods they attempt to replace. Imitation juices—whether canned, frozen, or powdered—may contain as much or more vitamin C as natural juice, but lack other vitamins and minerals found in real

Today, as in the Middle Ages, food is produced by farming, but the methods are very different. Do you think the Medieval farmers (left) would think this lettuce could grow without soil?

Not all of these products are natural juice. Which ones are probably the most nutritious? Why? What are the advantages and disadvantages of the other juice products?

juices. Some imitation juice products may have a high sugar and water content, and they often contain little or no natural juice.

## Adding Nutrients

Technology also aids in the enrichment and fortification processes which add nutrients to foods. When nutrients are added to replace, at least in part, those removed by refining or other manufacturing techniques, the process is called **enrichment.** Cereals, flour, and flour products are examples of foods that are often enriched.

Foods are sometimes supplemented with nutrients that are naturally lacking. This process is called **fortification.** For example, vitamin D is present in few foods and in small amounts, but it is required for the absorption and use of calcium. Therefore, it is often added to milk, which is a major source of calcium in the diets of most people. Many forms of milk and margarine are fortified with vitamin D. Fortified milk is a reliable and better source of vitamin D than is raw milk.

## Food Safety

For the most part, the food products you have to choose from are nutritious, safe to eat, of high quality, and convenient. They can be prepared so that they will be wholesome and pleasing. Occasionally, however, food can cause illness. A **food-borne illness** is caused by eating contaminated food. Food may be contaminated by poisonous substances called **toxins.** Some plants naturally develop toxins. You may know

Some toxins occur naturally in plants. It takes an expert to distinguish between the two poisonous Jack-o'Lantern mushrooms (top) and the edible chanterelles (bottom).

that eating certain kinds of wild mushrooms can cause illness. Over the years, humans have learned not to consume foods containing natural toxins, or they have learned to remove the toxins before eating those foods. Food-borne illnesses can also occur when foreign substances contaminate food. *Microorganisms,* such as bacteria, or insects and/or their eggs, occasionally find their way into a food product. Perhaps you have seen green mold on bread that has been kept too long, or have smelled "spoiled" milk or eggs that were not refrigerated properly. All of these are contaminated foods, foods that can make you sick. Contamination can also occur during processing and packaging. You have probably heard of canned goods or dairy products recalled by the producer because of salmonella or other bacterial "poisoning."

The discomfort caused by eating contaminated foods is known as **food poisoning.** This gastrointestinal discomfort can last from a few hours to several days and can be mild or severe. Some food-borne illnesses can be fatal. Diseases

## Safety Tip

- Do you know that raw eggs are a common source of food poisoning? Take these preventive measures. Check the date on the egg carton. Check the eggs to make sure that they are not cracked. Keep eggs and products that contain raw eggs, such as mayonnaise, eggnog, and some cake batters refrigerated and away from heat and the sun.

caused by bacteria or viruses may be contracted from food, milk, or water contaminated with microorganisms. The disease organisms themselves can be transmitted by animals, insects, humans, utensils, and equipment. (See pages 124–132.)

Foods are easily contaminated when they are prepared or stored in unsanitary wraps or utensils. Thus, the prevention of food-borne illness requires utmost cleanliness of facilities, equipment, utensils, and persons working with food. All foods should be stored at appropriate temperatures. Despite refrigeration, freezing, and other preservation techniques, a high incidence of food-borne illness still occurs.

## Getting Help from the Experts

As food technologists continue to develop new foods and to find ways to enrich or fortify familiar ones, the world of food continues to expand. The more choices there are available to you, the more important it is for you to look carefully at the nutrient content, quality, and safety of all foods. That way you can determine the best possible diet for you. Nutrition specialists study the characteristics of edible products and keep up with new developments in food production. They provide a wealth of educational

Cleanliness is extremely important in food preparation. Restaurant workers wear aprons, cover long hair, and use spotless utensils to prevent food-borne illnesses.

material to encourage people to consume appropriate and healthful diets. But the final selection is still up to you. This book, in giving you a guided tour through the world of food, will help you understand the information you need in order to make food preparation and consumption both healthful and enjoyable for you.

Scientists tell us that even the most basic foods are made up of combinations of ingredients.

## Food Choices

The world of food provides the essential nutrients for your good health, but you must select foods to provide an assortment of nutrients in good proportion to each other. There is no such thing as "the perfect food." Appropriate combinations of food do provide our nutrient needs. Chemical analysis shows that most foods are themselves a combination of a variety of nutrients such as carbohydrates, fats, proteins, vitamins, minerals, and water.

### Starting with Nutrition

From the world of food, you can choose both traditional and new foods. Begin your selections with foods from the nutrient-rich groups —the Vegetable-Fruit Group, the Bread-Cereal Group, the Milk-Cheese Group, and the Meat-

Poultry-Fish-Beans-Nuts Group—and then add other foods to complement your nutrient and kilocalorie needs. The four food groups are easy to use and will help you put together a nutritious diet. (See pages 57–63.) Nutritious foods are grouped according to similarity of protein, vitamin, and mineral content. There is also a fifth group, which contains foods with less nutritional value and/or a high sugar or fat content. These foods should be used rarely.

Many familiar combination foods, such as the stroganoff being prepared here, contain foods from all four of the basic food groups.

While food combinations such as casseroles and soups do not seem to fit into a specific food group, they are often very nutritious foods. These combinations of basic foods can be placed into the food group which reflects their main ingredient. Chapter 3 shows you how to use the food groups when you plan meals.

**Nutrient Density**  Foods that are rich in nutrients and have a low calorie count are said to be nutrient dense. When you select nutrient-dense foods from each of the four food groups, you get essential nutrients without consuming more kilocalories than you need. **Nutrient density** reflects the amount of nutrients provided per calorie; thus, nutrient-dense foods provide more nutrients than kilocalories. Foods that have low nutrient density can be said to have "empty calories." That means that a candy or soft drink, for example, is fattening without providing any worthwhile nutrients. A creamed soup, on the other hand, might be high in kilocalories, but it is also nutrient rich. The soup's calories are not "empty." Even more nutrient dense would be a low-calorie, nutrient-rich dish such as vegetable soup.

**Food and Physiology**  When you look at how various foods contribute different nutrients to your body, you are looking at the relationship between food and health. That relationship was also at the heart of the discussion of food-borne illnesses on page 4. The effect of what you eat on the normal or healthful functioning of your body, its organs, and its processes is the **physiological** effect of food.

At the most basic level, your body needs food to survive. Lack of food results in starvation. Lack of the *right* food—lack of proper nutrition—can result in illness and even death. Since your body requires a variety of nutrients, a balanced diet—one which provides those nutrients in the right proportions—is essential to good health.

While everyone requires a balance of nutrients, some people have particular food needs. They may be allergic to some foods, have a disease requiring them to limit certain kinds of foods, or a need to supplement a particular nutrient. They have a special need to watch their diet. However, everyone who is concerned about good health should be aware of the physiological effects of eating different foods. Later chapters of this book will discuss these effects in more detail.

### Psychological Influences

Some people say that they don't just eat to live; they live to eat. That expression reflects one of the psychological factors of food consumption: eating can be very pleasurable. There are many pleasures associated with eating: taste, aroma, texture, and even the appearance of food are among the most basic. But there are other pleasures that are more closely tied to emotional needs. Some people eat to relieve tension, others to reward themselves for a job well done, and still others to occupy themselves when they are bored. They are not satisfying their **hunger,** the physiological need to eat, when they snack for these reasons. Instead, they are trying to satisfy an **appetite,** or a psychological desire to eat.

Soft drinks contain empty calories. They add to your weight without offering much nutritive value. Low-fat milk, on the other hand, is nutrient dense. It offers a high proportion of nutrition per kilocalorie.

What makes food enjoyable? The aroma and appearance make it pleasurable even before you taste it. So do the setting and companionship of a family meal. There is also the added satisfaction of creating and sharing a well-prepared meal.

Appetite can relate to the habits you have developed over your lifetime. Have you ever vacationed in a different time zone and found that you got hungry at your "old" mealtimes even though you were eating regularly on a new schedule? Time is not the only factor to trigger appetite; association can cause you to desire particular foods in particular circumstances. Do you find you *must* have popcorn at the movies? *Need* to eat when you see others enjoying food? *Crave* a specific snack at bedtime? Does the sight or aroma of a certain food stimulate your appetite even when you are not truly hungry? You must be able to distinguish between true hunger, which indicates your body's *need* for food, and appetite, which is a psychological rather than a physiological reaction.

Think about some of the most memorable meals you have had. What made them special? The taste of the food? The atmosphere? The company? A sense of relaxed acceptances in a group or of being special and elegantly served? What psychological factors influence your consumption and enjoyment of food?

## Sociological and Cultural Influences

Special events—religious or national holidays as well as family celebrations—often revolve around a traditional meal. The customs associated with the meal—including the choice of food—often grow out of the social, cultural, and religious influences on our lives. Religious beliefs sometimes direct which foods may not be eaten at all, which under special circumstances, and which dishes for special celebrations. Cultural influences—the shared language, customs, and values of a society or group—are not so strict but still have a strong impact on a person's

Close friends feel like "one of the family" when they share a casual meal in the kitchen. A more formal, elaborate meal gives added importance to a special occasion or celebration.

While many Americans celebrate holidays with a turkey dinner, the meal below is traditional for Chinese New Year.

influence on your eating habits. Joining friends for a pizza after school or "going on a diet together" are just two ways that your friends can influence what you eat. While sharing food with friends can be a wholesome and pleasant experience, it is also a way that some people get swept into food fads or quack diets. Be sure you contribute some common sense and sound nutritional information to your group's choice of foods.

## Food Availability

The cultural and regional cuisines that developed many generations ago were based partly on what foods were readily available and how well they would keep in a particular climate. People who lived near the sea, for example, ate more fish than those on the wheat-producing prairies. Tropical fruits were plentiful in the diets of those in damp, equatorial regions and almost unknown in colder climates; on the other

Scandinavians get much of their food from their cold, northern waters (top) while tropical cultures make fruit available yearlong.

preference in food. If you grow up in a culture in which spicy food is traditional, you may find other cuisines too bland, while a visitor to your home may not be able to tolerate your "hot" dishes. On the other hand, exploring different ethnic foods, which reflect different cultures, and regional foods, which come from or are popular in particular sections of this country, can be an enjoyable way to increase your appreciation of other countries, areas, and lifestyles.

Family, too, influences not only what you eat but what seems "right" to eat. If your family considers doughnuts suitable only as a dessert, you may find it difficult to eat one for breakfast; it doesn't seem "right" to you. Or having your Thanksgiving turkey without the wild-rice stuffing traditional in your family may make the holiday less of a celebration for you. As you grow up, your friends or peers become a stronger hand, food did not spoil so readily where the temperature and humidity remained low.

Today, with advances in technology and transportation, food availability has a somewhat different meaning than it had only several generations ago. We no longer have to rely on what is locally grown and wait for its seasonal harvest. Many varieties of foods are available in various forms all year at the local supermarket. But again, the more options you have, the more carefully you have to examine your choices. Are out-of-season strawberries really a good choice at four times their summertime price? Do you like the taste and texture of the cheaper frozen ones? Are the more expensive imported berries really better than in-season native ones? Price, as it relates to quality, taste, and your budget, is one way to judge how "available" a food is.

Another consideration is time or convenience. While buying the raw ingredients for a chicken-and-noodle dinner and then preparing it yourself might be the most economical answer to "What are we having tonight?", your available time might be so limited that you consider a frozen prepared dinner instead. But if you had had time available earlier in the week, a more nutritious and economical solution might have been to cook some meals ahead and then freeze or refrigerate them. Having the food you prefer available at the price you can afford often requires a good deal of planning.

**Processing** One of the reasons that more foods are available in more places during all seasons is the development of food **processing,** the intentional treatment given to food before consumption. Foods are processed to prevent perishables from spoiling or deteriorating and to preserve them for future consumption. Spoilage is caused by microorganisms. Deterioration is the result of the action of enzymes, physical damage, or the influence of light, temperature, or oxygen.

The chief methods of food preservation use heat, refrigeration or freezing, dehydration or drying, or additives. Some additives improve the color, texture, flavor, and nutritional value of foods as well as prevent the growth of undesirable microorganisms. Sugar, salt, and vinegar were among the first food additives to be used.

Many people prefer fresh, locally grown fruits and vegetables sold at a farm stand when the produce is in season.

A View of a Stage also ij manner of Fishing for, Curing & Drying of Cod at NEW FOUND LAND: A. The Habit of the Fishermen. B. The Line. C. The manner of Fishing. D. The Dressers of the Fish. E. The Trough into which they throw the Cod when dressed. F. Salt Boxes. G. The manner of carrying the Cod. H. The Cleansing of the Cod. I. A Press to extract the Oyl from the Cods Liver. K. A Cask to receive the Water and Blood that comes from the Livers. L. another Cask to receive the Oyl. M. The manner of drying the Cod.

One of the oldest methods of food preservation is the use of salt curing. The drawing and caption on the left describe the method used in 1738. What method of preservation was used for the smoked whitefish shown below?

Processing can also change agricultural products into other forms which are more suitable, acceptable, or attractive to consumers. In addition, processing makes available certain components, or parts, of foods—such as flour, starch, sugar, and oil—which are not readily available from foods in their original forms.

**Manufactured Foods** In addition to developing food, food scientists and technologists have created new foods from traditional agricultural products and/or nonconventional agricultural products. These manufactured foods are sometimes called fabricated or engineered foods. When they contain one or more ingredients from nonconventional agricultural products, they are regarded as substitutes, or **synthetic foods.** These products may be blended to look and taste very much like the food they imitate. For example, many people find nondairy

Many manufactured foods, such as nondairy creamers, are widely used today.

creamers a satisfactory substitute for cream. Manufactured foods may have added vitamins or minerals and may include synthetic ingredients to enhance their color, flavor, or texture. Manufacturing processes also permit the replacement of animal fat and cholesterol with vegetable fats, making these products suitable for people on fat-and/or cholesterol-restricted diets. For example, cholesterol-free egg substitutes allow these people to enjoy some of their favorite dishes without going over their cholesterol limits.

## Packaging

Have you noticed that different types of food are packed in different ways? Packaging protects each particular food product from physical damage during transportation and handling. It is also designed to protect foods from oxygen, light, moisture, and heat.

You may have seen perforated-film bags for fresh fruits and vegetables, shrink film for poultry and cheese, opaque film to protect cured meats from oxygen, vacuum and nitrogen back-fill packages for luncheon meats, and moisture-proof packaging to prevent frozen food from drying out. Each of these packaging techniques is designed to suit the particular food it protects.

The storage needs of different foods require different packaging.

**Labels** Labels on food packages contain very important information about the products and their use. Labels identify the ingredients, including additives, and often supply nutritional and calorie information. They give directions for preparation and storage of the food as well as "freshness" or expiration dates. The size (in ounces or grams, for example) listed on the package helps you comparison shop for per-serving price. Recipes or coupons are sometimes an added bonus to be found on food packages.

One of the most recent additions to many food packages is the Universal Product Code (UPC) for computerized checkout. Each product has its own UPC symbol or grid which can be "read" by a computer. The items you purchase are recorded by means of this symbol as they pass an electronic optical scanner at the checkout counter. The computer prints the name and price of each item on a screen at the checkout and on your sales receipt.

From this label, what can you tell about the nutrient values of the product?

| NUTRITION INFORMATION PER SERVING | |
|---|---|
| SERVING SIZE | 4 OZ.—CONDENSED |
|  | (8 OZ. AS PREPARED—226 g) |
| SERVINGS PER CONTAINER | 2½ |
| CALORIES | 70 |
| PROTEIN (GRAMS) | 3 |
| TOTAL CARBOHYDRATES (GRAMS) | 8 |
| SIMPLE SUGARS (GRAMS) | 1 |
| COMPLEX CARBOHYDRATES (GRAMS) | 7 |
| FAT (GRAMS) | 3 |
| SODIUM | 870mg/serving |

| PERCENTAGE OF U.S. RECOMMENDED DAILY ALLOWANCES (U.S. RDA) | | | |
|---|---|---|---|
| PROTEIN | 4 | RIBOFLAVIN | 2 |
| VITAMIN A | 50 | NIACIN | 4 |
| VITAMIN C | * | CALCIUM | * |
| THIAMINE | 2 | IRON | 4 |

*CONTAINS LESS THAN 2% OF THE U.S. RDA OF THIS NUTRIENT.

## For Review

1. What is nutrient density? Why is it important to know whether a food is nutrient dense?
2. What is the difference between hunger and appetite?
3. What are three psychological reasons that people snack?
4. What is the influence of culture on eating habits?
5. What factors determine whether a food product is available for your use?
6. Why are foods processed? What are the chief methods of processing?
7. What are the purposes of packaging? What can you learn from package labels?

# Management— The Key

Good management is the key to efficient use of time, energy, money, equipment, foods and all other resources in the production of high-quality food products. Management includes all of the decision making and planning of the work activities to complete a task. When you are responsible for meals, you are the meal manager. You will see that you will have to consider your goals (aims, objectives) and values (ideals, attitudes) and those of your family when you make decisions and plans. Skillful management of all resources helps you to prepare and serve meals or to complete other tasks with a minimum of time and energy.

There is usually more than one way to complete a task. When you consider what, why, when, and how the task is to be done, you can select the best and quickest way to complete the task satisfactorily.

## Conserving Food Resources

As a meal manager, you will want to conserve all resources, including food resources. Food conservation means no waste of food before or after the meal. You can conserve food by doing the following: (1) buy only quantities of food that can be used before they become spoiled or stale; (2) shop carefully in sanitary markets, and select quality products; (3) quickly transport the purchased food from store to home to avoid spoilage and loss of quality; (4) do not leave perishable foods on the kitchen counter even for a short time; (5) store all foods properly to control waste and to keep foods safe for eating.

Home kitchens are often the sources of food-borne illnesses. Bacteria are present everywhere, even on foods, and are the causes of such illnesses. When the supply of food is more abundant than can be used immediately, preserve it for future use by canning or freezing.

You will also conserve food when you use basic (standardized) recipes, such as those in

Shop wisely and store properly. Buy perishables in quantities that you will use before they spoil, and refrigerate them immediately.

Chapters 12–30. You will read about the selection, language, and use of recipes in Chapter 9. Recipes will help you to use time and energy well, avoid waste, and produce quality products. Remember that any recipe is only as good as the measurements you make.

Every profession or trade has its own set of tools. Tools are as basic to cookery as is the food itself. You will learn about cookery tools and their uses in Chapter 7. Knowing which tool is best for each job is essential. You should know how to handle each tool and the cooking process for which it is suited.

## Energy Conservation

The conservation of energy is a matter of great concern today. There are a number of very practical ways to conserve energy in the preparation of food.

Whether you cook with electricity, gas, wood, coal, or any other fuel, there is always a need to conserve energy. You conserve energy when you cook foods on top of the range if you adjust the heat level of the unit (gas or electric) to provide only enough heat to cook at the desired temperature. Use only pans that fit the unit. Pans that are too large or too small waste heat and, therefore, waste energy. You use much less energy when you select pans with straight sides, a slight curve between the sides and bottom, and tight-fitting lids.

Cook foods only to the desired doneness to save energy. Electric units may be turned off shortly before the food is completely done. When using the oven, you will conserve energy by following these suggestions: (1) preheat the oven only when necessary; (2) use the full capacity of the oven; (3) set the oven 25 degrees lower when baking in glass, ceramic, or stainless steel tools; (4) open the oven door only when necessary; (5) turn off the oven shortly before cooking is completed.

Conserving energy in the use of the refrigerator is also important. Fill the refrigerator to the recommended capacity, and space the items in it to permit circulation of the cold air. The refrigerator and freezer compartments operate most efficiently when properly filled. Be sure to cover all foods: uncovered foods lose liquid into the air, forcing the refrigerator to work longer than is necessary. As with the oven, open the refrigerator door only when necessary.

The dishwasher uses energy to heat water, to operate the motor, and to raise the air temperature during the drying cycle. Operate the dishwasher only when filled to capacity. Use the energy-saver cycles when possible.

## For Review

1. What are three ways to conserve food resources?
2. What are two ways to conserve energy when cooking on a range?
3. List three ways to conserve energy when using the oven.

Save energy by running the dishwasher only when it's full.

# Making More Food Available to the World

Despite vast differences among the nations of the world, all share a common concern—making more food available to all people, and making that food count nutritionally. Technological advances in agriculture, food processing, medicine, and nutrition have contributed much toward these goals.

Nutrition challenges vary with living conditions. Different regions have different problems. However, world nutrition specialists have identified three main obstacles to proper nutrition: a lack in the quality and/or quantity of available food; poor health and unsanitary conditions; and life-style choices or psychological disorders. Consider some of the ways technology is used to overcome the barriers to nutrition.

## Agricultural Technology

Improved irrigation methods have opened up new land areas for farming. New types of farming, such as aquaculture and hydroponics (growing vegetables in nutrient-rich water), increase yields. The use of improved fertilizers and the knowledge of new tools also contribute to bigger yields.

## Biotechnology

Scientists have created new strains of plants through cross-breeding. These hybrids are bred for particular strengths, such as resistance to drought or resistance to certain diseases. Gene splicing is currently being experimented with as a way of producing hybrids that are resistant to diseases.

## Food Technology

Increased knowledge about nutrition and improved food processing have led to food-fortification programs. In some regions of South America where diets lacked protein, vegetable proteins were added to boost the nutritional value of a commonly consumed pasta. In parts of

A bioengineer performs experiments on crops.

Latin America, vitamin A was added to sugar to counter a diet deficiency. In the United States, iodine has been added to salt since 1924.

## Medical Technology

Disease interferes with an individual's ability to absorb essential nutrients. With increased knowledge of diseases and new forms of immunization, people in nations suffering from high disease rates can now be immunized. In addition, some nations now provide vitamin and mineral supplements to groups of people with deficient diets. Improved instruments for research are making it possible to identify the minerals and vitamins missing from some diets.

# The Study of Food

As you continue to study THE WORLD OF FOOD, you will learn about the foods of tomorrow and today; tools used in food preparation; techniques of meal planning, preparation, and service; methods of food preservation; and careers in food service. You will also learn more about the nutritional contribution of different foods and what methods of cookery best preserve those nutrients while providing the most pleasurable dining experience.

## Why Foods Are Cooked

Foods are cooked (1) to make them more palatable, or pleasing to the taste; (2) to develop, enhance, or alter flavor; (3) to improve digestibility; (4) to improve or enhance color; and (5) to destroy disease-carrying organisms and harmful

Dry-heat broiling promotes the browning of foods. The color and texture of this well-browned chicken add to its appeal.

A long, slow-cooking process blends the flavors of ingredients. A crockpot can cook a delicious stew while you are busy elsewhere.

substances that may be found in or on raw food. Nutrients are conserved when recommended temperatures are used and food is not overcooked. Water-soluble nutrients are conserved when foods are cooked in only small quantities of water.

**Palatability** Short periods of cooking (boiling, broiling) will maintain the original palatability of food, while long periods (roasting, baking, simmering) can enhance palatability. When you want to blend the flavors of ingredients in a combination dish (such as a casserole or soup), use a long, slow-cooking process. Dry heat (roasting, broiling) promotes browning, while moist heat (using water or steam) does not. Browned foods have a distinct, pleasing flavor. Microwave cooking, although it has the advantage of thawing, heating, and cooking very quickly, does not brown foods.

16

Microwave cookery has the advantages of quick thawing and rapid cooking. A frozen meal can be prepared in a few minutes.

Famine relief involves the management of food, energy, and financial resources on a worldwide scale.

**Texture**   Cooking usually softens the texture of food. The method you use and the length of cooking time determine how soft the food will become. Overcooking, regardless of method, causes undesirable changes in flavor, color, and texture.

### The Challenge

Your challenge as an individual is to make the best possible choices of food and of preparation techniques for the nutrition and pleasure of the people for whom you manage meals: yourself, family, friends, or perhaps an entire restaurant or dining hall. You will want to conserve your resources—food, energy, and finances —and still create tempting and healthful meals.

Our challenge as a society is similar. We need to produce and conserve both food and energy resources to provide a healthful and pleasing diet for as many of the world's people as possible. We will need to continue to use our technology and, at the same time, develop ways that will not waste or pollute our natural resources. The world's resources are limited and must be conserved and used carefully. The care we take of our environment—air, water, and land—directly affects the abundance and quality of the food we eat.

### For Review

1. What are three reasons food is cooked?
2. What method of cooking is best for blending the flavors of a combination dish? For browning meats?
3. How does cooking usually affect the texture of food?

# 1 Chapter Review

## Summary

Through the years, the variety of food that people can choose from has increased because of the advances of technology. When a person makes a food decision, it should include consideration of the food's nutritional value, since that is important to a person's health. However, influences such as appetite, family customs, holiday celebrations, and culture affect a person's food choices. Another factor that controls diet is food availability. Today there are many more foods available because of food processing and improved packaging.

While some foods are eaten raw, others are cooked. The cooking method should allow for the greatest nutrition. The conservation of food, energy, and financial resources is another important consideration for a meal manager.

## Vocabulary

Use the words below to complete the sentences in the paragraphs.

| | |
|---|---|
| appetite | nutrient density |
| enrichment | nutrients |
| food-borne illness | physiological |
| food poisoning | processing |
| fortification | synthetic foods |
| hunger | toxins |

The chemical building blocks that a body needs for nourishment are called __(1)__. So, to keep a body healthy, a person should try to avoid eating empty calorie foods, which have low __(2)__. The relationship of what a person eats to the normal functioning of the body and its processes is called the __(3)__ effect of food. When a person eats, it may be to satisfy __(4)__ or __(5)__. Occasionally, the food may be poisoned by substances that are called __(6)__. When this happens, a person becomes sick with a __(7)__, which is caused by eating contaminated food. The discomfort caused by eating contaminated food is called __(8)__.

To preserve foods for future use, it is important that they go through a __(9)__ method. Scientists' experiences with this method have led them to create new products called __(10)__, which contain one or more ingredients from nonagricultural products. In addition, technologists have discovered a way to add nutrients to foods through the processes of __(11)__ and __(12)__.

## Chapter Questions

1. Why does a person need food?
2. What three reasons have contributed to the increase of food choices?
3. Why are nutrients sometimes added to foods?
4. How are food technologists now helping consumers?

5. Why is it important to base a diet on the four food groups?

6. How do personal emotions, habits, culture, and family traditions affect people's choice of food?

7. What are some of the processed foods that you eat?

8. What are the advantages of packaged food?

9. What is the Universal Product Code, and how is it used?

10. What considerations are necessary for good food management?

11. Why is it important to manage all resources carefully when you prepare food?

12. What is the proper care that should be given perishable foods?

## Skill Activities

**1. Resource management** Keep a food journal in which you record your experiences in studying about and preparing foods. A notebook would be best for this purpose. Begin your journal by recording ways you managed food resources wisely when you cooked. For example, write the date, and then tell what you prepared and how you conserved food and energy resources. Look at the sample below:

September 15. Today when I baked cookies, I carefully measured the ingredients and did not waste any. I quickly returned the milk, eggs, and shortening to the refrigerator when I was through using them. I also stored the sugar and flour in dry containers. During the baking process, I only opened the oven door to remove the pan when the cookies were done. When I was through baking, I loaded the dishwasher with the dirty utensils, but waited to run it until it was filled to capacity. Then I used the energy-saver cycle.

**2. Social studies** On a sheet of paper, write these headings: perforated-film bags, shrink film, opaque film, vacuum and nitrogen back-filled, and moisture-proof packaging. Now look at the kinds of packaging used for food stored at home. Under the appropriate heading, write the name of the food that uses that kind of packaging.

**3. Critical thinking** Synthetic foods are manufactured to answer a need. Think about the needs for certain kinds of food for which there are currently no products available. If you could create some synthetic foods, what would they be? Write a report that describes your synthetic foods and that tells their benefits.

**4. Reading** Find two processed foods, and compare how each was processed. Then read the list of ingredients to determine whether nutrients and preservatives were added. If they were, make a list of these additives.

# 2 Technology and Choices

## As you read, think about:

- the characteristics of "natural," or "organic," foods.
- why additives are used.
- how and when to use convenience foods.
- which resources influence food choice.

**Vocabulary**
technology
convenience foods
fad diets
food additives
shelf life

The use of machinery, automation, and applied science, or **technology,** has increased the number of food choices that are available on the market today. Products no longer come directly from the field to the kitchen as they did a century ago. Today, most foods come from farms that are often thousands of miles away. They reach the family table only after passing through a food processing plant and being carried by truck, train, or plane to local food markets.

## Foods Today: Facts and Fallacies

Foods today can be purchased in a variety of forms: fresh, canned, frozen, dehydrated, partially prepared, ready-to-serve, and as packaged dry mixes. The boxes, bottles, and jars in supermarkets are often filled with new and improved food products. The idea of convenience was introduced into foods gradually when the first foods were canned, the first milk bottled, and the first bread sliced. These developments eventually led to cake and pastry mixes, and instant, just-add-water foods.

Today, most supermarket food is packaged. Which foods in this turn-of-the-century market needed to be measured and wrapped? Which were sold in packages similar to those used today?

The many prepared and semiprepared food products have revolutionized the task of preparing daily meals. These foods are often called **convenience foods** because they have been processed to shorten preparation or cooking time. They can save time and energy in the kitchen, but they do not eliminate the need to understand the principles of nutrition and food preparation.

The variety of convenience foods today is almost endless. How many different kinds are shown here? What kinds are not shown?

## Organic Nature of Food

Foods are basically composed of carbon, hydrogen, oxygen, and nitrogen. All foods are organic, or natural. However, the terms *organic* and *natural* are often specifically used to identify foods that are not processed in any way, are grown on soils which have no chemical fertilizers, and are not sprayed for pest destruction. These organic foods usually spoil or deteriorate more quickly than do other foods since they have not been processed.

Organic foods are sold in special stores or in special sections of markets. They have no miraculous qualities and are not richer sources of nutrients than other foods. The usual deteriorative changes occur in all foods, organic or otherwise, unless they are processed.

You should be aware that some promoters of organic foods change existing facts to suit their purpose. Vitamins in organic foods are no different from synthetic, or laboratory-produced, vitamins and are not more plentiful than

in regular foods. Salespersons in health-food stores are likely to offer you free medical advice and prescribe one of their products. Their natural-food diets are often very unbalanced nutritionally and can be dangerous. In addition, organic foods are usually more expensive than regular foods.

## Information and Misinformation About Food

Technology not only brings us new foods, it also brings all kinds of information about foods, nutrition, health, and diet. Books, newspapers,

Organic farming does not use chemical fertilizers or pesticides. This man is using fish as a fertilizer.

radio, and television spread information and advertising faster than ever before. Not all of this material is accurate information, however; there can also be misinformation. Myths and fads as well as scientific studies appear in the media. Commercials can be useful to introduce new products or suggest new uses for familiar ones, but advertisers can also mislead consumers by implying exaggerated benefits—such as popularity or romance—for their products. After all, the advertiser's purpose is to *sell* rather than inform. There are even cases in which misinformation is spread by quacks who are trying to sell products they know to be useless or even dangerous.

**Myths About Food**   You probably know that a myth is a story that is partly or totally fictional but that can sometimes have a great influence on a culture or group of people. Myths are often handed down from one generation to another as part of a society's tradition. From the myth of Ceres, the ancient Roman goddess of grain and agriculture, whose activities were said to control seasonal changes, we get the word *cereal.*

While no one believes the myths about Ceres anymore, there are still food myths that are popular today. Particular foods are used to "cure" illnesses or to bring good luck. Many food taboos, or bans on eating particular foods, are based on cultural or family traditions and have no basis in scientific fact. Large numbers of people continue to hold certain beliefs about food even though those beliefs have been scientifically disproven: for example, the myth that brown eggs are more nutritious than white eggs has been proven false by scientists.

**Food Fads**   While food myths come from the past, food fads represent the newest of the new. A fad is a temporary fashion, and its appeal is usually that it's "the latest" rather than the

Each of these foods "had its day" as the "in" thing to serve at parties. Can you name them? What is popular today? Why do you think food fads change so quickly?

most sensible thing. You are familiar with fads in clothing and hair styles. Fads of earlier generations, such as hula hoops or swallowing live goldfish, probably seem foolish to you now. Can you think of any recent food fads? They might include the "in thing" to serve at a party or the newest kind of restaurant. These kinds of fads come and go like other fashions.

There are food fads, however, that can be dangerous. Eating raw goldfish or eating only one type of food, such as grapefruit, to gain strength or lose weight are examples of unhealthful food fads. **Fad diets,** crash diets to lose weight, have always had their followers, but advances in technology have increased their popularity. "New scientific breakthroughs" or "scientifically created" complete liquid diets —often sold at high prices—are tempting to people who look for a shortcut to good health, weight loss, or beauty. So are vitamin fads.

Fad diets come and go as fast as fad foods. What does that tell you about how effective they are?

While large doses of one vitamin may be praised highly as a cure-all one year, megadoses of a different vitamin are likely to be popular the next year. In all cases of food fad and fashion, remember that a *balanced* diet is necessary for good health. Very large doses of nutrients that are beneficial in small amounts are often useless (because the body cannot absorb or store the extra amounts) or dangerous. Relying on one food to the exclusion of others is also unhealthy. Use the knowledge you gain from this book and your own natural common sense before you indulge in any food fads.

**Food Quacks**   Have you ever heard anyone referred to as a "snake-oil salesman"? Generations ago, people would go from town to town selling snake oil or some equally useless or potentially dangerous concoction as a cure for almost everything. They were usually far from town by the time the cheated purchasers had a chance to test the product's benefits.

There are still "snake-oil salesmen" or food quacks today. They write books or place advertisements promoting wonder drugs, amazing cures, complete foods, or superdiets. In general, it's wise to follow this rule: the greater the claim for a food product, the more carefully you should examine its validity. Check with respected scientific or medical sources or with qualified nutritionists. Technology has made great strides, but it has not yet created miracles.

## Additives

Without additives, many of our foods would not exist, and others would have a much shorter

Does this advertisement for a cure-all look old-fashioned? You can probably find similar claims in some magazines or on television.

# POPULAR OPINION

Has decided that Ayer's Sarsaparilla is the best of all blood-purifiers.   Among the numerous complaints for which it is the specific are pimples, boils, carbuncles, scrofulous sores, eczema, humors, headache, dyspepsia, nervous prostration, catarrh, rheumatism, and scrofulous consumption.   For all diseases originating in impure blood, medical men recommend Ayer's Sarsaparilla in preference to any other.   Safe—pleasant—economical.

"For ten years past I have prescribed Ayer's Sarsaparilla and find it highly efficacious in the treatment of all disorders of the blood."—R. R. BOYLE, M. D., *Philadelphia, Pa.*

"I regard Ayer's Sarsaparilla as the best blood medicine on earth, and know of many wonderful cures effected by its use."—J. W. SHIELDS, M. D., *Smithville, Tenn.*

## Ayer's Sarsaparilla

Prepared by Dr. J. C. Ayer & Co., Lowell, Mass.   Sold by all Druggists.

### Has Cured Others, Will Cure You.

storage life. **Food additives** are substances added to foods to improve or protect flavor, color, and texture, and to retain the nutritional qualities. Through animal studies, the safety of the additives must be established by the food producer before they may be added to foods during preparation, processing, or packaging.

Additives serve special needs. A number of additives are identical to the substances found in nature. For example, synthetic vitamins are the same as those found in foods, and are used by your body in the same way. Vitamins and minerals are added to foods to improve the nutrient value and to replace those which have been lost in processing.

*Antioxidants* (ant-ee-OK-suh-dents) prevent undesirable color and flavor changes in vegetables and meat products. Ascorbic acid and vitamin E are natural food antioxidants. The BHA (butylated dehydroxyanisole) and BHT (butylated hydroxytoluene) on labels identify common antioxidants. Bleaching agents such as chlorine dioxide and nitrosyl chloride reduce the time required for aging flour to improve its baking quality.

Natural and synthetic coloring agents are used to improve acceptability and appearance of foods such as carbonated beverages, dairy products, and some meats. The 1960 Color Additive Amendment to the Federal Food, Drug, and Cosmetic Act controls the certification and listing of color additives which may be used in foods, drugs, and cosmetics.

A number of preservatives are used in food products to extend the **shelf life,** or length of time the food remains fresh. These preservatives are identified as antioxidants, inhibitors, or fungicides. Commonly used stabilizers and thickening agents include gelatin, pectins, and vegetable gums (carrageenan). These additives promote the smoothness of confectionery products and frozen desserts and add body (viscosity) to beverages.

You can recognize that most of the foods that are necessary for good health are highly perishable. Meat, milk, fruits, and vegetables would soon spoil if they were not frozen, dehydrated, or preserved by a suitable technique.

Federal, local, state, and city governments exert considerable efforts to protect our food supply. Some of the important federal agencies are the Food and Drug Administration (FDA), the United States Department of Agriculture (USDA), the Federal Trade Commission (FTC), and the United States Public Health Service. In addition, state and local governments also promote the safety of food sold in their areas.

**For Review**

1. What are some advantages of so-called organic, or natural, foods? What are some disadvantages?
2. What is the difference between a food fad and a food myth?
3. What is the difference in the way your body uses vitamins found naturally in food and synthetic vitamins?
4. Describe some of the purposes of food additives.

# Shortcuts in Food Preparation

Convenience foods permit shortcuts in food preparation. The increasing number of convenience foods includes mixes for cakes, cookies, casseroles, breads, salad dressings, soups, frostings, and others. Some need only the addition of water or another ingredient to complete the preparation of the product.

You should consider several points when deciding whether to use a convenience food instead of a similar homemade product. Although convenience foods usually require less time and energy, you should also consider their nutritive value, cost, and quality in comparison to the homemade version, as well as your skill in food preparation.

## Canned Foods

When foods are canned, most of the work of preparation has been done during the canning processes. For example, the cleaning, peeling, slicing, and cooking have all been completed before the food is canned. It is ready to serve or requires only heating. The variety of canned foods includes vegetables, fruits, soups, meats, chicken, fish, puddings, and relishes. Main-dish foods such as stews, spaghetti, and chow mein also come canned. Canned foods can be used

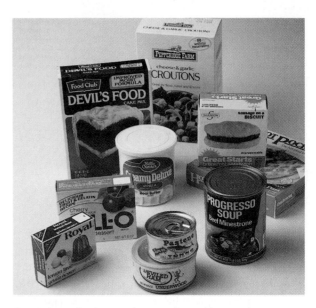

Convenience foods come in many forms. How much preparation time and effort does each of these products save?

This assembly line in a peach cannery does the washing, halving, and coring for you. When you open a can of peaches, they are ready to serve.

# What Goes into a Package?

You've just created a new cookie. It's delicious, and you're sure you'll sell a million packages . . .

Because every food product is unique, developing the right package for your new cookie could be a long and involved process. For months before your cookies can be sold in stores, people such as scientists, food-tasters, and market researchers will test many different packages to determine the right kind for your cookie.

In general, three companies test and create new packaging. The end-user company is your cookie company, the company that will package the cookies. The raw material supplier is the company that sells the foil, plastic, paper, or cardboard that will eventually protect your cookies. The converter company buys the raw materials and actually manufactures the packaging.

## In the Desert and Jungle Rooms

To develop the right package, the companies first identify materials that have successfully protected similar foods in the past. These materials might include foil, different kinds of plastic wrap, and cellophane. The cookies are wrapped in the different materials.

Scientists then place the wrapped cookies in rooms or sealed jars that have different temperatures and levels of humidity. The hot, dry rooms are called desert rooms. The hot, moist rooms are the jungle rooms.

After a set amount of time, the scientists weigh the product in each kind of wrapping. If the cookie wrapped in cellophane, for example, weighs less after three weeks, they know that the cookie has probably lost water. It will not stay moist in cellophane. Sometimes the scientists will test the air surrounding the wrapped cookie in the jar. They take samples of the air and analyze it to determine exactly what qualities of the cookies were lost through the packaging. In these ways, scientists can eliminate some of the less effective packaging materials.

## From Tasting to Your Table

Food-tasters play a vital role in choosing the right package for your cookies. Food-tasters sample the product to see how the packaging materials affect the taste. For example, food-tasters would try your cookies after they had been wrapped in cellophane in the jungle room.

After all the packaging materials have been tested under different conditions—by tasting and by chemical analysis—the materials are chosen. Most packages consist of many layers. For example, your cookie package could consist of plastic wrap on the outside, foil in the middle, and coated paper next to the cookie.

Once the materials are chosen, you have to decide what seal to use, what type of ink to use on the package, what words and pictures you want on it, and how you want it to open and reclose. Then the converter company manufactures the packages, and you are then on your way to selling your first million.

Packaging is often more important than the product itself. What packaging materials can you identify here?

alone or in combination with other foods. Canned vegetables are used in salads, soups, and stews. Undiluted canned soups may be used as cream sauces in casseroles, or over vegetables or meats.

## Frozen Foods

Frozen foods make available a year-round supply of fruits, vegetables, meats, fish, and seafoods. The wide variety of frozen, ready-prepared dishes includes appetizers and desserts as well as main dishes.

Foods are often frozen raw for later cooking, or frozen after they are partially or completely cooked. Meats, fish, and poultry are frequently frozen raw and need to be cooked before eating. Most vegetables are partially cooked before freezing in order to destroy enzymes that cause changes in texture, color, and

flavor. When cooked foods have been frozen, they need only be heated to serving temperature. Some meats, fish, and poultry as well as whole dinners are available as cooked frozen foods. Frozen fruit is ready to serve after defrosting, but frozen juices require dilution with water.

The efficiency (time and energy gained) of using frozen foods depends on the kind of food and the form it replaces. The use of frozen foods saves a considerable amount of preparation and clean-up time. Be sure you consider the time required for defrosting foods, and include it in your meal planning.

## Ready-to-serve Foods

Ready-to-serve foods require little time and effort. They can be eaten as they are or added to other foods. Breads, crackers, sliced cold meats,

Main dishes, side dishes, and desserts can all be prepared from convenient frozen products.

breakfast cereals, cheeses, a variety of jams, jellies, pickles, and bakery products are included in the ready-to-serve category.

## Ready-to-use Foods

Ready-to-use foods are those in which all of the preliminary preparation has been done. They require only cooking or heating to be ready to serve. Foods of this type include instant coffee, tea, cocoa, prepared stuffing, brown-and-serve rolls, instant potatoes, chopped meat, washed spinach, canned foods, some frozen foods, shredded cabbage, and chopped vegetables for both salads and stews.

## Cost of Convenience

The price of convenience foods includes the cost of the food plus the cost of processing, packaging, labor and management, shipping, and marketing. For some prepared mixes, packaging costs may be just as high or higher than the cost of the ingredients themselves. It is difficult to compare the cost of home-prepared foods with commercial mixes because similar products may contain different proportions of ingredients. The cost of a rich, homemade cake may be higher when compared with the cost of a plain cake mix. It is also important to consider the number of servings from a packaged mix and the cost of ingredients such as eggs, milk, or nuts which may have been added to the mix. Convenience foods may cost the same or more than home-prepared foods. However, the difference in price may be made up by the amount of time saved in the kitchen. To the working person, this convenience may be worth the extra cost.

## Ingredients in Convenience Foods

Because the ingredients in convenience foods may not be of the same kind and in the same proportion as those in homemade products, there can be a difference in nutritive values. For example, the flour in a mix may or

You may not think of these (top) as convenience foods, but imagine the time farm families spent baking bread, making cheese, and preserving fruit in order to produce similar products.

may not have been enriched; a minimum of egg, milk, or fat may have been used in an effort to reduce cost. The commercial mix may make use of the highly stabilized fats which do not contain vitamin A. It is important to read the labels on all convenience products so that you know their contents.

However, it is possible that some convenience items can be higher in nutritive value than the fresh products. For example, frozen foods can be more nutritious than fresh foods stored for several days before use.

Many of the convenience foods that are on the market today are those known as dry mixes. Any of those ingredients which can be converted to a dry form are suitable for use in the making of mixes. For example, the most common dry ingredients which are used in cake mixes include flour, some type of leavening agent, some type of shortening, sugar, milk solids, salt, and powdered vanilla.

## Packaging of Convenience Foods

The packages in which convenience foods are sold are designed to protect them from contamination and prevent deterioration caused by contact with air, light, or heat. The most serious problem with convenience foods is prolonged storage, which tends to reduce quality. High temperature and humidity also hasten the rate of deterioration.

Convenience foods, like all other packaged foods, must meet the general requirements of the United States Food and Drug Administration for all foods shipped across state lines. Therefore, convenience foods must be prepared from wholesome foods and must be fit to eat. Each label must list the name of the product, net contents of the package, ingredients used, the nutrient content, name of the manufacturer or distributor, and place of manufacture.

## Cookery Principles

Successful products can be prepared from convenience foods when directions are followed carefully. Better products can be prepared when you understand why specific directions are given. For example, you will make more satisfactory pastry from mixes when you understand that overmixing or handling can develop too much gluten and result in a poor-quality, tough product.

Science and technology created convenience foods within the framework of the basic principles of food preparation. Although convenience foods save the time of assembling, measuring, and mixing ingredients, they have not eliminated the need for learning the basic principles, correct techniques, and basic skills of cookery. For convenience foods to give you the greatest satisfaction, basic cookery principles must be learned, understood, and followed.

Similar convenience products made by various manufacturers may have different formulations and recipes. Therefore, it is necessary to use the other ingredients that are suggested in the directions provided on the package in order to get the best results. Convenience foods practically eliminate the individual errors in ingredient selection and measurement, but they do not eliminate the possibility of failure due to the inability to follow directions accurately.

## When to Use Convenience Foods

It will be easier to know how and when to use convenience foods instead of homemade foods when you give consideration to the quality desired in the final product, your preparation ability, the time available, cost, nutritive value, and the equipment, supplies, or ingredients required. Your meals are likely to be a combination of traditional, prepared-from-ingredients foods and convenience products. The wide range of available foods makes planning ahead and shopping more complicated jobs than ever before —and more exciting.

## Using Convenience Foods Creatively

While convenience foods are designed to produce the same results each time they are used, they do not have to stifle your creativity in the kitchen. You can use convenience foods imaginatively by adding ingredients to them or by using them as ingredients in other dishes. You can even create your own homemade convenience foods and store them for future use.

**Ingredient Convenience** Many mixes are valuable both for their intended purpose of reducing preparation time and effort, and as ingredients for creating new dishes. Soup mixes can go into dips and casseroles or can flavor meats and sauces. A packaged casserole may be a ready-made meal in itself, or the base for a gourmet meal of your own creation. A gelatin mix may be used alone for a light dessert, or you may add fruits or vegetables to make it into a salad.

Packaged croutons can be a crunchy addition to a mixed vegetable salad. When crushed, they become a topping for a casserole or a coating for poultry. Canned or dehydrated soups can be used as the bases for gravies or the sauce for baked dishes. They can also be added to vegetable loaves or croquettes. Frozen cherries or berries can become the chief ingredients in cobblers, pies, or tarts. Precooked rice can replace the potato as an accompaniment to meat, poultry, or other vegetables. Dried vegetables, when reconstituted and added to broth, become a quick soup.

**Homemade Convenience** Products prepared at home can also be convenience foods. For instance, homemade breads, cookies,

Using convenience foods does not have to mean boring meals. These bacon bits, croutons, and dressing add variety to salads.

You can make your own convenience foods. The puréed tomatoes being prepared here can take the place of canned tomatoes.

Chapter 2—Technology and Choices **31**

cakes, and casseroles can be stored in the freezer for later use. The basic ingredients of flour, leavening, salt, and shortening can be made into a dry mix, refrigerated, and used later in making muffins, biscuits, pastry, and cookies. The quality of any of the products made from homemade convenience mixes can be equal to that of those made by conventional methods.

**Creating Variety** Because they are mass-produced, convenience foods often lack variety, but you can use your own creativity to solve this problem. However, before you can be creative with convenience foods, basic cookery principles must be mastered. Creativity through variations in mixes is possible only when the proportions of basic ingredients are not changed. Variety in convenience foods can be achieved in several ways. Different garnishes or ingredients appropriate to the convenience food can be added. Raisins, nuts, spices, herbs, cheese, and bacon are some examples of creative garnishes. (See Chapter 12.) The convenience item can be used as an ingredient in a homemade product such as a pie made with a homemade pastry and a convenience filling. A change in the size and shape or the arrangement of the food will also give some variation and reveal your personality and creative ability. The

widespread use of convenience products presents a challenge to create new food combinations to satisfy the need for a variety in eating.

## Assembling a Good Diet

Modern technology gives you the opportunity to assemble food into healthful eating patterns and to make selections from the greatest variety of food ever available. The world of food is surrounded by the world of management, which involves goals, values, decisions, and actions. You are your own meal manager. You decide what foods your body will receive. The variety of foods available forces you to make choices among them. You as the meal manager must make many decisions—what to serve, when and where to shop, how to prepare, and how and when to serve the foods. Your food decisions involve the resources of money, time, energy, personal effort and skills, and your ability to plan, purchase, prepare, and serve food. Your food choices will be influenced by your early experiences, traditions, positive and negative food associations, and food availability. It is your responsibility, however, to make good choices because they affect your entire life.

When the food groups set the pattern for your food intake (see Chapters 3 and 5), your food choices can contribute adequate nutrients without an excess of kilocalories. Depending upon which foods you select and how you prepare them, the food groups can contribute about 1000 to 1400 kilocalories. Active young adults require more kilocalories than the food-group recommendations provide. Some of the kilocalories still needed could come from larger servings, margarine, salad dressing, sugar, and desserts. Another choice is to use any spare kilocalories for iron-rich and other nutrient-rich foods. Any time more kilocalories are needed

**For Review**

1. List the forms of convenience foods and one advantage of using each.
2. Why is it important to read the labels of convenience foods carefully?
3. List five factors you should consider when deciding whether to use a convenience food instead of a homemade food.
4. What are two ways to use convenience foods to create variety in meals?

It takes planning to assemble a balanced meal from many ingredients. What food groups are represented here? What dishes could be prepared from these ingredients?

than the basic food-group choices provide, they should come through the choices you make carefully rather than unintentionally or impulsively through high-calorie foods or snacks.

When fewer calories are desired, select lean meats, skim or low-fat milk, and hard cheeses. Avoid adding sugar, fat, salad dressing, gravy, or alcohol to your diet. Consume fresh fruits and vegetables to satisfy your appetite, and add variety to your meals by selecting different foods each day. The meal patterns in Chapter 3 make it easy for you to arrange your food choices into meals.

Whatever the source of food or the technology involved in its production, you determine the nutritional adequacy of your diet. You have the opportunity to be well nourished. Whether this goal is reached is a matter of your choice and knowledge. The information you need is in the chapters that follow. The choice is yours.

## For Review

1. Approximately how many kilocalories are provided by a diet based on the four food groups?
2. What is a healthful way to add more kilocalories to your diet?
3. What foods should you select if you want to limit calorie intake?

# 2 Chapter Review

## Summary

Today many convenience foods exist because of the use of additives. These convenience foods have been processed to eliminate or reduce the preparation required for cooking. Although convenience foods reduce the time and effort necessary for preparation, they do not eliminate the importance of knowing the principles of nutrition and food preparation.

The meal manager must plan wisely to serve a nutritious, cost-effective, well-balanced diet. The decision of what to prepare should include considerations of cost, quality, nutritive value, and skill necessary for food preparation. Although much misinformation exists about the benefits or dangers of certain foods, the meal manager should know that all foods are organic and foods labeled as "organic" or "natural" are no more nutritious than regular foods.

## Vocabulary

Match each numbered vocabulary word with its definition.

1. convenience foods
2. fad diets
3. food additives
4. shelf life
5. technology

a. The length of time that food remains fresh.
b. Substances used to improve or protect the flavor, color, and texture of food and to keep its nutritional qualities.
c. The use of machinery, automation, and applied science to increase the number of food choices.
d. Prepared and semiprepared food products that have been processed either to make unnecessary or to reduce the cooking and preparation time.
e. Diets designed to lose weight quickly.

## Chapter Questions

1. How have convenience foods revolutionized the task of meal preparation?
2. What are the characteristics of "natural," or "organic," foods?
3. Describe a recent food fad or fad diet. Tell whether the diet or food is healthy or unhealthy and why.
4. Explain three advantages of additives used in foods.
5. Compare canned and frozen foods.
6. Why is it difficult to compare the cost of ingredients in home-prepared foods with commercial mixes?

7. What are three causes that hasten deterioration in packaged mixes?

8. What must be listed on each convenience food label?

9. Pudding and gelatin mixes are convenience foods that may be used to make other foods. Select one of these, and tell how it can be used as an ingredient to create a new food or to make a homemade product.

10. How can home-prepared products become convenience foods?

11. What are some of the factors that affect a meal manager's decision about what to serve, where to shop, and how to prepare the food?

12. What influences a person's food choices?

## Skill Activities

**1. Decision making** In your food journal or in a card file box, start a collection of recipes that use convenience foods. You can find recipes in magazines, on the packages of convenience foods, and on the display boards in supermarkets. Organize your collection into sections that cover beverages, soups, salads, meats, fish, poultry, casseroles, snacks, breads, cakes, cookies, pies, and desserts. Add to this collection as you discover other interesting recipes.

**2. Resource management** Keep a record for a week of the convenience foods used in your home. Note how and why they were used. Compare your record with those of your classmates.

**3. Communication** Write an invitation to a chef from a local restaurant to speak to your class. Prepare a list of questions that you would like to ask. Include in your list a question about whether the chef uses either commercially prepared or restaurant-prepared convenience foods and how they are used.

**4. Math** Look at the directions on a package of cake mix and at a home recipe for the same kind of cake. Estimate the time necessary for the preparation of each cake. Also, compare the cost of ingredients necessary to make the finished product. (For the purposes of measuring, estimate that one cup equals 8 ounces, a tablespoon equals 0.5 ounces, and a teaspoon equals 0.17 ounces.) Is the cake prepared from the mix or the recipe more cost effective?

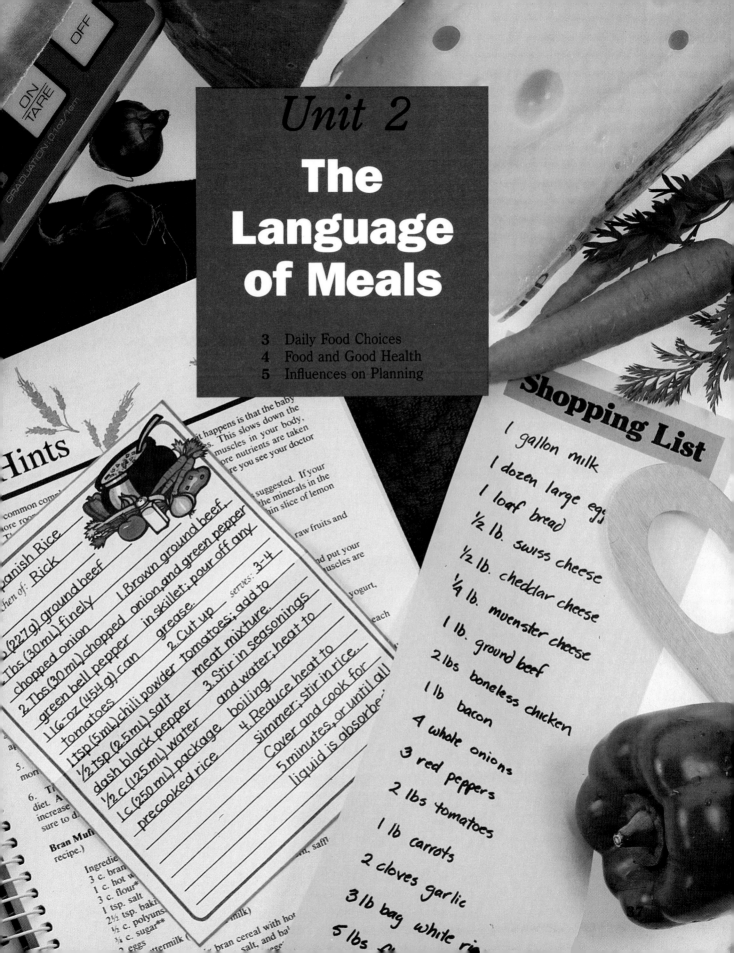

# Unit 2

# The Language of Meals

3 Daily Food Choices
4 Food and Good Health
5 Influences on Planning

# 3 Daily Food Choices

## As you read, think about:

- how to balance kilocalories in your meals.
- the characteristics and sources of carbohydrates, proteins, fats, vitamins, and minerals.
- how each of the different nutrient groups is important for good health.
- how to use the four nutrient-rich groups of the Daily Food Guide to plan meals.

### Vocabulary

kilocalories
carbohydrates
cellulose
fats
cholesterol
proteins
amino acids
complete
  proteins
vitamins
minerals
trace elements
RDA

In the preceding chapters, you learned about the expanding world of food choices and some of the factors that influence what you choose to eat. You looked into the importance of technology in both food production and food preparation. Now you are ready to examine the principles involved in meal planning.

Attractive, nutritious meals do not just happen. They have to be planned. There are several important factors to remember when planning meals. They include your personal nutrient needs, the nutritional needs of those who will eat with you, and the time, energy, and money available to you. Making the meals as attractive and tempting as possible is also a consideration. Your knowledge and skill in food preparation and the equipment you have available will limit any menus you plan. The importance you attach to each meal will also influence your overall planning.

When planning menus, you should think of all the meals for a particular day at the same time. That way you can divide and balance the nutrient requirements among the three meals. Whether you plan simple or elaborate meals, your first responsibility is to make sure the meals provide all the needed nutrients.

## Kilocalories in Your Meals

Your body has a very special need for energy, just as it has for nutrients. The energy needs of your body and the energy your body obtains from food is measured in **kilocalories.** (One kilocalorie is equal to 1000 calories.) Carbohydrates and fats provide most of the body's energy needs, and protein contributes the remainder. Fats contribute 9 kilocalories per gram, while carbohydrates and protein give 4 kilocalories per gram. The amount of fat, carbohydrate, and protein in a food determines its kilocaloric value. Although some foods are rich sources of fat and other foods are rich sources of carbohydrate or protein, most foods contain varying amounts of each energy nutrient.

Because British sailors used to be given limes to prevent scurvy, they acquired the nickname "limeys."

This simple rule will help you identify the energy-rich foods: the greasy, fat-crisp, gooey, sticky, or sweet foods contribute many kilocalories and are therefore energy rich, while the juicy, water-crisp foods have few kilocalories.

Your body needs energy (kilocalories) for play and work and for the various reactions taking place within your body's cells. The kilocalories in the meals you eat should equal those required for your daily work and the work of your body's cells. In other words, kilocalories eaten (coming into the body) should equal the kilocalories consumed (spent in work and cellular activity). When you eat more kilocalories than

The energy-rich, fat-crisp, or gooey-sweet foods (left) contrast with the nutrient-rich, nonfattening, water-crisp foods (right).

your body uses each day, you will gain weight. When you eat fewer kilocalories than your body needs each day, you will lose weight. When the kilocalories taken in equal those spent, your weight remains constant. You will neither gain nor lose weight.

## Maintaining a Desirable Weight

When the weight you maintain is desirable for your age and height, you have reached a kilocaloric balance. This simply means that you are eating the right amount of food to provide the kilocalories your body needs to function. You are eating the kilocalories to match the energy you spend each day. A gain in weight means you are eating more food than is needed to replace the energy you are spending each day. When this happens, you should take a good look at the foods you are choosing as well as when and how much you are eating. The best place to begin cutting down is with the greasy, gooey, sweet foods. These foods quickly add up to a kilocalorie overload, but contribute very few, if any, of the essential nutrients.

The recommended servings from the four nutrient-rich food groups provide most of your nutrient needs and give you about 1300 to 1500 kilocalories (depending upon the foods you choose and their methods of preparation). This amount of energy (1300–1500 kcal) is probably less than your body spends each day and would permit you to lose unwanted weight gradually. When weight loss occurs slowly, your body is given a chance to adjust to the reduced food intake and your weight loss can be permanent.

Whenever more energy is taken into the body than is spent, the body has no choice but to store it as fat in *adipose* (AD-uh-pohss) tissue. Excess kilocalories occurring day after day allow more and more fat to be stored. This leads to obesity. Individuals weighing about 20 percent above desirable weight are said to be obese. Overweight is a serious health problem in the United States. Obese individuals are found in every age group. Obesity detracts from personal appearance, increases the likelihood of cardiovascular diseases, complicates other diseases, and shortens the life span.

There are no easy solutions to overweight or obesity. Kilocalories in excess of need are the direct cause of gained weight, regardless of whatever may be the indirect cause. If miracle diets eliminated excess weight, there would be no overweight people among us today!

A good weight-reduction diet is based on a balanced diet and uses few high-energy foods. It employs cooking techniques that do not add calories, such as broiling, steaming, baking, and boiling. Large servings of fruits and vegetables are substituted for the decreased intake of the energy-rich fats, sugars, and desserts.

Consuming more kilocalories than you need causes weight gain.

### For Review

1. What determines a food's kilocaloric value?
2. What are usually the characteristics of energy-rich (high in kilocalorie) foods?
3. What is a kilocaloric balance?
4. What causes obesity? What are the disadvantages of being overweight?

# Nutrients in Your Meals

You recall that foods contain varying amounts of nutrients and that most foods are made of more than one nutrient. Nutrients are the building blocks of food. They can be classified into six general groups: carbohydrates, fats, proteins, vitamins, minerals, and water.

The nutrients from food serve your body in three general ways. Carbohydrates and fats supply the energy for your work and play; proteins build and repair your body; and vitamins, minerals, and water regulate and protect your body processes.

You will need all of these nutrients as long as you live. However, during periods of rapid growth, from birth through adolescence to adulthood, you will have a greater need for nutrients so that your body can grow and develop.

## Carbohydrates

Carbohydrates are important nutrients in a balanced diet. They are the major suppliers of energy in the diet, and help the body make the best use of proteins.

As their name indicates, **carbohydrates** (kahr-bo-HY-drates) are made up of carbon, hydrogen, and oxygen. There are three types: simple carbohydrates, or sugars; complex carbohydrates, or starches; and cellulose. Most carbohydrates are found naturally in plant foods, although one type of sugar, lactose, is found in milk. "Refined" or "processed" carbohydrates are those taken out of their natural sources; they can then be added to other foods. White table sugar is an example of a refined carbohydrate.

**Sugars** These simple carbohydrates can be divided into two groups. The simple sugars include *glucose* (also called dextrose), *fructose,* and *galactose.* Double sugars, such as *sucrose, lactose,* and *maltose,* are broken down into simple sugars during digestion. All kinds of sugars supply the same amount of energy per gram.

Sugars are not just found in "sweets." Table sugar, made from the sucrose in sugarcane or sugar beets, is what we usually mean when we use the word *sugar* in conversation. But fructose, the sweetest of all the sugars, occurs naturally in ripe fruits and some vegetables; and lactose, or milk sugar, is found in dairy products. When you are checking labels for the ingredients in a food product, you should be aware of all the different kinds of sugars and the variety of terms for sugar products; for example, corn syrup and molasses add sugar content to a product.

**Starches** These complex carbohydrates are broken down into simple sugars during digestion. They are found most often in grain products, rice, and legumes.

**Cellulose** Sometimes called fiber or roughage, **cellulose** (SELL-yuh-lohss) is a complex carbohydrate found in plant cells. It is tough and stringy and does not break down completely during digestion. Therefore, fiber aids in digestion, prevents constipation, and is now thought

All of these very different foods are good sources of carbohydrates. What kind of carbohydrate is found in each?

to prevent some intestinal diseases. Recently, medical and nutritional experts have urged Americans to add more fiber to their diets. Cellulose is found in bran, whole-grain products, some raw vegetables and fruits as well as in legumes and nuts.

While it is true that carbohydrates are energy-rich foods, natural carbohydrates (such as fruits, vegetables, and grains) have a good ratio of nutritional value to kilocalories in addition to providing essential fiber. If you are concerned about your calorie intake, cut down on refined or processed sugars and starches rather than the natural carbohydrates you need to stay healthy. A lack of carbohydrates can cause the body to have difficulty using fats efficiently and to burn protein for energy, instead of using it to build and maintain body cells. A lack of vitality may be a sign that your diet is low in carbohydrates.

### Fats

**Fats** are the most energy-rich nutrients. They provide two and one-fourth times as much energy (calories) as an equivalent weight of carbohydrates or proteins. If they are not used by the body for energy, however, you may find them accumulating as extra pounds. Carbohy-

The cooking methods you use can turn low-fat foods into high-fat dishes. These potatoes originally were a nutrient-rich, nonfattening food. Are they a healthy choice now? Why?

drates and proteins that have not been burned as energy will also be stored by the body as fat.

You probably recognize most of these oily substances as fats: butter, margarine, oil, and the fat layers in meat. You probably also know that egg yolks and whole milk are rich sources of fat. Some foods high in fat may surprise you: walnuts and lean meats, for example, contain fat you cannot see.

Fats help with some essential functions in your body. They supply fatty acids, some of which are essential nutrients. However, all but one of these fatty acids, linoleic acid, can be made by your body and so do not need to be consumed in food. Linoleic acid can be obtained from vegetable oils. Fats also contain certain fat-soluble vitamins that cannot be carried in water. Your body would not be able to use these vitamins without the help of fats. A lack of fats can slow growth and cause unhealthy skin.

**Saturated and Unsaturated Fats** The fatty acids supplied in fats are of two types. *Saturated fats* tend to be solid at room temperature. They include butter, hard cheese, and lard. *Unsaturated fats,* which contain less hydrogen, are liquid at room temperature. They include vegetable oils. Recent medical studies have indicated that saturated fats may cause the body to produce a substance called cholesterol, while *polyunsaturated* (POL-ee-un-SACH-uh-ray-tid) *fats* (fats with the least amount of hydrogen) may actually reduce the level of cholesterol. Nutritionists feel that the American diet is generally too high in fats, and many people are now trying to limit their intake of fats in general and to replace saturated with unsaturated fats in particular. (See Chapter 27 for more information on fats.)

**Cholesterol** While **cholesterol** (kuh-LESS-tuh-rohl) is a substance found normally in all body cells, there is medical evidence that an excess of blood cholesterol can contribute to heart disease. Many people are therefore limiting their intake of foods that are high in cholesterol. These include eggs, organ meats, and some shellfish—all foods of animal origin. Since it is also believed that saturated fats cause the body to produce cholesterol, limiting or eliminating saturated fats is also recommended for people with a high cholesterol level. The body does need cholesterol to manufacture some essential chemicals and to aid digestion, but it can make all the cholesterol it needs. The typical American diet, most experts feel, is too high in cholesterol and cholesterol-producing substances. Many health professionals recommend cutting down on all fats for a more healthful diet.

Complete proteins occur naturally in meats, but they can be made by combining nonmeat foods, such as peanut butter and whole wheat.

## Proteins

All body cells are composed of **proteins.** New cells needed for growth or cells damaged by illness or injury require a supply of proteins from the diet. Even in a healthy adult, proteins are constantly being broken down and need replacement. The human body thus has a constant need for protein supplies. This need is even greater for children and adolescents who are growing quickly and for pregnant women and nursing mothers.

Proteins are also important in making *antibodies,* the body's defense against infection, and in forming *hormones,* which help regulate body processes. If other sources of energy (such as fats and carbohydrates) run low, the body will burn proteins for energy.

**Amino Acids**   Proteins are made up of **amino** (uh-MEE-no) **acids**, which are chemical compounds containing carbon, hydrogen, oxygen, and nitrogen. There are about twenty amino acids. At least eight of these are essential amino acids, which cannot be made by the body. *Essential amino acids* must be supplied by diet; the remaining *nonessential amino acids* can be produced by the body, using the essential eight.

Some foods contain adequate amounts of all the essential amino acids. These are called **complete proteins** or high-quality proteins. Most animal foods are of this type. Usually, a single plant food cannot supply all the essential amino acids in the proper proportion, but combinations of plant foods can make up a high-quality protein meal. Rice with beans is an example of a high-protein food that serves as a staple in the diet of some cultural groups or in regions where meats are not customarily available or affordable. Other complete-protein combinations, such as peanut butter on whole wheat bread, are popular with vegetarians who choose to avoid eating meat.

Because amino acids cannot be stored by the body, you need to replace your supply of them with complete-protein meals every day. It is particularly important to eat a high-protein breakfast since your supply of amino acids is bound to be low after approximately ten hours without food.

A lack of protein can stunt growth and cause fatigue and weakness of the muscles. The resulting lack of antibodies creates a tendency to infection and disease.

### Vitamins

Even though vitamins do not provide energy or build and repair cells, they are a very important part of a healthful diet. **Vitamins** are the complex chemicals that help regulate the chemical reactions necessary for the body's growth and health. You probably know many of the vitamins by their letter names, such as vitamin C, which is found in citrus fruits, and vitamin D, which is added to milk. Some vitamins are also known by their chemical names, such as ascorbic acid for vitamin C. It is helpful, especially when reading labels, to be familiar with both names.

Vitamins can be divided into two groups. The *water-soluble vitamins,* B complex and C, dissolve only in water. They are not usually stored by the body, and excess amounts are flushed out as waste. Thus, water-soluble vitamins need to be replaced daily. The *fat-soluble vitamins*—A, D, E, and K—dissolve only in fats. Since they can be stored by the body, excess amounts are not flushed out and can build up to harmful levels. You should be especially careful of taking large doses of vitamin supplements; a balanced diet should provide all the vitamins you need.

**Vitamin A (retinol)**   This fat-soluble vitamin promotes healthy growth, especially the development of healthy bones and teeth. Vitamin A is also good for the eyes (by preventing night blindness) and for the skin and hair. In addition, it helps prevent infection of the linings of the mouth, nose, throat, and digestive tract.

Vitamin A occurs as retinol and can also be found in a protovitamin (a substance that can be turned into a vitamin by the body) called carotene. *Carotene* gives certain vitamin A-rich foods, such as carrots and pumpkins, their distinctive yellow color, or it mixes with chlorophyll to produce a deep green, as in broccoli. Dairy products, liver, and eggs also contain high proportions of vitamin A.

Because vitamin A is stored by the body, overdoses can occur. Too much vitamin A can lead to headaches, nausea, and skin problems.

These vegetables get their beautiful color from the protovitamin carotene. The presence of what vitamin is indicated by the yellows and deep greens of carotene?

**B Vitamins** This group of related, water-soluble vitamins (referred to as the B-complex vitamins) was once thought to be one vitamin. Now scientists have found that each of the following has a slightly different function.

- Vitamin $B_1$ (thiamin) helps in the use of carbohydrates for energy. It also aids digestion, promotes good appetite, and helps to keep nerves healthy. An extreme deficiency of vitamin $B_1$ can result in the disease *beriberi*. Good sources of vitamin $B_1$ include whole grains, pork and other meats, poultry, fish, and dried beans.
- Vitamin $B_2$ (riboflavin) aids the body in the use of protein and energy foods, promotes good eye function, and maintains smooth skin. A lack of vitamin $B_2$ can cause premature aging. Vitamin $B_2$ occurs in dairy and grain products, eggs, meats, fish, and dark-green vegetables.
- Niacin helps the body use other nutrients and maintains healthy nerves and digestion. Niacin deficiency results in the disease *pellagra* (puh-LAG-ruh). Good sources of niacin are whole grains, dairy products, meat, fish, poultry, and peanuts.
- Folic acid is important for the health of red blood cells. A lack of it causes a form of anemia. Sources of folic acid are deep-green leafy vegetables, grains, meat, and eggs.
- Other B vitamins include $B_6$ (pyridoxine), $B_{12}$ (cobalamins), pantothenic acid, and biotin. All are necessary for health, and must be replaced daily because the body does not store them.

**Vitamin C (ascorbic acid)** This water-soluble vitamin works with calcium to create and maintain healthy bones and teeth. It helps in blood formation and the strengthening of blood-vessel walls. Vitamin C also helps the body fight infection and aids in the healing of cuts and wounds. In addition, it helps form *collagen* (KOL-uh-jen), which binds together the cells of body tissue.

Citrus fruits are not the only foods from which to get vitamin C. All these foods are good sources of that important vitamin.

Citrus fruits are especially good sources of vitamin C. Other fruits, broccoli, and cabbage, as well as mustard, turnip, and collard greens are high in vitamin C.

The disease *scurvy* is caused by a lack of vitamin C. Bleeding gums, bruising easily, and fatigue may also indicate vitamin C deficiency. Some people believe that large amounts of vitamin C prevent or cure colds, but too much vitamin C (more than 100 to 200 milligrams a day) can be harmful and cause diarrhea.

**Vitamin D (calciferol)** This fat-soluble vitamin can be made by the body when the skin is exposed to sunlight. Since it is found naturally in very few foods, the best dietary source of this important nutrient is vitamin D-fortified milk.

Working with calcium and phosphorus, vitamin D helps build and maintain strong bones and teeth. Thus, it is especially important for children, who can develop the disease *rickets* from a long-term deficiency of vitamin D. Even in adults, a lack of vitamin D can cause softening of

Your body makes vitamin D when your skin is exposed to sunlight. The best food source of this nutrient is fortified milk.

the bones. On the other hand, since the body stores vitamin D, overdoses can occur, causing weight loss, nausea, diarrhea, and sometimes even bone deformities.

**Vitamin E (tocopherols)**　This fat-soluble vitamin is important as an antioxidant. That is, it protects cell membranes, vitamin A, and fatty acids from damage caused by too much oxygen. It also aids in the use of energy foods.

Vitamin E is found primarily in oil, shortening, and margarine. Other sources include whole grains, milk, eggs, liver and green leafy vegetables. Because vitamin E is stored by the body, overdoses can occur, causing nausea, dizziness, and blurred vision. Eventually, muscle weakness and extreme fatigue can be caused by too much vitamin E.

**Vitamin K**　This fat-soluble vitamin is important in helping blood to clot properly. The body manufactures vitamin K, but it is also found in dark-green leafy vegetables, cabbage, and cauliflower. Only a small amount of vitamin K is needed for good health.

## Minerals

Minerals are an important part of a healthful diet. Because the body cannot make them, minerals must come from food. **Minerals,** like vitamins, help regulate some body processes.

There are two groups of minerals. Calcium, phosphorus, magnesium, chlorine, potassium, and sodium are needed by the body in large amounts. They are easily found in food. The body needs only small amounts of the second group, called **trace elements,** but they are still vital to health. Iron, iodine, and zinc are the most common trace elements.

**Calcium and Phosphorus**　These two minerals work closely together to build and maintain healthy bones and teeth. Ninety-nine percent of the calcium and eighty percent of the phosphorus in the body are found in bones and teeth. The body continues to need these nutrients for bone maintenance even after growth stops. A lack of calcium in the diet causes the body to take stored calcium out of the bones. This can result in *osteoporosis* (OSS-tee-o-puh-RO-siss), a condition in which bones become porous, fragile, and break easily. Older people, particularly women, often get this condition. Many experts now feel that most American adults do not get enough calcium in their diets. They recommend calcium-rich foods such as dairy products, broccoli, and turnip and mustard greens.

Milk has a particular advantage. It supplies the correct balance of calcium and phosphorus so that they can work together. Too much phosphorus can cause the bones to lose calcium. Some foods, such as soft drinks, have so much phosphorus that they may unbalance this delicate mineral teamwork.

Calcium has other important uses, too. It helps blood to clot and aids in the functioning of the heart and nervous system. Researchers think it may even lower high blood pressure. In

A lack of calcium can lead to osteoporosis, in which bones become porous and brittle. Recently, many experts have emphasized the need for foods rich in calcium to prevent this condition.

addition to working with calcium, phosphorus also has some functions of its own. It helps the body produce energy and use other nutrients. Phosphorus is found in dairy products, whole grains, meats, dried beans, and peas.

**Magnesium** This mineral is important for the health of the nervous system and muscles. It helps *enzymes* (EN-zimes), substances that speed up chemical reactions, to perform their functions, and aids the body in the use of carbohydrates and proteins. Magnesium also forms part of the skeleton, soft tissues, and blood.

A balanced diet should satisfy the body's need for magnesium. Dairy products, eggs, organ meats, whole grains, nuts and leafy green vegetables are among the good sources of the mineral. Some people whose lifestyles do not include good eating habits develop magnesium shortages. A symptom of magnesium deficiency is muscle tremors, or shaking.

**Sodium, Chlorine, and Potassium** These three minerals team up to regulate body fluids. They maintain the water balance of the body and help nutrients to enter cells and waste products to pass out. Sodium, chlorine, and potassium also influence muscles, including the heart, and nerves.

Many foods contain these minerals. Table salt (as its chemical name *sodium chloride* indicates) is a rich source of both sodium and chlorine. Most foods have some sodium, and it is often added to processed foods in the form of salt, soy sauce, and sodium compounds such as monosodium glutamate. Brine, in which pickles

**Health Tip**
- If you want to limit salt intake but like the taste of salt in foods such as soups and casseroles, add a little vinegar.

The minerals your body needs as nutrients are the same substances found in rock and soil. The nutrients enter the food chain when plants absorb them or when they are mined, as at this salt mine.

part of red blood cells. Hemoglobin carries oxygen to the cells of the body and carries away the carbon dioxide waste. Iron is also found in body cells, helping them to use the oxygen they receive from the blood.

The body can store and reuse iron, but some iron still needs to be supplied by diet. A lack of iron causes iron-deficiency anemia, which is marked by fatigue and weakness, poor appetite, and pale skin color. Many people take iron supplements to avoid anemia, but too much iron can be harmful, causing constipation. Iron overdoses can be toxic and damage the liver. Good food sources of iron are organ meats, eggs, meat, dried fruits and legumes, whole grains, and dark leafy greens.

**Iodine**   A small amount of this trace element is necessary for the thyroid gland to regulate metabolism, the body's rate of growth and energy use. Lack of iodine produces *goiter,* an enlargement of the thyroid.

Most people easily get enough iodine in their diets. Saltwater fish and iodized table salt are good sources of the mineral, and many other foods contain small amounts.

**Zinc**   This trace element plays many important roles in the growth and maintenance of the body. Zinc helps in the use of carbohydrates, proteins, and fats. It is contained in enzymes, tissues, and bone. Zinc also helps in healing wounds and in the protection against disease, as well as in growth and reproduction.

Many foods contain zinc. Among the best sources are seafood, meat, eggs, dairy products, and whole grains. It is possible to build up too much zinc. The result can be fever, nausea, and vomiting.

### Water

You are probably aware that water is necessary to life. Human beings can do without food much longer than they can live without water.

are packaged, and cured foods, such as sausage and bacon, also contain high levels of sodium. Because research indicates that high sodium levels may contribute to high blood pressure, many people are now cutting down on their use of table salt and other sodium-rich products. Another medical problem associated with excess sodium in the body is the buildup of water in the tissues, leading to *edema* (uh-DEE-muh), or swelling.

On the other hand, sodium, chlorine, and potassium can be lost through heavy perspiration. They often need to be replaced after strenuous exercise, very hot weather, or illness. Symptoms of a deficiency of these minerals include fainting and vomiting. Some medications can cause a loss of potassium. Foods rich in potassium include citrus fruits, bananas, dried fruits, fish, and meat.

**Iron**   This trace element is essential to good health even though the body needs only small amounts. Iron and protein make up *hemoglobin* (HEE-muh-glo-bin), an important

Much of the body itself—from two-thirds to three-quarters—is water, and water escapes from the body in perspiration, excreted waste products, and as water vapor in every breath.

Water is an important part of many body fluids, such as blood and digestive juices. As part of the digestive juices, it helps change consumed food into nutrients the body can use. As part of the blood, it helps carry those nutrients to the cells and carries away cellular waste products. Water also helps to regulate body temperature; the evaporation of perspiration from the skin is one way the body is able to cool off.

Of course, the best source of water is drinking water itself. The body needs about six cups of fluids each day. Soups, sauces, and other dishes made with water contribute water as do drinks of various kinds. Water is also present in "juicy" foods such as fruits and vegetables.

## Nutrients and Food Sources

The chart on pages 50–51 will help you review your need for the various nutrients and the foods in which they are found. Refer also to Chapters 13 through 29 for information on the nutrient contributions of particular foods.

## Recommended Daily Dietary Allowances

On pages 52–54 you will find the Table of Recommended Daily Dietary Allowances. These are the amounts of the essential nutrients that the Food and Nutrition Board, on the basis of available scientific knowledge, considers adequate to meet the known nutritional needs of practically all healthy persons, from infancy through adulthood. There are also estimated safe and adequate intakes for additional selected vitamins and minerals.

**RDA,** Recommended Dietary Allowances, are recommendations for the amounts of nutrients that should be eaten daily. Since there are some losses of nutrients that occur during the processing and preparation of food, you must

Don't forget that water is an important part of a healthful diet.

allow for these losses in planning your daily intake of food.

You will notice that dietary allowances are listed in the table according to age and sex; in this way, adjustments in the nutrient allowances are made to meet the demands of the different growth periods. Even though you stop growing at adulthood, your body continues to have a need for all nutrients. You will notice that most of the nutrient values are listed in grams and milligrams (454 grams = 1 pound, and 1 mg = one-thousandth of a gram), and that vitamins A and D are listed in International Units (one I.U. = 0.3 micrograms, or less than one-millionth of a gram). Vitamin A is now also listed in a new unit, the R.E. (retinol equivalent) recommended by the FAO/WHO (Food and Agriculture Organization/World Health Organization) Expert Committee. A retinol equivalent equals one microgram of retinol. You will find these recommended allowances listed on labels on food packages.

## Nutrients and Food Sources

| Nutrient | Food Sources | Body Needs | Nutrient Shortage |
|---|---|---|---|
| Carbohydrates | breads, cereals, spaghetti, macaroni, noodles, potatoes, lima beans, peas, sugar, syrup, jellies, honey | supply energy; supply roughage or cellulose | fatigue; constipation |
| Fats | butter, margarine, cream, salad dressings, shortenings, lard, fat of meat, invisible fat in lean meats, egg yolks, cheese | supply energy, essential fatty acids, and fat-soluble vitamins; to protect body organs; to insulate and retain heat | retarded growth; unhealthy skin |
| Protein | meat, poultry, fish, milk, cheese, dried peas, beans, nuts, breads, cereals | to build and repair body tissues; to build necessary components such as enzymes and antibodies | poor growth; weak muscles; shortage of antibodies and enzymes |

### Minerals

| Nutrient | Food Sources | Body Needs | Nutrient Shortage |
|---|---|---|---|
| Calcium | milk, cheese, ice cream, broccoli, turnip and mustard greens | bones and teeth; regulate nerve and muscle activity; to clot blood | poor bones and teeth; poor muscles; poor nerve control |
| Phosphorus | milk, cheese, whole-grain cereals and breads, meats, dried beans and peas | bones and teeth; regulate body; cell activity | poor bones and teeth; poor growth |
| Sodium, Chlorine, and Potassium | for sodium and chlorine: table salt, sodium compounds used as additives, brine, cured foods; for potassium: citrus fruits, bananas, dried fruits, fish, meat | help maintain water balance; influence heart muscles, nerves | fainting; vomiting |
| Iodine | seafoods; iodized salt | activity of thyroid gland | goiter |
| Iron | liver, meats, eggs, whole-grain and enriched cereals and breads, dark leafy greens, dried peas, beans, prunes, raisins | for hemoglobin of red blood cells | anemia |
| Magnesium | whole grains, leafy greens, meat, milk, legumes, nuts | muscle and nerve function; bones, teeth | tremor |
| Zinc | meats, liver, seafoods, eggs, whole grains, milk | growth, enzymes | retarded growth; impaired sense of taste |

## Nutrients and Food Sources *(continued)*

| Nutrient | Food Sources | Body Needs | Nutrient Shortage |
|----------|-------------|-----------|-------------------|
| **Vitamins** | | | |
| Vitamin A | whole milk, cream, butter, margarine, cheese, dark-green and deep-yellow vegetables | good skin and mucous membranes; growth; eye pigment | night blindness and eye diseases; poor growth; poor skin condition |
| Vitamin $B_1$ (thiamin) | enriched or whole-grain cereals, pork and other meats, poultry, fish, dried beans and peas | health of nerves; digestive function; helps release energy from carbohydrates; promotes good appetite | fatigue, poor appetite, poor growth, beriberi |
| Vitamin $B_2$ (riboflavin) | milk, cheese, ice cream, whole-grain and enriched cereals, eggs, meat, liver, poultry, fish, dark-green vegetables | smooth skin, good eye function; aids body in use of protein and energy foods | poor skin, premature aging, poor vision, poor growth |
| Vitamin $B_{12}$ | meats, organ meats, fish, poultry, eggs, milk | red blood cell formation; nerve function | pernicious anemia; neurologic degeneration |
| Folic Acid | deep-green leafy vegetables, muscle meats, eggs, whole grains | mature red blood cells | macrocytic anemia |
| Niacin (part of B complex) | enriched and whole-grain cereals and breads, milk, cheese, meat, fish, poultry, peanuts | helps body use other nutrients; maintains good nerves and digestion | pellagra, fatigue, poor digestive and nerve function |
| Vitamin C (ascorbic acid) | oranges, lemons, limes, tomatoes, strawberries, cantaloupe, dark-green leafy vegetables, cabbage, broccoli | helps to firm cementing material of cells and strong blood vessel walls | scurvy, bruise easily, bleeding gums, fatigue |
| Vitamin D | vitamin-D milk, egg yolks, butter, margarine, fish-liver oils | helps body use calcium and phosphorus for strong bones and teeth | rickets, poor bones and teeth |
| Vitamin E (tocopherols) | oil, shortening, margarine, whole grains, dairy products, eggs, liver, green leafy vegetables | protects vitamin A and salty acids against much oxygen; aids in use of energy foods | blood cells may rupture; muscles may become wasted |
| Vitamin K | dark-green leafy vegetables, cabbage, cauliflower | helps blood clot properly | poor blood clotting; loss of calcium from bones |

The RDA applies to both sexes at all stages of life.

## Nutrition Labeling

Nutrition labeling on a food product will tell you the nutritive value of the food. Nutrition labeling was developed by the Food and Drug Administration and the food industry to provide the consumer with the nutrient content of most foods. It is important for you to have this information if you are to plan and prepare healthful meals.

Look at some labels on food products. Near the top of each label, locate the section identified as "Nutrition Information." The label tells the size and number of servings in the container. Next are listed the number of calories and the amounts of protein, carbohydrate, and fat in one serving. The lower part of the label gives the percentages of the U.S. RDA of protein and seven vitamins and minerals in a serving of the

## Food and Nutrition Board, National Academy of Sciences—National Research Council Recommended Daily Dietary Allowances,[a] Revised 1989

Designed for the maintenance of good nutrition of practically all healthy people in the U.S.A.

| | Age (years) | Weight[b] (kg) | Weight[b] (lbs) | Height[b] (cm) | Height[b] (in.) | Protein (g) | Fat-Soluble Vitamins Vitamin A (μg RE)[c] | Vitamin D (μg)[d] | Vitamin E (mg α T.E.)[e] | Vitamin K (μg) | Water-Soluble Vitamins Vitamin C (mg) | Thiamin (mg) | Riboflavin (mg) |
|---|---|---|---|---|---|---|---|---|---|---|---|---|---|
| Infants | 0.0–0.5 | 6 | 13 | 60 | 24 | 13 | 375 | 7.5 | 3 | 5 | 30 | 0.3 | 0.4 |
| | 0.5–1.0 | 9 | 20 | 71 | 28 | 14 | 375 | 10 | 4 | 10 | 35 | 0.4 | 0.5 |
| Children | 1–3 | 13 | 29 | 90 | 35 | 16 | 400 | 10 | 6 | 15 | 40 | 0.7 | 0.8 |
| | 4–6 | 20 | 44 | 112 | 44 | 24 | 500 | 10 | 7 | 20 | 45 | 0.9 | 1.1 |
| | 7–10 | 28 | 62 | 132 | 52 | 28 | 700 | 10 | 7 | 30 | 45 | 1.0 | 1.2 |
| Males | 11–14 | 45 | 99 | 157 | 62 | 45 | 1000 | 10 | 10 | 45 | 50 | 1.3 | 1.5 |
| | 15–18 | 66 | 145 | 176 | 69 | 59 | 1000 | 10 | 10 | 65 | 60 | 1.5 | 1.8 |
| | 19–24 | 72 | 160 | 177 | 70 | 58 | 1000 | 10 | 10 | 70 | 60 | 1.5 | 1.7 |
| | 25–50 | 79 | 174 | 176 | 70 | 63 | 1000 | 5 | 10 | 80 | 60 | 1.5 | 1.7 |
| | 51+ | 77 | 170 | 173 | 68 | 63 | 1000 | 5 | 10 | 80 | 60 | 1.2 | 1.4 |
| Females | 11–14 | 46 | 101 | 157 | 62 | 46 | 800 | 10 | 8 | 45 | 50 | 1.1 | 1.3 |
| | 15–18 | 55 | 120 | 163 | 64 | 44 | 800 | 10 | 8 | 55 | 60 | 1.1 | 1.3 |
| | 19–24 | 58 | 128 | 164 | 65 | 46 | 800 | 10 | 8 | 60 | 60 | 1.1 | 1.3 |
| | 25–50 | 63 | 138 | 163 | 64 | 50 | 800 | 5 | 8 | 65 | 60 | 1.1 | 1.3 |
| | 51+ | 65 | 143 | 160 | 63 | 50 | 800 | 5 | 8 | 65 | 60 | 1.0 | 1.2 |
| Pregnant | | | | | | 60 | 800 | 10 | 10 | 65 | 70 | 1.5 | 1.6 |
| Lactating | 1st 6 months | | | | | 65 | 1,300 | 10 | 12 | 65 | 95 | 1.6 | 1.8 |
| | 2nd 6 months | | | | | 62 | 1,200 | 10 | 11 | 65 | 90 | 1.6 | 1.7 |

a   The allowances are intended to provide for individual variations among most normal persons as they live in the United States under usual environmental stresses. Diets should be based on a variety of common foods in order to provide other nutrients for which human requirements have been less well defined.

b   Weights and heights of Reference Adults are actual medians for the U.S. population of the designated age. The use of these figures does not imply that the height-to-weight ratios are ideal.

c   Retinol equivalents. 1 Retinol equivalent = 1 μg retinol or 6 μg β-carotene.

d   As cholecalciferol. 10 μg cholecalciferol = 400 I.U. vitamin D.

e   α-tocopherol equivalents. 1 mg d-α-tocopherol = 1 α-T.E.

## Estimated Safe and Adequate Daily Dietary Intakes of Selected Vitamins and Minerals[a]

| | Age (years) | Vitamins | | Trace Elements[b] | | | | |
| | | Biotin (μg) | Pantothenic Acid (mg) | Copper (mg) | Manganese (mg) | Fluoride (mg) | Chromium (μg) | Molybdenum (μg) |
|---|---|---|---|---|---|---|---|---|
| Infants | 0.0–0.5 | 10 | 2 | 0.4–0.6 | 0.3–0.6 | 0.1–0.5 | 10–40 | 15–30 |
| | 0.5–1.0 | 15 | 3 | 0.6–0.7 | 0.6–1.0 | 0.2–1.0 | 20–60 | 20–40 |
| Children and Adolescents | 1–3 | 20 | 3 | 0.7–1.0 | 1.0–1.5 | 0.5–1.5 | 20–80 | 25–50 |
| | 4–6 | 25 | 3–4 | 1.0–1.5 | 1.5–2.0 | 1.0–2.5 | 30–120 | 30–75 |
| | 7–10 | 30 | 4–5 | 1.0–2.0 | 2.0–3.0 | 1.5–2.5 | 50–200 | 50–150 |
| | 11+ | 30–100 | 4–7 | 1.5–2.5 | 2.5–5.0 | 1.5–2.5 | 50–200 | 75–250 |
| Adults | | 30–100 | 4–7 | 1.5–3.0 | 2.5–5.0 | 1.5–4.0 | 50–200 | 75–250 |

a Because there is less information on which to base allowances, these figures are not given in the main table of the RDA and are provided here in the form of ranges of recommended intakes.
b Since the toxic levels for many trace elements may be only several times usual intakes, the upper levels for the trace elements given in this table should not be habitually exceeded.

## Food and Nutrition Board, National Academy of Sciences—National Research Council Recommended Daily Dietary Allowances,[a] Revised 1989

Designed for the maintenance of good nutrition of practically all healthy people in the U.S.A.

| | Water-Soluble Vitamins | | | | Minerals | | | | | | |
| | Niacin[f] (mg NE) | Vitamin B6 (mg) | Folate (μg) | Vitamin B12 (μg) | Calcium (mg) | Phosphorus (mg) | Magnesium (mg) | Iron (mg) | Zinc (mg) | Iodine (μg) | Selenium (μg) |
|---|---|---|---|---|---|---|---|---|---|---|---|
| Infants | 5 | 0.3 | 25 | 0.3 | 400 | 300 | 40 | 6 | 5 | 40 | 10 |
| | 6 | 0.6 | 35 | 0.5 | 600 | 500 | 60 | 10 | 5 | 50 | 15 |
| Children | 9 | 1.0 | 50 | 0.7 | 800 | 800 | 80 | 10 | 10 | 70 | 20 |
| | 12 | 1.1 | 75 | 1.0 | 800 | 800 | 120 | 10 | 10 | 90 | 20 |
| | 13 | 1.4 | 100 | 1.4 | 800 | 800 | 170 | 10 | 10 | 120 | 30 |
| Males | 14 | 1.7 | 150 | 2.0 | 1200 | 1200 | 270 | 12 | 15 | 150 | 40 |
| | 20 | 2.0 | 200 | 2.0 | 1200 | 1200 | 400 | 12 | 15 | 150 | 50 |
| | 19 | 2.0 | 200 | 2.0 | 1200 | 1200 | 350 | 10 | 15 | 150 | 70 |
| | 19 | 2.0 | 200 | 2.0 | 800 | 800 | 350 | 10 | 15 | 150 | 70 |
| | 15 | 2.0 | 200 | 2.0 | 800 | 800 | 350 | 10 | 15 | 150 | 70 |
| Females | 15 | 1.4 | 150 | 2.0 | 1200 | 1200 | 280 | 15 | 12 | 150 | 45 |
| | 15 | 1.5 | 180 | 2.0 | 1200 | 1200 | 300 | 15 | 12 | 150 | 50 |
| | 15 | 1.6 | 180 | 2.0 | 1200 | 1200 | 280 | 15 | 12 | 150 | 55 |
| | 15 | 1.6 | 180 | 2.0 | 800 | 800 | 280 | 15 | 12 | 150 | 55 |
| | 13 | 1.6 | 180 | 2.0 | 800 | 800 | 280 | 10 | 12 | 150 | 55 |
| Pregnant | 17 | 2.2 | 400 | 2.2 | 1200 | 1200 | 320 | 30 | 15 | 175 | 65 |
| Lactating | 20 | 2.1 | 280 | 2.6 | 1200 | 1200 | 335 | 15 | 19 | 200 | 75 |
| | 20 | 2.1 | 260 | 2.6 | 1200 | 1200 | 340 | 15 | 16 | 200 | 75 |

f 1 NE (niacin equivalent) is equal to 1 mg of niacin or 60 mg of dietary tryptophan.

Adapted from *Recommended Dietary Allowances*, 10th Edition, 1989, with the permission of the National Academy of Sciences, Washington, D.C.

## Estimated Sodium, Chloride, and Potassium Minimum Requirements for Healthy Persons[a]

| | Age (years) | Weight (kg) | Weight (lbs) | Electrolytes Sodium (mg)[a, b] | Electrolytes Chloride (mg)[a, b] | Electrolytes Potassium (mg)[c] |
|---|---|---|---|---|---|---|
| Infants | 0–0.42 | 4.5 | 10 | 120 | 180 | 500 |
| | 0.5–0.92 | 8.9 | 20 | 200 | 300 | 700 |
| Children | 1.0 | 11.0 | 23 | 225 | 350 | 1000 |
| and | 2–5 | 16.0 | 34 | 300 | 500 | 1400 |
| Adolescents | 6–9 | 25.0 | 56 | 400 | 600 | 1600 |
| | 10–18 | 50.0 | 104 | 500 | 750 | 2000 |
| Adults | 18+ | 70.0 | 154 | 500 | 750 | 2000 |

a No allowance has been included for large, prolonged losses from the skin through sweat.

b There is no evidence that higher intakes confer any health benefit.

c Desirable intakes of potassium may considerably exceed these values.

Adapted from *Recommended Dietary Allowances*, 10th Edition, 1989, with the permission of the National Academy of Sciences, Washington, D.C.

food. The U.S. RDA represents the amounts needed each day by most people, plus a margin of safety (30 to 50 percent) to allow for individual differences. To insure enough vitamins, minerals, and protein, the percentages for each food should add up to about 100 percent each day.

Look at the labels shown below. The one on the left shows that one serving of the food contains 4 percent of the U.S. RDA for protein, 2 percent of the U.S. RDA for vitamin C, and so on. Some labels will list other vitamins and minerals, polyunsaturated and saturated fats, cholesterol, and sodium. Nutrition information is especially helpful to persons on weight-reduction, diabetic, and other medical diets.

The nutrition information panel gives you an easy way to learn about the nutritive value of foods. You can compare the information on the labels from different types of foods to determine which nutrients are commonly found in each food, and which foods are particularly good sources of certain vitamins and minerals.

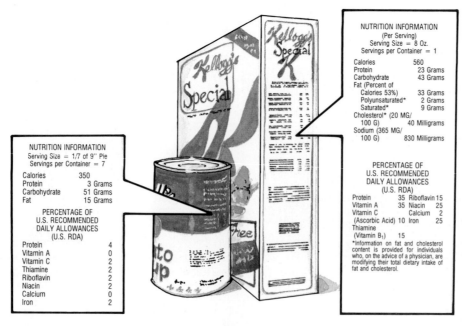

The labels on food packages allow you to select foods for nutritionally balanced meals as well as to watch your calories. How do these labels help people with particular medical problems?

# Fuel for the Day—Breakfast

Would you pass up a chance to be more alert, get more accomplished, or feel less tired—in the morning? If you regularly skip breakfast, you could be passing up such a chance. Millions of Americans omit this important meal every day. Half of all American schoolchildren and one or two members of half the American families routinely skip breakfast. Since 1978, one survey found, this breakfast-skipping trend has increased by slightly over 30%. Yet evidence increasingly suggests that these breakfast-skippers may be cheating themselves.

Many of the nutrients in typical breakfast foods are not consumed to a large extent at other meals. Also, the body consumes many of these nutrients better if they enter the body in small amounts. Protein and calcium are two such nutrients. One study found that teenagers who skip breakfast end their day with 40% less calcium and vitamin C, and 10% less iron and thiamin than the suggested RDA.

Breakfast can help your performance at school or on the job. After a night of sleep, your body is low in nutrients and energy. It needs to be refueled. Think of all the activities you go through in the morning. A balanced breakfast provides you with fuel for those activities.

Although the findings are not conclusive, several studies link breakfast consumption with better morning performance. At the University of Iowa Medical College, researchers found that breakfast-eaters showed higher productivity, faster reaction times, and less muscle fatigue than breakfast-skippers. Another study linked breakfast-abstaining students with listlessness and an inability to concentrate.

Many weight-conscious dieters, thinking that they are avoiding calories, skip breakfast. In a study done on rats, researchers found that eating infrequently during the day actually encouraged the rats' bodies to store energy in fat cells. A study of men who eat only one or two meals a day found that they had higher cholesterol levels and an increased number of fat cells compared with men who ate the same amount of calories but ate more frequently.

What does a balanced breakfast include? Protein is a must. Breakfast should include about one-third of your protein needs for the day. Protein helps you to be alert and discourages mid-morning hunger pangs. Cottage cheese, milk, yogurt, cheese, eggs, fish, and peanut butter are good choices. Any fruit or juice that contains vitamin C is also a good choice. For energy, you need to eat some complex carbohydrates—whole-grain bread, bran muffins, or cereal are examples.

If you remain unconvinced of the importance of breakfast and you are still tempted to skip it, consider this. In a ten-year study of 7,000 men and women, researchers from the University of California at Los Angeles found only one factor in common among all the healthier people in the group. They all took time to eat breakfast almost every day. Although eating breakfast may not prolong your life, it does reflect your attitude toward your health.

A healthful breakfast provides you the fuel for the day.

By carefully comparing different kinds of foods, you can learn much about which foods contribute substantial amounts of nutrients and which ones do not. New food products can be compared with familiar ones to find out whether they are good nutritional buys. Eating a variety of foods each day along with using this nutrition information will insure that you are getting the nutrients for a healthful diet.

## Nutrients in Meatless Meals

While everyone needs the same nutrients, people can pick and choose the foods that supply them. Some individuals choose to follow the vegetarian style of eating and prefer meatless meals. The *vegetarian* diet consists almost entirely of foods of plant origin. Although vegetarianism may be practiced in a variety of forms, there are really only two basic diet patterns —the *vegan* and the *lacto-ovo*.

The vegans, or pure vegetarians, do not eat any animal products. They select a diet of legumes, nuts, fruits, vegetables, and grains. The vegan may have some difficulty getting enough energy (kilocalories) eating only foods of plant origin, since these foods are bulky. When the diet is short in kilocalories, the body is forced to use protein for energy rather than for body building and maintenance.

Beans with corn in tortillas make a complete protein.

Meats supply complete proteins which contain all of the amino acids your body requires and those which your body cannot make. You also know that plant proteins are incomplete since they lack some of the essential amino acids. When your diet includes foods of animal origin, such as meat, milk, and eggs, amino acids are easily provided. The protein content of a vegan diet can sometimes be inadequate in essential amino acids and in protein.

Legumes—such as navy beans, lima beans, kidney beans, pinto beans, soy beans, black-eyed peas, chick-peas, and peas—along with grains are the chief sources of proteins in the vegan diet. A careful combination of legumes and grains (including seeds and nuts) can provide all the essential amino acids and result in high-quality protein dishes. Succotash, (a mixture of lima beans and corn), and beans with a cornmeal product or with rice provide complete protein.

Another nutrient lacking in the vegan diet is vitamin $B_{12}$, which is found only in foods of animal origin. When soy milk is fortified with vitamin $B_{12}$ and calcium, it becomes a valuable source of these nutrients for vegans. Vegans also need to include generous amounts of fresh dark-green vegetables, which provide some iron and calcium. Leafy greens are good sources of riboflavin, which is best provided by milk.

Vegetarians who consume only milk with the foods of plant origin are known as lacto-vegetarians. The lacto-ovo vegetarians do not eat meat, poultry, or fish, but they do eat eggs and dairy products. The eggs, milk, and cheese provide these vegetarians with the nutrients usually contributed by meats but which are lacking in foods of plant origin.

An adequate diet must contain a balance of a variety of nutrients. If you eliminate certain types of foods—whether for religious, philosophical, health, or any other reasons—you must be careful to find another source of the nutrients you have lost.

## For Review

1. What three ways do nutrients serve your body? Which group or groups of nutrients perform each function?
2. How many types of carbohydrates are there? List them.
3. What is fiber? What is its importance in the diet?
4. Why is a low-fat diet good even though your body needs fats for good health?
5. What is the difference between essential and nonessential amino acids? What foods contain all the essential amino acids?
6. What are two differences between water-soluble and fat-soluble vitamins? Which vitamins make up each category?
7. What is osteoporosis? What causes it? What foods help prevent it?
8. What health problems are associated with too much sodium? How can your body lose sodium? What happens when you have too little sodium, chlorine, and potassium in your diet?
9. What is RDA? What is one way to find out the RDA supplied by packaged food products?
10. What nutrients are often lacking in a vegetarian diet? How can they be made up?

# Meal-Planning Guides

To check the nutrient value of each food and to see that you meet your RDA for each nutrient is very time-consuming. Nutritionists have set up an easy guide for food selection. It is called the Daily Food Guide.

The Vegetable-Fruit Group contains foods that can be served as main dishes, side dishes, desserts, or snacks.

## The Daily Food Guide

Your daily food choices can be listed in five general groups. They are the Vegetable-Fruit Group; the Bread-Cereal Group; the Milk-Cheese Group; the Meat-Poultry-Fish-Beans-Nuts Group; and the Fats-Sweets Group. The first four of these food groups are rich in nutrients and are referred to as the Daily Food Guide, the Four Food Groups, or the Basic Four. The fifth group includes foods with a high sugar and/or fat content and should only be used in small quantities.

**The Vegetable-Fruit Group** Each day, you must be careful to include the dark-green leafy or deep-yellow vegetables for their rich supply of vitamin A in the form of carotene. You also need to include one serving of foods rich in vitamin C, such as citrus fruits, canta-loupes, or strawberries; or two servings of foods that are fair sources of vitamin C, such as raw cabbage, green pepper, tomato, or asparagus. Four or more servings are recommended each day from the Vegetable-Fruit Group (½ c (125 mL) cooked vegetable or fruit, or 1 whole fruit or vegetable such as an apple or potato = 1 serving).

**The Bread-Cereal Group** All whole-grain, enriched, restored, or fortified cereals and breads, macaroni, spaghetti, and noodles are in this group. Rolls, biscuits, muffins, and other quick breads such as waffles and pancakes are included when they are made with enriched flour. To meet daily requirements, you need to select four or more servings each day (1 slice of bread, ¾ to 1 c (185 to 250 mL) of cereal or macaroni product = 1 serving). Cereals and breads are rich in starch, a carbohydrate, and provide the B vitamins, some iron, and incom-plete proteins.

Foods from the Milk-Cheese Group are found in many combination dishes, such as custard, ice cream, and some cakes. Where else do you find dairy products? What is your favorite source of these important foods? Do you usually meet your daily whole-milk requirement?

The foods called "the staff of life"—breads and rice—are included in the Bread-Cereal Group. What other foods are part of this group? Which is your "staff of life"?

**The Milk-Cheese Group** This group includes the various forms of milk and cheese. Milk (whole, skim, nonfat, dry, evaporated), chocolate milk, other milk beverages, cheese, and ice cream are included. A portion of your milk requirement can be used to make custards, milk puddings, and cream soups. The table below gives the daily requirements for different age groups.

**Whole Milk**
- **Children** 3 or more c (750 mL)
- **Adolescents** 4 or more c (1 L)
- **Adults** 2 or more c (500 mL)
- **Pregnant Women** 3 or more c (750 mL)
- **Nursing Mothers** 4 or more c (1 L)

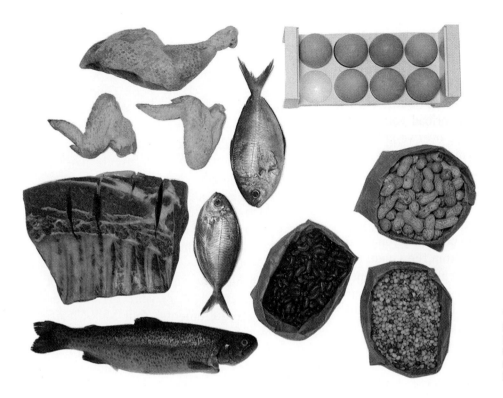

The foods of this group are important sources of protein. Which ones provide complete protein? Which ones supply incomplete protein?

The Milk-Cheese Group will provide you with these nutrients: calcium, protein, riboflavin, and other B-complex vitamins. You will receive vitamin A from whole milk and vitamin D from fortified milk. Low-fat milk (2 percent) and skim milk may be fortified with vitamins A and D and will give you about one-half the number of calories provided by whole milk.

**The Meat-Poultry-Fish-Beans-Nuts Group** This group is made up of all kinds of meat, including beef, veal, pork, lamb; variety meats such as liver, kidney, heart; poultry and eggs; all fish; and dried beans, peas, and nuts. To help meet your daily protein requirement, you will select two or more servings (4 oz (113 g) raw meat or 3 oz (85 g) cooked meat = 1 serving) from this group. This group can supply either complete or incomplete protein, depend-

ing upon which food you select. Meat, poultry, fish, and eggs provide complete protein, while dried peas, beans, and nuts provide incomplete protein. When you choose a food with incomplete protein, such as dried peas or beans, include a complete protein food such as milk, cheese, or egg in the same meal. The milk will provide the kind of amino acids which are missing in foods that contain incomplete protein. These foods will also provide the B vitamins and iron. Liver is the richest food source of iron.

**The Fats-Sweets Group** You will notice that foods rich in fats and sugars (pastries, cookies, cakes, and jellies) are not included in the Daily Food Guide. These foods are rich in calories but provide almost no vitamins, minerals, or proteins. They are used to add flavor to other foods, such as melted butter or margarine on vegetables or added sugar in puddings and beverages. When you are active, you do need some foods that contain fat and sugar. Foods rich in fats and sugars are considered harmful when they crowd out other needed foods (fruits, vegetables, milk) and when they overload your body with extra calories that cause overweight. Because fats and sugars are so high in calories, it is better to include them only in small quantities to complement the Daily Food Guide, rather than to use them to replace foods in the Guide.

The Daily Food Guide makes it easy for you to plan meals that include the nutrients you need each day. If you select foods from the Guide for each meal and are careful to include the amounts of food recommended from each group, your nutrient needs will be met. Learn to think of meal planning in terms of the Daily Food Guide.

The foods of the Fats-Sweets Group should be eaten only in moderation, after basic nutritional needs have been met. They provide little nutrition in proportion to kilocalories.

**For Review**
1. List the four basic food groups that make up the Daily Food Guide. How many servings per day should you include from each group?
2. What kinds of foods are included in the fifth group, the Fats-Sweets Group? When and why should you include foods from this group?
3. Which foods from the Vegetable-Fruit Group are rich in vitamin A in the form of carotene? Which foods are rich in vitamin C?
4. What different varieties of food can you choose to make up your Bread-Cereal Group requirements? Your Milk-Cheese Group requirements?
5. Can peas, beans, and nuts replace meat in your diet? Why or why not?

# The Meals of the Day

Food habits and customs differ with countries and cultures; not all countries serve three meals a day. In some countries, it is customary to have five or six meals a day. Your diet, however, probably consists primarily of breakfast, lunch, and dinner.

## Meal Patterns

A meal pattern serves as a blueprint or guide and reminds you to include certain types of foods in your meals. When you do not follow a guide, it is easy to omit certain essential foods such as milk, vegetables, or fruits. Well-planned meals include at least one food from each group of the Daily Food Guide. Your menus should provide calories and protein as well as your vitamin and mineral needs.

No single meal will provide all your nutrient needs, but the meals for an entire day can supply these needs when you plan them well. The following meal patterns will help you choose or plan good meals.

### Breakfast Pattern
Fruit (often citrus)
Main Dish (cereal and/or egg, waffles, etc.)
Bread
Milk or Other Beverage

### Lunch or Supper Pattern
Main Dish (protein food in casseroles, soups, salads, or sandwiches)
Vegetable and/or Fruit
Bread
Milk or Other Beverage

### Dinner Pattern
Main Dish (meat, poultry, fish, or other protein)
Two Vegetables (or vegetable and a fruit)
Salad
Bread
Milk or Other Beverage

## Breakfast

Breakfast is the first meal of the day. It breaks the "fast" of the long night. Some people often skip breakfast, but nutritionists and scientists tell us that breakfast is an important meal. Without breakfast, it is difficult to get the daily nutrient needs. Breakfast skippers are less alert, more subject to illness, and tend to overeat later in the day. This practice often leads to overweight.

A good breakfast includes foods from the Daily Food Guide. It should supply from one-fourth to one-third of your total daily nutrients and calories. When you do not include a citrus fruit or another fruit that is high in vitamin C for breakfast, plan to include some other sources of vitamin C in the other meals of the day. When you do not include cereal, use an additional serving of bread and drink a glass of milk for your beverage.

The type of breakfast for you will depend upon your energy needs. For example, if you are very active, you may prefer a heavy breakfast. When you include the foods listed in the breakfast pattern, you will have a medium breakfast. You can easily adjust a medium breakfast to meet your individual needs. When energy needs are great, include both cereal and egg and/or additional foods (waffles, pancakes, bacon, sausage) or use larger servings. When energy needs are small, use smaller servings or fewer foods.

Customarily, the variety of foods served for breakfast is smaller than that for other meals. All foods from the Daily Food Guide can be served for breakfast if you choose. If conventional breakfast foods do not appeal to you, arouse your morning appetite with such unconventional and nutritious foods as cheeseburgers, chili, pudding, pizza, or soup.

Foods you choose for breakfast should be determined by your energy needs as well as the foods that you will choose for other meals of the day. The other meals of the day do *not* replace your need for breakfast.

## Lunch

In contrast to breakfast, lunch is a moderately heavy meal served at noon; when the same type of meal is served in the evening, it is called supper. Different cultures and lifestyles determine at which time of day—noon or evening—people eat this moderately heavy meal.

Your lunch should supply one-third of your nutrient needs. It should not be so heavy that it interferes with your activity the remainder of the day. Use the basic lunch pattern to plan a satisfying and nutritious lunch.

For the main dish, you may choose from soups, sandwiches, hearty salads, casseroles, or

Traditionally, Americans eat their main meal of the day, dinner, (bottom) in the evening and have a lighter meal for lunch or supper. Although usually a light meal, why should breakfast (top) be particularly nutritious?

creamed foods. Lunch is usually more satisfying when at least one hot dish is included. It is a good time to serve foods such as eggs or vitamin C-rich foods when they have not been included for breakfast.

When you select your lunch from a school cafeteria or pack your lunch, follow the lunch pattern and include foods from the Daily Food Guide. Fruits, fresh vegetables, meats, and desserts may be left over from family meals and used creatively in a packed lunch. You can add variety to sandwiches by using different breads as well as different fillings. For a packed lunch, wrap each food in waxed paper or transparent wrap to protect freshness and prevent mixing of flavors.

Lunches, too, can be light, medium, or heavy, depending upon your activity and the foods that you include in your other meals. When you include the foods listed in the lunch pattern, you will have a medium lunch. You can adjust the basic lunch pattern to meet your individual needs in the same way as the breakfast pattern; that is, by using additional foods or larger servings. Good lunches, whether purchased, packed, or prepared at home, require careful planning.

## Dinner

Dinner is considered to be the largest and most elaborate meal of the day and may be served either at noon or in the evening. During the week, dinner may be served in the evening when all of your family members are at home. On Sundays and holidays, it is often served in the afternoon.

The dinner main dish is usually meat, poultry, fish, or occasionally a cheese or egg dish. You should choose the other foods in the dinner pattern to enhance and complement, or complete, the main dish. The other menus for the day are often based on the main dish chosen for dinner. If you first plan dinner, it will be easier to include the foods in breakfast and lunch that will complete your daily nutrient needs.

Although dinner often consists of one course—the meat, vegetable, and salad—you may have a dessert and at times an appetizer course. The appetizer should be light, such as a clear soup, tart fruit, or juice.

When you include the foods listed in the dinner pattern, you will have a medium dinner. Dinners, too, may be light, medium, or heavy, as the basic pattern is adjusted by adding or subtracting foods or by adjusting portion size.

## Other Food Consumption

You will notice that desserts and snacks were not included as part of the meal patterns discussed above. That is because they tend to be high in fat and sugar and lack other nutrients. However, if chosen carefully, desserts and snacks can be healthful additions to the meals of the day.

**Desserts**    After daily food requirements are met, desserts can be used as the additional foods that provide the energy required for your activity. Fruits, custards, and milk puddings are wholesome desserts and contribute to your nutrient needs. Sweeter and/or more fattening desserts should not take the place of any necessary nutrients or add unnecessary kilocalories. When you maintain the weight desirable for you, you are doing a good job of matching the food you eat with your energy needs.

**Snacks**    Between-meal eating, when it does not interfere with your appetite for main meals, can serve two useful functions. First, a snack can fill a nutritional gap left by your main meals. For example, if you missed your orange juice at breakfast, a tangerine would make a good snack later in the day. Second, snacks can supply extra energy—especially after vigorous exercise. An ice cream sundae after team prac-

Snacks do not have to be bad for you. A carefully selected, nutritious snack can be an important part of a busy, active day.

tice is energy rich. It can also supply some nutrients you may have missed during the day if, for example, you drank juice rather than milk at lunch. However, if the sundae takes you over your kilocaloric balance for the day, you might want to skip the pastry or french fries at dinner.

### For Review
1. How can using meal patterns help you plan your food consumption?
2. What proportion of your nutrient need should be met by breakfast? By lunch? By dinner?
3. How can you adjust the meal patterns for higher energy needs? Lower energy needs?
4. What are two useful functions that are sometimes performed by snacks and desserts?

# 3 Chapter Review

## Summary

Nutritional meals provide the proper balance of kilocalories to meet the energy needs of your body. Carbohydrates and fats provide most of the body's energy needs, and proteins contribute the remainder. The nutrients in foods supply energy for your work and play, help your body grow and heal, and regulate and protect your body processes. To help people plan healthful meals, the Food and Nutrition Board has provided recommendations for the amounts of nutrients that should be eaten daily. To plan nutritional meals that meet the recommended dietary allowances, a meal manager should refer to the nutrition label that appears on most foods, to the Daily Food Guide, and to the meal patterns.

## Vocabulary

| | |
|---|---|
| amino acids | kilocalories |
| carbohydrates | minerals |
| cellulose | proteins |
| cholesterol | RDA |
| complete proteins | trace elements |
| fats | vitamins |

1. The energy needs of your body and the energy your body gets from food is measured in _____.
2. The major suppliers of energy in the diet that help the body make the best use of proteins are called _____.
3. _____ is a complex carbohydrate that is sometimes called fiber or roughage and is found in plant cells.
4. _____ are the most energy-rich nutrients that provide two and one-quarter times as much energy as carbohydrates or proteins.
5. _____ is found normally in the blood, tissues, and digestive juices, but saturated fats in the diet may cause the body to produce too much of this substance, which can contribute to heart disease.
6. _____ are nutrients that are important for building and repairing body cells and for protecting the body from infections.
7. _____ are chemical compounds that contain carbon, hydrogen, oxygen, and nitrogen and make up proteins.
8. When foods, such as most animal foods, contain adequate amounts of all the essential amino acids, they contain _____.
9. The complex chemicals that help regulate the chemical reactions necessary for the body's growth and health and that are found in foods such as milk and citrus fruits are called _____.
10. _____ are an important part of a healthful diet because they can help regulate some body processes, and they become part of bones, teeth, tissues, and blood.
11. The group of minerals that the body needs in only small amounts and that consists of iron, iodine, and zinc are called _____.
12. _____ are recommendations for the amount of nutrients that should be eaten daily.

# Chapter Questions

1. What are ways that you can balance kilocalories in your meals?
2. What are the characteristics of a good weight-reduction diet?
3. What are the names of the six general groups of nutrients?
4. In what ways are fats important for maintaining a healthy body?
5. How are minerals and vitamins alike and different?
6. Why is it important for you to plan a diet that includes the recommended daily amounts of nutrients?
7. What nutrient information is provided on a nutrition label?
8. How can you use the information on a nutrition label to plan a balanced diet?
9. What is the Daily Food Guide?
10. How is the Daily Food Guide helpful?
11. Why should you follow a meal pattern?
12. Why is it easier to plan dinner first and then the other meals?

# Skill Activities

**1. Social studies** In your food journal, list the foods you eat during a day and the food groups to which they belong. Write the following headings: "Vegetable-Fruit Group," "Bread-Cereal Group," "Milk-Cheese Group," "Meat-Poultry-Fish-Beans-Nuts Group," and "Fats-Sweets Group." Leave room to write the food examples.

When you finish the chart, ask yourself these questions: Did I eat food from each group? Did I have more foods from one group than the others? Were my food choices healthful?

**2. Math** Make a chart with the headings "Brand Name," "Size of serving," "Calories per serving," "Protein," "Carbohydrate," and "Fat." Visit a grocery store, and find two pancake mixes that are prepared by just adding water. Read the nutrition labels. Beside each heading, write the information. Now look at the differences between the mixes. Does one mix have fewer calories per serving? If so, which one? Compute the difference. Does one mix have fewer nutrients than the other? If so, which one? Compute the differences. Make a statement about the relationship between calories and nutrients.

**3. Critical thinking** Plan meals for yourself for a three-day period. To help you make good food choices, refer to the meal-planning guide and the meal patterns. Check the RDA to see if your meals are nutritionally balanced. If not, rework your plan and recheck. Analyze where you have made your improvements.

**4. Science** Pick a vitamin and research who discovered it, how it was discovered, the benefits of the vitamin, and the diseases or problems that can occur as a result of a shortage of the vitamin. Report your findings to the class.

# 4 Food and Good Health

## As you read, think about:

- how digestion turns food into usable nutrients.
- how absorption delivers nutrients to the bloodstream.
- how the circulatory system delivers nutrients to body cells.
- how the body uses energy and what affects the rate of energy use.
- what the nutritional needs are of different stages of the life cycle.
- what causes weight problems and how dieting can solve weight problems.

### Vocabulary

digestion
absorption
peristalsis
circulatory system
basal metabolism
basal metabolic rate (BMR)
aerobic exercise
insomnia
overweight
obese
deficiency
malnutrition
anorexia nervosa
bulimia

Do you ever wonder how the breakfast you ate this morning became the fuel that is now keeping you alert, warm, and healthy? How the meals you ate yesterday turned into the materials that can build and repair your cells today? And what about that ice cream sundae you really shouldn't have had but did? Where did the various parts of it end up? As protein building blocks? As energy burned during your bike ride home? As fat?

The answers to these questions begin with **digestion,** the process that breaks down the foods you eat into the nutrients your body can use. Through the process of **absorption,** the usable nutrients from the digestive system are delivered to the circulatory system, or bloodstream. The blood carries the nutrients to all body cells and removes cellular waste products.

Some nutrients are burned to produce the energy that powers all body processes. Some

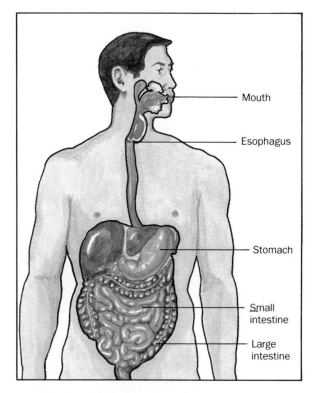

Digestion is a complex process. It begins in the mouth and continues in the esophagus, stomach, and small intestine. Waste is processed for elimination in the large intestine.

nutrients that are not immediately needed are stored. You recall that calcium is stored in bones. Other "storage areas" include adipose tissue, or fat. Some nutrients in oversupply are eliminated as waste along with parts of food that cannot be digested. You remember that cellulose is a carbohydrate that aids digestion and the regular removal of wastes because its fiber cannot be completely digested.

## Digestion

Digestion includes the processes that break down food. These processes take place in the digestive, or gastrointestinal, tract: the mouth, esophagus, stomach, and small intestine. The large intestine prepares waste for elimination.

This 1499 woodcut shows how scientists used to describe the human digestive and circulatory systems and brain.

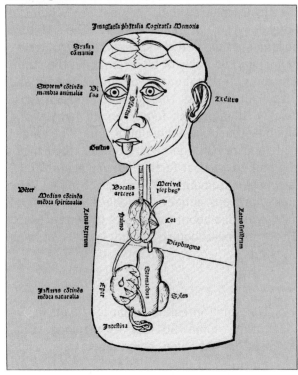

Just the sight and smell of a favorite food is "enough to make your mouth water." What foods make your mouth water?

## Esophagus

After swallowing, which is an involuntary reflex, the food is moved along by another involuntary process, muscular contractions called **peristalsis** (per-ih-STAL-siss). Peristalsis takes place in the esophagus, the tube that connects the mouth to the stomach.

## Stomach

The stomach is a saclike organ about 10 inches (25 cm) long and is located above the waistline. When you say, "I have a stomach ache," you may actually be referring to a pain in either the small or the large intestine. They are located below the waistline.

The stomach produces gastric juices —sometimes even at only the sight or aroma of food—that contain hydrochloric acid and enzymes. The peristaltic waves, or muscular contractions, of the stomach churn and break up food particles that are then mixed with the gastric juices. The enzyme *pepsin,* along with the hydrochloric acid, begins the chemical breakdown of proteins. Finally, the mixture becomes a thin, watery substance called *chyme.*

Different kinds of food remain in the stomach for different lengths of time. Liquids and carbohydrates pass through the stomach most quickly, high-protein foods remain longer, and fats take the longest amount of time. The longer that food remains in your stomach, the longer you will go without feeling hungry again. Thus, fats, which remain in the stomach about four hours, prevent hunger the longest. A balanced meal will take about four hours to be processed by the stomach before moving on to the small intestine.

## Small Intestine

The small intestine is hardly small! It is a coiled tube about 20 feet (6 m) long. *Bile,* produced by the liver, helps digest fats, while

## Mouth

Many of the digestive processes depend upon digestive juices, and some of these juices can be stimulated even before you actually "eat" anything. The sight and/or aroma of a food you like can make your mouth "water," or cause saliva to be produced by the salivary glands in your mouth, even before you taste the food. Not only does saliva soften and moisten the food in your mouth, it also contains an enzyme that begins the digestion of starch. When food is chewed, it is broken into more easily digestible pieces, which helps it mix with saliva and makes it easier to swallow.

other enzymes break down proteins into amino acids and starches into sugars. Peristaltic waves continue to move the chyme through the digestive system. Once digestion is complete, the nutrients are absorbed by the small intestine, and wastes move on to the large intestine.

## Waste Elimination

Indigestible substances from food move into the large intestine along with a small percentage of nutrients that cannot be used or stored. They continue to be processed in the large intestine. Water is absorbed and sent to the kidneys for later elimination. Solid waste moves along through the large intestine and is eventually eliminated.

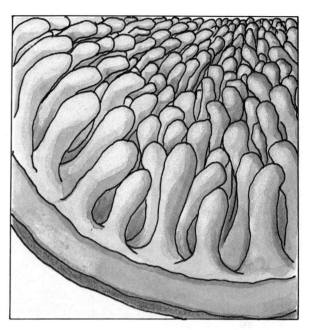

Hairlike villi increase the surface of the small intestine and thus speed absorption.

**For Review**
1. What causes the production of digestive juices such as saliva?
2. Briefly explain what digestive processes occur in the mouth, the stomach, and the small intestine.
3. How long does it take the average meal to be processed by the stomach? What nutrient prevents hunger the longest?

# Absorption

Absorption removes the newly digested nutrients from the digestive tract and prepares them for transportation to the cells by way of the bloodstream.

## Villi of the Small Intestine

The first phase of absorption takes place through the villi of the small intestine. *Villi* are small hairlike projections of the lining of the small intestine. They increase the surface area of the intestinal lining and thus allow fast absorption of nutrients.

The nutrients are now divided according to their destination. Vitamins and minerals that can be used right away are carried by the bloodstream to the body cells and systems that need them. Sugars, amino acids, and fatty acids are transported to the liver where they are converted into more usable or storable forms. Some fatty acids, glycerides, and vitamins go directly to the lymphatic system, another body network that carries body fluids.

## The Liver

Further changes in the forms of nutrients occur in the liver. This important organ changes certain sugars and some digested fats into glucose, or blood sugar. Glucose is the fuel for cellular activity and is particularly important for the brain and the nervous system. Protein can also be changed into glucose by the liver if other sources are not readily available. Glucose that is not needed immediately is stored by the liver as glycogen, which can be changed back into usable glucose when the blood-sugar level gets low. Excess glucose is stored as body fat.

A portion of the digested fats is converted by the liver into immediately usable energy. Some amino acids are produced by the liver and can be stored there briefly. The liver can also turn them into other chemicals. Vitamins and minerals are stored or passed on by the liver, depending on the body's needs. The liver even breaks down a variety of harmful substances so they will not cause damage.

If you think of the liver as a complex processing plant, storehouse, and stock manager, you will have some idea of how important this amazing organ is.

## Circulatory System

Imagine a 20-second trip through 60,000 miles (96,500 km). Now imagine that the journey includes the delivery of important products as well as the removal of unwanted materials for each of trillions of customers. This delivery of oxygen and nutrients to all the cells of the body by the blood certainly puts the old Pony Express

to shame! The route the blood follows includes the *capillary system,* the network of blood vessels that are so narrow that red blood cells can fit through only one at a time. The blood, pumped by the heart, an organ the size of a fist, constantly and continuously takes this vital journey through the circulatory system.

Technically, the **circulatory system** includes the heart, lungs, and blood vessels. Oxygen absorbed through the lungs is carried by the red blood cells. The *plasma,* or liquid part of the blood, carries the nutrients that have been processed by digestion and absorption. The heart pumps the blood through its network of vessels; the tiniest vessels, the capillaries, reach every body cell. There, the blood makes its pick-ups and deliveries. Nutrients and oxygen are absorbed from the blood through the cell walls, or membranes; carbon dioxide and waste fluids pass out into the blood through the same membranes. When the blood passes through the kidneys, it deposits the waste fluids there for later excretion, and delivers the carbon dioxide to the lungs to be exhaled. The rhythmic pumping of the heart helps the blood circulate on its amazing journey again.

Medical specialists can learn a great deal about your health and nutrition by analyzing samples of your blood.

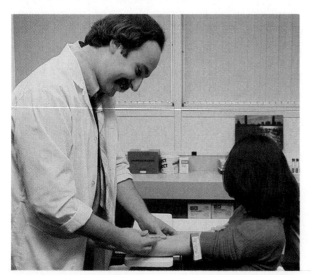

### For Review

1. What is the importance of the shape of the villi of the small intestine?
2. List at least three important processes performed by the liver.
3. What are the three parts of the circulatory system? What is the major function of each?
4. How do nutrients reach each and every body cell? How do they get into the cells?
5. What are the waste products of cells? What happens to them?

# Metabolism: How the Body Uses Energy

What goes on in the body cells after nutrients and oxygen have been delivered to them determines a person's metabolism. **Metabolism** (muh-TAB-uh-liz-um) is the sum of the processes or chemical changes that occur in living cells.

## Basal Metabolism

You are probably aware that some people can consume more kilocalories than others without gaining weight. You may even have heard someone say, "Oh, she can eat like that all day and not put on an ounce because of her metabolism." This expression really refers to **basal metabolism,** the amount of energy a particular person needs for necessary life processes.

Basal metabolism is the rate at which foods are burned. It is measured by the amount of body heat given off when a person is at complete rest 14–18 hours after eating. In other words, it does not include physical activity (walking uses less energy than running), digestive activity (the body works harder to deal with a big meal than a glass of water), or emotional activity (being angry enough to get "hot under the collar" uses more energy than relaxation). Basal metabolism refers to the amount of energy needed simply to stay alive, but it still varies according to body size and type, age, health, and the activities of certain body organs. The higher your **basal metabolic rate (BMR),** the more kilocalories you use up just staying alive, and the more you can consume without gaining weight.

Larger people usually have a higher BMR than smaller people. The more lean tissue (as opposed to fatty tissue) a body has, the more energy per unit of body weight it requires. Also, the more growth the body is engaged in, the higher the BMR. Have you ever heard anyone

say, "He's eating so much because he's having a growth spurt"? Body temperature can affect the basal metabolism, too. High fever uses more energy; very low temperature (such as the hypothermia suffered by people who have been almost "frozen" in snowbanks or fallen into extremely cold water) slows body processes and uses less energy. Finally, glands such as the thyroid regulate the rate at which body processes are carried on. If these glands do not function properly, weight problems can result. You have probably felt the effects of **adrenalin** (uh-DREN-uh-lin), produced by the adrenal gland, in times of stress. It makes your heart pump faster and speeds up other body processes as it prepares the body for "fight or flight" (the response to stress either by physical action or by running away).

## Energy and Body Processes

As you have seen, there are a lot of activities that go on in your body without your having to think about them. Cellular activities, breathing, digestion, and circulation are all automatic processes, and they all require energy. When you say, "I have no energy today," you probably

Is this runner really "out of energy"? Even when you feel exhausted, your body is generating and using energy to keep body processes going. What are some of these processes?

mean you don't feel up to any additional activities, such as riding your bike or taking an exam. However, you certainly do have energy; without it, your body processes would stop. All life requires energy.

**Energy from Nutrients** When you build a campfire to create warmth, you are using oxidation to release energy. The oxygen in the air combines with the fuel (in this case, wood) and produces energy (heat and light); carbon dioxide and water are produced as waste. A similar oxidation process occurs in body cells. The fuel is glucose. When glucose combines with oxygen (which, along with food, has also been delivered to the cells by the blood), it produces energy (heat as well as power that can be used by the cells). This process also releases carbon dioxide and water as waste products. The expression "to burn energy" means that the cellular process releases energy through oxidation, or "burning." In the cells, however, energy can be stored in ATP (adenosine triphosphate). The ATP then provides energy to the body when needed.

**Measuring Energy—Kilocalories**
You remember that the energy needs of your body as well as the energy provided by food are measured in kilocalories. Fats, as you recall, contribute the most energy value: 9 kilocalories per gram. Carbohydrates and protein contribute 4 kilocalories per gram.

As you have seen, different people "burn" kilocalories at different rates, depending on their particular BMR, or basal metabolic rate. The following chart will give you an idea of the kilocalorie intake needed to maintain health and body weight for general groups of people. Note that the last column provides a range (in parentheses) of requirements, thus allowing for other differences that affect basal metabolic rates.

A bomb calorimeter is used to determine the energy value, or caloric content, of food.

## Exercise and Health

Most people are aware of the importance of exercise for "staying in shape;" that is, having a weight, physical appearance, and stamina (endurance) that both looks and feels good. However, exercise is also important for even more basic health reasons.

The body needs some exercise to keep functioning properly. Approximately an hour of fairly vigorous exercise three times each week should maintain good muscle tone as well as strengthen the heart and lungs and improve circulation of the blood. Regular exercise also improves resistance to disease and infection.

## Recommended Daily Energy Needs (in Calories) Based on Age, Weight, and Height

| Persons | Age | Weight (Lbs) | Height (Inches) | Energy Needs (Calories) (Range Based on Varying BMR)* |
|---|---|---|---|---|
| Infants/ Children | 0– 1 | 18 | — | lb. × 52 (+ /− 7) |
| | 1– 3 | 29 | 34 | 1300 (900–1800) |
| | 3– 6 | 40 | 42 | 1600 (1300–2200) |
| | 6– 9 | 53 | 49 | 2100 (1700–3100) |
| Boys | 9–12 | 72 | 55 | 2400 (2000–3400) |
| | 12–15 | 98 | 61 | 3000 (2600–3400) |
| | 15–18 | 134 | 68 | 3400 (3000–3800) |
| Girls | 9–12 | 72 | 55 | 2200 (1800–3000) |
| | 12–15 | 103 | 62 | 2500 (2100–2900) |
| | 15–18 | 117 | 64 | 2300 (1900–2700) |
| Women | 18–35 | 128 | 64 | 2100 (1700–2500) |
| | 35–55 | 128 | 64 | 1900 (1500–2300) |
| | 55–75 | 128 | 64 | 1600 (1200–2000) |
| Lactating | | | | add 1000 calories |
| Pregnant | | | | add 200 calories |
| Men | 18–35 | 154 | 69 | 2900 (2500–3300) |
| | 35–55 | 154 | 69 | 2600 (2200–3000) |
| | 55–75 | 154 | 69 | 2200 (1800–2600) |

*Indicated range based on activity level and differing basal metabolic rates.

Exercise is important for health as well as for pleasure at every stage of life.

Those who lead a lifestyle of little physical activity, are more likely to suffer heart disease, diabetes, ulcers, and lower back pain. Also, tension, anxiety, depression, and a general feeling of tiredness can often be relieved by regular exercise.

**Exercise and Kilocalories**   The more you exercise, the more energy or kilocalories you burn. Exercise affects the rate at which the body burns kilocalories, speeding up the use of energy-rich foods. Also, as you recall, muscle tissue burns more kilocalories than fat tissue does. Many kinds of activities, not just sports, burn calories.

# Caloric Cost of Various Activities

(for a 154-pound person)

| Calories used per hour (approximate) | Activities |
|---|---|
| 72–84 | Sitting<br>Conversing |
| 120–150 | Strolling 1 mph<br>Standing<br>Playing cards |
| 150–240 | Level walking 2 mph<br>Level cycling 5 mph<br>Typing on manual typewriter<br>Riding lawn mower<br>Golfing, using power cart<br>Canoeing 2.5 mph<br>Horseback riding (walk) |
| 240–300 | Cleaning windows<br>Mopping floors<br>Vacuuming<br>Pushing light power mower<br>Bowling<br>Walking 3 mph*<br>Cycling 6 mph<br>Golfing, pulling cart<br>Horseback riding (sitting to trot)<br>Volleyball (6-man, noncompetitive)<br>Badminton (social doubles) |
| 300–360 | Scrubbing floors*<br>Walking 3.5 mph*<br>Cycling 8 mph*<br>Table tennis (Ping-Pong)<br>Badminton (singles)<br>Volleyball<br>Golfing, carrying clubs<br>Calisthenics (many)*<br>Ballet exercises*<br>Dancing (foxtrot)<br>Tennis (doubles)<br>Raking leaves or hoeing |
| 360–420 | Walking 4 mph*<br>Cycling 10 mph*<br>Ice skating* |

| Calories used per hour (approximate) | Activities |
|---|---|
| 360–420 | Roller skating*<br>Horseback riding (posting to trot)*<br>Canoeing 4 mph<br>Digging garden<br>Disco dancing |
| 420–480 | Hand lawn-mowing*<br>Walking 5 mph*<br>Cycling 11 mph*<br>Tennis (singles)*<br>Badminton (competitive)<br>Downhill skiing (light)<br>Water skiing<br>Cross-country skiing 2.5 mph*<br>Folk (square) dancing*<br>Splitting wood<br>Snow shoveling |
| 480–600 | Sawing hardwood*<br>Digging ditches<br>Jogging 5 mph*<br>Cycling 12 mph*<br>Downhill skiing (vigorous)<br>Touch football<br>Paddleball<br>Horseback riding (gallop)*<br>Basketball<br>Mountain climbing*<br>Ice hockey* |
| 600–660 | Running 5.5 mph*<br>Cycling 13 mph*<br>Handball (social)*<br>Squash (social)*<br>Fencing<br>Basketball (vigorous)*<br>Cross-country skiing (4 mph)* |
| More than 660 | Running 6 to 10 mph*<br>Cross-country skiing 5 or more mph*<br>Handball (competitive)*<br>Squash (competitive)* |

Note: Continuous swimming is also an excellent aerobic exercise that can burn a significant number of calories. However, the caloric range is very wide, depending on such factors as the skill of the swimmer, percentage body fat, stroke used, temperature of the water, and presence of a current.

*This means that the activity can result in cardiovascular conditioning.

Reprinted from Jane Brody's *Good Food Book, Living the High-Carbohydrate Way,* by Jane E. Brody. By permission of W. W. Norton & Company, Inc. © 1985 by Jane E. Brody.

**Different Exercises for Different Purposes** Exercises can be divided by type as well as by how strenuous they are. Some exercises are particularly useful for particular results, such as flexibility or strength. You would expect a ballet dancer and a weight lifter to engage in different exercise programs. Sometimes, very specific exercise programs are developed for particular individuals. You may be familiar with exercises used to restore limbs that have been in casts or to improve the strength of someone who has been ill or has had a heart attack. You may want to develop certain muscle groups to improve your endurance before a day-long bike trip, or your strength for an arm-wrestling contest. There are exercises, however, that are good for several of these results as well as some that promote overall fitness and good health. A few of the benefits that can be gained from different kinds of exercise are:

1. Strengthening the heart and lungs. Any exercise that makes the body take in more oxygen is called an **aerobic** (air-O-bik) **exercise.** Brisk walking, swimming, and bicycling—all good aerobic exercises—make the heart and lungs work harder and thus strengthen the cardiovascular (heart and blood vessels) system. The increased blood supply brings more oxygen to the cells and aids in the removal of carbon dioxide waste as well. The increased and more efficient cardiovascular functioning increases endurance and helps prevent fatigue.

Training for both of these activities requires exercise. What kinds of exercises are most important for the dancers? Why? What is most important for the weight lifter? What exercise needs do they have in common?

**Health Tip**

- To burn extra kilocalories while you are walking for exercise, move your arms energetically.

2. Improving flexibility. Some exercises help make the muscles and joints more elastic and flexible, thus increasing their range of motion. This makes many movements easier and more graceful. Stretching exercises improve flexibility.
3. Conditioning the muscles. Regular exercise makes muscles stronger and able to do more work for longer periods of time. Different kinds of exercise condition different muscle

groups, as you have probably found out from some muscle-aching experiences of your own. Shoveling snow, for example, may strain "muscles you didn't even know you had," even if you think that your sports program keeps you in good shape. Taking up a new sport, even for a well-conditioned athlete, often requires starting slowly and building up strength in muscles that were not strenuously used by other activities. General strengthening and conditioning exercises include sit-ups, push-ups, walking, and bicycling. Benefits of overall muscle conditioning include strengthened stomach and back muscles, which help prevent lower back pain, and strengthened diaphragm muscles, which help improve the functioning of the lungs.

What is this man doing? Warming up, of course. Stretching exercises improve the flexibility of joints and muscles. They also help prevent injury to muscles during more strenuous exercise. What other warm-ups do runners do?

## Psychological Benefits of Exercise

Here is a surprising fact about exercise: even though it is strenuous activity, it is relaxing. Exercise relieves both physical and psychological stress. Perhaps you know someone who uses a punching bag at home or who goes to a gym or health club to "work out" when tension builds up. Or someone who takes a brisk walk "to cool off" when angry. Regular exercise also lowers overall stress and tension. People who jog or swim regularly will probably tell you how much they miss this activity when they give it up for a while.

When you exercise, you increase your intake of oxygen. More oxygen reaches the brain, and you feel more alert. Thus, exercise is often a good "cure" for feeling tired or depressed. The improved conditioning of your muscles and the improved functioning of your lungs and cardiovascular system also promote a sense of well-being. Since a well-toned body is more attractive than a flabby one, and flexible joints and muscles move more gracefully than unconditioned ones, exercise improves appearance. This, too, often makes a person feel better about himself or herself. Regular exercise can also prevent overeating by relieving the tension which causes some people to snack when they are not really hungry. Finally, exercise can be done either in a group, for companionship, or alone, "to get away from it all." There are many kinds of exercise to choose from and even more good reasons for participating.

### Sleep

Just as your body needs to be active during part of the day, it needs to be inactive part of the time, too. Sleep is restorative—it replaces, repairs, renews, and refreshes. Body cells are replaced more quickly during sleep than during active hours. Energy supplies are also built up when strenuous activities are not going on. Muscles need rest to get rid of the waste products that build up in them during strenuous exercise. When you are very active, these wastes build up faster than the process of cellular waste disposal can keep up with. During sleep, the built-up cellular waste can be disposed of by the bloodstream.

Sleep is important psychologically, too. Research shows that dreaming is important to psychological well-being. Many people are not just tired but also irritable if they don't get enough sleep.

Both physical and psychological reasons can cause **insomnia,** the inability to get enough sleep. Excitement or worry can prevent sleep. So can eating too little or too much, or feeling too hot or too cold. Being overtired can even make it difficult to fall asleep. Because sleep is so important, insomnia can become a serious health problem.

There are many myths associated with curing insomnia. One, drinking a warm glass of milk before bedtime, does have a basis in scientific fact. The amino acid *tryptophan* (TRIP-tuh-fan), found in milk, can aid in causing sleep. Taking a warm bath or playing soft music is relaxing and can help you fall asleep. While vigorous exercise increases alertness, a few mild stretching exercises to ease tense muscles is a good aid to sleep. Regular sleep hours and a regular routine of preparing for sleep are also helpful. Obviously, right before bedtime, you should not eat anything that might cause indigestion. Nor should you take sleeping pills. They can become habit-forming and may cover up the real causes of insomnia. Generally speaking, good diet and exercise promote healthy sleep patterns. If you have serious sleep problems, you should see your doctor.

### Stress and Emotions

You have seen how stress can affect sleep patterns and how, in turn, exercise can help lessen stress. Digestion, too, can be affected by feelings. Whether the stress or excitement is pleasant or upsetting, the body's hormone balance is affected. *Hormones* are chemicals that control the rate of digestion as well as the rates of other body processes such as breathing and blood pressure.

There are several ways that emotions affect the digestive operations of the stomach. Anger, it is often said, "ties the stomach in knots." In reality, this emotion causes the churning motion —peristaltic action—of the stomach to increase. Food is pushed along to the small intestine before the proper digestive processes have been completed, and indigestion results.

Feelings of resentment or aggression also affect the stomach, causing it to produce the gastric juices which help to digest food. Usually,

Getting enough sleep is vital to good health. Scientists can study both normal sleep patterns and sleep disorders in a sleep-laboratory setting. Electrodes attached to the patient help take important measurements of eye and brain activity.

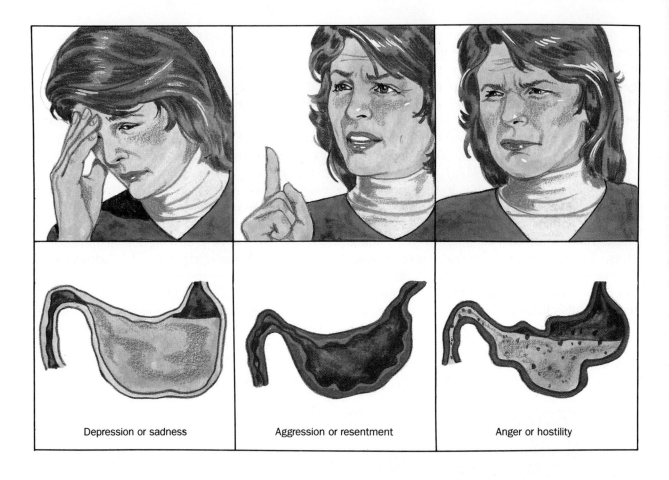

| Depression or sadness | Aggression or resentment | Anger or hostility |

there is little or no food to digest at these times, since people don't often eat much when feeling resentful or aggressive. Thus, the hydrochloric acid in the stomach builds up and leads to "heartburn." This pain may seem to be near the heart or elsewhere in the chest, the abdomen, or the back.

Fear, on the other hand, slows down the production of digestive juices such as saliva. That's why your mouth is often dry when you are afraid. Sadness, disappointment, and depression also stop the production of gastric juices and close off the capillaries to the stomach lining. The undigested food feels as though it's "lying like lead" in the stomach.

Emotions often affect digestion. Depression blocks production of gastric juices so that digestion stops. Aggression and resentment increase the production of gastric juices; if there is no food to digest, heartburn results. Anger speeds up peristalsis, pushing food along before it is ready and causing indigestion.

## Health Tip

- Always wind down slowly after vigorous exercise. To stop abruptly is bad for your heart.

# Food for Thought

Feeling calm or sleepy? Maybe you feel full of energy. Are you forgetful? Recent research suggests that the foods you eat may affect your moods and your memory. This research is leading some doctors to experiment with special diets and with foods to combat depression and other psychological disorders. The research may also lead to development of special enriched medical foods.

Carbohydrates, the research suggests, tend to make us feel calmer because they stimulate the production of insulin. Insulin moves amino acids from the blood into the muscles. This clears a path to the brain for an amino acid called tryptophan. When tryptophan reaches the brain, the brain produces serotonin. Serotonin is the chemical that makes us relaxed and sleepy. It also makes us less sensitive to pain. Some patients who suffer from chronic pain are currently experimenting with high carbohydrate diets.

Proteins, according to research, may make you feel peppy. A chemical called tyrosine is in many protein foods. It causes the brain to make norepinephrine, a chemical that picks up your spirits. One major hospital is currently experimenting with tyrosine added to chocolates for depressed patients.

Eggs, liver, and soybeans all contain choline. Choline stimulates the brain to produce acetylcholine, a chemical involved in the memory process. Scientists hope that choline added to the diet will help to improve memory, but research into this area is too little and too new for conclusions.

Scientists do not guarantee that food has a mind-bending power. All of the research is still too new. It seems, however, that the effects of the chemicals are most powerful on an empty stomach. So, if you are trying to change your mood or your memory, eat a healthful breakfast.

Bread, eggs, pasta, tofu, and liver are considered by some researchers to affect your moods and memory. Which of these foods are carbohydrates? Which are proteins? How do insulin, tyrosine, and choline affect your mood or memory?

It's easy to "read" this man's emotions from his face and from his body language. These emotions are also affecting his digestive system, thus adding to his discomfort.

**For Review**

1. Explain four factors that affect a person's BMR (basal metabolic rate).
2. Describe the energy-producing "burning," or oxidation, that occurs in body cells. What chemicals are involved? What are the waste products?
3. List and explain at least three benefits of exercise.
4. Why does the body need sleep?
5. Explain three ways emotions can affect digestion.

## Food and the Life Cycle

Food sustains all of us for today and helps build and maintain our bodies for a lifetime. Nutrition affects each person, even before birth.

### Pregnancy

Nutrients for the unborn child's growth and development come from the mother. This means her diet during pregnancy is especially important. The woman who reaches childbearing age well nourished and maintains a good diet during pregnancy is likely to avoid complications and have a healthy baby. Pregnancy can be a problem when the expectant mothers are still adolescents. The teen body must cope with its own growth needs as well as those of the child it bears. This can lead to complications for both the mother and the child. The daily diet during pregnancy should provide generous amounts of nutrients according to the Daily Food Guide. There is a need to cut down on nutrient-poor foods such as sweets, fried foods, and other fats to avoid overweight and to assure that nutrient needs are met.

Stress or excitement also affect the body another way. You may feel "a rush of adrenalin" as your heart and breathing rates increase. The body prepares for physical action and sends energy-rich nutrients into the bloodstream. If you take part in "fight or flight," these changes are useful. If, as is often the case in modern times, the stress is psychological and you cannot or do not take physical action, the feeling of your pounding heart may just add to the distress of the situation. Exercising when you feel this way is often very helpful.

## Food Guide: Child, Teen, Adult, Pregnant or Lactating

| | Fruits and Vegetables | | | | | |
| | Vitamin A Rich | Vitamin C Rich | + Others (to Total) | Grain Products | Milk and Milk Products | Meats and Alternatives |
| --- | --- | --- | --- | --- | --- | --- |
| Children[a] (6 months to 9 years) | 1 | 1 | 4 | 4 | 2–3 | 2 |
| Children (9–12 years) | 1 | 1 | 4 | 4 | 3 | 2 |
| Teenager | 1 | 1 | 4 | 4 | 4 | 2 |
| Adult | 1 | 1 | 4 | 4 | 2 | 2 |
| Pregnant or Lactating | 1 | 2 | 5 | 4 or more for adequate weight gain | 4[b] | 3 |

a For preschool children, serving size is 1 tablespoon per year of age.
b For pregnant teenagers, increase to 5 servings.

Extra nutrients are needed during pregnancy both to build the baby's tissues and to protect the mother's health. Special requirements of the pregnant woman include an increased need for kilocalories, for protein, and for calcium, folic acid, and iron. Although it is said that a pregnant woman is "eating for two," she does not need to double her kilocalorie intake. An increase of 300 calories a day is sufficient for the growth of the fetus (unborn baby) and for the mother's increased BMR; too much weight gain can complicate pregnancy. On the other hand, the expectant mother needs 50 percent more protein than the average adult for the production of all the new body cells that are being created. Because calcium helps build teeth and bones, the pregnant woman needs to take in enough of this mineral for both her own health and her baby's growth. If her diet does not supply enough calcium, the fetus will use the reserves stored in the mother's bone tissue. The new red blood cells forming in the fetus require additional supplies of folic acid and iron. These high

Pregnant women need more calcium and protein than the average adult, but only 300 calories per day. Doctors often recommend low-fat milk. Why should the child also drink milk?

requirements often have to be filled by iron and B-vitamin supplements. Other increased nutrient needs should be met by diet. A pregnant woman should discuss her own and her baby's nutrient needs with her doctor throughout her pregnancy.

### Infancy

Children grow and develop more rapidly during their first two years of life than at any other time. Good nutrition is especially important for mental as well as physical development. Poor nutrition can lead to mental retardation and permanent brain damage. Milk is baby's first food, from the breast or as bottled formula. Milk supplies a large proportion of nutrients and is easy for the baby to digest. Foods such as cereals, strained fruits, and vegetables are gradually added to the baby's diet, according to the baby's increasing ability to digest complex foods. As children grow, the balanced diet begun in infancy should continue with progressively larger servings of foods from all of the groups in the Daily Food Guide.

Adults control what small children eat. As they grow up, they choose more of their own diet. Thus, it's important to instill good eating habits early in life.

### Adolescence: The Teen Years

The balanced diet controlled by a child's parents is often significantly changed during the teen or adolescent years. As teenagers become more independent, they choose many of their own foods, especially snacks, and have more meals away from home. Many teens go on crash, or fad, diets or just skip meals in an effort to lose weight. They often become deficient in calcium, iron, and vitamins A and C.

Adolescence, it is important to remember, is a time when a balanced diet is critical. The teen years, like infancy, are a time of rapid growth. Boys, at about 16 or 17, and girls, at about 12 or 13, usually have noticeable growth spurts and require high-energy and nutrient-rich foods. Calcium is needed for bone growth. Protein, which is also needed for growth, will be used instead for energy if carbohydrates and fats are lacking. Girls need a high supply of iron when they begin menstruating. Another problem often associated with the physical changes of adolescence is acne. Science has not been able to show a link between this skin problem and particular kinds of foods. On the other hand, good nutrition—a balanced diet selected from the Daily Food Guide—does promote healthy skin, hair, and teeth while ensuring enough energy for the important growth needs of the teen years. Snacks can help "keep you going" during this active period of your life, but they should also be chosen from the Daily Food Guide. You will read more about weight maintenance and control later in this chapter.

### Adulthood

You will never outgrow your need for the nutrients given in the Daily Food Guide. These nutrients give the cells the ability to maintain themselves and slow down aging. As people become older, they generally need fewer calories. However, their need for nutrients remains about the same. *Osteoporosis,* the age-related

Many teens go through sudden growth spurts. What special needs does this boy have at this time of his life—besides a new wardrobe?

bone loss, can be slowed or prevented by a high calcium intake, regular exercise, moderation in alcohol and caffeine consumption, and by not smoking.

Many adults are surprised to find that they are suddenly gaining weight although they are not consuming more kilocalories. There are several reasons for this. One is that adults, unless they are pregnant, are not experiencing the high-energy needs of growth. The BMR slows during adulthood. Another reason is that many adults lead inactive lives. They spend much of their time at a desk or in a car and often do not think they have the time for regular exercise. Excessive weight gain can lead to a variety of health and disease problems, so exercise and a balanced lower-calorie diet are important for adults.

## Living Alone

Many people live alone at some time during their lives. Unmarried young adults often live alone, as do many older people. Whatever the age, living alone can create some extra problems for getting the proper nutrition. Many of those living alone are tempted to "take the easy road" and just snack on junk food. It does not seem worthwhile to prepare a meal that will be eaten alone in a few minutes, and the same leftovers for days afterward is equally unappealing. Therefore, those who live alone often suffer from poor nutrition.

People who live alone should keep their nutritional needs in mind even though they buy in small quantities. Special dishes that take more effort to prepare can be a satisfying activity for a

People who live alone often do not cook full meals each day. A practical solution is to cook large amounts and then freeze single-serving portions for later use.

rainy day and result in several frozen portions for future use. Often, the best solution to boring or lonely meals is to invite a friend. Sharing the cooking as well as the eating can help make a meal into an enjoyable event.

## Food for Athletes

Some coaches mistakenly believe that athletes need a diet different from nonathletes. Athletes require the same balanced meal pattern suggested for the average person, except that the total amount of food eaten may be increased to meet the increased energy expenditure. Your energy expenditure is related to the intensity and duration of activity. When you choose extra calories from a variety of foods in the food groups, you will also get additional vitamins and minerals at the same time. There

is no evidence to support the belief that a high-protein diet, vitamin supplements, or special health foods improve athletic performance or work.

The salt usually used in food preparation or added at the table is adequate for the athlete. The last meal should be eaten at least three hours before a sports event. Athletes prevent excess water loss by adequate water intake before and during practice or competition. You should not rigidly restrict water before or during athletic contests as some athletes mistakenly believe.

## Older Adults

The percentage of older adults (over age 65) in the population is increasing every year. Many of these people are healthy and active, but their nutritional needs are still somewhat different from those of other ages. There are also large numbers of the elderly who have health, emotional, financial, or other problems that affect their nutritional needs and their abilities to meet those needs.

The major difference in the dietary requirements of older adults is in their kilocaloric needs. The BMR continues to slow down as people get older, and most people over 65 do not get as much exercise as they once did. Because the nutrient needs of older people remain the same while the kilocaloric needs decrease, older adults need to concentrate on foods with a high nutrient density. Many older people, however, simply cut down on their overall intake of food. This often leads to serious nutrient deficiencies, particularly in the B vitamins, iron, calcium, and protein.

Many older people do not buy fresh fruits, vegetables, and meats because these items are too expensive and spoil quickly. Other foods are often available in family-size rather than single-serving sizes, or require more complex preparation than some older people can manage. Older

Many older people are healthy and vigorous and can still give time to help others. The man on the right volunteers in a senior center where other people come for companionship and a hot, nutritious meal.

people who live alone often do not feel it is worthwhile to prepare a balanced meal just for themselves; they miss the companionship of family members. Other reasons that complicate food preparation are difficulty in movement (caused by arthritis or other health problems) and poor eyesight. Changes in vision affect how tempting food looks. Taste and smell also become less sharp, and many foods seem bland and uninteresting. Older people who have dental problems or who have lost their teeth find chewing difficult. For those older people who live alone, all these difficulties may make food preparation seem too much to bother with. They may even forget meals or not get the proper amount of fluids. Most communities have local programs, such as Meals on Wheels, which deliver balanced meals to older people; some

even provide the companionship that makes eating seem worthwhile.

## Medical Conditions and Nutrition

Patients with some short-term medical conditions require special diets for a short time. These people recover quickly and soon go back to their normal eating patterns. You probably have had a "stomach flu" or "24-hour virus" yourself and have been restricted to very bland, easily digestible foods for a short while. Some more complicated problems are also temporary. People recovering from surgery or taking certain kinds of medication are often on restricted diets. These food plans are designed by professionals, medical personnel and dieticians, and should always be followed carefully. Because these diets are often quite bland, attractive

Well-presented meals and cheerful companionship help make special medical diets more pleasant for patients.

arrangement and presentation of the food, as well as cheerful companionship while the meal is eaten, can help make these meals a more pleasant experience.

Long-term medical conditions affect a person's diet all through life. Again, professional medical advice should always be followed. *Diabetes* is one of the most well-known of these conditions. In the diabetic, high blood sugar results from a lack of or a problem with the insulin in the blood. Low-sugar diets are usually recommended. Many people today are on low-sodium diets to control or prevent such conditions as high blood pressure and heart or kidney disease. They usually eliminate table salt altogether and avoid other high-sodium foods. High blood pressure and heart problems are also reasons for low-cholesterol diets. People with these problems avoid foods high in saturated fat, such as eggs, whole-milk products, and fatty meats. Some people are allergic to a particular food and must avoid it. Never tempt someone who has a food allergy to "try just one bite."

Allergic reactions can range from hives and other rashes to headaches, weakness, and breathing difficulties.

## For Review

1. Why are there likely to be health and developmental problems if a pregnant woman is still an adolescent?
2. In what stage of life does the most rapid growth occur?
3. What are two nutritional problems associated with adolescence?
4. Why do adults often put on weight even though they are not eating more than they did as teenagers?
5. What different nutritional needs do athletes have?
6. Describe four problems that make it difficult for some older people to get proper nutrition.

# Maintaining the Proper Weight

The amount of time, energy, and money spent by Americans on trying to change (usually, trying to reduce) their body weight makes weight control one of this country's most "popular" activities. Many people find it difficult to maintain their proper weight. Many others strive for impossible goals; they try to look like a favorite movie star or model or like an imaginary and idealized picture they have of themselves. A surprising number of people—many of them teenage girls—actually make themselves ill in an effort to achieve the perfect figure.

## What Is Your Proper Weight?

What is the proper weight for you? Is it the same as for your friends? Of course not. Neither is your clothing size a good measure of what you "should" weigh. Different people have different size frames and body types as well as different BMRs. What's right for one of your friends may not be right for another friend or for you.

**Body Type** Heredity, the physical characteristics you got from your parents, has a lot to do with your size and shape. It's easy to see that height is inherited, and few people even think of trying to change it. However, many people fight a losing battle against the body type they have also inherited.

Scientists use three categories to classify body types. *Ectomorphs* have a slender, angular build and delicate features. They tend to be lean. *Endomorphs* have a more rounded shape and broader frame. They are often plump, with weight centered in the abdomen. *Mesomorphs* have a build somewhere between the other two. They have a muscular frame. As you can imagine, even if they are the same height, the ideal weight for an ectomorph, endomorph, and mesomorph could be quite different.

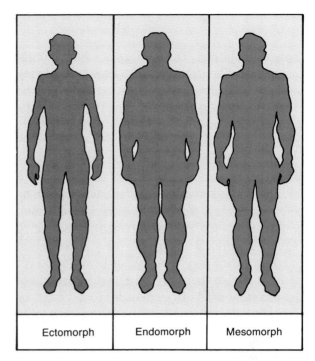

| Ectomorph | Endomorph | Mesomorph |

These people are the same height, but have different frames and builds. Each represents one of the basic body types. Therefore, the ideal weight will be different for each one.

**Appearance** If you take a good, long, critical look in the mirror, you can probably determine which of the body types most closely describes you (many people fall somewhere between two types). You can also get a good idea of whether you are underweight or overweight. Do not compare yourself to some ideal. Instead, look for rolls of fat or bulges. They indicate overweight. (Some flabbiness may indicate lack of muscle tone which can be corrected by exercise without a change in weight.) If you see protruding hipbones and ribs, you are probably too thin. Now, adjust your posture and look again. Straightening your spine, throwing back your shoulders, and pulling in abdominal muscles can do wonders for the way you look. You may find that your "overweight," particularly around your middle, was merely the product of a slouch.

**Skinfold Test** To get a more precise picture of how much fat your body has, you can try a skinfold test. Doctors use a caliper to get this measurement, but you can use the following method for a good approximation. You will be measuring the layer of fat under the skin of the back of your upper arm, calf, or waist (or the midriff on a male). Pinch the skin between your thumb and forefinger. The skin and fat layers should pull away from the muscle and make a fold. If you "pinch more than an inch," you may be overweight. A person of normal weight usually measures a fat layer of between ½ and 1 inch (12 and 24 mm). Some people carry their weight unevenly. They may have thin or heavy arms yet be normal elsewhere. Try the test in several of the recommended places in order to get a better idea of the average thickness of the fat layer under your skin.

**Height-Weight Charts** Another way to judge if your weight is suitable for your height and frame is to use a height-weight table like the one on page 89. Health professionals develop these charts for adults, according to height and frame. Since teenagers grow and mature at different rates, they are not included on these tables. Note the range of weights even within one column. Remember the body types described on page 87. You can see that the chart gives only a rough idea of how much a person should weigh. However, using the chart along with the skinfold test and a realistic interpretation of what you see in the mirror can probably give you a good idea of whether your present weight is right for you.

### Overweight

What should you do if you have determined that you really do weigh more than you should? What's wrong with being overweight? When does too much weight become a health risk?

There is a difference between overweight and obesity. **Overweight** describes people who are up to 10 percent above their desirable weight. **Obese** (o-BEESS) people are at least 20 percent above normal weight for their height and frame. While a pound or two above your ideal weight might make you technically overweight, it should not become a health problem if you get the proper nutrition, exercise regularly, and sleep well. As a matter of fact, many athletes are technically overweight not because they have too much fat but because they have a large amount of muscle. Obesity, on the other hand, is an excess of body fat, and can pose a serious health risk.

According to studies by life insurance companies, obese people have a shorter life expectancy than people of normal weight. They run higher risks of cancer, diabetes, heart diseases, high blood pressure, and other health problems. The body organs, including the heart and lungs, have to work harder to power an obese body than a lean one. Muscles and bones are also under added strain. A body overinsulated by fat has trouble cooling itself, and perspires more easily. The obese person tires easily and may find healthful exercise difficult to manage.

**Causes of Overweight** Often, there are medical reasons for obesity. Body type also has an influence. An endomorph may never look as slim as an ectomorph but still can maintain a proper and healthful weight for that type of build. Research indicates that the number of fat cells in a person's body never decreases, although the individual cells can become smaller in size. That means that obesity as a child or teenager may make it harder to control weight as an adult.

The major reason for overweight and obesity, however, is related to kilocaloric balance. It means that the body is taking in more fuel (kilocalories) than it is burning (including growth and exercise). The excess is being stored by the body as fat. You have seen that exercise is a way of influencing your kilocaloric balance.

## 1983 Metropolitan Height and Weight Tables*

| | Height | | Frame Size | | |
|---|---|---|---|---|---|
| | Feet | Inches | Small | Medium | Large |
| Men | 5 | 2 | 128–134 | 131–141 | 133–150 |
| | 5 | 3 | 130–136 | 133–143 | 140–153 |
| | 5 | 4 | 132–138 | 135–145 | 142–156 |
| | 5 | 5 | 134–140 | 137–148 | 144–160 |
| | 5 | 6 | 136–142 | 139–151 | 146–164 |
| | 5 | 7 | 138–145 | 142–154 | 149–168 |
| | 5 | 8 | 140–148 | 145–157 | 152–172 |
| | 5 | 9 | 142–151 | 148–160 | 155–176 |
| | 5 | 10 | 144–154 | 151–163 | 158–180 |
| | 5 | 11 | 146–157 | 154–166 | 161–184 |
| | 6 | 0 | 149–160 | 157–170 | 164–188 |
| | 6 | 1 | 152–164 | 160–174 | 168–192 |
| | 6 | 2 | 155–168 | 164–178 | 172–197 |
| | 6 | 3 | 158–172 | 167–182 | 176–202 |
| | 6 | 4 | 162–176 | 171–187 | 181–207 |
| Women | 4 | 10 | 102–111 | 109–121 | 118–131 |
| | 4 | 11 | 103–113 | 111–123 | 120–134 |
| | 5 | 0 | 104–115 | 113–126 | 122–137 |
| | 5 | 1 | 106–118 | 115–129 | 125–140 |
| | 5 | 2 | 108–121 | 118–132 | 128–143 |
| | 5 | 3 | 111–124 | 121–135 | 131–147 |
| | 5 | 4 | 114–127 | 124–138 | 134–151 |
| | 5 | 5 | 117–130 | 127–141 | 137–155 |
| | 5 | 6 | 120–133 | 130–144 | 140–159 |
| | 5 | 7 | 123–136 | 133–147 | 143–163 |
| | 5 | 8 | 126–139 | 136–150 | 146–167 |
| | 5 | 9 | 129–142 | 139–153 | 149–170 |
| | 5 | 10 | 132–145 | 142–156 | 152–173 |
| | 5 | 11 | 135–148 | 145–159 | 155–176 |
| | 6 | 0 | 138–151 | 148–162 | 158–179 |

*Reprinted through the courtesy of Metropolitan Life Insurance Company.

From our earliest years, food—particularly sweet desserts—is used as a reward in our society (left). Adults, too, often celebrate special occasions as well as personal achievements in this way (right).

Chapter 4—Food and Good Health **89**

The other way, obviously, is by changing what you eat. The fewer kilocalories you consume, the fewer will remain to be stored as fat after the body's metabolic needs have been met.

Why, then, is losing weight so difficult for so many people? People overeat for psychological and social reasons. Eating patterns are often related to stress, boredom, and habit. Food is often treated as a reward in our society. Children rewarded with a cookie for good behavior are likely to grow up to be adults who reward themselves with sweets for a job well done. They may also reward others with food, celebrating special occasions with elaborate, fattening meals and putting out snacks to welcome guests. Advertisements constantly remind the public of the availability and desirability of food. Commercials associate their food products, particularly high-calorie snacks and fast food, with popularity and good times. They show slim, healthy models indulging in food habits that tend to make most people overweight.

Why is it a good idea to get personalized advice from a health professional when you plan to diet to lose weight?

**How to Lose Weight** With all the temptations around you to eat too much and to indulge in high-calorie, low-nutrition foods, and with all the modern conveniences that can lead to a sedentary, or inactive, lifestyle, what is the best way to reach and maintain your ideal weight? The answer begins with a question: How important is it to you to lose weight?

First, you must reach a serious decision to lose weight. You must add up the advantages to both your health and your appearance. Think how much better you will feel about yourself. You must really want to lose weight and have the willpower to stick with your decision.

Second, visit your physician. A check-up by your doctor will reveal if your weight problem has any medical causes or if you have any nutritional **deficiency** (dih-FISH-en-see), the lack of a particular nutrient that can lead to a health problem. You can also discuss with your doctor any emotional problems you think are related to your weight. There is little sense in planning a reducing diet unless emotional reasons for overeating are also considered.

Your physician will probably want to know about your usual eating habits. For two or three days before your visit, keep a record of what you eat, and when, where, and how much you eat. Don't forget snacks. You and your doctor will study your eating habits to see how they can best be modified for healthy weight loss. Be prepared to discuss the amount of exercise you usually get, too.

Finally, your doctor will give you a diet suited to your health, age, body size and type, and usual level of activity (you may also be told to increase your exercise level). The diet will be balanced to ensure proper nutrition and good health. If supplements are needed, the doctor will prescribe them. That is not a decision you should make on your own.

If you are planning to lose only a few pounds, or if you are pleased with your weight but fear you may not be able to maintain it, you can use the Daily Food Guide to plan a nutritious, nonfattening diet. Limiting foods from the Fats-Sweets Group and looking carefully at snacks will help. If, however, you need to lose a lot of weight or have had trouble dieting on your own, it is best to follow a physician's advice. Crash diets, fad diets, commercially sold liquids and pills, and skipping meals all can lead to serious health problems.

### Some Do's and Don't's for Dieters

*Do* set realistic weight-loss goals for yourself. Your doctor can help you do this. Break down long-term goals (your ideal weight) into more easily reached short-term goals (pounds lost per week). Weight loss is not perfectly regular, so *don't* be discouraged if you do not lose the same amount each week. *Do* reward yourself with a nonfood present or special activity when you reach a goal. You deserve it!

*Don't* believe the exaggerated claims of fad diet books or diet plans or even of acquaintances who tell you how much they lost in a week or month. *Don't* set unrealistic goals for your body type or plan to lose more weight than is healthy at one time. Unrealistic goals lead to frustration; sudden and severe weight loss can lead to illness.

*Do* develop new eating habits as you diet. You will need these new, sensible habits to maintain your desired weight once you reach it. Look carefully at when you overeat and why. Then try to avoid those temptations. Prepare low-calorie snacks in advance for times when you feel you must eat between meals, or plan a different activity, preferably one involving calorie-burning exercise, for those times. Taking a biking break from homework is preferable to a snack break. Pre-cut carrot sticks are just as convenient to carry to the TV as a box of cookies or a bag of chips.

*Don't* get caught in seesaw dieting. Losing

It's just as convenient to take a piece of fruit or pre-cut carrot and celery sticks to munch on while watching TV as it is to take a bag of chips—and much healthier!

a lot of weight on a crash diet, then gaining it back, then dieting again is not only discouraging, it's also bad for your health. The severe adjustments your body has to make to each weight swing can cause thyroid and heart problems.

*Do* seek support from friends—or even from diet groups or clubs—when you diet. Encouragement from people "who have been there" can be very helpful. However, *don't* go on fad diets just to help out a friend or be one of the group. Stay away from single-food diets, diets based on commercially sold supplements or "complete foods," diet pills and suppressants, and diets with exaggerated claims. Nutritional deficiencies, more serious health problems, and even deaths have resulted from following some of these fads without a doctor's supervision.

*Do* increase your exercise level. Exercise not only burns calories and thus increases weight loss, it also helps prevent the flabbiness that sometimes accompanies the loss of many pounds.

*Don't* be embarrassed to "trick" yourself into good eating habits. Using smaller plates makes portions look larger. Taking smaller mouthfuls, chewing slowly, and putting down your fork between bites helps make smaller meals last longer. Drinking a glass of water before a meal may also make you feel less "empty."

Finally, *do* use this book to help you learn to prepare tempting and healthful meals that are also low in kilocalories. Use the Daily Food Guide as your basic nutritional guide. Watch not only the ingredients but also the methods of food preparation of the dishes you eat at home and in restaurants. Check for low-calorie recipes and nutrient-dense foods. Eating well is certainly a challenge, but it does not have to be a chore.

## Weight-related Health Problems

Being too heavy is not the only weight-related problem. Some people weigh too little and are underweight. They need to follow many of the same steps as those who are overweight in changing their diets, but of course they will be adding rather than reducing calories. Other individuals weigh enough but still suffer nutrient deficiencies or are generally malnourished. Still others suffer from the dangerous eating disorders known as anorexia nervosa and bulimia.

**Deficiencies and Malnutrition**  It is easy to understand how people who cannot obtain or afford enough food or the right food can suffer from deficiencies in nutrition. In times of famine, whole societies can suffer **malnutrition,** the result of not getting the right nutrients in the right amounts, while many people actually starve to death. Some people, even in wealthier societies, cannot afford the

Thin is in! Fashion and advertising promote an unusually slender figure. Not everyone can achieve this "look;" some anorexics actually starve themselves trying to attain it.

foods for a balanced diet and are concerned only with feeling "full." They, too, often become malnourished.

The most common deficiency diseases suffered in this country are *anemia* (uh-NEE-mee-uh) (a lack of oxygen in the red blood cells, caused by too little iron, folic acid, or vitamin $B_{12}$) and *osteoporosis* (brittle, porous bones caused by lack of calcium). Few Americans today get *rickets* (a bone-softening disease of childhood caused by lack of vitamin D) or *scurvy* (a serious illness caused by lack of vitamin C), which were common in past centuries. A long-term lack of proper nourishment—including both calories and nutrients—can stunt mental and physical development LIM in children and cause emotional as well as physical problems in adults.

In addition to people who are too thin, some overweight people also suffer from malnutrition. That is because they eat too much of the wrong foods. Too many sweet and fatty foods not only add pounds, but they can also "crowd out" the nutrient-dense foods. It's hard to work up much enthusiasm for a well-balanced dinner of lean meat and vegetables when you've just consumed french fries and a shake.

**Eating Disorders**   Two weight-related health problems have recently received increased publicity. They are both serious disorders that often affect teenagers, and you should be aware of their characteristics and their dangers. These conditions seem to be associated with a desire to lose weight but continue even after the victim has become very thin. They have complex psychological causes and are often triggered by stress. Victims need both medical and psychological help, and they need it quickly.

**Anorexia nervosa** (an-uh-REK-see-uh ner-VO-suh) is a disorder which at first seems to be crash dieting to achieve a very thin figure like that of a model or a movie star. Anorexics, however, have distorted images of their own bodies. They constantly complain that they are fat even when they are painfully and unhealthfully thin. Some anorexics stop eating almost entirely and can literally starve themselves to death.

**Bulimia** (buh-LIM-ee-uh) victims, too, want to lose weight but they also want to eat,

and they carry both these desires to extremes. First they binge (eat as much as they can, up to four or five times the normal amount for a meal) and then they make themselves vomit to purge, or rid, themselves of the calories. This binge-purge pattern becomes a habit, and bulimics become unable to digest food. They, too, can starve to death.

Both anorexia and bulimia are much more than just dieting. They are serious psychological and medical problems that require professional attention.

## Balance Is the Key

On the whole, you should avoid extremes: extremes in eating behavior, extremes in claims for diet foods and plans, extremes in goals for your own weight-loss or weight-gain program. Balance is the key: a balanced diet from the Daily Food Guide, a balance of kilocaloric intake and use, a balance of food and exercise, and a balance in the times and types of foods you eat. As you have seen, good health is a balance of many processes. "Keep your balance" and you will promote good health.

### For Review

1. Describe three methods you can use to determine your proper body weight.
2. Why is obesity a health problem?
3. What are the benefits of visiting your doctor to work out a plan for weight reduction?
4. What are fad diets? Why should they be avoided?
5. How can someone who is overweight still be malnourished?
6. Why are anorexia nervosa and bulimia so dangerous?

# $4$ Chapter Review

## Summary

The nutrients in the food a person eats are important to good health. Once food is swallowed, the digestive processes begin. The nutrients in the food are broken down and carried by the bloodstream to build body cells, or they may be stored in the body for later use. The substances not needed are excreted as waste. The nutrients combine with oxygen to give a person energy, which is needed to carry on all life processes. The kilocalories in food affect the amount of energy a person has. Too many kilocalories, however, cause an unhealthy condition. A balanced diet—planned according to the Daily Food Guide—sufficient exercise, and plenty of sleep help people remain healthy and maintain their proper weight.

## Vocabulary

Use the words below to fill in the blanks.

| | |
|---|---|
| absorption | deficiency |
| aerobic exercise | digestion |
| anorexia nervosa | insomnia |
| basal metabolic rate (BMR) | malnutrition |
| | metabolism |
| basal metabolism | obese |
| bulimia | overweight |
| circulatory system | peristalsis |

When a person swallows food, muscular contractions, __(1)__, move the food along through the esophagus to the stomach. After a person eats, the foods are broken down in the stomach into nutrients for the body by a process called __(2)__. In the next step, __(3)__, the usable nutrients are taken from the digestive system and delivered into the bloodstream. The blood carries the nutrients to all the body cells through the __(4)__, which includes the heart, lungs, and blood vessels.

The processes that occur in the body cells after the nutrients and oxygen have been delivered is known as __(5)__. Some people can eat foods with more kilocalories than others and not gain weight because their __(6)__, which is the amount of energy a person needs to carry on the necessary life processes, varies according to body size and type, age, health, and the activities of certain body organs. Often larger people can consume more kilocalories without gaining weight because they usually have a higher __(7)__. Kilocalories can be burned up through walking briskly, and bicycling, which are a form of __(8)__. To restore the body from the day's activity, a person requires sleep, but some people suffer from __(9)__, which is an inability to get enough sleep.

The consumption of too many or too few kilocalories can cause weight problems. One weight problem is caused by a nutritional __(10)__, which is the lack of a particular nutrient, and another is __(11)__, which is the result of not getting the right nutrients in the right amounts. People who weigh too much are __(12)__ or __(13)__. Some people become so concerned with their weight problem that they may develop one of two serious health disorders — __(14)__ or __(15)__.

# Chapter Questions

1. How does digestion turn food into usable nutrients?
2. Briefly explain how the process of absorption delivers nutrients to the bloodstream.
3. How does the circulatory system deliver nutrients to the body cells?
4. What are the four automatic body processes that require energy?
5. What is the relationship between exercise and kilocalories?
6. What are causes of insomnia and what are ways to overcome it?
7. How do the nutrient needs of your mother and father differ from your nutrient needs?
8. What kinds of diets are usually recommended for people with heart problems?
9. When does too much weight become a health risk?
10. Why does a person who is obese as a child or teenager usually find it difficult to control weight as an adult?
11. Why is losing weight difficult for many people?

# Skill Activities

**1. Decision making** In your food journal or in a card file box, start a collection of recipes that are for low cholesterol or low sodium diets. You can find these recipes in magazines, in the food pages of newspapers, on supermarket display boards, and on the packages of specially marked products. In addition, some producers of margarine with no cholesterol provide menus and recipes for low-cholesterol meals. Organize your collection into sections that cover beverages, soups, salads, meats, fish, poultry, casseroles, snacks, breads, cakes, cookies, pies, and desserts. Add to this collection as you discover other recipes for appetizing meals.

**2. Communication** Write an invitation to a physical therapist to speak to your class. Prepare a list of questions that you would like to ask her/him to talk about. Include in your list, questions about the kinds of exercises that strengthen the heart and lungs, that improve flexibility, and that condition the muscles.

**3. Reading** On the left-hand side of a sheet of paper, write the headings "Brand name," "Ingredients," "Serving size," "Calories," "Protein," "Carbohydrate," "Fat," and "Sodium." Visit a grocery store, find the canned fruits section, and select brands of the same kind of fruit, such as pears. Read the nutritional labels. Beside each heading, write the information you find. Now look at the differences between the products. Which brand has the least amount of calories? Which brand has the most calories? What is the difference in calories between the two brands? Why do you think one brand has more calories than another? Which brand has the least amount of sodium? Which brand has the most sodium? Which brand has the least carbohydrates? Which brand has the most carbohydrates?

# 5 Influences on Planning

## As you read, think about:

- how to manage resources in food preparation.
- how to achieve variety in meals.
- how to select nutritious restaurant meals.
- how to keep carry-away foods safe.

**Vocabulary**
management
menu
generic brands
texture
à la carte
salad bar
entrée
Heimlich
  Maneuver

Please note heating directions

In addition to the meal-planning guides, there are some other ways to help you create meals that are not only nutritious but also efficiently prepared as well as attractive and tempting.

To achieve this goal, you should think about a number of things. Think about the people for whom you are planning meals. To begin with, you will probably cook for your family, so think about family customs or traditions. There are probably a number of dishes that are especially important to your family. Cost, time, and energy must also be considered. Of course your meals should have variety in color, size and shape, texture, flavor, and temperature of foods.

There are also times when you will eat away from home. On these occasions, you should be just as careful to balance your nutrient intake and avoid calorie overload. Consider all the foods you eat—those you prepare yourself, those prepared for you at home, and those you eat out—as parts of your daily food intake. Use the Daily Food Guide to balance all parts of your daily diet.

## Planning Home-prepared Meals

Most of your experience with food comes from your family meals. Your family food customs or traditions have made certain foods and methods of cooking important to you. These familiar foods continue to give you enjoyment, satisfaction, and a feeling of security. Chicken with potato salad may be the food that appeals to some people. Others may think of boiled corned beef and cabbage as their special meal. Still others may enjoy refried beans and enchiladas. As you plan meals, you will probably include some of your favorites.

When you are away from home or with people who have different food customs, your

Your taste in food has been influenced by customs handed down in your family. Tea from a samovar is a Russian tradition.

experiences with food may broaden. You will probably come to enjoy many different foods. Some foods from other countries may become as popular with you as those you are used to eating. For example, many people enjoy fresh pineapple, shrimp, pizza, spaghetti, fried noodles, tacos, stir-fry vegetables, and barbecued ribs. Family food favorites and new foods will make your meals interesting and a pleasure to prepare.

### Managing Your Resources

There are many things to consider when you plan and prepare a meal. You want your final product to be nutritious and appealing—to look, smell, and taste good as well as to be good for you. You also want all parts of the meal ready to serve at the proper time. You have to think about what you need in order to prepare the meal—equipment as well as ingredients—and the cost of obtaining or using these materials. Finally, you need to consider your skills in the kitchen. There may be times when you will want

When you manage meal preparation well, you can be justly proud of the nutritious, flavorful, and attractive results.

carries through to the conservation of energy and leftovers. Skillful management, as you saw in Chapter 1, allows the completion of a given task using the least time and energy while achieving the best results.

**Cost of Food** One important consideration in the management of a meal is what many corporate and business managers call "the bottom line": the cost.

Fortunately, the cost of food is not determined by its nutrient value. You can purchase nutritious foods that are well within your food allowance. Inexpensive foods from each food group may include canned vegetables and vegetables in season; nonfat dry milk and margarine; less tender cuts of meat; poultry; enriched or whole-grain breads; and cereals that need to be cooked.

Meats are the most expensive, while grains and breads are the least expensive groups of foods. From the meat group, poultry and fish are usually less expensive than meats. Cheese, eggs, and milk are other more economical sources of complete protein.

Your best guide for comparing the cost of food is to determine the cost of each serving. Divide the cost of the food by the number of servings to obtain the cost per serving. For

to experiment with new dishes and other times when you will want to serve foods that you already know how to prepare.

Good **management,** all of the decision making and planning of work activity to complete a task, is the way to coordinate these factors. It begins with decision making (determining the **menu,** the dishes to be prepared and the order in which they will be served) and

Often, the larger the package size, the lower the unit price (at left on each shelf label). Always check the unit price to be sure; specials and sales can sometimes make the smaller size a better buy.

You can save money by choosing generic brands. These wholesome foods and useful products come in simply marked packages. There is usually only a limited selection of generic products.

example, when the cost of a whole chicken is $7.98 and it serves 4 people ($7.98 divided by 4), the cost per serving is approximately $2.00.

Unit pricing is another way to make food-cost comparisons. When the price per pound (kilogram), per ounce (gram), or per quart (liter) is listed on the package label or market shelf, you can easily compare prices, even of different sized packages. Do your shopping at stores that have unit prices clearly displayed.

It is usually wise to buy a less expensive form of a food if it will serve your purpose. For example, the chili you prepare using Grade C canned tomatoes (which come in pieces of varying size) can be just as delicious as if you used the more expensive, Grade A, whole tomatoes. The largest and most perfect foods are more expensive, but their nutritional value is the same as smaller, cheaper sizes of the same food.

Another way to cut costs at the supermarket is to buy **generic brands** instead of national brands or store brands. Generic food products are wholesome foods. They come in simply marked packages that list only the name of the product, such as sweet peas, the ingredients, net content, and name of manufacturer or distributor. Generic brands are lower in price than national or store brands because of inexpensive packaging, little advertising, and limited selection. Sometimes the contents are of somewhat lower quality (USDA Grade C, and some Grade B), but they are adequate for many purposes.

When you want to spend less money for food, you can reduce the amount of meat you buy and stop buying extras such as potato chips, pretzels, and carbonated beverages. You can choose recipes with less sugar, fat, and egg, and those which have optional ingredients such as mushrooms, toasted almonds, or some other ingredient. Recipes that use canned soups, prepared puddings, or canned onion rings add to the cost of food. Heat-and-serve products, salad dressings, gravy mixes, and foods in pressure cans also add to cost.

Why is it not a good idea to cut down on milk, citrus fruits, and the dark-green and yellow vegetables? Foods that provide little if any nutrients, such as cola beverages and sweets, are the truly expensive foods because their return in essential nutrients needed for health is so limited. When you shop, consider not only cost per serving but also cost related to nutrient value.

**Time and Energy** Time, as well as money, is often limited. You will be preparing meals each day, but on some days you will have more time for food preparation than on others. The time and energy you will have to spend in preparation will be influenced by the foods and the food forms you buy. Some foods, such as less tender cuts of meats, yeast breads, and baked beans, take more time to prepare than other foods. Raw or fresh foods require less preparation and therefore less time and energy. There may be times when your schedule permits little time for food preparation. If your budget allows, at these times you may decide to use prepared mixes, canned or frozen foods, or heat-and-serve convenience items.

Some methods of food cookery, such as broiling and frying, require more attention than others, such as roasting and braising. Small or thin pieces of food cook more quickly than large or thick pieces. Foods such as roasts or casseroles cooked in the oven usually require more time than do many foods cooked on the range surface. As you saw in Chapter 1, you can conserve energy—electricity or gas—by turning off the oven a few minutes before the food is completely done. The retained heat will continue to cook the food. Another energy-saving strategy is to cook side dishes in the oven when you have it on to prepare the main course. Baked potatoes might be a particularly good choice if the oven is already on at the right temperature. No additional energy use would be required.

Some foods can be prepared by more than one method. You can choose the method that best fits your time schedule. Drop biscuits, baked potatoes, and strawberry cobbler require less preparation and attention than rolled biscuits, french fries, and strawberry chiffon pie.

Foods that cook slowly and those that require less attention allow you to do other tasks at the same time the food is cooking. Mashing potatoes, making gravy or white sauce, and broiling foods are last-minute details that can complicate meal preparation. A meal will be more easily prepared if you include no more than one food that requires any last-minute preparation or attention.

## Using a Meal Preparation Plan

The preparation of a meal involves following a time schedule as well as the recipe directions. Making a plan or schedule using four "time zones" is especially important for the success of the beginning cook. Select the recipes you wish to use, and note suggested cooking times as well as temperatures or heat settings (low, medium, or high).

Divide the foods of your menu into four preparation time zones: (1) foods that can be prepared in advance; (2) foods that require an hour or longer to cook; (3) foods that require less than an hour to cook; (4) foods that require last-minute preparation. Foods that can be prepared in advance maintain their good eating quality even if prepared early in the day or the day before. They do not harden, dry out, or toughen. Cakes and pies are often prepared in advance. Many foods that take longer than an hour to cook, such as casseroles or pot roasts, can be "held" or kept warm for a little while without losing their eating quality. Most dishes that require short cooking periods are best served as soon as they are cooked. Pan-broiled foods, vegetables, and fried or broiled foods should be served immediately for best flavor and texture. Leave time for last-minute jobs, such as making gravies and mashing potatoes.

As you divide the preparation of a meal into the four time zones, you also group the foods into a logical order, beginning with the foods that take the longest to cook. Notice how the menu on the opposite page can be divided into preparation time zones. In addition to the time zones, you should list the actual time at which you will perform each activity.

You must allow time for preparation of a dish in addition to the cooking time required. It will be easier for you to judge the preparation time required when you first list all of the steps involved in a recipe. For example, when you prepare scalloped potatoes, you must estimate how long it will take you to make the white sauce (measure ingredients, combine them, and cook the sauce); to pare, slice, and arrange potatoes in a casserole; and to cover them with the sauce. If you estimate that it will take 15 minutes to assemble the dish, you should begin preparing the potatoes 15 minutes ahead of the time that the dish is to be put into the oven.

# Meal Preparation Plan

**Menu:** Baked Ham
Scalloped Potatoes
Fresh Asparagus Spears
Lettuce Salad   French Dressing
Crescent Rolls
Fresh Strawberry Sundae
Coffee   Milk

**Serve:** 6 P.M.

| | Preparation Time Zones | Time Schedule |
|---|---|---|
| Advance Preparation: | 1. Prepare ham for baking<br>2. Wash potatoes<br>3. Wash, trim asparagus, refrigerate<br>4. Wash, cut lettuce into wedges, refrigerate<br>5. Wash, prepare strawberries, refrigerate<br>6. Measure coffee into percolator basket | Complete these preparations at any convenient time in your schedule before 4 P.M. |
| More Than an Hour to Cook: | 1. Set oven to preheat and set table.<br>2. Place ham into oven<br>3. Prepare scalloped potatoes<br>    Bake scalloped potatoes<br>4. Clean up work area | 4:00<br>4:10<br>4:11<br>4:30 |
| Less Than an Hour to Cook: | 1. Cook asparagus<br>2. Prepare coffee in percolator<br>3. Shape refrigerated cresent rolls and bake<br>4. Select required serving dishes and arrange conveniently near range | 5:35<br>5:36<br>5:44 |
| Last-Minute Preparations: | 1. Remove butter or margarine from refrigerator and pour milk<br>2. Arrange lettuce wedges on plates, add dressing<br>3. Remove rolls from oven and arrange in napkin-lined bread basket<br>4. On serving platter, arrange ham and asparagus<br>5. Remove scalloped potatoes from the oven<br>6. Serve the main course<br>7. Just before serving dessert, arrange ice cream and strawberries in sundae dishes. | 5:50<br>5:52<br>5:54<br>5:55<br>5:58<br>6:00 |

You should list the convenience foods (refrigerated rolls, for example) and any heat-and-serve items in your time plan. A written time plan will help you realize the steps involved in meal preparation, develop good work habits, and build self-confidence, in addition to helping you get all the food ready for serving at the proper time. Even experienced cooks make written time plans when preparing elaborate or special meals. As you gain experience, you will be able to prepare meals without detailed written plans, but with plans you keep in mind.

**Skills** Whether you are a skilled, experienced cook or a beginner determines how much written planning you need to do for a meal as well as the type of menu you will select. Be realistic about your food-preparation skills. Beginners should start with simple recipes that do not require many complicated steps or several steps occurring at the same time. However, do not be afraid to branch out and experiment when you have time and a suitable audience. Your family will probably be tolerant of not-quite-successful results. For company, stick with dishes you know how to prepare well.

**Equipment** Another factor to consider when planning a menu is the equipment you have available in your kitchen and how well you know how to use it. The brand-new microwave or food processor is useful in meal preparation only after you have taken the time to learn to use it properly.

Read through any recipes you are considering to see if they require special equipment. Some recipes give a choice: beating ingredients either in an electric mixer or by hand; stir frying in a wok or frying pan. Others are very specific; only a soufflé dish or a waffle iron will do. In other cases, you can see that without some electric aid (a food processor, electric mixer, or pasta machine), a recipe will be too lengthy or too complicated for you.

Even simple recipes require the use of special equipment. Waffles are fun and easy to prepare if you know how to use the waffle iron. What other dishes require special equipment?

Also, be sure to consider all the dishes you are preparing. If you are roasting the main dish in the oven at 350°F (180°C), you cannot brown another dish at 450°F (230°C) at the same time. Even if the temperatures are the same, will all items fit in the oven together? Are there enough burners on your range for all the foods you are planning to cook or warm there? Will everything fit in the refrigerator? Few home kitchens have the refrigerator, range, and oven space that is available to chefs on television who whip up elaborate meals with the aid of unseen assistants and whole rows of appliances.

### Variety in Menus

Remember the old saying "Variety is the spice of life"? You will probably quickly agree that variety adds interest to food. Boring sameness can really dull the appetite. Even though you may follow the same meal pattern, you can

# Dietary Guidelines

In 1982, a committee of the National Academy of Sciences presented a report on the links between diet and cancer. The report resulted from the efforts of 13 top scientists who studied all the available research on how the foods we eat can influence the development of cancer. The committee included scientists with different areas of expertise and different notions about the link between diet and cancer. Wary of myths, quacks, fraud, and inconclusive scientific evidence, the committee cautiously approached their task.

Despite this caution, the committee found compelling scientific evidence linking diet and cancer. From their two years of research they issued a set of dietary guidelines. These guidelines, if followed, could help people improve their chances of avoiding cancer. The committee was quick to point out, however, that they could not now and would never be able to issue dietary rules that would protect everyone from developing cancer.

## The NAS Dietary Guidelines

1. Decrease fat consumption. The typical American consumes 40 percent of his or her total calories in fat. The committee suggests a target of 30 percent for most people. High fat consumption is linked to common cancers, particularly breast and colon cancer.

2. Eat more vegetables, fruits, and whole grains. Citrus fruits with their high vitamin C content, and dark-green and dark-yellow vegetables with their high vitamin A content seem to be important in preventing cancer. Cabbage and related vegetables are also important.

3. Avoid smoked, salt-cured, and salt-pickled foods. This recommendation is based on strong evidence from China, Japan, and Iceland where people eat large amounts of foods preserved in these ways. In these countries, there are high rates of cancer of the stomach and esophagus.

4. Efforts by government, industry, and consumers to improve food safety should be continued. Substances in food that are suspected of causing cancer can occur naturally. They also may be added during production, processing, and storage. Food should be tested regularly to make sure that suspected substances do not exceed permissable levels.

5. Possible cancer-causing substances in foods should be identified and further testing should be done. Substances that cause mutations in laboratory animals should be removed from food if this does not affect the nutritional value.

6. Drinking alcohol has been linked to higher rates of respiratory cancer and upper gastro-intestinal cancer. Adults who choose to drink alcohol should do so only in moderate amounts. (Others not yet of legal age to drink should not drink at all.)

Fruits and vegetables seem to be a good guard against cancer.

have variety in meals by varying color, size and shape, texture, flavor, temperature, and methods of cooking.

Because foods must look good before you are willing to eat them, it is often said that "you eat with your eyes." Pleasing combinations of foods add attractiveness and stimulate the appetite. When you plan menus, include a variety of foods that will look attractive together.

**Color**   You may be very aware of color and color combinations in the clothes that you wear. Color in food requires the application of these same color principles to the food combinations included in a meal. Contrasting colors add interest and complementary colors enhance the appearance of foods. You not only want foods to look good together, but you also want their colors to harmonize with the dishes, place mats or tablecloth, and centerpiece.

**Size and Shape**   In addition to color, the size and shape of the foods served can add variety and attractiveness. Repetition of the same shapes is not interesting. When you serve a combination of foods cut into small pieces as in casseroles or stews, serve the accompanying vegetable or salad so that the definite shape and identity of the vegetable or salad ingredients are retained.

**Texture**   Texture in food refers to the way the food feels when you chew it. When you have a variety in the textures, you add a pleasing contrast to a meal. Choose foods which are crisp, crunchy, hard, soft, and tender for additional eating pleasure. Too many foods of the

**Practical Tip**
• Keep several one-dish meals in the freezer to pull out on busy days.

The many shapes, sizes, and colors of pasta can add variety whether they are used in the main dish or as a side dish. A sauce with a contrasting color can then be added.

same texture, whether soft or crisp, will detract from your meal.

**Flavor**   Contrasts in food flavors add interest to a meal. Avoid serving foods with similar flavors (broccoli, cabbage, brussels sprouts) at the same meal. Also avoid serving too many sweet, sour, or highly seasoned foods at the same time.

**Temperature**   Contrasts in food temperatures will also make meals more pleasing. Some foods will be hot, others cold, and still others served at room temperature. Even during the summer months, including at least one hot food makes a meal more acceptable and satisfying. A good rule to follow is to include something hot in a cold meal, and something cold in a hot meal.

**Preparation Methods**   You will be able to achieve additional variety in meals by using

different methods of preparation. Creamed shrimp, creamed potatoes, and creamed peas are all too much the same consistency. They make for an uninteresting meal.

**Nutritional Variety** Meals will be more pleasing when there is no excess of carbohydrate, fat, or protein. A variety of nutrients makes a meal palatable and nutritionally adequate. Include only one fat-rich or sugar-rich food in a meal.

Color, flavor, texture, and size and shape, along with a variety in temperature, method of preparation, and nutrient values are all factors that contribute to the enjoyment and attractiveness of meals.

These favorite meals from different cultures all use the contrast of texture, color, shape, and flavor to add interest. What dessert would you suggest for each meal? Why?

**For Review**

1. Explain three ways to lower the cost of meals without loss of either nutrients or appeal.
2. What are the four food preparation time zones? Why should you write out a food preparation time schedule?
3. What are five factors that add variety to meals? Give a specific example for each.

# Food away from Home

Work, school, social occasions, celebrations, and vacations may involve foods or meals eaten away from home. All foods consumed, including those eaten away from home, are a part of your total daily food intake. At any time food is eaten—either at home or away—take care to provide the nutrients your body needs without a calorie overload. The Daily Food Guide and the meal patterns will help you to choose nutrient-rich foods and to plan balanced meals.

Foods eaten at school or work replace a meal that might have been eaten at home. Regardless of where a meal is eaten, it should contribute approximately one-third of your daily nutrient and energy needs. Between-meal snacks are not an adequate substitute for any meal. If you want to have some snacks in your pattern of eating, be sure to have them in your total food plan. Foods such as fruit, sweets,

Eating away from home is no reason to have poor nutrition. Bring your own meal or buy a well-balanced one in the school cafeteria. Lunch "out" is still part of your daily diet.

sandwiches, and beverages may be saved from your regular meals to eat as snacks. Unless snacks are a part of your daily food plan, they can be sources of unwanted calories and nutrient-poor foods.

Routine activities and social occasions that involve food should be planned as part of a daily pattern of eating. At these times, adjust the foods that you eat at home to include only nutrient-rich foods. Control the size of portions, and eliminate fat-rich or sugar-rich foods to avoid a calorie overload. Fruits and vegetables are not always included abundantly in all away-from-home food functions. When this is the case, include the daily vegetable-fruit allowances in the meals that you do have at home.

## Selecting Food in Restaurants

Eating away from home often means buying food in either traditional or fast-food restaurants. Many types of restaurants offer a sit-down meal to be selected from a menu. Other restaurants may be cafeteria-style and offer a wide range of foods that you can look at and choose from as you walk through a line.

A number of table-service restaurants do not include a prepared vegetable (other than potatoes, rice, and salad) as an accompaniment to the main course. A variety of vegetables and fruits is not included. Milk is only available at an added cost. When you plan to eat in a restaurant, consider the food choices offered and then try to include at home those foods that are not available at the restaurant.

**Traditional Restaurants** There are many varieties of traditional, or sit-down, restaurants. There are expensive, elegant places with strolling musicians and flaming desserts as well as family restaurants where menus and seating are geared to those dining with young children. Other restaurants cater to different patrons at different times of the day; you have probably heard of lunch-time specials featured at restaurants located near office buildings. There are also coffee shops, delicatessens, and various ethnic (such as Chinese or Mexican) restaurants from which to choose. In all of these, diners are seated at tables, or occasionally at counters, and they choose meals from a menu.

A restaurant menu lists the available dishes and their prices. Occasionally there is a choice between complete dinners—which often come with appetizer, dessert, and beverage included in the price—and **à la carte** foods, for which each item is priced separately. You can select more carefully to avoid fattening or nutrient-poor foods if you order à la carte.

In a cafeteria, all the food is displayed for patrons as they walk through a line with a tray. Desserts are usually presented first, when you are still hungry and before you have selected the other parts of your meal. It is often wise to skip dessert the first time through the line. If you are still hungry when you have finished the rest of your meal, you can always go back and choose a dessert which complements the nutrient and calorie choices you have already made. Prices are usually posted for each selection in a cafete-

ria. A cashier at the end of the line totals your selections, and you pay either as you leave the line or as you leave the restaurant.

Foods in cafeterias are usually held in a steam table or under hot lights until they are purchased. Many foods, particularly vegetables, will deteriorate in quality if they are held this way for a long time. You should be aware that many sit-down restaurants also hold previously prepared vegetables or other foods on steam tables in the kitchen. The quality of cooked foods can be retained if they are prepared close to the time they are to be served. Dishes prepared "to order" are often more expensive because more time and effort is involved.

Recently, a new style of food choice has become popular in all kinds of restaurants, from formal dining rooms to fast-food places. The **salad bar** displays and keeps cold the ingredients for salads of all kinds, including the vegetables, garnishes, and dressings. Prepared salads are often available, too. There are salad bars so elaborate that they almost provide an entire buffet meal, including soup, cheese, bread, and fruit. Diners may order their **entrée** (AHN-tray), or main course, at their table and then

Traditional restaurants provide table service, and patrons order from a menu. This is a relaxing way to enjoy good food and conversation.

Salad bars can range from a few tossed-salad ingredients to entire buffet meals. What food groups are represented here? What main dishes would complement these selections?

The typical fast-food meal is high in calories and low in nutrition. What choices here would provide the healthiest meal?

select from the salad bar to complement their other choices. Many restaurants allow customers to choose the salad bar as an entire light meal. Fast-food restaurants may also offer salad bars as side-dish selections or as entire meals.

**Fast-food Restaurants** Nearly all meals that are served in fast-food restaurants contribute a super abundance of calories. Choose foods with care in order to avoid a calorie overload. A meal that includes a hamburger, fries, and a quick shake provides more than half the 2700 calories recommended for the active male adult.

Colas and thick shakes contribute to an abundance of calories with little nutrient value. Quick shakes average about 334 kcalories, and colas about 111 kcalories. Quick shakes are not milkshakes; they usually contain some fat-free milk solids, sweeteners, and thickeners.

Typical fast-food meals are usually adequate in protein, and are rich sources of carbohydrate and fat. They provide some nutrients but often are below one-third of the RDA. Most

fast-food meals are lacking in one or more essential nutrients; some are lacking in as many as ten. This lack is largely due to the omission of fruits, vegetables, and milk. The nutrients most often lacking are vitamin A, folacin, pantothenic acid, iron, and copper. (See pages 41-48.) On the other hand, fast foods are likely to be extremely high in sodium, a factor which has to be considered, especially when a sodium-restricted diet is necessary.

On days when you plan to eat in fast-food restaurants, include milk, vegetables, and fruits in the meals you have at home. Try to eat at fast-food restaurants that have salad bars or other ways of choosing vegetables and real dairy products.

As you probably know, most fast-food restaurants have menus, including prices, posted above the counters where food is ordered. You pay when you order, and then carry your food to a table. Again, you usually order your dessert with your meal, before you know if you will still be hungry for it when you have finished your main course. However, ordering all at once does give you a chance to try to create a nutrient balance as you place your order.

**The Heimlich Maneuver** Many restaurants post a chart like the one opposite. The

# First Aid For Choking

**1**

- **ASK: Are you choking?**
- If victim cannot breathe, cough, or speak...

**2**

- **Give the Heimlich Maneuver.**
- Stand behind the victim.
- Wrap your arms around the victim's waist.
- Make a fist with one hand. PLACE your FIST (thumbside) against the victim's stomach in the midline just ABOVE THE NAVEL AND WELL BELOW THE RIB MARGIN.
- Grasp your fist with your other hand.
- PRESS INTO STOMACH WITH A QUICK UPWARD THRUST.

**3**

- **Repeat thrust if necessary.**

- **If a victim has become unconscious:**

**4** • Sweep the mouth.

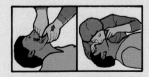

**5** • Attempt rescue breathing.

**American Red Cross**

**6** • Give 6–10 abdominal thrusts.
- Repeat Steps 4, 5, and 6 as necessary

Everyone should learn how to perform the steps above for choking and how to give rescue breathing and CPR. Call your local American Red Cross chapter for information on these and other first aid techniques.
Caution: The Heimlich Maneuver (abdominal thrust) may cause injury. Do not *practice* on people.

**LOCAL EMERGENCY TELEPHONE NUMBER:** _____

chart explains how to perform the **Heimlich Maneuver,** a quick, simple method to save someone who is choking on a small piece of food. You should familiarize yourself with this procedure so you can use it at home or anywhere someone might need it. Many lives have been saved by the Heimlich Maneuver. Even a five-year-old child has used it to save the life of a playmate.

### Food for Social Occasions

Foods are frequently a part of social occasions and celebrations. At such times, there is usually an abundance of different foods. Again, think about your total daily needs, and do your best to consume the kind and amount of food that suit your needs. You are not obligated to take large servings. It is quite acceptable to eat less food than you are served. Concentrate on eating a balanced diet, and avoid rich sauce, gravy, and excess salad dressing. Desserts and beverages are calorie-rich, but you can control the amount you consume. If you have a weight problem, concentrate on eating fruits and vegetables, and small quantities of other foods.

### Cooking Outdoors

In addition to going to restaurants and to parties, there is another way to "get out of the kitchen" at mealtime: cooking outdoors. Poultry, fish, and tender cuts of meat are best for the barbecue, since grilling is a dry-heat method of cooking. Less tender cuts of meat must be tenderized before they are grilled. Meat cooked on the grill is often basted with sauce to keep it from drying out. Either a tomato-based or fruit-based sauce may be used, with a variety of spices to suit individual tastes and creativity.

Vegetables such as ears of corn and potatoes can also be cooked on a grill. Rolls and breads may be warmed for serving. Foods may even be placed in a skillet or pan or wrapped in heavy-duty aluminum foil and placed on the grill.

You can still select a balanced diet from the variety of foods served at social occasions. Limit the amount of each type of food you eat, and avoid fattening dishes.

Remember to keep hot foods hot and cold foods cold, and to keep food and utensils clean when you cook and eat outdoors.

### Carry-away Food

Foods prepared at home to be eaten elsewhere should be planned into your daily food intake. Carry-away foods need not be calorie-rich. Instead they can contribute essential nutrients. Attractively arranged fresh vegetables and fruit trays, well-prepared and arranged vegetable dishes, and vegetable-meat casseroles are welcome additions to pot-luck or covered-dish gatherings. Covered-dish meals often include too many desserts, but this does not have to be the case.

Home-prepared foods are also a part of

Carry-away foods should be chosen with care in order to avoid spoilage. Foods likely to spoil should be kept at proper temperatures. What foods need special attention?

45°F (7°C) for cold foods. A vacuum container (thermos) will keep liquid or semiliquid foods hot or cold. An insulated chest will protect hot or cold foods. However, the food has to be thoroughly heated or thoroughly chilled before it is put into a thermos or an insulated chest. Ice or reusable cold-packs will help keep foods cold. Failure to keep foods at the proper temperatures can result in illnesses if the food spoils and is then eaten.

Therefore, carry-away foods should be chosen on the basis of keeping quality. Foods that have a low acid content should not be stored at room temperature. Because they are likely to spoil quickly, it is recommended that milk- and egg-rich foods—creams, custards, cream-filled puffs, meringue pies, and low-acid egg-milk salad dressings—should not be part of a carry-away food unless the appropriate temperature can be maintained.

packed lunches, picnics, cookouts, and camping and bicycling trips. If you use carry-away foods, food safety becomes particularly important.

**Safety of Carry-away Food**   Regardless of where food is served, it should be wholesome, uncontaminated, well prepared, attractive, and nutritious. Home-prepared foods to be eaten elsewhere must be protected from contamination in order to keep their good eating quality until served. Personal cleanliness, as well as sanitation of food, utensils, and carrying containers are essential if food-borne illnesses are to be avoided. To guard against possible increased bacterial count during food transport and holding, you should keep a temperature above 140°F (60°C) for hot foods and below

**For Review**

1. What foods are often lacking in restaurants? How can you make up for this?
2. Where are desserts usually offered in a cafeteria line? Why?
3. What proportion of the calorie needs of a normal adult male is provided by a fast-food meal of a hamburger, fries, and a quick shake? What nutrients do fast-food meals supply adequately? What nutrients do fast-food meals lack? What do they have in oversupply?
4. Can you contribute significantly to your Milk-Cheese Group needs by having a fast-food quick shake? Why or why not?
5. What temperature protects hot foods from spoiling? What temperature protects cold foods? How can you keep carry-away foods from spoiling?

# 5 Chapter Review

## Summary

In planning a menu, food managers must consider their skills and the equipment that is available. During the preparation of the meal, attention to the cost of the food and energy as well as the management of time are important. To make a meal appealing, the food should have a variety of color, texture, flavor, and different sizes, shapes, and temperatures.

Some people find it difficult to maintain a balanced diet when they eat away from home. However, by following the Daily Food Guide, the meal patterns, and eating wisely at home, they can maintain a healthful diet and not overload on calories. Cooking and eating outdoors and eating carry-away foods are other ways of eating away from home. In both instances, it is very important to maintain sanitary conditions and control the temperature of the food to prevent any bacteria growth.

## Vocabulary

Match each numbered vocabulary word with its correct lettered meaning.

1. à la carte
2. entrée
3. generic brands
4. Heimlich Maneuver
5. management
6. menu
7. salad bar
8. texture

a. A plan that describes the dishes to be prepared and the order in which they will be served.
b. The main course of a meal.
c. The decision making and planning of work activities needed to complete the task of meal preparation.
d. The way food feels when you chew it.
e. Food products that do not have a brand name but list only the name of the product, ingredients, net content, and the name of the manufacturer or distributor.
f. A quick, simple method to save someone who is choking on a small piece of food.
g. A restaurant menu that lists a separate price for each food item.
h. A display of ingredients for salads of all kinds, including the vegetables, fruits, cheeses, garnishes, and dressings.

## Chapter Questions

1. Briefly describe how your family food customs have made certain foods and methods of cooking important to your family.
2. How can you wisely manage individual skill, equipment, economic, food value, time, and energy resources in menu planning and food preparation?
3. No matter where a meal is eaten, how much should it contribute to your daily nutrient and energy needs?

4. Why should the inclusion of snacks be part of your total food plan?
5. What are ways to adjust your pattern of eating when you plan to attend a social function where food will be served?
6. What are advantages and disadvantages of eating meals from fast-food restaurants?
7. What are important considerations to remember when cooking a meal outdoors?
8. How can you select nutritious restaurant meals?
9. What are the ways to keep carry-away foods safe of food-borne illnesses?

## Skill Activities

**1. Communication**   In your food journal, write a recipe for a traditional meal that is a family favorite. Be sure to include the name of the dish, the ingredients, and the way they should be put together. Also tell the number of people the recipe will serve and the length of time the food should cook and at which temperature.

**2. Resource management**
With your class, plan a dinner menu to serve four people. Include a salad, an entrée that includes chicken, and a dessert. In planning what to serve, consider your skills and the equipment that is available for your use. Decide which dishes to prepare, the recipes to use, and the order in which the food will be served. To assist with your management of time, use the Meal Preparation Plan to develop a schedule.

**3. Reading**   There are many articles about the caloric and nutritional values of fast foods. Try to find articles that refer to the kinds of meals that are served in the fast-food restaurants in your area. Read several of these articles, paying attention not only to what foods are available but also to what ingredients are added as the food is prepared. Then prepare a report to tell about your findings. Tell which of the prepared foods have the highest calories and which foods have the lowest calories. Tell which foods you think are the most nutritious and why you think so.

**4. Critical thinking**   Visit two fast-food restaurants in your area to learn the variety of food items that are available. Then plan a lunch menu of a healthful meal a person could order at each restaurant. In order to meet the requirements of the Daily Food Guide and meal patterns, decide which foods a person should eat at home because they are not available at the restaurant. Which restaurant provided the best opportunity for ordering a healthful meal?

# Unit 3

# Food Management

Apple-Walnut Bread
Baked and Frozen
November

# 6 The Kitchen

## As you read, think about:

- how to design and organize a kitchen for efficient and pleasurable work.
- how to evaluate a kitchen for safety, sanitation, and durability.
- how to prevent food-borne illnesses through personal and kitchen cleanliness and proper food storage.
- how to guard against and treat kitchen accidents.

### Vocabulary

**work centers**
**work flow**
**work triangle**
**grounded**
**sanitation**
**personal hygiene**
**spoilage**
**microorganisms**
**salmonella**
  **poisoning**
**botulism**
**contaminants**
**dry storage**
**pretreatment**
**antidotes**
**antiseptic**

PART TWO

NOTES ON KITCHEN DESIGN

### BASIC CONSIDERATIONS

A kitchen is more enjoyable if it is organized efficiently. A few moments taken now to think through the design of your kitchen will save countless hours in its future use.

The three main work areas—clean-up, cooking, and refrigeration-storage—should be arranged in a triangle with the distance between the elements a minimum of 4 feet and a maximum of 8 to 10 feet and with the total triangular distance not exceeding 27 feet. This work triangle should be located outside of major household traffic patterns to allow the cook uninterrupted pathways. Beyond these basic work centers, you may want to provide space for special use: a planning desk, a mixing/baking counter, a hobby area, a table or bar for eating, etc.

### COMMON LAYOUTS

There are several generic types of kitchen layout, each with its own advantages and disadvantages. (See illustrations 8a-f.)

SINGLE COUNTER KITCHENS align the three work areas along one wall. The short distances between work centers allows for high efficiency without the usual 'work triangle.' In this plan, the sink is best located in the center. Try to avoid doors at each end of the counter; these can create a flow-through traffic pattern which interrupts work.

CORRIDOR (GALLEY) KITCHEN This type functions best if the distance between the two counters is between 4 and 5 feet, and if only one end of the corridor is open to household traffic. One wall can also be opened up between counter top and overhead cabinets for easy communication with adjacent rooms.

L-SHAPED KITCHENS have their counters and work centers along two adjacent walls. Here, the work flow triangle stays outside the main traffic flow. The corner kitchen in an open family room is a good example

U-SHAPED KITCHENS have each work center located on its own counter, the one generally at the base of the U. This type is highly efficient, but requires at least feet in each direction. The work tri is clear of traffic flow, and the cou is continuous. Two cooks can use comfortably.

If space is available, both and the U-shaped kitchen by adding an island. One ters can be located here, counter space, or the for extra preparation

Illus. 8

# Kitchen Organization

While it is true that many modern time-saving conveniences and efficiently organized work centers were designed to "help get you out of the kitchen" more quickly, it is also true that mixers, microwaves, and food processors have encouraged a new interest in cooking. Many people now cook as a hobby as well as a necessity. Time-saving devices have actually *increased* their time in the kitchen! They look for safe and efficient organization of appliances and work areas as well as attractiveness when they design or even just dream about a kitchen.

## Work Centers

The equipment you have and the way it is arranged in your kitchen will have a considerable influence on the amount of time and personal energy you need to spend in food preparation. It will also influence how efficiently you can work and how much you will enjoy preparing meals.

Think of the kitchen as having three major areas, or **work centers;** that is, a particular area in which to do each of the three major activities of storage, preparation and cleanup, and cooking and serving. Even when there is some overlap of these areas, they are basically divided into the following work centers.

**Refrigerator Center**   This area is used for both food storage and preparation. Perishables (for example, milk, eggs, meats, and fresh vegetables) and frozen foods are stored in the refrigerator-freezer, and staple foods (for example, flour, sugar, canned and bottled goods) are stored in nearby cabinets. Counter space is needed for unpacking groceries and for some mixing and assembling of foods. This work center is where most meals usually begin, as ingredients are selected and collected for food preparation.

**Sink Center**   This area is used for all activities that require water. Here, fruits and vegetables are cleaned and prepared for cooking. Other dishes that require the addition of water in their preparation (for example, rice,

Although it lacks a stove, this room is recognizable as a kitchen. What functions and activities of this colonial kitchen have been replaced by technology? Which activities unrelated to meal preparation still go on in modern kitchens?

Perishables and frozen foods are stored in the refrigerator center (top). How are foods prepared for cooking at the sink center?

The range center (below) is where food is actually cooked. All three centers should provide suitable storage and work areas.

pasta, and add-water mixes) may also be assembled here before cooking. Counters in the sink center may hold small appliances such as the blender, food processor, and coffee maker. Some major appliances such as the dishwasher, trash compactor, and waste disposer are also located in the sink center. Cabinets in this work area store tools such as knives, peelers, and strainers. Dishes, glassware, and flatware should be stored here, too, so that they can be conveniently put away after washing. Since the sink center is where dishes are washed, cleaning supplies (for example, detergents and sponges) should also be stored in this area.

**Range Center** This is the cooking and serving center of the kitchen. The range, oven, and possibly a microwave oven are located here. Cabinets in this area store pots, pans, cooking tools, and potholders. There should be enough counter space on which to put food after it is cooked and while it is being arranged for serving. It is helpful if serving dishes can also be stored nearby.

### Work Triangle

The three work centers are where you will spend most of your food-preparation time. Most often, the **work flow** of food preparation, the order in which the tasks are done, is to take ingredients from the refrigerator center; to clean, assemble, or prepare the food at the sink center; and to cook and serve the food from the range center. Ideally, the three work centers should be arranged so that you can move easily from the refrigerator center to the sink center to the range center.

Since different parts of a meal are prepared at different times and in different stages, you will probably need to use all three work centers many times in the preparation of the average meal. Therefore, a **work triangle,** an arrangement in which the three work centers form the

The work triangle of a kitchen links the three work centers. You will usually walk along the "sides" of this imaginary triangle many times during meal preparation. Long sides require more walking; short sides cut down on counter and storage space.

points of an imaginary triangle, is the ideal shape for the work area of a kitchen. The total distance of the three sides of the work triangle should be no more than 22 feet (6.6 m).

## Kitchen Plans

While all arrangements of refrigerator center, sink center, and range center are called work triangles (the cook moves along a triangle from center to center), the floor plans can take a variety of shapes. The following are the most common kitchen plans. As you read, look at the diagrams on page 120. Think about how efficiently space is used in each one and how much time and effort it probably takes to prepare a meal in each type of kitchen.

**U-shaped Plan**  This is the most efficient arrangement because of the short distance from work center to work center as well as the amount of cabinet and counter space. The con-

**Safety Tip**
- To prevent the overloading of circuits, use separate outlets for high-heat appliances such as toasters and coffee pots.

tinuous U shape also discourages walk-through traffic from interfering with the cook.

**L-shaped Plan**  This arrangement of continuous appliance counter space on two adjoining walls is also efficient. Note, though, how the triangle spreads out. The more counter and cabinet space, the longer the walk between range and refrigerator.

**Corridor Plan**  This arrangement opens the U-shaped kitchen at its closed end, so its major disadvantage is walk-through traffic. Note the short distance between work centers.

**Straight-line Plan**  This arrangement is the least efficient for two reasons: there is usually not enough counter and storage space, and the step-saving triangle has been flattened into a less efficient straight line. These one-wall kitchens are usually found in small apartments or other places where space is severely limited.

**Island and Peninsula Plans**  These arrangements are similar: they both include an addition to one of the other plans, usually the U-shaped plan. They require a large, spacious area and make use of what would otherwise be wasted space. An island or a peninsula that contains a work center can shorten one or more sides of the work triangle. If it does not contain a work center, the added counter and cabinet space is still useful. Note that the island "floats" in the middle space, while the peninsula is an extension of a wall counter.

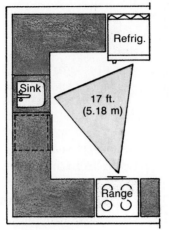

U-shaped Plan

17 ft. (5.18 m)

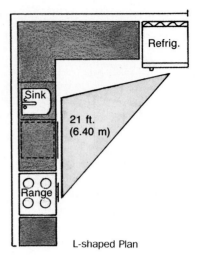

L-shaped Plan

21 ft. (6.40 m)

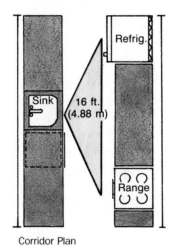

Corridor Plan

16 ft. (4.88 m)

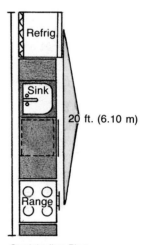

Straight-line Plan

20 ft. (6.10 m)

Various arrangements of kitchen work areas are possible. Almost any kitchen will fit one of these plans. Which plan does your kitchen at home fit?

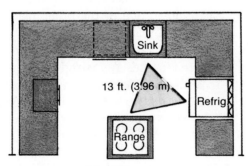

Island Plan

13 ft. (3.96 m)

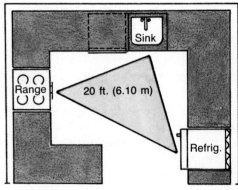

Peninsula Plan

20 ft. (6.10 m)

Three-hole electrical outlets usually indicate that a grounding wire has been installed. Adapters allow appliance plugs with three prongs to be used in two-hole outlets, but an electrician should make sure that the system is properly grounded.

# The Working Kitchen

Most cooks have a dream kitchen; some are lucky enough to find or design one. The majority of people, however, do not have the opportunity to start from scratch in kitchen design and must make do with what they find. There are, though, certain points to consider as you evaluate your kitchen for safety, efficiency, and the pleasure of preparing food in it.

### Electrical Wiring

Kitchens use a lot of electricity to operate motors and produce heat. If motor-driven appliances are not operating at full speed, if heat-producing appliances are slow, or if lights dim when electrical appliances are on, the electrical circuits may be overloaded. If any of these warnings of inadequate wiring occur, you should have a qualified electrician find and correct the problem.

Wiring and plugs on small appliances should be kept in good repair. Fraying of the insulation around wiring is dangerous. If you must use extension cords in the kitchen, use the heavy-duty type designed for small appliances. Ordinary cords become hot and can cause fires. Any cord is a hazard if it can be tripped over, if it can pull an operating appliance off a counter, or if it can come in contact with direct heat.

Appliances with plugs having three prongs are **grounded** appliances. The round prong grounds the appliance when it is plugged into a three-hole outlet that has an installed grounding wire. If there is a problem in the electrical circuit, the electricity will flow to the ground and not to the person touching the appliance, as long as the appliance is properly grounded. Three-hole outlets usually indicate the presence of a grounding wire, but the best way to be sure is to have an electrician check. If there is no grounding wire, ask the electrician how to use an adapter to ground your appliances, or if changes in your wiring system are necessary. The National Electric Code now requires that new homes have a grounding wire.

### Counters

One of the major complaints about kitchens is lack of counter space. Tables, stands, or portable cabinets can provide extra work surfaces. Laminated plastic counter surfaces are durable and easy to clean. They resist moisture but not heat. More expensive ceramic tiles are heatproof and sturdy, but the grouting between tiles can be difficult to keep clean.

## Storage

Very few cooks feel they have enough kitchen storage. Stackable bins, cabinets on casters, wall shelves, or hanging baskets can be added for more storage space. Extra drawers can be hung under upper cabinets, and narrow shelves attached inside cabinet doors. Round revolving shelves, called lazy susans, and pull-out shelves usually allow a more efficient use of cabinets. Hanging the pots, pans, and utensils on the wall, or storing small objects in containers on counter tops can free cabinet space for larger objects. Often, efficiently reorganizing your present storage areas can provide needed storage space.

There are many space-saving storage products on the market. The containers above are airtight yet transparent. The arrangement below provides easy access in an attractive setting.

## Wall Coverings

This aspect of kitchen decorating offers the widest choice of materials and creative effects. Paint is often the easiest and least expensive solution; use enamel (rather than latex) paint for easier cleanup. Wallpaper is also popular; be sure to get washable paper or vinyl. Ceramic or metal tile is durable and easily washed, but it can be quite expensive. Tile splashbacks (behind the sink or range) are useful and attractive. Paneling, if it is both grease- and water-resistant, can also be used in a kitchen. It is particularly useful for hiding damaged or unattractive walls.

## Floor Coverings

For both comfort and easy cleanup, many people choose vinyl floor coverings, either in sheet or tile form. They are available with a no-wax finish for easy care, and they may also be padded for walking and standing comfort. Hard surfaces, such as ceramic tile, wood, or brick, are attractive and durable but not so comfortable. Carpeting designed for kitchens is comfortable and reduces noise, but it requires frequent vacuuming and quick attention to spills.

## Kitchens for the Handicapped

People who are handicapped or disabled often value their independence even more than the rest of us. One important kind of independence is the ability to select and prepare food. The average kitchen presents many problems for the disabled. People in wheelchairs cannot reach high cabinets, get close to the sink, or see inside pots on the range. Those who require walking aids cannot carry things while using crutches or walkers. People with arthritis, with other problems affecting grasping, or with the use of only one hand may have difficulty grasping small drawer pulls or keeping a mixing bowl steady. Major remodeling can create a kitchen

This kitchen has been designed for wheelchair use. Notice the lower work surfaces and the wide spaces under the table and stove. Are the refrigerator and oven models good choices? Why?

tailored to the use of the handicapped, but there are also simpler and less expensive changes that will give many handicapped people their independence in the kitchen.

**Equipment and Storage** There are some appliances, such as those with Braille controls, designed specifically for the handicapped. However, selecting carefully among the styles that are usually offered to the general public can provide appliances accessible to many handicapped people. For example, a side-by-side refrigerator-freezer allows those in wheelchairs easier access to either compartment. Front-loading dishwashers with controls on the front are easiest for the disabled to use. Pull-out racks on both these appliances are a great help. A shallow sink with a rear drain and a single-control faucet at wheelchair level can be extremely helpful.

Many handicapped people find separate small appliances, such as toaster ovens, microwaves, electric broilers, and electric skillets, easier to use than regular ranges. Among standard ranges, an electric model—without an open flame—may be preferable. Controls on cooktops should be in the front; those with burners in one row eliminate the need to reach over heat and flame. If the cabinet below the cooktop is removed, wheelchairs can be positioned right next to the range. A mirror hung above the range allows seated cooks to see inside pots. Self-cleaning wall ovens mounted at a convenient height are a great help to those in wheelchairs or those who have difficulty lifting.

Storage space can be modified for the handicapped. Placing large, easy-to-grip handles on cabinet doors and drawers helps; removing the doors is often even better. Lazy Susans, pull-out shelves and baskets, and lightweight cabinets on wheels all increase the ability of the handicapped to store and reach things without aid.

**Other Kitchen Aids for the Handicapped** Many of the simplest things you do in the kitchen become difficult, if not impossible, for the handicapped person. Fortunately, many of the solutions are simple, too. Standard counter tops are often too high for those in wheelchairs to use. Built-in trays or boards that pull out provide good work surfaces for those who must work sitting down. A wide shelf hung at wheelchair height or a wooden tray mounted right on the wheelchair can be indispensable. A dining table atop a pedestal allows wheelchair seating. A rolling cart helps people who cannot walk and carry heavy objects at the same time to get from one work center to another. Suction cups or wet sponges help hold mixing bowls and cutting boards for one-handed use, while long-handled tongs are useful for reaching and pulling out refrigerator racks or oven shelves. Hardware stores carry many "kitchen aids" that are useful to the general public and indispensible to the handicapped. Among these are salad spinners, jar-lid openers, electric can openers, and long-handled utensils.

---

**For Review**

1. What are three warning signals of inadequate kitchen wiring? How can extension cords pose a hazard?
2. How can you add storage and counter space to a kitchen?
3. List three kinds of floor coverings and three wall coverings suitable for kitchens. Give one advantage and/or disadvantage for each one.
4. Explain three ways to remodel a kitchen for use by a handicapped person.

---

# Sanitation

Even a dream kitchen doesn't guarantee great meals. It doesn't even guarantee safe meals. **Sanitation**—keeping the kitchen, all equipment, food, and yourself clean and as free as possible from bacteria—must be practiced in *every* kitchen to prevent food-borne illnesses (see page 4).

## Personal Sanitation

You have been reading about ways in which the kitchen can be adapted to make food preparation safe, efficient, and pleasurable. Now it's time to think about the cook. How do the cook's **personal hygiene** (individual cleanliness), clothing, and habits contribute to the safety and efficiency of food preparation?

Keep your own safety in mind when thinking about your cleanliness and clothing in the kitchen. You want to avoid wearing loose garments that might catch fire or get caught in kitchen appliances. You also want to avoid transferring illness-causing bacteria and other germs to the food you are preparing.

Following these guidelines, based on food-service industry rules, can help you maintain personal cleanliness in the kitchen:

1. Keep your hands clean. This means not only washing them with hot soapy water *before* you begin food preparation but also *after* coughing or sneezing, playing with a pet, or handling raw meats, fish, poultry, or eggs.
2. Avoid touching your face or hair while working in the kitchen. If you do, rewash your hands.
3. Use separate towels for drying your hands and for wiping dishes.
4. If you have an open cut or sore on your hands, use plastic gloves for handling food.
5. Tie your hair back or cover it so it will stay out of the food.

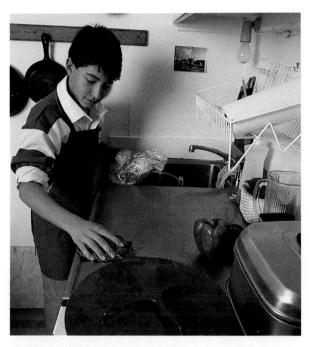

Cleaning up as you cook not only saves time later, but also prevents the growth of microorganisms on utensils and work surfaces.

der to avoid food-borne illnesses and to make your food preparation environment a pleasant place to work.

1. Wash counter tops, tables, and other work surfaces before you begin cooking. Dirt may have built up since you cleaned up after your last food preparation.

2. Keep work surfaces and utensils clean as you work. Wipe up spills right away. Thoroughly clean utensils—and the cutting board—after each use. This is especially important after contact with raw foods. Use hot soapy water. A plastic cutting board is less likely than a wooden one to get scratches in which bacteria can grow.

3. Wash pots, pans, and dishes in hot soapy water as soon as possible after using them. If you cannot wash them immediately, at least rinse them to remove food particles that can attract pests or breed germs. Keep dirty dishes and pots away from your food-preparation area.

Personal sanitation is essential to safe food preparation. This girl has tied back her hair, rolled up her sleeves, and put on an apron. How do these precautions help prevent contamination?

6. Be sure your clothes are clean. Avoid loose items that can accidentally touch food (or catch fire or get caught in appliances). Roll up long sleeves.

7. Wear an apron. It will not only keep your clothes clean, but it can be easily washed to remove any germ-carrying food stains that may get on it during food preparation.

8. If a dish towel or utensil falls on the floor, do not use it again until it has been rewashed.

9. Always use a separate spoon for tasting —never the same one you are using for stirring.

## Kitchen Sanitation

As you can see, kitchen cleanliness is closely related to the work habits and hygiene of the cook. Make sure you follow the guidelines for both personal and kitchen cleanliness in or-

4. Wash tools and utensils that have been used on raw foods before you use them on cooked foods. The cooking process will probably destroy most bacteria in the food, but a spoon or knife used before the food was cooked can reintroduce bacteria into the finished product.
5. Change dish towels and hand towels often.
6. Dispose of all food wastes properly. Remove garbage from the kitchen often—at least once a day—and clean the garbage can often.
7. Clean up well after food preparation. Be sure work surfaces have been washed and dried. Don't forget to sweep crumbs from the floor. Leave the kitchen in the condition you would like to find it when you begin to prepare your next meal.

### Proper Food Storage

You already know how important proper food storage is. As you read in Chapter 1, food-borne illnesses can result from food spoilage. **Spoilage** is a change in food caused by *enzymes* (chemicals present in food that can cause undesirable changes in its eatability) and by **microorganisms,** tiny living things that can be poisonous or that can cause changes in food. While some of these changes are desired (for example, yeast is a microorganism that makes bread rise), others can make you ill.

**Food Poisoning** Food poisoning, as you saw in Chapter 1, can result from eating some kinds of microorganisms or poisonous bacterial waste products known as *toxins*. Food poisoning

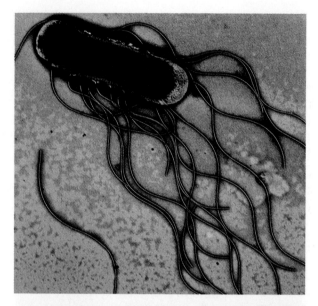

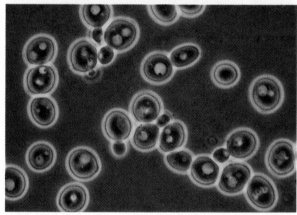

Microorganisms cannot be seen with the naked eye, but they can affect your food and your health. Food contaminated with salmonella bacteria (top) can make you ill. Yeast (bottom) makes bread rise.

can also come from naturally poisonous foods, such as certain varieties of mushrooms. Contamination by chemicals, such as pesticides or other soil, air, and water pollutants, may also make food poisonous. Plants and animals that live in other animals can cause severe health problems. For example, a small worm that lives in pork products can cause the serious illness *trichinosis* (trik-uh-NO-siss) (see page 359).

> ### Safety Tip
> • Clean off canned food lids before opening in order to avoid contaminating food with store dirt and bacteria.

# Working to Keep Kitchens Clean and Safe

"Food establishments have to be extraordinarily clean," comments Lisa Witomski. Lisa should know—she has served as a chef in a small restaurant and a large hotel, studied hotel and restaurant management, and worked for a national food manufacturer. Today, she and her father, Charles Witomski, own and operate T. Frank McCall's, which provides cleaning chemicals, floor finishes, cleaning equipment, and paper products to many different food establishments.

Among T. Frank McCall's customers are food manufacturers, hotels, restaurants, hospitals, nursing homes, and company-run employee dining rooms.

These customers can purchase products to meet their unique sanitation needs. Hospitals and nursing homes purchase plastic bags treated with chemicals that prevent the spread of bacteria and kill insects. Small restaurants buy small amounts of cleaning agents. Large food manufacturers require 55-gallon drums of cleaning chemicals. In addition, customers can obtain trash cans, paper products for cleaning, protective gloves, and hair nets. Lisa points out that T. Frank McCall's is not primarily a restaurant-supply business: "Restaurant-supply places have 'millions' of doilies, glassware, disposable foam containers, and specialized paper products for food." Instead, T. Frank McCall's concentrates on helping customers maintain the sanitary conditions necessary for their businesses.

A vital component of Lisa's customer calls is making sure that cleaning products are used correctly. "Cleaning is very technical. If you use too much of one chemical or mix chemicals, people can get hurt or even die."

To prevent inappropriate use of chemicals, T. Frank McCall's provides training. "We have a series of videotapes, and we do lectures. We talk about a subject, for example, 'Maintaining a Tile Floor.' We show a video, discuss the product, and do a demonstration."

When Lisa returns to her office, concern for safe use of chemicals remains a priority. The most common mistake is that people do not properly dilute the highly concentrated cleaning chemicals. Lisa is currently investigating a machine that would dilute chemicals properly. To serve customers better, it is necessary to keep up with new products and equipment.

Beginning in 1987, federal law mandated that every employee has a right to know about dangerous chemicals in the workplace. As a result, chemical suppliers are required to provide every customer with a Materials Supply Data Sheet (MSDS) for each product. The MSDS includes a list of the chemical ingredients, procedures to follow in case of an accident, and a phone number to call for further treatment. Employers are responsible for holding seminars to inform employees about the chemicals and for making the MSDSs easily accessible. Lisa makes sure that MSDSs are on file for all T. Frank McCall's products and that all customers receive the appropriate MSDSs.

While in the office, Lisa also prepares bids for contracts and participates in financial planning for the company. This diversity makes her job interesting and exciting.

A chemical supplier explains an MSDS.

"Seconds" that have been left at room temperature—especially uncovered outdoors—can cause food poisoning. Keep hot foods hot and cold foods cold to prevent the growth of microorganisms.

You may have heard or read reports in the media about various types of food poisoning. In some cases, people get "sick," but seem to recover quickly. In other cases, there are deaths, and the government or the manufacturer orders the recall of the affected foods. You may have wondered which types of food poisoning are the most serious and how to tell one kind from another.

The least dangerous form of bacterial food poisoning is commonly called "staph" poisoning because it is caused by the *staphylococcus aureus* bacteria. Staph bacteria thrive at room temperature and can be found on healthy people as well as in food. Personal cleanliness and quick refrigeration of rich foods, such as custards and dressed meat and vegetable salads, can help prevent staph illness. If you get staph food poisoning, the nausea, vomiting, diarrhea, and cramps will probably begin 8 to 20 hours after eating the contaminated food, and will last up to two days.

*Salmonella* (sal-muh-NELL-uh) and *clostridium perfringens* bacteria cause more severe food poisoning. Salmonella bacteria thrive at room temperature, but can easily be killed by thorough heating. Perfringens bacteria also thrive at room temperature, so perfringens poisoning is most common at buffets and other places where food has been left out for long periods. The symptoms of **salmonella poisoning,** which can last as long as three days, include a severe headache and fever, in addition to stomach upset. Perfringens symptoms, which begin 4 to 22 hours after eating and last about a day, include stomach pain and discomfort.

**Botulism** (BOCH-uh-liz-um) is the most deadly form of food poisoning. The bacteria *clostridium botulinum* produces a toxin so strong that a tiny bit can kill you. Therefore, never taste a food to see if it is "still good." Improperly processed canned goods are the most common source of botulism. Never buy or use a leaking or bulging can; check for unusual color, smell, or appearance. If you are suspicious, do not buy or use the food. "Better safe than sorry" makes good sense here. Botulism attacks the nervous system, and its symptoms, occurring 12 to 36 hours after eating, include double vision and difficulty speaking, swallowing, and breathing. Immediate medical attention is essential; over half the cases of botulism are fatal.

**Time and Temperature** These two *T*'s will help you remember how to prevent the growth and survival of many **contaminants,** dangerous foreign substances in food. Temperature and time are the important factors. Bacteria grow and multiply at room temperature, from

Never buy or use damaged cans. Denting or leaking may mean that contaminants have gotten into the food. A bulging can may indicate botulism, the deadliest kind of food poisoning.

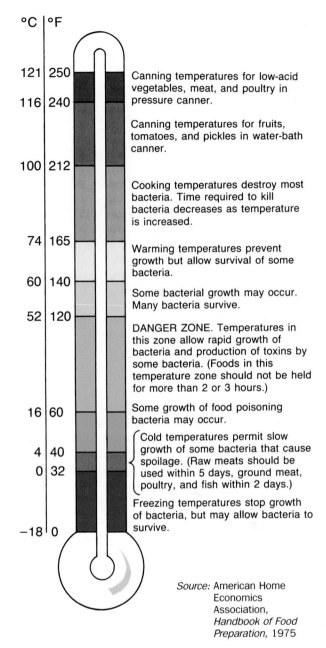

| °C | °F | |
|---|---|---|
| 121 | 250 | Canning temperatures for low-acid vegetables, meat, and poultry in pressure canner. |
| 116 | 240 | |
| | | Canning temperatures for fruits, tomatoes, and pickles in water-bath canner. |
| 100 | 212 | |
| | | Cooking temperatures destroy most bacteria. Time required to kill bacteria decreases as temperature is increased. |
| 74 | 165 | |
| | | Warming temperatures prevent growth but allow survival of some bacteria. |
| 60 | 140 | |
| | | Some bacterial growth may occur. Many bacteria survive. |
| 52 | 120 | |
| | | DANGER ZONE. Temperatures in this zone allow rapid growth of bacteria and production of toxins by some bacteria. (Foods in this temperature zone should not be held for more than 2 or 3 hours.) |
| 16 | 60 | Some growth of food poisoning bacteria may occur. |
| 4 | 40 | Cold temperatures permit slow growth of some bacteria that cause spoilage. (Raw meats should be used within 5 days, ground meat, poultry, and fish within 2 days.) |
| 0 | 32 | |
| | | Freezing temperatures stop growth of bacteria, but may allow bacteria to survive. |
| −18 | 0 | |

*Source:* American Home Economics Association, *Handbook of Food Preparation,* 1975

Temperature of Food for Control of Bacteria

60-125°F (15-52°C). The longer food is kept at room temperature, the more bacteria will multiply. High temperatures, above 165°F (74°C), kill most microorganisms. That is why you should thoroughly heat or reheat prepared foods even though the "cooking" has already been done. Cold, below 40°F (5°C), or freezing temperatures keep bacteria from multiplying but do not kill them.

Time, then, is the other important factor in keeping food "fresh." Never give microorganisms time to multiply at room temperature. Serve hot foods while still hot; refrigerate perishable ingredients and leftovers immediately; do not thaw frozen foods on the counter. Even when stored at the correct temperature, food cannot be kept forever.

**Freezer Storage** Whether you have a separate freezer or a combination refrigerator-freezer, the freezer temperature should be 0°F (−18°C) or lower. At this temperature, many previously prepared as well as uncooked foods can be kept for months. In general, avoid freezing foods that contain mayonnaise, cooked egg

To protect food, always wrap it properly for the freezer and defrost it in the refrigerator. Wrappings should be airtight to prevent freezer burn. Mold heavy-duty foil around odd shapes.

grow on the warmer outside surface. Many foods can be cooked frozen if you have forgotten to defrost them in time. You have probably noticed this statement on many prepared frozen-food products: "If product thaws, heat and enjoy immediately. Do not refreeze." This is good general advice. Foods that were frozen before they were cooked may be frozen again after cooking.

**Refrigerator Storage**   To keep perishables from spoiling without freezing, refrigerator temperatures should be about 40°F (5°C). Wrap refrigerated foods properly to protect against loss of moisture, nutrients, and flavor, and against "swapping smells" with other foods. Don't store lidless cans; place contents in tightly closed containers. Meat and poultry need only be wrapped loosely in waxed paper or left in store wrap. Use the refrigerator meat trays and vegetable bins if you have them. If not, store meats and other easily spoiled foods, such as dairy products, near the freezer compartment, where the temperature is coldest. Fresh fruits and vegetables can go in the lower part of the refrigerator, which is usually somewhat warmer. Always leave room for air to circulate so that all parts of the refrigerator are cold enough to protect perishables. Never lean foods against a refrigerator wall; they may freeze.

whites, gelatin, or custard. Fresh vegetables may be frozen if they will be cooked before eating.

It is important to package foods correctly for the freezer to prevent "freezer burn" and loss of eating quality. Use heavy-duty foils and bags, freezer paper or cartons, and heavy plastic containers with tight-fitting lids. When wrapping for the freezer, mold and seal closely around the food. Get out as much air as you can. Keeping a list of the foods you have in the freezer is a good idea. Many foil packages look alike; opening them to take a peek damages the wrapper or lets air into the container. You also want to distinguish between the container of stew you made last month and the one you made last week. Then you can use the older package first, thus "turning over your inventory."

When you decide to use an item from your freezer, cross it off the inventory list and *thaw it in the refrigerator.* Do not thaw frozen foods at room temperature. Even while the inside of a food is still frozen, microorganisms will begin to

Never put open cans in the refrigerator. Instead, transfer their contents to tightly closed containers.

**Dry Storage**   The least perishable foods in your kitchen may be kept in **dry storage;** that is, in any cool, dry, dark place. You have probably seen food packages that specify a cool, dry place for their products or that warn against exposure to direct sunlight. Warmth and moisture can cause foods to lose their eating quality quickly, so do not store foods above the range, refrigerator, radiator, or sink. Steam and heat will cause spoilage. The ideal temperature for dry storage is 55-70°F (13-21°C). Never store food under the sink or near cleansers and chemicals. Leakage or contamination in these areas can be very dangerous. However, a shelf in a pantry or basement is fine if it is clean, dry, cool, and protected from constant direct light.

Dry storage is fine for unopened cans, jars, and boxes of foods (unless the package specifies otherwise) as well as for most properly wrapped grain products. Once cans are opened, the contents should be transferred to tightly closed containers and then refrigerated. Food in boxes that do not reclose easily, such as cereals and pastas, should be transferred to airtight containers, but they can remain in dry storage. Onions, potatoes, dried beans and peas, and unripe fruits may be kept in dry storage. Once fruit becomes ripe, however, it should be refrigerated. Whole-grain products should also be refrigerated if they will not be used within two months.

Unopened boxes may be stored in cabinets. If a box does not reclose tightly, transfer its contents to a container with a lid.

Outdoor parties present special food-safety problems. Note the thermos and disposable paperware above. What other precautions have been taken? What should have been done differently?

## Sanitation for Outdoor Meals and for Parties

Sanitation and food safety are important any time you prepare and serve food, not only in your kitchen or for family meals, but also for outdoor meals and for parties. For outdoor meals, the main points to remember are to keep hot foods hot, cold foods cold, and all utensils and food containers clean. Insulated bags and storage chests, dry ice and frozen gels, thermos or vacuum containers, and tight or insulated wrappings can help protect against food-borne illnesses. The use of disposable containers, paper plates, and throw-away "silverware" reduces the need to bring dirty dishes back home. Always be extra careful with both sanitation and food temperature when you take or cook food away from home.

There are special indoor occasions that call for extra care, too. Parties and other large gatherings where food is served present special problems. There are often large quantities of food, much of it prepared in advance. Don't be tempted to prepare too far in advance. If you must keep cooked food more than one or two days, freeze it rather than refrigerate it. If you are keeping a lot more food in your refrigerator than usual, be careful not to overload it. An overloaded refrigerator will not stay cold enough to protect food from spoiling. Be sure, also, that you have enough oven and range space for last-minute food preparation. You don't want foods sitting on the counter "waiting their turn" to be heated or served. Keep foods in the refrigerator until they can be properly heated or served cold.

Many large-group meals are served buffet style, with food displayed so guests can choose and help themselves. Use warmers, chafing dishes, and hot trays for hot foods, and set cold foods on ice. These precautions work only temporarily, however, so set out only a small amount of food at one time. Keep extra helpings at the right temperature in the kitchen (in the oven or refrigerator) and refill serving dishes as needed.

Disposable dishes, very useful at parties, can be thrown away immediately after use, so dirty dishes and food remains do not accumulate. Any leftover food to be used again should be refrigerated promptly.

## Kitchen Cleanup

Kitchen cleanup may be the part of meal preparation that you like least, but it is one of the most important. The cleaner the kitchen, the safer and easier it will be to use again.

**Cleanup at the End of a Meal**  Every good cook leaves the kitchen clean. Wise cooks clean as they go along. When you do not let foods harden or dry out on utensils or plates, dishwashing is much easier. Cleanup after meals will also be easier if you wash utensils and dishes and return them to their storage space as you are cooking. In this way, your kitchen will be clean and orderly rather than cluttered and

While no one enjoys doing it, cleaning up after cooking or eating is necessary. If everyone pitches in, cleanup goes faster and seems less like "work."

crowded when you serve the meal. You will have more counter space for arranging serving dishes and platters that you are planning to use on the dining table. You will also have counter and sink space for those dishes that have been removed from the table during the service of the meal.

Your kitchen will also be neater at mealtime if you rinse and dispose of any empty jars or cans, waste paper, and garbage as you cook. Foods that remain in discarded containers may attract flies and rodents, and produce bad odors.

When the meal has ended, clear the table and take the soiled dishes to the sink area. Scrape food from dishes, and rinse them. Store leftover foods immediately.

Stack the dishes on one side of the sink in the order they are to be washed: glasses, flatware, cups and saucers, plates, serving dishes, utensils. The general rule is to wash the least soiled items first and then follow in order to the most difficult-to-clean items. If you use a dishwasher, follow the manufacturer's directions for loading it.

## Pretreatment and Stain Treatment for Pans

**Kind of Pan**

| | |
|---|---|
| Aluminum | To remove discoloration due to water or alkali: Use 2 teaspoons (10 mL) of cream of tartar for each quart of water, and simmer until stain disappears (about 10 minutes). Vinegar and acid foods, such as tomato, will also brighten aluminum. |
| Enamel | To remove burned food: Use 1 teaspoon (5 mL) of baking soda for each quart (liter) of water, and boil until food is loosened. |
| Glass | To remove burned food: Soak in concentrated baking soda solution made with 3 tablespoons (15 mL) of baking soda for each quart (liter) of water. |
| Iron | To remove burned food: Use 1 teaspoon (5 mL) of baking soda for each quart (liter) of water, and heat to a boil. |
| Stainless Steel | To remove burned food: Soak in hot water with soap or detergent added. Scour if necessary with household cleanser. Brown spots caused by overheating pans cannot be removed; they are permanent. |
| Teflon | To remove stains: Mix 2 tablespoons (10 mL) of baking soda and ½ cup (125 mL) of liquid household bleach with 1 cup (250 mL) of water. Boil this solution for five minutes in the stained utensil. *Wash thoroughly,* rinse, and dry; then wipe teflon surface with salad oil before using. |
| Tin | To remove burned food: Soak in a solution of 1 teaspoon (5 mL) of baking soda for each quart (liter) of water. Do not scour. Scouring will remove the tin coating. |

When you wash dishes by hand, add a measured amount of detergent or soap (to avoid waste) and fill the sink or dishpan about one-third full of hot water. Hold the dish near the level of the dish water as you wash it. Place the washed item into the drainer and rinse with scalding hot water. Be sure to rinse both the inside and outside of the cups, glasses, and bowls, and both sides of plates. Dishes that are scalded dry quickly and do not require drying with a cloth.

Wash and dry wooden items and items with wooden handles quickly so that they do not become warped. Pick up knives one by one and wash them carefully. Place them apart from the other items so that you will not cut yourself. Wash the remaining pots and pans last.

After the items are dry, return them to their proper storage space. In this way, you will be able to locate any item quickly when you wish to use it again.

Use a damp cloth to wipe the counter top and the surfaces of the range and refrigerator. Empty the wastebasket and garbage (unless you have a garbage disposer) before washing the dishes. Leave the sink clean and dry, especially stainless steel sinks, which will water-spot if not wiped dry.

Make sure that all cupboards are closed and that the range is turned off. As the final touch, you may need to dry mop or vacuum the kitchen floor and the dining area. Also, after you use the dining table, make sure that it is clean and that the chairs are placed properly. Your kitchen and dining area are now in order.

**Pretreatment of Pots, Pans, and Dishes** The **pretreatment** (rinsing or soaking before washing) you give to pots and pans or dishes will depend upon the type of soil and the kind of pan. Refer to the chart on page 133 for specific guidelines.

Always allow very hot pans to cool for a short while before adding water; otherwise you may be burned by the steam formed. Avoid any sudden changes in temperature that can cause glass to break, enamel to chip, and thin metal pans to warp.

Use cold water to soak pans or rinse dishes that contained egg, milk, flour, starch, or cereal mixtures. Hot water will cook on these foods, making them more difficult to remove. For dishes that held sugar or syrup, use hot water to dissolve any remaining traces.

For pans that contained greasy food, first pour off the remaining fat while the pan is still warm. Then wipe out the pan with a paper towel, add a small amount of detergent, and fill the pan with hot water.

When you use pans properly (by controlling the heat so they do not scorch) and clean them well after each use, very few stains will develop.

## For Review

1. When working in the kitchen, at what times should you wash (or rewash) your hands?
2. Why should you wash utensils that have been used on raw food before you use them for the finished, cooked product?
3. List three types of bacterial food poisoning, their causes, and their symptoms. Which is the most dangerous? The least dangerous?
4. What are the two *T*'s to remember to prevent food-borne illnesses? Explain why they are important.
5. How should foods be wrapped for storage in the freezer? For storage in the refrigerator? For dry storage?
6. What are three sanitation guidelines to follow for outdoor meals or for parties?
7. In what order should dishes be washed?
8. Why should some dishes and pots and pans be pretreated?

# Preventing Accidents in the Kitchen

Not surprisingly, the room that is the site of most home accidents is the kitchen. You should be particularly careful when you work in the kitchen, understand the kinds of hazards found there, and know how to deal with accidents if they do occur.

## Burns and Fires

To prevent burns and fires in the kitchen, use pans that are large enough to hold food without boilovers, and turn the handles of all pots away from the outer edges of the range to prevent them from being tipped over. Be sure pot handles are not placed over a heat source, and always use dry potholders to handle pans and to remove items from the oven. Never put your hands into the oven; pull out the rack instead. Don't reach across the flame on a gas range or the hot elements on an electric range. When you lift the lids of pots and pans, tilt them away from you so that steam will be blocked from your face and hands, and always use tongs to remove food from hot water or hot grease.

Hot grease can catch fire, so never leave it to cook unattended, and always use a broiler pan with a drip tray to catch the fat. All grease and dirt should be cleaned from the stove, oven surfaces, and the exhaust hood after each use so it will not catch fire the next time the heat is turned on. Before deep-fat frying, be sure all water is drained from the food, and always use a utensil to lower the food slowly and carefully into the hot fat.

Keep all flammable materials away from sources of direct heat. That includes your clothing (long, wide sleeves can easily catch fire when you cook) as well as curtains, towels, paper goods, cleaning fluids, and aerosol cans. Plastics may melt and give off poisonous fumes if they come in contact with direct heat. Always store matches in a metal container away from direct heat. When you light a match, strike it away from you and hold it upright so the flame burns more slowly. Before discarding a match, run cold water over the tip to make sure it is out. If you must light a gas appliance by hand, light the match before turning on the gas. Escaping gas can cause an explosion.

Never place paper towels near a flame (top); they may catch fire. Turn pot handles away from other burners so they don't get hot; if they stick out from the stove, the pots can be knocked over.

Always make sure that the range and other appliances are turned off after use. It is difficult to tell if an electric range is off because there is no flame. A gas burner may still be on if the flame has blown out, and gas will build up in the kitchen.

## Electric Shock and Fire

Make sure that any electric appliance you use is in good repair. Pay particular attention to cords and plugs. Avoid using extension cords; if you must, use the heavy-duty type. Be sure that all electrical appliances are grounded and that circuits are not overloaded. See page 121 for more information about grounding and electrical wiring. Use appliances only for their intended purposes and according to the manufacturer's directions. Leave appliances unplugged when not in use, and always hold the plug when removing it from the outlet. Never just yank the cord. Do not let any metal object touch the working parts of any connected electric appliances. If you must "fish out" your toast with a fork, unplug the toaster first.

Beware of water coming in contact with electricity, which can cause a severe shock. Always unplug appliances before cleaning them, and do not place an appliance in water unless it is labeled "immersible." Do not touch electrical appliances with wet hands, if you are standing on a wet surface, or if you are in contact with the sink or any other plumbing. If you keep portable appliances on the counter near the sink, be sure the counter tops are dry and that cords and plugs do not become wet.

## Falls

Tripping and falling can be particularly dangerous in the kitchen because of hot surfaces, electrical appliances, and the possibility of broken glass. The use of water and other liquids and the dampness caused by cooking vapors can make the kitchen floor slick. Always wipe up

Unplug appliances before washing them. Make sure parts are immersible; keep cords dry.

Damaged or poorly repaired plugs and wires may cause electrical fires.

Pull the rack out of the oven and use pot holders when uncovering a pot or casserole. Tip the cover away from you so that escaping steam will be blocked from your face and hands.

Use a well-balanced stepstool, not a chair, to reach above you.

An open cabinet door "just asks" to be bumped into.

You are less likely to hurt yourself with a sharp knife than a dull one. Always slant any knife away from you when cutting.

It is easy to cut yourself in the kitchen. Sharp knives sticking up from the dishwasher basket and jagged can lids are typical hazards. If glass breaks, always use a dustpan and brush—not your bare hands—to clean it up.

spills immediately to prevent slipping. Never leave objects in the middle of the floor where they can be tripped over, and close drawers and doors so you won't bump into them. If you need to reach a high shelf, stand on a stepstool or ladder designed to balance and support you; don't use a chair. Never climb on counters or appliances. The use of throw rugs in the kitchen is generally not a good idea. If you must use a throw rug, make sure it has a nonskid backing.

## Cuts

Knives are often the cause of personal injury. Sharp knives, however, are safer than dull ones. You use extra pressure to cut with a dull blade, and your hand or the knife is thus more likely to slip. Whenever you cut with a knife, slant the blade away from you and use a cutting board. Pass a knife to another person handle first, and if the knife starts to fall, don't try to catch it in midair. Wash knives separately; never search for them in soapy water. Then store them separately with the handles toward you. In a dishwasher, load knives point down. Of course, you should use knives—and other kitchen utensils—only for their intended purpose.

Broken glass is another source of cuts in the kitchen. Do not use cracked or chipped dishes and glassware. If glass does break, never clean it up with your bare hands. Sweep large pieces into a dustpan, and use several thicknesses of wet paper towel for the small chips.

Use a can opener that leaves smooth edges, and completely remove the can lid, which should be discarded immediately. Keep your fingers away from the moving parts of any appliance. Use extra care when you must touch the blades; unplug the appliance so it cannot start suddenly while your hands are near it.

## Poisoning and Choking

Poisons should always be kept separate from foods, out of reach of children and pets, and tightly closed in their original containers. Labels on cleaners, chemicals, and pesticides list **anti-dotes** (remedies to counteract the poison) and other emergency procedures. Each time you use poisonous products, follow their directions carefully. Remember that breathing poisonous fumes can be just as deadly as swallowing a poison. Always use a spray can in well-ventilated areas, and point the can away from you. Natural gas from a faulty gas range or oven, and fumes from a charcoal grill, burning plastic, and certain other fabrics are toxic and dangerous.

Choking is another hazard that can occur when preparing or eating food. Avoid choking by not running or talking with food in your mouth, by not eating large pieces of food, and by chewing well before you swallow.

## Special Precautions for Special People

All of the hazards described above are more likely to occur among several groups of people.

Older adults, children, and the handicapped run special risks. Many older people whose reflexes have slowed and who may have vision, hearing, or strength loss still want to prepare their own meals. They should use small, lightweight utensils and cookware, and unbreakable dishes. A blender, mixer, or food processor can eliminate hand mixing and slicing. Nonskid mixing bowls, roll-out shelves, and Lazy Susans can also help. Of course, all work areas should be well lit.

Children, on the other hand, often operate at top speed, and may run through the kitchen. Keep the floors clean and dry, and cabinet doors and drawers shut. Children are curious to see, touch, and taste things. Hot foods, electrical cords, and sharp objects should be kept out of their reach. Use childproof locks when storing poisons, matches, or medicines. Put childproof safety plugs in unused electrical outlets. Discourage children from climbing on chairs, counters, or appliances to get a snack for themselves.

It is worthwhile—and fun—to teach children to do simple kitchen tasks. Not only will they learn proper methods, but they will also be less likely to have an accident.

Hot grease can easily catch fire and should not be left cooking unattended. If there is a fire, turn off the heat source, and smother the flames with baking soda or salt.

If someone's clothing catches fire, wrap the person in a blanket and roll him or her around on the floor to smother the flames. If it is your clothing, don't run! Drop to the floor and roll around.

Make sure they understand the dangers of operating appliances and heat sources. Take the time to teach them to do easy kitchen tasks correctly, and warn them against procedures that are too difficult.

## Emergency Action

No matter how careful you are in the kitchen, accidents may happen, and you should know what to do if they occur. Don't be embarrassed to call for help in an emergency. Keep emergency telephone numbers—police, fire department, ambulance, poison control center—posted near the telephone. Include the gas company if you have gas appliances. Teach children to use these numbers to get help. If an accident does occur, a child may be the only person around to make the call. Children should also know their own phone number and address to aid rescue workers.

**In Case of Fire** If a small grease fire starts in a pot or oven, turn off the heat source immediately. Cut off the fire's air supply by closing the lid or oven door or by pouring a lot of salt or baking soda on the flames. Do not use

water. A fire extinguisher may be used on small fires. However, if the fire is spreading, immediately leave the house or apartment and call the fire department from a nearby phone. If someone's clothing catches fire, use the stop-and-drop procedure. Do not run! Drop to the floor, and roll around to smother the flames, or wrap

Place emergency numbers near the telephone. Then, even a young child can quickly call for help if it is needed.

# Rescue Breathing

   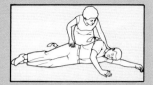

**1. Check for Unresponsiveness**

Tap or gently shake victim

Rescuer shouts "Are you OK?"

Partner says "Unconscious"

Rescuer says "Unconscious"

Rescuer shouts "Help!"

**2. Position the Victim**

Roll victim onto back, if necessary

Kneel facing victim, midway between victim's hips and shoulders

Straighten victim's legs, if necessary, and move arm closest to you above victim's head

Lean over victim, and place one hand on victim's shoulder and other hand on victim's hip

Roll victim toward you as a single unit; as you roll victim, move your hand from shoulder to support back of head and neck

Place victim's arm nearest you alongside victim's body

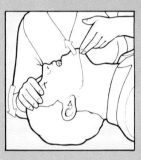   

**3. Open the Airway:** Use head-tilt/chin-lift method

Place one hand on victim's forehead

Place fingers of other hand under bony part of lower jaw near chin

Tilt head and lift jaw—avoid closing victim's mouth

**4. Check for Breathlessness**

Maintain open airway

Place your ear over victim's mouth and nose

Look at chest, listen and feel for breathing for 3 to 5 seconds

Partner says "No breathing"

Rescuer repeats "No breathing"

**5. Give 2 Full Breaths**

Maintain open airway

Pinch nose shut

Open your mouth wide, take a deep breath, and make a tight seal around outside of victim's mouth

Give 2 full breaths at the rate of 1 to 1 1/2 seconds per breath

Observe chest rise and fall; listen and feel for escaping air

**6. Check for Pulse**

Maintain head tilt with one hand on forehead

Locate Adam's apple with middle and index fingers of hand closest to victim's feet

Slide fingers down into groove of neck on side closest to you

Feel for carotid pulse for 5 to 10 seconds

Partner says "No breathing, but there is a pulse"

Rescuer repeats "No breathing, but there is a pulse"

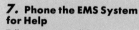   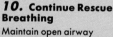

**7. Phone the EMS System for Help**

Tell someone to call for an ambulance

Rescuer says "No breathing, has a pulse, call
_____." (Local emergency number or Operator)

**8. Now Begin Rescue Breathing**

Maintain open airway

Pinch nose shut

Open your mouth wide, take a deep breath, and make a tight seal around outside of victim's mouth

Give 1 breath every 5 seconds at the rate of 1 to 1 1/2 seconds per breath

Observe chest rise and fall; listen and feel for escaping air and the return of breathing

Continue for 1 minute—about 12 breaths

**9. Recheck Pulse**

Tilt head

Locate cartoid pulse and feel for 5 seconds

Partner says "Has pulse"

Rescuer repeats "Has pulse"

Next look, listen, and feel for breathing for 3 to 5 seconds

Partner says "No breathing"

Rescuer repeats "No breathing"

**10. Continue Rescue Breathing**

Maintain open airway

Give 1 breath every 5 seconds at the rate of 1 to 1 1/2 seconds per breath

Recheck pulse every minute

**11. What to Do Next**

While the rescuer is rechecking pulse and breathing, the partner should read one of the following statements:

1. Victim is breathing but is still unconscious.

2. Victim has a pulse but is not breathing.

Based on this information, the rescuer should make a decision about what to do next, and continue giving the right care.

the victim in heavy material, such as a blanket, and roll him or her around on the floor. If there is heavy smoke, *crawl* away; smoke is thinner near the floor. If you smell gas, turn off all appliances, open windows, and leave the house to call for assistance.

Treat minor burns by cooling them under cold water or with ice packs. Then cover them with clean, dry bandages. Never use butter on a burn. Do not clean the burn or break blisters. Only apply ointments on a doctor's advice. For severe or large-area burns, keep the patient warm and in a flat position, and get medical help.

**In Case of Electric Shock** Never touch someone who is still in contact with electricity. The current will pass through you as well. Turn off the current by pulling out the plug or removing the fuse. Use a nonconducting material (such as wood, rope, or cloth, which do not carry electricity) to break the connection between the victim and the electric current. Begin rescue breathing if necessary, and call for help immediately.

**In Case of Falls** If there are open wounds as the result of a fall, treat them like cuts (see below). If you think a bone may be fractured, do not move the victim, but get medical help. If there is a head injury (headache, dizziness, difficulty speaking, and vomiting are warning signals), call for help. Do not give the person anything to eat or drink. Minor bumps, bruises, and sprains can be treated with ice packs and bed rest. If discomfort continues, consult a doctor.

**In Case of Cuts** Minor cuts can be treated by washing with mild soap and water and then blotting dry. Apply a clean, dry bandage. An **antiseptic** (a substance that kills germs and prevents infection) can also be used. In case of severe bleeding, press firmly on the wound with a thick cloth, and get medical help. Puncture wounds can be serious even though they do not bleed much. Consult a doctor immediately.

**In Case of Poisoning** Call for help immediately, whether the poison has been swallowed, inhaled, or sprayed in the eyes. Read the package label to find out what antidote to use, or call the poison control center or the hospital emergency room for guidance. A person who has inhaled smoke or poisonous fumes should be taken to a well-ventilated area. Use rescue breathing if necessary. Flush irritated eyes with large amounts of water. Again, in all poisoning cases, get emergency medical help immediately.

**In Case of Choking** If someone is choking on food or an object lodged in the throat, use the Heimlich Maneuver described in the chart on page 109. Get medical help quickly.

## For Review

1. List three important tips for preventing each of the following: burns and fires, electric shock, falls, cuts, poisoning, and choking.
2. What kitchen aids are particularly helpful for older adults? Why?
3. What special precautions should you take to "childproof" a kitchen?
4. For which kitchen emergency should you leave the house *before* you call for help? Why?
5. How can you put out minor grease fires? Fires in clothing?
6. How can you safely break the electrical connection when someone is getting an electric shock?

# 6 Chapter Review

## Summary

Kitchens are designed and organized to make food storage, preparation and cleanup, and cooking and serving efficient. Durable floor and wall coverings, plenty of space for food storage and preparation, and enough electrical outlets help make kitchens safe. So does careful and correct use of electrical appliances. A good food manager is concerned with personal and kitchen cleanliness, proper food storage as well as the time and temperature used for preparing the food to prevent food-borne illnesses.

Since most home accidents occur in the kitchen, care should be used when cooking. It is important to know how to treat minor burns and wounds and to know the telephone numbers for getting emergency medical help for more serious injuries.

## Vocabulary

Use the words below to complete the numbered sentences.

| | |
|---|---|
| antidotes | pretreatment |
| antiseptic | salmonella |
| botulism | poisoning |
| contaminants | sanitation |
| dry storage | spoilage |
| grounded | work centers |
| microorganisms | work flow |
| personal hygiene | work triangle |

1. _____ are the three major areas in the kitchen where storage, preparation and cleanup, and cooking and serving occur.
2. The _____ of food preparation is the order in which the tasks are done, going from the refrigerator, to the sink, then to the range center.
3. The three work centers should be arranged as a _____, which is the ideal shape for the work area of any kitchen.
4. Appliances that have three prongs are _____ appliances.
5. Proper _____ is needed to keep the kitchen, equipment, food, and yourself clean and as free as possible from bacteria.
6. Your individual cleanliness, or _____, is important to safe food preparation.
7. Food-borne illnesses can result from _____, which is a change in food caused by enzymes.
8. Tiny living things that can be poisonous or that can cause changes in food are called _____.
9. A severe headache and fever, as well as an upset stomach are symptoms of _____, which is a form of food poisoning.
10. The most deadly form of food poisoning that attacks a person's nervous system is _____.
11. Time and temperature are important factors to prevent the growth of dangerous foreign substances in food that are called _____.
12. _____ is a cool, dry place where the least perishable foods may be stored.

13. Heavily soiled pots and pans are easier to clean when you use the _____ of rinsing and soaking before washing them.
14. _____ are remedies that should be used to counteract poison.
15. A substance that can be applied to a minor wound to kill germs and prevent infection is an _____.

## Chapter Questions

1. How should work centers be arranged and why should they be in that arrangement?
2. Evaluate your kitchen for safety and efficiency.
3. What are two reasons why it is important to wash counters and other work surfaces before, during, and after food preparation?
4. Evaluate your kitchen for cleanliness.
5. Determine the steps to follow to prevent a food-illness if you were to prepare a meal that used a frozen food ingredient.
6. As a meal is prepared and served, what are at least three ways good cooks use to keep the kitchen clean?
7. What are at least five important precautions to follow when using the stove?
8. If you have to use a knife or fork to remove your toast from a toaster, why should you unplug the appliance?
9. What are three safeguards you can use to avoid getting cut in the kitchen?
10. If you or a family member gets burned while cooking, what should you do?

## Skill Activities

**1. Communication** In your food journal, keep a record of the guidelines you followed for personal cleanliness and kitchen sanitation when you prepared a meal. For example, write the date, tell what you prepared, and the ways you maintained a high standard of personal hygiene as well as the ways you kept the kitchen clean during the food preparation. For a list of personal hygiene guidelines, refer to page 124 and for a list of kitchen sanitation guidelines, refer to page 125.

**2. Resource management** Use lined paper to make freezer inventory sheets. Write one of these headings at the top of each piece of paper: "Breads," "Cakes and Cookies," "Casseroles," "Meats," "Vegetables." Then make three columns and label them "Type of Food," "Date of Freezing," and "Date of Removal." If you use these sheets, it will help you to know the food that is available in the freezer as well as how long the food has been stored in the freezer.

**3. Social studies** If you do not have a list of emergency telephone numbers posted near your telephone, make a list now. List the telephone numbers for the police, fire department, ambulance, and poison control center. Put this list beside your telephone.

# 7 Appliances, Equipment, and Tools

## As you read, think about:

- how to select, use, and care for major appliances.
- how to select, use, and care for small appliances.
- how to shop and budget for appliances.
- how to select, use, and care for cookware, bakeware, and kitchen tools.

## Vocabulary

credit
Underwriters
   Laboratories
   (UL) seal
American Gas
   Association
   (AGA) blue star
EnergyGuide
   labels
warranty
full warranty
limited warranty
cookware
bakeware

If you could have only one basic piece of equipment in a kitchen, what would it be? A range on which to cook food? There are meals that can be prepared without heat, but how would you keep perishables from spoiling? Did you choose the refrigerator-freezer? That is certainly an important appliance, but humanity survived for centuries—and prepared countless meals from the most basic to the most elaborate —without refrigeration. Most people, however, did have access to water—for cleaning foods, for use as an ingredient, and for cleaning up after meals. Perhaps then, the sink and dish-washer form the most important work center in the kitchen. What do you think?

You may have some personal experience in doing without the appliances we usually take for granted. Do you remember a time when your house lost electricity after a storm? How did you manage without the refrigerator and electric range? Or were you lucky enough to have a gas range? Did you ever have your water turned off for plumbing repairs? Could meals be prepared during that time?

Now think about the smaller appliances and tools you use in food preparation. Which of these are "essential" and which are luxuries? It is not merely a question of price. A good-quality knife is essential but more expensive than a melon-ball cutter, which is certainly a luxury. What tools and small appliances would you buy first to equip a kitchen? How would you know if you were getting your money's worth? If you could afford only one new major appliance to update an old kitchen, which would it be: a range, refrigerator-freezer, or dishwasher? What features would you choose to be sure the appliance contributes the most to your cooking efficiency and pleasure? A close look at the features, uses, and care of kitchen appliances, equipment, and tools will not only make you a better purchaser, it will also make you a better cook.

What appliances are totally lacking in this kitchen? Note the wooden sink and coal stove. How have they been improved since the 1870s?

# Major Appliances

Major appliances are not only a major help in food preparation, they are also a major purchase. They are expensive to buy; you will not purchase them often, so you want to make the right choice the first time. It is definitely worth your while to do some research into what's available, and to do some comparison shopping for price. You should also think about the features you really need. Often the newest, fanciest features are not really the most useful, but they are usually the most expensive. Think, too, about the costs of operating different models. Energy efficiency is an important consideration when buying appliances.

Major appliances are also expensive to repair. You want to purchase top-quality appliances that are durable and reliable. You also want to be sure you learn to use and care for them correctly. Finally, major appliances can make an important difference in the amount of time you spend in the kitchen and the kinds of meals you prepare. Taking the time to learn to use all the features of a new appliance when you first bring it home will save you time later and increase your enjoyment in the use of the appliance.

This ultramodern electric range can be used for many methods of food preparation. What are the advantages of electric ranges? What are the disadvantages?

## The Range

The range includes both the cook-top and the oven/broiler, but they need not be in one unit. There are two basic styles. The *freestanding ranges,* which stand on their own, usually have one oven below the cook-top. Double-oven or split-level ranges have an additional oven above the cook-top. Some ranges have a separate broiler below the lower oven; others have broiling capacity within the oven. *Built-in ranges* have separate cook-tops and oven units built into the kitchen counters. There are usually cabinets below the cooking surface. Depending on the height of the oven or double oven, there may be storage above and below these appliances, too.

Ranges may be fueled either by gas or electricity, although gas lines are not available in all areas. There are people who prefer each kind of fuel. Some differences between gas and electric cook-tops affect the way food is cooked, while induction cook-tops often require the use of particular kinds of pots and pans.

*Gas cook-tops* have burners and cook by flame. You can set the temperature by using the controls to regulate the size of the flame. Heat is produced as soon as the flame appears, and heat stops as soon as the flame is turned off. This gives the cook good control over the amount of heat under pots and pans. Some gas ranges have continuous pilot lights. If they blow out, fumes may accumulate until the gas is turned off or the pilot light is relighted. *Never strike a match if you think gas may have accumulated.* If you are lighting a gas oven or burner, light the match first and then turn on the gas. Newer gas ranges have a pilotless ignition, which eliminates the need for the pilot light to burn continuously and therefore uses less fuel.

*Electric cook-tops* have wire coils called heating elements. When the electricity is turned on, the coil slowly heats; when the electricity is turned off, the coil slowly cools. Foods take longer to get hot on an electric heating element than on a gas burner. Also, food will continue to receive heat after the control is turned off, so you must be careful of overcooking and burning. Most electric range controls have several temperature settings (such as high, medium-high, low, and simmer), but it takes time for the element to get hotter or cooler when you change the setting. If a food is burning or has finished cooking, you may need to lift the pot or pan from the heating element for a few moments or move it to another burner until the coil responds to the change in setting.

*Induction cook-tops* have a glass ceramic surface over the heating elements. The production of heat depends upon the magnetic attraction between the heating element and a pan made with iron (for example, cast-iron or stainless steel). Other types of cookware do not produce this attraction and cannot be used on an induction cook-top.

**Special Features** There are a variety of features to be found on different range models. They affect both the convenience of using the appliance and its price. You must decide which features are worthwhile for you.

Ranges come in a wide variety of styles. This gas range has a built-in, stove-top grill and accompanying microwave oven. What are the advantages of this arrangement?

*Automatic cleaning* is a feature of most new ranges. *Self-cleaning* ovens have a special, very hot cycle that burns off grease and food spills. You may need to use a damp cloth to wipe up the ash that remains after this cycle. *Continuous-cleaning* ovens have walls with a special surface that causes food to be burned away whenever the oven is on.

*Ventilating hoods* are located over the cook-top. They remove heat, steam, and odors. Many have filters that absorb grease and smoke. *Thermostatic controls* on some cook-tops work like an electric skillet to keep the heating element or burner at a constant temperature. *Built-in clocks* and *timers* are available on many ranges to help you keep track of cooking times. Some turn the oven on and off at preset times. Other useful features include built-in meat thermometers and add-on grills, rotisseries, and griddles. Windows in oven doors and lights inside the oven allow you to check on food without opening the oven door.

**Use and Care** Before using a range, always read the owner's use-and-care manual. It will give directions for safe operation, the use of special features, and cleaning suggestions.

All parts of the range require cleaning: the cooking surface, oven, and broiler unit. With proper care, you will retain the beauty of your range even though you use it often.

As you recall from Chapter 6, controlling the heat setting of surface burners and units and using the correct size pots and pans will help to prevent boilovers. Should spills occur, wipe them up immediately. If you let them build up, they will bake onto the surface and become more difficult to remove. Use a dry cloth or sponge to wipe spills when the range is hot; use warm, soapy water when it is cold.

The surface units, including the drip trays, should be cleaned often. The chromium trim needs only to be cleaned with soap and water. Avoid using steel wool or soap pads on chromium or enamel; the abrasiveness of these materials will scratch the surface.

Spills on the surface of the range should be wiped up as soon as possible, before they have a chance to dry or "bake on." Avoid using abrasives, such as steel-wool pads; they can scratch the surface.

Clean the broiler pan after each use. Allow the pan to cool for a few minutes after the food is removed, pour out the fat from the drip tray, and wipe it with absorbent paper. Place soap or detergent into the drip tray, add hot water, and let the tray soak while you wash other dishes. If the use-and-care manual recommends it, line the broiler's drip tray with foil before cooking in order to make cleanup easier.

Electric heating elements are self-cleaning. When the unit becomes hot, the food will burn off. You need only to clean the drip pans under the elements by washing them in soapy water. For cleaning gas burners, follow the directions given with your gas range.

If you wipe a cooled oven after each use, you will avoid the difficult task of removing baked-on food, vapors, and grease. You may place a piece of aluminum foil (slightly larger than the pan or dish) under a dish that is likely to spill over while baking. Commercial oven cleaners may be used to clean up burned-on food, but they should be used with care. They can be harmful to the skin and eyes, and should be used only in well-ventilated areas. Protect yourself with rubber gloves, and spread newspapers over the floor or nearby surfaces.

## The Refrigerator-Freezer

This appliance helps to keep perishables from spoiling and provides longer-term storage for frozen foods. Refrigerator-freezers come in a variety of sizes. Choose a size according to how many people you serve, how often you shop, how often meals are eaten at home, and how much long-term storage you need in the freezer. Refrigerator capacity is given in cubic feet or liters. For a four-person household, 16 cubic feet (456 L) of refrigerator space and 8 cubic feet (228 L) of freezer space is a good general guide. Always measure before you buy to make sure that the unit will fit in the allotted space in your kitchen.

All refrigerator sections should keep food at 32 to 40° F (0 to − 4° C). Freezers should be − 5 to 5° F (− 21 to − 15° C). Some freezing compartments in one-door refrigerators hold food at only 10 to 15° F (− 12 to − 9° C). These are suitable *only* for short-term storage of already frozen items.

Refrigerator-freezers are available in several styles. *Top-mounted two-door models* have the freezer above the refrigerator. This style is the most common. *Side-by-side models* have the freezer next to the refrigerator. It is easier to see and reach the frozen foods (particularly for children or those in wheelchairs) in this arrangement, but some people find the narrower shelves inconvenient. *Bottom-freezer models* are the reverse of the top-mounted style. Here, the more frequently used foods are at eye level, thus eliminating much bending down. *One-door models* have a freezing compartment—not a true freezer—inside the refrigerator. *Portable models* are often small enough to slide under a desk or to sit on a counter. These models have

Give the advantages of a water/ice dispenser in the door.

ice-cube trays but usually cannot hold frozen foods. They are most often used in college dormitories and in offices.

**Special Features** There are a variety of features available in refrigerator-freezers. Some affect the cost of operating the appliance; most affect the price of buying it. Choose the ones that provide the most convenience at the least cost for your particular needs.

*Automatic defrosting* can save you all or some of the chore of defrosting. *Frost-free models* defrost themselves completely. Ice does not build up in either the refrigerator or the freezer. These are the most expensive to buy and operate. *Cycle defrost* or *automatic defrost* models, less expensive than frost-free models, defrost only the refrigerator section; you must defrost the freezer yourself. *Manual defrost* models are the least expensive to buy and operate—and the least convenient. Both compartments must be defrosted by hand.

The various refrigerator-freezer styles have different advantages and disadvantages. While access to frozen foods is awkward in this bottom-freezer model, foods that are used more often, such as fruits and vegetables, are at eye level in the upper section.

*Adjustable shelves* are a very useful and relatively inexpensive feature that allows you to design your own storage space by moving the shelves up and down. *Specialized storage bins* are designed for the temperature and moisture requirements of meat, cheese, or fresh produce. Some have adjustable controls. *Automatic ice makers require a special plumbing hook-up and add considerably to the cost of the unit. Ice and water dispensers* allow you to save energy because you do not need to open the door to fill a glass with ice or ice water. This feature requires a water hook-up and adds considerably to the price of the unit. Other useful features are energy-saving switches, reversible door hinges, and textured doors, which hide dirt.

**Use and Care** The owner's use-and-care manual is the best guide for efficient use and cleaning of your refrigerator-freezer. Of course, you should set the controls to provide the right temperatures for both compartments (see page 149). The appliance should be located away from sources of heat. Another way to prevent the unit from overworking is to limit the number of times you open the door. Never leave the door open while you decide what you want. Decide first; then open the door. Organize foods so you can find them easily.

The freezer section should be packed full for maximum efficiency. However, air needs to circulate freely in the refrigerator section; overloading it will cause it to work harder. Be sure to wrap all foods properly (see pages 130-131). Place an open box of baking soda in both sections to absorb odors. Also wipe up spills immediately to help keep the refrigerator smelling fresh, as well as to prevent the growth of bacteria. Wipe food containers before you place them in the refrigerator.

To clean the outer surface of the refrigerator, wipe it with a damp cloth whenever necessary. Never use strong detergents or abrasive cleansers, as they can spoil the finish and damage plastic parts. If your refrigerator-freezer is self-defrosting, it will still need occasional cleaning with a baking soda and water solution.

For other units, defrost when freezer ice is about ¼ inch (6.35 mm) thick. A build-up of ice keeps the unit from operating efficiently. Turn the control to "off" or "defrost." Remove frozen foods and wrap them in several sheets of newspaper to prevent thawing. You may place pans (not ice trays) of hot water into the freezer compartment for quicker defrosting. Remove all food from the refrigerator, and clean the interior and the freezer with a baking soda and water solution. When you are finished, turn the control to the normal setting and replace the food. Wash the ice trays and the outside of the refrigerator

For maximum efficiency of the appliance, a freezer should be packed full, but items in the refrigerator compartment should be arranged so that air can circulate around them.

with warm water and a mild detergent or soap. The owner's manual will give you complete instructions.

About every six months, move the unit away from the wall, unplug it, and vacuum the dust and lint from the coils and base.

### The Freezer

A separate freezer can be a great convenience if you have the space for it. It allows you to buy in large quantities, which can save both money and time spent food shopping.

Freezers come in two basic styles. *Upright freezers* look like and are about the same size as most refrigerators. Food is easy to see and to reach in these models, and they don't require much floor space. Some upright freezers are frost-free. *Chest freezers* are less expensive than upright models, but they take up more floor space. Foods at the bottom are not really accessible without unloading much of the unit. Many chest freezers are placed in basements or garages. They should have a lock to prevent children from opening the units and crawling or falling in. Chest freezers need to be defrosted several times a year.

**Special Features** There are a variety of features available in both kinds of freezers, as well as features particular to each type. Both types may have *door locks* for safety and security, and *safety lights* or *alarms,* which signal that power is off or that the temperature is too high to keep food safely frozen.

The special features of chest freezers include lids that stay up automatically once they are raised, lift-out storage baskets, and sliding dividers for added convenience.

Upright freezer features include fast-freeze shelves, door shelves that allow packages to be placed upright, and energy-saving switches that regulate the moisture-control devices on frost-free models.

Select chest-freezer models with lids that stay up automatically, so they don't close on the person using them, and with locks to prevent small children from climbing inside.

**Use and Care** Freezers should be located in a cool, dry place. Be sure the temperature controls are correctly set and that the door seals fit tightly. Open the door as little as possible. In general, the fuller the freezer, the more efficiently it will operate.

Of course, the freezer should be kept clean, and foods should be properly wrapped. Manual defrost models should be defrosted when ice becomes about ¼–½ inch (6.35–12.7 mm) thick. Vacuum the condenser coils every six months. Also refer to the owner's manual for use and care of your freezer.

### The Dishwasher

While a dishwasher is not an essential appliance, it is a very useful one. It saves time and personal energy that can be better spent doing more creative kitchen activities. It also cleans and sanitizes dishes better than many people do when washing dishes. In order to accomplish this, the dishwasher should operate with 140° F (60° C) water and adequate water pressure.

There are two basic types of dishwashers. *Built-in dishwashers,* loaded from the front, fit under the counter and are permanently connected to the kitchen plumbing. They need to be installed professionally. *Portable dishwashers,* loaded either from the top or the front, are rolled to the sink when used and are connected to the faucet with a hose. A drain hose allows water to drain into the sink. When not in use, portables can be stored anywhere and their tops used as extra counter space.

Dishwashers give you a choice of cycles. Most provide a normal cycle for average loads; a heavy-duty, or pots-and-pans, cycle; and a short, or gentle, cycle for china and crystal. Some have a rinse-and-hold cycle and a plate-warmer cycle as well. Usually, the more cycles, the higher the price. Think about your usual needs before investing in extra cycles you may never use. The dishwashing process is usually a noisy one. Look for models that have good insulation, as they will operate more quietly.

This portable dishwasher can be hooked up to the sink for water supply and drainage. When not in use, it rolls away, and the specially treated top provides an extra work surface.

**Features** In addition to cycles and insulation, there are other differences in dishwasher features. *Interior surfaces* are available in porcelain, enamel, plastic, or stainless steel. *Multiple wash arms* provide more spray points to reach more dishes directly. *Adjustable racks* allow you to make room for large or oddly shaped items. *Soft food disposers* chop up food particles so that they can drain out and not accumulate in the appliance. *Hot water boosters* maintain the temperature of the hot water during cleaning. The *delay-wash* feature allows you to set the appliance to go on at a later time. *Interchangeable front panels* of various colors allow you to change the color scheme of your kitchen without replacing your dishwasher.

**Use and Care** It is more energy efficient to run the dishwasher when it is full. However, you should be careful to arrange items so they do not block other items from the water jets, so water drains off properly (particularly so cups and glasses do not fill up), and so they will not touch the moving arms of the dishwasher. Always refer to the owner's manual for correct loading and operating of the dishwasher. Energy can also be saved by using the shortest cycle for the amount of soil in the load. The no-heat drying feature allows dishes to dry naturally and saves electricity.

Use only the specially made dishwasher detergents in the amounts recommended by the manufacturer. Always scrape food particles and bones from dishes before you load the dishes into the dishwasher. However, it is not necessary to rinse dishes if you will be using the unit right away.

**Practical Tip**
• Dry tin bakeware in a warm oven to keep the utensils from rusting.

## For Review

1. What is the best source of information on the use and care of a particular appliance?
2. What are the three kinds of cook-tops? Explain one advantage or one disadvantage of each.
3. Which compartment of a refrigerator-freezer should be well filled to operate efficiently? Which should have air circulating for the best operation? Why?
4. What is one advantage and one disadvantage of a chest freezer? Of an upright freezer?
5. What are three things to be careful of when loading a dishwasher?
6. For two major appliances, describe the style and features that would be best for your family. Explain your choice.

# Small Appliances

It often seems as though there is a small electric appliance to do almost any kitchen task you can think of. While these appliances are not essential to food preparation, they do have many advantages. Some save time and personal energy. Slicing, grating, and whipping can be done faster—and often better—by food processors and mixers than by hand. Others save electrical energy, and thus save money, too. Heating several dinner rolls or baking a potato in a small toaster oven is more energy efficient than turning on a large conventional oven for the same purpose. Because small appliances are usually portable, they can be moved wherever you need them. For many people, using these appliances is one of the things that makes cooking fun. For example, some cooks enjoy experimenting with all the operations the food processor can accomplish. For others, however, small appliances actually make cooking possible. Older adults, the handicapped, and people with little time available rely extensively on these appliances to save time and energy and make kitchen work easier. For these groups of people, though, careful selection of small appliances and a thorough knowledge of how to use them are essential. Unless the appliance is easy to use, clean, and store, it will not be a true convenience. As with major appliances, you should consider your needs, your skills, and the space you have available, as well as the quality, features, and price of each appliance before you make a purchase.

## Toaster

One of the earliest and most popular of small appliances, the toaster not only browns

Food processors perform many tiresome kitchen tasks quickly and efficiently. They encourage people to experiment with recipes that might otherwise seem to require too much tedious "work."

A toaster oven is a very versatile appliance for its size. What different cooking tasks can it perform?

bread on both sides but also prepares many specially manufactured products such as toaster-tarts, waffles, and pancakes. Toasters come in two- and four-slice models. Look for controls that allow easy regulation of degree of brownness, and for lowering and raising the toast. Make sure that the toast—or whatever product you will be toasting—is raised high enough out of the toaster to be removed easily.

### Toaster Oven

As its name suggests, the toaster oven combines features of both a toaster and an oven. In addition to toasting, it can warm, top brown, and bake small amounts of food. Some toaster ovens also have broiling capacity. They come in a variety of sizes, so you can choose the size that best suits your needs.

### Mixer

An electric mixer blends, beats, whips, and mixes ingredients. There are three basic types.

*Hand-held,* or *portable, mixers* can do light-weight jobs and then be stored away easily. *Stand mixers* have a counter-top stand and a large and small mixing bowl to fit on the turntable. These models can do most mixing jobs. *Heavy-duty mixers* can manage larger and thicker batters. Special attachments allow them to knead bread dough. Because of their size and weight, stand and heavy-duty mixers are usually stored on the counter top. Look for the type of bowls—glass or stainless steel—and range of speeds that you will use most often. Make sure the motor is powerful enough for the jobs you have in mind and that you have room to store the model you select.

### Blender

A blender chops, blends, purées, and lique-fies foods. A tall glass or plastic container with a cover sits on a stand containing a high-speed motor. Blades in the bottom of the container do the work. There are usually five or six speeds; make sure the blender you select has the speeds suitable for the jobs you do most often. Also look for removable blades for easy cleaning. An extra

Many cooks feel that a kitchen is not complete without a mixer. Of these three kinds—the stand mixer, the heavy-duty type with bread-kneading capacity, and the portable, hand-held variety—which would be best for you? Why?

# Simple Tools That Work

An old saying tells us that simplicity is a virtue. In the kitchen, technology need not be complicated to be effective. In fact, some of our most useful kitchen tools are simple. Consider one centuries-old tool, the knife.

The three tools described below are relatively new technologies, but they are also simple tools that work.

**Heat Pipes**   Heat pipes are used to roast meats more efficiently in the oven. Shaped like an arrow, a heat pipe consists of a long metal cylinder. One end is pointed. The other end is fashioned with finlike metal pieces. The cylinder contains a small amount of liquid.

You pierce the meat with the heat pipe near the bottom of the roast and push toward the opposite, upper side. The heat pipe is positioned diagonally through the middle of the roast. As the roast cooks, the heat pipe absorbs and transfers heat into the interior of the roast. Thus, the inside of the roast cooks almost as quickly as the outside. This reduces both cooking time and shrinkage of the meat.

**Garlic Press**   Peeling and chopping fresh garlic cloves can be a time-consuming process. A garlic press makes this job more efficient and less messy. Garlic presses are made out of metal or plastic. There are a variety of different styles, but a basic garlic press consists of two leverlike pieces attached at one end. At the attached end, one piece is hollowed out and has small holes in it. The other end is flat. When you put a clove of garlic in the hollowed-out end and then push, you get instant minced garlic.

**Liquid Crystal Egg Timer**   To achieve perfect hard-cooked or soft-cooked eggs, you can use a liquid crystal egg timer. This simple device consists of a liquid crystal enclosed in plastic. You simply put it in the pan with the eggs. As the water heats, the crystal changes color. The color change will gradually extend to a marker labeled "soft," then another labeled "medium," until it finally reaches "hard." This simple tool takes the guesswork out of boiling eggs.

A garlic press and an egg timer are two of the simplest tools used in the kitchen.

feature is small containers with covers; these are useful both for blending small amounts and for storage of the blended product.

## Food Processor

A food processor makes food preparation much easier. It can slice in various thicknesses, chop, shred, grind, grate, and mix ingredients. A removable bowl and cover sit on the base, which contains the motor. A pusher, or "feed tube," fits through a chute in the cover and enables you to "feed" ingredients into the bowl while the unit is on or off. A variety of blades and discs for various tasks usually comes with the unit.

## Electric Skillet

An electric skillet can do more than just fry foods. It also simmers, roasts, pan-broils, and bakes. A thermostat keeps the heat at the temperature you select. Electric skillets come in several sizes and shapes; some have extra high sides and covers. Skillets with nonstick surfaces are also available. Be sure to get a skillet with a removable heating control so the pan can be easily cleaned.

Slow cookers and electric skillets have thermostats to keep temperatures constant, and slow cookers can be left unattended for hours.

## Slow Cooker

A slow cooker cooks foods slowly over a long period of time. It is useful for stews, soups, and roasts. Slow cooking retains the juices and flavors of foods and tenderizes tough cuts of meat. Because a slow cooker can be set in the morning and work safely unattended for hours, it can provide a hot, finished meal to working people when they return home at dinner time. The heating element of a slow cooker is in the base. Look for a removable food container for easy cleaning.

## Pressure Cooker

Although the pressure cooker is not an electric appliance, it is a useful appliance that reduces cooking time and also prevents loss of nutrients. The temperature in the pressure cooker rises above the boiling point, and steam pressure builds to cook and tenderize foods quickly. The build-up of steam can also be dangerous. Be sure to follow the manufacturer's directions when you use a pressure cooker. Always let the cooker cool and the steam subside before removing the lid.

## Electric Coffee Maker

Electric coffee makers are of two types. Electric *percolators* first heat the water and then force it up through a stem in the unit into a basket of coffee grounds. This process is repeated until the coffee is at the desired strength. In *automatic drip coffee makers,* the water is first heated in a reservoir and then drips through a basket of grounds below. The container into which the coffee drips can be removed for pouring; when it is replaced, a heater in the base keeps the coffee warm. Both types of coffee makers usually have controls for the selection of brewing strength, and both come in various sizes, or cup capacity. Some of the drip models have preset timers.

An in-sink disposal is very convenient to have. It eliminates much of the food waste otherwise stored in garbage cans by grinding it up and flushing it away.

## Food Waste Disposer

Also called an in-sink disposal, this appliance conveniently disposes of food garbage. It is installed under the sink. Food enters the disposal unit through the sink drain and is then ground into small particles and flushed into the drainage system. While most modern disposers will grind up bones and stringy vegetables, older models will not. Check the owner's use-and-care booklet.

There are two types of in-sink disposers. *Batch-feed* models take only a small load at a time and operate only when the cover (which acts as the switch) is in place. This system prevents unwanted objects from getting into the system while it is operating. *Continuous-feed* disposers are more convenient but not as safe to use. They are operated by a wall switch, and waste can be fed in continuously. You must be careful not to drop utensils or other nonwaste objects into continuous-feed models. Look for disposer reset buttons, which turn the unit back on after it has jammed. Some units also come with anti-jam buttons.

## Counter-top Ovens

A small oven that can be placed on a counter top can be a very useful addition to a kitchen. If the oven has broiling capacity, it can eliminate the need to use the ankle-high broilers in some gas ranges. Small ovens are more energy efficient for small amounts of food. They are also handy as an "extra" when you are entertaining a large group. Two of the most popular of these counter-top ovens are the convection oven and the microwave oven.

**Convection Ovens** These ovens have fans that circulate the heated air all around the food. Because heat hits the food from all sides, foods cook more quickly and evenly and with less energy than in conventional ovens. Preheating is not necessary, and lower temperatures can be used. Foods also brown more evenly and remain juicier. Look for models with digital control panels and with temperature probes for testing doneness. Ordinary bakeware can be used in convection ovens.

**Microwave Ovens** These appliances cook foods differently than other ovens. Microwave ovens do not get hot. Instead, they give off microwaves, which are similar to radio waves, that bounce off the metal interior walls. Food is hit from all sides by these microwaves, which enter the food to a depth of about ½–1½ inches (1.3–3.8 cm). The microwaves cause the food molecules to rub against each other, which creates friction and, thereby, heat. Food cooks very quickly—about four times faster than in conventional ovens. Microwave ovens use less energy than conventional ovens, but they require particular kinds of cookware (glass, plastic, paper, or ceramic) through which microwaves can pass. Usually, foods do not brown in a microwave oven, and some must be rotated or stirred for even heating. You will read more about microwave cookery in Chapter 10.

Convection ovens use fans to circulate heated air so that it hits food from all sides. Therefore, preheating is not necessary, lower temperatures can be used for cooking, and foods cook more quickly and evenly. Convection ovens produce well-browned foods with the juices sealed in. Ordinary bakeware can be used.

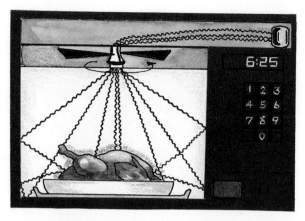

In a microwave oven, a magnetron tube produces microwaves, which are guided toward a slowly rotating fan. The fan blades reflect the microwaves. Some hit the food directly; others bounce off the oven surfaces and then hit the food. The microwaves cause food molecules to vibrate, thus creating heat. Food cooks quickly but does not brown. Special bakeware is required.

Microwave ovens come in various sizes and with different power ranges. The higher the power, the faster the oven will cook. Look for these features in a microwave oven: defrost setting, variable power levels, timers, temperature probes with automatic shut-offs, and special browning elements to brown foods at the end of microwave cooking. Some ovens have shelves to allow more foods to be cooked at one time; some microwaves also have rotating platforms for even cooking.

Since exposure to large doses of microwaves can be hazardous, be sure any oven you buy meets safety standards and remains in perfect working order. Have it checked for leakage every few years. Follow the manufacturer's instructions very carefully when you operate or clean your microwave oven.

## Use and Care of Small Electrical Appliances

As with major appliances, the owner's manual is your best source for information on the use and care of small appliances. In general, handle these appliances carefully, and avoid dropping or banging them. Never use or store them near water. Do not plug too many of these small electrical appliances into one electrical circuit.

Always turn an appliance to "off" before disconnecting it. Then disconnect it by grasping the plug—not by pulling the cord. Connect the appliance by plugging the cord into the appliance first, and then into the electrical outlet. Remove the plug from the outlet before you remove the cord from the appliance.

Heating units of appliances are never placed into water unless they are water sealed and clearly marked "immersible."

Clean small appliances after each use. Let them cool first. Check in the owner's manual to see which parts—such as beaters, blades, bowls, or containers—may be placed in the dishwasher. Power units or motors need only be wiped with a damp cloth. Chrome or plastic parts can be cleaned with a soapy cloth, rinsed, and dried. Immersible parts may be washed in the sink.

Clean small appliances after each use. First make sure the appliance is off; unplug it; and then follow the manufacturer's directions.

## For Review

1. What are the two most obvious advantages of a toaster oven over a conventional toaster?
2. What are the three types of electric mixers? Give a good reason that a person might have for choosing each type of mixer.
3. Explain a major advantage for using each of the following appliances: blender, food processor, electric skillet, slow cooker, pressure cooker.
4. What are the two types of food waste disposers? Which type is the safer one to use? Why?
5. Briefly describe how food cooks in a convection oven. How food cooks in a microwave oven.
6. What steps should you follow when connecting and disconnecting a small electric appliance?

# Buying Appliances

As you have seen, the range of appliance styles, features, sizes, and price is almost endless. Add to this the number of dealers and "deals," and shopping for an appliance may seem to be an overwhelming task. Taking some time to think through your needs, your available work and storage space, and your budget will help narrow your choices. Doing some research on safety, durability, reliability, and convenience of different brands and styles will help even more. Finally, comparison shopping will provide you with the best combination of price and service.

## Personal Factors to Consider

Before you begin shopping for a major or small appliance, consider three personal factors.

**Need** Do you really "need" a new appliance, or is the old one adequate? Do you really "need" the most up-to-date, nonessential appliances, or is it just fashionable to have them?

One way to answer the first question is to compare the features of the appliance you want to buy and the one you have. Will these features really make a difference in your time and effort in the kitchen or in the kinds of foods you are able to prepare? Of course, if an appliance has become unsafe to use or no longer reliably performs its major function, it should be replaced.

To answer the second question, think honestly about how often you would use the appliance. Once a year? Once a week? Would you be reluctant to use it because it is difficult to clean? A nuisance to store? Do you have other appliances that can do the same job? If you would use it often and it would improve your efficiency and pleasure in the kitchen, consider that you do "need" it, and move on to the next two factors.

Many small electrical appliances are nice to have but not essential. Which of these do you "need"? Why?

When you shop for small appliances, consider whether you will keep them on the counter top or store them away. Do you have space to use them? To store them? Are there portable or hang-under-the-cabinet styles that would do the same job in less space? If you must store a mixer away in an already crowded cabinet, will you still be willing to use it often?

**Budget** Consider whether you can afford to buy a small appliance "outright" in one lump sum. If not, would you feel more comfortable saving up for it or buying it on credit? Most major appliances are purchased using **credit,** a method of paying small amounts of the purchase price over a period of time. For the benefit of having extra time to pay, *interest* or a *finance charge* is also paid. Therefore, you eventually pay more money for a purchase when you buy on credit than when you "pay cash."

Three kinds of credit purchases are common for appliances. The first is the *installment plan,* an arrangement between the purchaser and retailer to pay a down payment and then to

**Space** When you shop for a major appliance, you must be careful that the models you are considering will fit in your kitchen. Measure floor space, height, and depth. If the appliance (such as a refrigerator or oven) has doors, consider which direction the doors open and if there is space in your kitchen for the doors to open fully.

You can save space in a small kitchen by using small appliances designed to hang under cabinets rather than rest on the work surfaces. Both coffee makers and microwave ovens come this way.

pay out the rest of the cost with interest. Another choice is a *bank loan.* The purchaser borrows money from the bank and makes an agreement to repay with interest; then the purchaser pays the retailer in cash. In a *credit-card purchase,* the purchaser pays a minimum amount each month to the credit-card company, which charges interest; the retailer is paid by the credit-card company. It is wise to shop for credit as carefully as you shop for the appliance itself. Be sure you know the yearly interest charges, penalties for late payments, and any other conditions before you agree to a credit-purchase program.

## Research: In the Library and in the Store

Before making a major purchase, it is wise to find out as much as possible about the item you are considering. You will want to know how long it will last, how well it will perform, and how often it will need repairs. You also want to know how convenient it is to operate and clean. These are important questions for the purchase of small appliances, too. Before you buy a dishwasher, a food processor, or even a toaster, read about the appliance and ask friends or neighbors what they like about the brands and styles they have.

**Library Research** While advertising is helpful in letting you know what new products or features may be available, your basic research should be in consumer magazines. Some magazines test products, list frequency-of-repair statistics, and give suggested retail prices. A magazine like *Consumer Reports,* which does not accept advertising, is a good place to do research before you go to the store. Consumer magazines also often suggest questions you may want to ask the dealer when you shop.

Comparison shopping is important for expensive appliances you will keep a long time. Do research, ask questions, have features demonstrated, and compare prices, warranties, and services.

**Comparison Shopping** Once you get to the store, you are comparing two separate things: the appliances, as to features, models, and list prices; and the dealerships or retailers, as to actual price, delivery or installation charges, and service. Don't be embarrassed to ask questions about the appliance or to have the salesperson demonstrate its features. Be sure you understand the terms of the sale, including returns or repairs, and any credit plans offered.

Compare appliances on these important points:

1. Safety—Look for the seals that indicate an appliance meets standards of safety. On electrical appliances, it is the **Underwriters Laboratories (UL) seal.** For gas appliances, look for the **American Gas Association (AGA) blue star.** Read any special safety information applying to the product. It may require special wiring or outlets. Be sure you are buying an appliance that will be safe in *your* kitchen.

2. Durability—Keep in mind your library research as you check appliances for durability.

The EnergyGuide label can help you determine which appliances are most energy efficient.

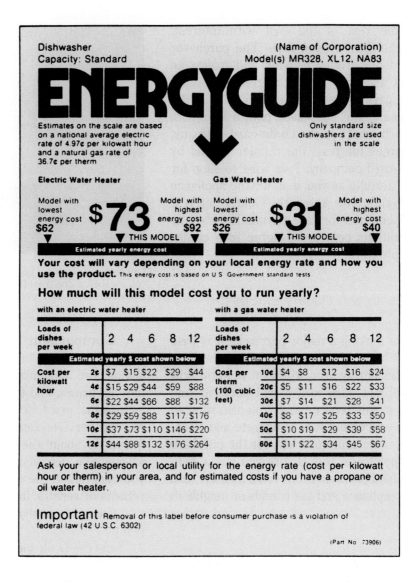

Dishwasher
Capacity: Standard

(Name of Corporation)
Model(s) MR328, XL12, NA83

# ENERGYGUIDE

Estimates on the scale are based on a national average electric rate of 4.97¢ per kilowatt hour and a natural gas rate of 36.7¢ per therm

Only standard size dishwashers are used in the scale

**Electric Water Heater**

| Model with lowest energy cost | | Model with highest energy cost |
|---|---|---|
| $62 | **$73** | $92 |

▼ THIS MODEL

Estimated yearly energy cost

**Gas Water Heater**

| Model with lowest energy cost | | Model with highest energy cost |
|---|---|---|
| $26 | **$31** | $40 |

▼ THIS MODEL

Estimated yearly energy cost

**Your cost will vary depending on your local energy rate and how you use the product.** This energy cost is based on U.S. Government standard tests

## How much will this model cost you to run yearly?

**with an electric water heater**

| Loads of dishes per week | | 2 | 4 | 6 | 8 | 12 |
|---|---|---|---|---|---|---|
| Estimated yearly $ cost shown below | | | | | | |
| Cost per kilowatt hour | 2¢ | $7 | $15 | $22 | $29 | $44 |
| | 4¢ | $15 | $29 | $44 | $59 | $88 |
| | 6¢ | $22 | $44 | $66 | $88 | $132 |
| | 8¢ | $29 | $59 | $88 | $117 | $176 |
| | 10¢ | $37 | $73 | $110 | $146 | $220 |
| | 12¢ | $44 | $88 | $132 | $176 | $264 |

**with a gas water heater**

| Loads of dishes per week | | 2 | 4 | 6 | 8 | 12 |
|---|---|---|---|---|---|---|
| Estimated yearly $ cost shown below | | | | | | |
| Cost per therm (100 cubic feet) | 10¢ | $4 | $8 | $12 | $16 | $24 |
| | 20¢ | $5 | $11 | $16 | $22 | $33 |
| | 30¢ | $7 | $14 | $21 | $28 | $41 |
| | 40¢ | $8 | $17 | $25 | $33 | $50 |
| | 50¢ | $10 | $19 | $29 | $39 | $58 |
| | 60¢ | $11 | $22 | $34 | $45 | $67 |

Ask your salesperson or local utility for the energy rate (cost per kilowatt hour or therm) in your area, and for estimated costs if you have a propane or oil water heater.

**Important** Removal of this label before consumer purchase is a violation of federal law (42 U.S.C. 6302)

(Part No 73906)

The American Gas Association (AGA) tests gas appliances for safety and performance. Those that pass receive this safety seal.

Electrical appliances are tested for safety and performance by Underwriters Laboratories. This UL seal signifies their approval.

Look at the finish: is it smooth and durable? Check door seals: do they fit tightly? Examine handles: are they fastened securely? Look at moving parts: are they sturdy and do they move easily?

3. Convenience—Make sure that the appliance will be easy for *you* to operate and clean. Are controls in a convenient location for your use? Can removable parts be taken out easily? Are all parts easy to clean, including

corners and accessories? Is a portable or hand-held appliance light enough to be handled comfortably?

4. Energy Efficiency—Saving energy is important for two reasons; it saves the consumer money and it preserves natural resources. Many major appliances now come with black-and-yellow **EnergyGuide labels** that help you compare the energy efficiency of different models. Spending a little extra on an energy-efficient model may "pay for itself and then some" as you use the appliance.

5. Warranties—A **warranty** promises the purchaser that the product will work properly for a certain length of time. If not, the manufacturer or dealer takes all or part of the responsibility to repair or replace it. A manufacturer's **full warranty** completely covers parts, labor, and shipping costs over a stated time period. A **limited warranty** has more restrictions than a stated time period; it may cover only certain parts, require the purchaser to pay mailing costs, or require the purchaser to pay labor costs for repairs. Always read a warranty carefully, fill out the registration card (if there is one), and keep it in a safe place. Occasionally, a dealer or retailer will supply an additional warranty to supplement the manufacturer's.

## For Review

1. What three personal factors should you consider before buying an appliance?
2. What useful kinds of product information can you get from advertising? From consumer magazines?
3. On what points should you compare dealers or retailers?
4. What are two good reasons to choose an energy-efficient appliance?

# Cookware and Bakeware

**Cookware** and **bakeware** are the objects that actually hold food while it is being cooked: bakeware in the oven and cookware on the cook-top. Food is placed either in or on them, so their surfaces should be of nontoxic materials that do not transfer tastes and odors to food. They should also be easy to clean so that they will be spotless when they are reused. In addition, cookware and bakeware should be able to withstand cooking temperatures and to transfer heat evenly to food. They should be easy for the cook to handle when hot, and convenient to store when not in use. Additional benefits are attractive designs that allow bakeware to be brought to the table as serving dishes, and the ability to go from freezer to oven without breaking. Refer to the following illustrations for the various types of cookware and bakeware.

### Cookware

*Saucepans (with lids)
   cooking foods in liquids: in standard sizes of 1 quart, 1½ quart, 2 quart, and 3 quart (or in metric sizes of 1 L, 1½ L, 2 L, and 3 L)
*Skillets or frying pans
   frying, pan-broiling, and sautéeing foods: in assorted sizes, some with lids
Dutch oven
   slow cooking of meat and poultry
Double boiler
   heating and cooking foods, such as custards and sauces, that burn easily
*Large pot
   cooking soups, pasta, or large quantities of food, usually 6 quarts (6 L) or more
Griddle
   cooking pancakes, sandwiches, and eggs
Teakettle
   boiling water

*Items marked by an asterisk are generally considered essential for a basic kitchen.

Saucepans

Roasting pan
and rack

Broiling
pan

Skillets

Casseroles

Double boiler

Dutch oven

Griddle

Large pot

Kettle

Cake pans

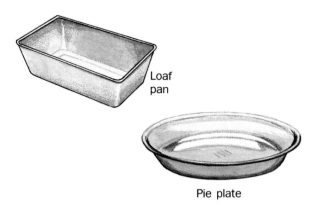

Loaf pan

Pie plate

Jelly-roll pan

Muffin tin

Tube pan

Cookie sheet

Custard cups

## Bakeware

*Roasting pan and rack
   roasting meat and poultry
*Broiling pan
   broiling foods
*Casseroles (with lids)
   baking food combinations: in assorted sizes
*Cake pans (square, round, and oblong)
   baking cakes and bar cookies
*Loaf pan
   baking bread, pound cake, and meat loaf
*Pie pan (metal or glass)
   baking pies and quiche
*Cookie sheet
   baking cookies
*Muffin tin
   baking muffins, cupcakes, and rolls
Tube pan
   baking angel-food, sponge, and chiffon cakes
Jelly-roll pan
   baking jelly rolls, bar cookies, and sheet cakes
Individual custard cups
   baking custards and individual servings of many foods

## Materials: Characteristics and Care

There are many materials suitable for cooking and baking using conventional cook-tops and ovens. However, microwave ovens require particular kinds of bakeware (see page 157), and so do induction cook-tops (see page 147). The most common materials for cookware and bakeware are described below. For special stain-removal tips, see the chart on page 133.

**Aluminum** This is the most popular cookware and bakeware material because it conducts heat rapidly and evenly. The thicker the aluminum, the better it will stand up over time. The major disadvantage of aluminum is that it develops stains from acid foods and from dishwasher detergent.

**Stainless Steel**  By itself, this material is durable, strong, and easy to clean. However, stainless steel conducts heat unevenly and slowly. Hot spots can cause sticking and burning. Therefore, stainless steel is often combined with better heat conductors (such as aluminum, copper, or carbon steel).

**Cast Iron**  An extremely heavy and durable metal, cast iron holds and conducts heat well. However, it is porous (marked by tiny holes into which liquid can seep and collect) and therefore must be "seasoned" with oil and heat to prevent rust. In addition, cast iron should not be scoured and must be absolutely dry when stored to keep it from rusting.

**Glass**  Use only specially designed heat-resistant glass as cookware and bakeware. This material conducts heat unevenly, and it will chip and break if mishandled. Glass should not be scoured. Food can be seen through the glass and is often brought to the table in an attractive glass baking dish. Some treated glass can go directly from freezer to oven without breaking.

**Glass-ceramic**  This attractive material is much more durable than clear glass, and it can go from freezer to oven. It does tend to develop hot spots if the heat source is uneven, so be careful that food does not stick. Glass-ceramic is easy to clean and can be scoured.

**Enamel**  Enamel, glass baked on metal, has the heating properties of the underlying metal. While its surface often comes in very attractive colors and patterns, enamel chips easily and should not be scoured.

**Copper**  This is an extremely attractive material for the outsides of teakettles and pots and pans, but frequent polishing is required to remove tarnish. While copper conducts heat well, it reacts with foods when heated and forms poisonous compounds. Therefore, tin, stainless steel, or chrome are used to line the cooking surface. Do not scour this thin lining; if the copper is exposed, the cookware can become dangerous to use. Clean the outside with special copper cleaner.

**Earthenware**  This attractive material retains heat well, keeping food hot for serving, but it conducts heat slowly and unevenly. Earthenware is often used for cook-and-serve casserole dishes. It should not be scoured, and it chips and breaks easily.

## Choosing and Buying

Cookware and bakeware range from the very expensive and durable to the cheap and flimsy. You can buy attractive sets to display as

Bakeware comes in a variety of materials and styles. Some are merely utilitarian. Others are attractive enough to bring right to the table but may require special cleaning and handling.

Copper is one of the most attractive cookware materials, but it requires frequent polishing to keep its beautiful shine.

well as use, or you can buy restaurant-quality, heavy-duty pieces that can last a lifetime. Completely supplying a kitchen with cookware and bakeware is a major decision and a major investment. As with appliances, buying the best quality you can afford is usually economical in the long run. Avoiding pieces you don't need (that often come as parts of sets) saves not only money but storage space. The more attractive but harder-to-care-for pieces should be added after the basics have been acquired.

When shopping for cookware and bakeware, do not be guided totally by price. Just because an item is expensive does not mean it is of good quality. On the other hand, a very low price should cause you to look extra carefully at a pot or pan. Consider the following points when choosing cookware and bakeware:

1. Cookware should be well balanced to avoid tipping over, even when empty. A flat bottom not only provides balance but also conducts heat more evenly.
2. Lids should fit firmly. They should have knobs or handles that can be grasped easily.

3. Handles on cookware should be heat resistant and attached securely with accessible screws in case they need tightening. Handles on bakeware should be large enough to be grasped easily with a potholder.
4. The finish should be smooth as well as durable. There should be no sharp or rough edges.
5. For the best quality construction, look for a one-piece main body with no seams. All parts should be easy to clean. Remember that the thicker the metal, the more resistant it is to damage.
6. If you buy a nonstick finish, choose the more durable, premium variety. Read the directions for its care before you make your final selection.
7. Test the piece in your hand. Are the handles comfortable to you? Is the piece too heavy? The best pot for someone else may not be the best for you.

This set of cookware has the advantages of nonstick finish and multi-use lids.

8. If you have limited storage, look for items or groups of items that are easy to store or that have several uses. Many cookware sets can be hung by their handles or stacked inside one another.

9. Finally, read the use-and-care booklet *before* you buy. Make sure you will be willing to clean and care for the item properly and that it can be used for its intended purposes.

Sometimes it seems as though there are more cookery tools available than you could ever hope to use. Always consider your specific needs when shopping for these items.

## For Review

1. Which cookware material can be stained by acid foods and dishwasher detergent? Which one is porous and likely to rust?
2. What are some advantages of copper as a cookware material? What are some disadvantages?
3. What are the four most important factors to check in determining the quality of a piece of cookware or bakeware?

## Cookery Tools

If you have ever browsed through a display of cookery tools in a gourmet kitchen shop—or even in a supermarket—you have probably seen countless knives, spoons, slicers, and gadgets. Some are advertised as all-purpose or multipurpose necessities. Others claim to be the ultimate in professional, specialized utensils for the "serious cook." Which of the tools do you really need? Which are useful but not essential? Which gadgets will probably end up in a jumble at the back of a drawer?

As with large and small appliances, you should consider several factors before purchasing cookery tools. These factors include your real needs (including your skills and usual cooking methods), your storage space, and your budget. Buying the best quality you can afford and then using the tool carefully, keeping it clean, and storing it properly will probably give you the best value for your money. But where should you begin?

Obviously, every cook needs to be able to do several basic things: cut and slice, stir and transfer foods (spoon liquids and small solids, and pierce, clasp or carry larger solids), and measure both liquid and dry ingredients. Since many ingredients now come in cans, can openers have become essential kitchen tools. Mixing bowls, too, are obviously a necessity. Some cooks feel that tools such as food grinders, apple corers, and grapefruit knives are also essential. As you read about the many cookery tools, think about which ones you would buy first if you were equipping your own kitchen. Also think about which tools you would add later on.

## Cutting Tools

French, or chef's, knife
    mincing, cutting, and chopping vegetables, fruits, and other foods
Slicing knife
    slicing meat and poultry
Bread knife (serrated)
    slicing bread or cake
Paring knife
    paring and cutting fruits and vegetables
Carving knife
    carving and slicing meat and poultry
*Butcher knife
    cutting large fruits, vegetables, and cuts of meat
*Utility knife
    many uses such as cutting, slicing, and paring
Boning knife
    cutting poultry; boning meat and poultry
Grapefruit knife
    cutting around sections of citrus fruit
Sharpening steel
    sharpening knives
Kitchen shears
    trimming pastry; cutting dried fruits, vegetables, and herbs
Peeler
    scraping and peeling fruits and vegetables
Apple corer
    removing cores from fruit
*Cutting board
    protecting counter tops when cutting

*Items marked by an asterisk are generally considered essential for a basic kitchen.

Potato masher
    mashing cooked potatoes
Food grinder
    grinding meat, nuts, and vegetables
*Grater
    grating cheese, fruits, and vegetables to varying degrees of fineness

## Stirring and Transferring Tools

Wooden spoons (graduated sizes)
    mixing; creaming shortening and sugar; stirring hot foods or sauces
*Slotted spoon
    lifting food out of liquid
*Large spoon
    basting and stirring
Baster
    basting
*Ladle
    serving soups and stews
Kitchen fork
    many uses such as turning and lifting large cuts of meat and holding meat and poultry securely while carving
Tongs
    lifting vegetables and meat; turning meat without piercing
*Turner
    lifting and turning such foods as pancakes, hamburgers, and eggs

## Measuring Tools

*Measuring spoons
    measuring small amounts of dry, liquid, and solid ingredients: in standard sets of ¼ teaspoon, ½ teaspoon, 1 teaspoon, and 1 tablespoon (or in metric sets of 1 mL, 2 mL, 5 mL, 15 mL, and 25 mL)
*Liquid measuring cups
    measuring liquids: in standard sizes of 1 cup, 2 cup and 4 cup (or in metric sizes of 250 mL, 500 mL, or 1 L)

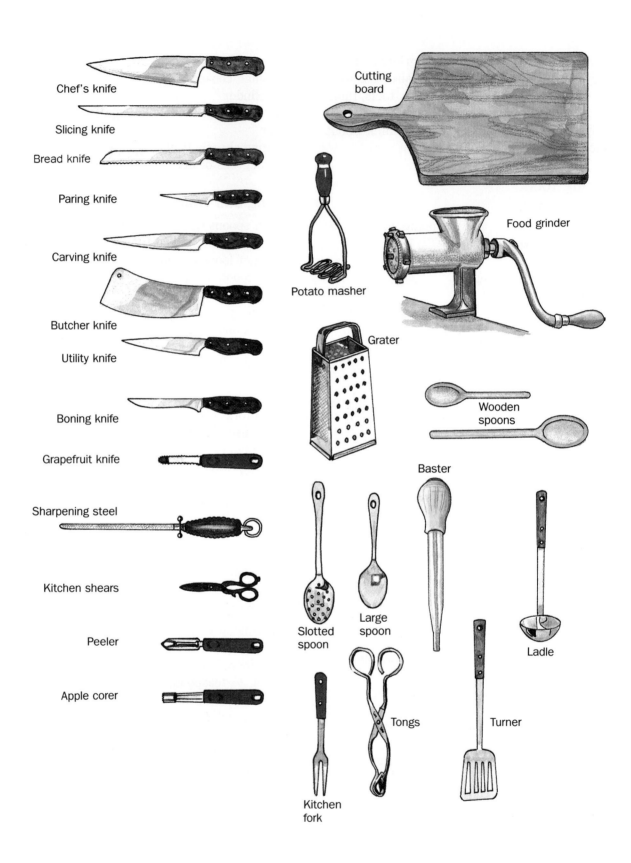

Chef's knife

Slicing knife

Bread knife

Paring knife

Carving knife

Butcher knife

Utility knife

Boning knife

Grapefruit knife

Sharpening steel

Kitchen shears

Peeler

Apple corer

Cutting board

Potato masher

Food grinder

Grater

Wooden spoons

Baster

Slotted spoon

Large spoon

Ladle

Kitchen fork

Tongs

Turner

Measuring spoons

Liquid measuring cups

Dry measuring cups

Kitchen spoon

Small rubber scraper

Straight-edged spatulas

Wire whisk

Rotary beater

Steamer

Frying basket

Colander

Strainers

Sifter

Pastry blender

Rolling pin and cover

Pastry cloth

Pastry brush

Rubber scraper

Cookie cutters

Mixing bowls

Wire rack

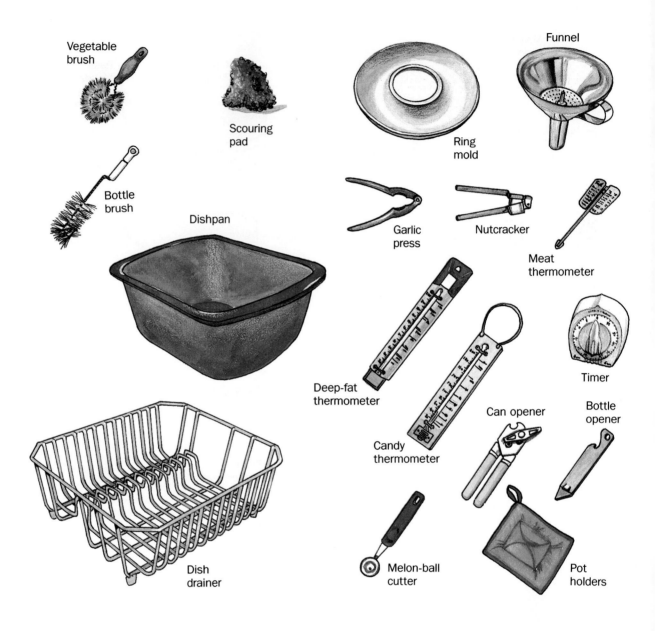

Vegetable brush

Scouring pad

Funnel

Ring mold

Bottle brush

Dishpan

Garlic press

Nutcracker

Meat thermometer

Deep-fat thermometer

Timer

Candy thermometer

Can opener

Bottle opener

Dish drainer

Melon-ball cutter

Pot holders

*Dry measuring cups
    measuring dry and solid ingredients: in standard sets of ¼ cup, ⅓ cup, ½ cup, and 1 cup (or in metric sets of 50 mL, 125 mL, and 250 mL)
Straight-edged spatulas (large and small)
    leveling off dry ingredients when measuring
Kitchen spoon
    spooning ingredients into measuring cups

Rubber scraper (small)
    scraping out measuring cups

## Separating and Mixing Tools

Rotary beater
    beating icings and eggs; whipping cream
*Wire whisk
    beating air into egg whites; blending; stirring sauces

Steamer
    holding vegetables above boiling water to steam them
Frying basket
    holding foods above oil to deep-fat fry them
*Strainers (large and small)
    straining; separating solids from liquids; draining foods
Colander
    straining coarse foods; puréeing fruits and vegetables; draining foods such as pasta
*Flour sifter
    sifting and adding air to flour and other dry ingredients

## Baking Tools

Pastry blender
    cutting shortening into dry ingredients
Pastry board and cloth
    kneading dough; rolling out pastry
Pastry brush
    greasing pans; brushing dough with melted butter
*Rolling pin and cover
    rolling out dough and pastry
Rubber scraper (large)
    scraping out bowls
*Mixing bowls (small, medium, and large)
    many uses such as mixing, dividing, and holding ingredients
Cutters (various shapes and sizes)
    cutting cookies, biscuits, and doughnuts
Wire cooling rack
    cooling cakes, cookies, and breads

## Cleaning Tools

Vegetable brush
    washing vegetables
Scouring pad
    cleaning stubborn food soil from pans
Bottle brush
    cleaning bottles
Dishpan
    soaking and washing dishes and utensils

Dish drainer
    draining washed dishes and utensils

## Miscellaneous Kitchen Tools

Ring mold
    forming puddings, fancy desserts, and salads
Funnel
    filling bottles or jars with liquid
Garlic press
    crushing garlic cloves
Nutcracker
    cracking nuts
Meat thermometer
    measuring internal temperature of roasts and whole poultry
Deep-fat thermometer
    measuring temperature of deep fat
Candy thermometer
    measuring temperature of sugar syrup
Timer
    timing kitchen activities
*Bottle opener
    opening bottles
*Can opener
    opening canned foods
Melon-ball cutter
    cutting ball-shaped pieces of foods such as melons, potatoes, and butter
Potholders
    protecting hands from hot cookware and bakeware

### For Review

1. List three tools that have more than one use, and describe the different functions each can perform.
2. List three tools that have a very specialized purpose that can also be accomplished by a more general-use tool. What multipurpose tool can also perform its function?

# 7 Chapter Review

## Summary

Major and small appliances contribute to the ease of food preparation if they are used and maintained properly. To care for and properly use an appliance, the owner's manual is the best guide. When you decide to purchase an appliance, consider not only your personal needs and financial resources but also the appliance's features, its durability and reliability, and its price. It is important to research a product and do comparison shopping before making the purchase to get the best deal. Once you make a decision, the appliance may be purchased using cash or a method of credit. In addition to appliances, several kinds of cookery tools, cookware, and bakeware are useful to fully equip a kitchen. This cooking equipment comes in a vast range of products, materials, prices, and features. However, only a small number of items are absolutely essential in a basic kitchen.

## Vocabulary

Match each numbered vocabulary word to the lettered statements. Some vocabulary words have more than one matched statement.

1. American Gas Association (AGA) blue star
2. bakeware
3. cookware
4. credit
5. EnergyGuide labels
6. full warranty
7. limited warranty
8. Underwriters Laboratories (UL) seal
9. warranty

a. Seal that the electrical appliance meets the standards for safety
b. A promise from the dealer that the product will work for a certain period of time
c. Saucepans
d. Seal found on a gas stove, for instance
e. An object that holds food while it is being cooked in the oven
f. A promise from the manufacturer or dealer that completely covers parts, labor, and shipping costs over a stated period of time if the product should fail to perform properly
g. A seal found on toasters and blenders
h. Installment plan
i. A label that provides the energy costs for operating an appliance
j. A statement from the dealer that has more restrictions than a stated time period
k. Frying pans
l. A seal that the gas appliance meets the standards for safety
m. Appliance labels used to compare the energy efficiency of different models
n. An object that holds food while it is being cooked on the stove top
o. A statement that may cover only certain parts or require the purchaser to pay mailing costs or labor costs for repair
p. Roasting pan and rack
q. Interest or finance charges

## Chapter Questions

1. What are the two small appliances you would buy first for a kitchen? Tell why.

2. What can you do to keep a refrigerator and freezer smelling fresh?
3. List the advantages of small appliances.
4. Before you purchase a major or small appliance, what factors should you consider?
5. Compare the ways convection and microwave ovens are alike and different.
6. What is comparison shopping?
7. Compare a full warranty and a limited warranty.
8. What are the four things you should do to get the best value for your money when you purchase a cookery tool?
9. If you were equipping your own kitchen, what are ten cookery tools you would buy first? Why?
10. Tell which cookery tools are recommended for each of these preparation procedures:
    a. mixing and creaming shortening and sugar
    b. beating egg whites
    c. mincing and cutting celery and onions
    d. determining the doneness of roasts
    e. cleaning bottles

## Skill Activities

**1. Communication** In your food journal, keep a record of the cookware, bakeware, and cookery tools you used when you prepared a meal. In your journal, write the date, what you prepared, and then the heading "Cookware and Bakeware." Under that heading, write the items you used. Then write the heading "Cookery tools." Under that heading, write the items you used. For a list of cookware and bakeware items, refer to pages 163–165. For a list of cookery tools, refer to pages 169–173.

**2. Decision making** Investigate the costs of operating different kinds of refrigerator-freezers. To do this, compare the information found on the EnergyGuide labels as well as other labels that may be on the appliance. Before visiting a store, prepare sheets on which to record the information you find. Write one of these headings at the top of each sheet of lined paper: "Automatic defrosting," "Frost-free," and "Manual defrost." On the left-hand side of each sheet of paper, write the headings "brand," "size," "type of model," "features," "price," and "operating costs." Now visit a store where refrigerators are sold. Read the information on the labels of each model, and enter the appropriate material on your sheets. Which model has the lowest price? Which model has the highest price? Which model is the most energy efficient to operate? Which model costs the most to operate? Which model has the most features? If you were going to purchase a refrigerator-freezer for your family, which one would you buy? Why?

**3. Resource management** Examine the various small cookery tools in your home. Make a list of those that are especially helpful as time and energy savers. Which tools are seldom used? Why are some tools more useful than others?

# 8 Food Buying

## As you read, think about:

- what your resources are as meal manager.
- how to plan for food shopping.
- how to comparison shop.
- how to use labels as consumer aids.
- how to get help from consumer-protection and information agencies.

**Vocabulary**

comparison
  shopping
name brands
store brands
generic brands
unit price
imitation food
GRAS list
standards of
  identity
nutrition label
open dating
UPC

# Resource Management

Management, as you read in Chapter 5, includes all of the decision making and planning of work needed to complete a task. Good management is the key to efficient use of time, energy, money, and equipment. Like any manager, a meal manager must carefully consider the best use of all resources to produce the best-quality result.

## Materials

What are your resources when you are in charge of preparing meals for a family? Obviously, the ingredients that go into the meals are an extremely important resource. You will choose them according to their quality. You will also make choices depending on the "clients" for those meals; in other words, the people who will be eating and their particular needs and preferences. Special diets and occasions will also be considered. Shopping for ingredients wisely, storing them properly, and preparing them so that they provide nutritious and appealing meals are some of the tasks of a meal manager. To accomplish this goal, the food itself is not the only resource you must consider.

## Time

Time is always an important and limited resource. For many busy people today, time is more limited than ever. In many families, all the adults work. Teenagers old enough to take over or help with meal preparation are also busy with school, homework, sports, and other activities that may even include part-time jobs of their own. Thus, time becomes a very precious resource. How can it be "saved" or used to the best advantage?

**Saving Cooking Time** One place to save time is in the actual preparation of food.

People have not always bought food in self-service supermarkets. Years ago, clerks waited on customers and did some of the weighing and packaging as well. Which method do you prefer? Why?

Prepared foods, heat-and-serve dishes, and frozen and canned goods all save time. However, they often cost more than made-from-scratch dishes. One of your tasks as a meal manager is to decide which resource—money or time—you can afford to "spend" in order to "save" the other.

Another way to save food preparation time is to use time-saving appliances. Convection and microwave ovens cook faster than conventional ovens (see Chapter 7). Blenders, mixers, and food processors save time, but they—like the specialty ovens—cost money to purchase.

**Saving Cleanup Time** While many people are willing to put in some extra minutes

Today's busy families often use time-saving appliances to prepare nutritious meals that fit in to their schedules. Preparing food ahead of time for reheating in the microwave saves time at the dinner hour.

adding creative touches to meals, few enjoy the time they spend cleaning up. A dishwasher cuts cleanup time considerably. Again, however, this appliance is a major expense and then costs money each time it operates. Even if you wash dishes by hand, there are time-saving strategies to kitchen cleanup. The most important is cleaning up as you go along. Spending a little time at first often saves a lot of time later.

**Saving Shopping Time** Perhaps the most time-consuming task of all—particularly if it is not done efficiently—is food shopping. Trips to the store take time. Trips to several stores take more time. Trips *back* to the store for essential items that were forgotten not only take even more time but often cause anger and frustration.

There is also the time spent in the store. Do you shop when the store is most crowded, and stand in long lines? Do you spend extra time deciding what goes with what and then retrace your steps through the aisles as you plan meals while in the store? Planning ahead—taking a few minutes at home to make a useful shopping list—can save many minutes in the store and eliminate those extra trips for forgotten items.

### Energy

While energy is not the same as time, it is closely related. Personal energy is "spent" over time. Cutting down on the time a task requires usually cuts down on the personal energy you need to accomplish that job. On the other hand, many time-saving appliances use other kinds of energy while they save yours. They use more electrical (or gas) energy than other methods of accomplishing the same task. They "spend" energy resources as they work to save your personal energy.

**Personal Energy** You have already learned a great deal about conserving personal energy in the kitchen from planning work centers and work triangles to cleaning up as you cook. Your personal energy is an important resource and should not be wasted when you shop any more than when you cook. Planning *before* you go shopping can save energy two ways: it can save you energy in the store, and it can save you energy when you do the actual meal preparation. Careful selection of ingredients—geared to the time, skills, and appliances you have as well as the type of meals you wish to prepare—can save you personal energy and make meal management a pleasurable task rather than an exhausting chore.

**Appliances and Energy** Appliances and other kitchen equipment are among your resources as meal manager. Using appliances wisely can save energy resources. First, it is always best to buy energy-efficient models (see page 163). Second, select the appliance in your kitchen that uses the least amount of energy for a particular job. The toaster oven is a better choice for a single-serving frozen dish or a baked potato than the larger conventional oven. The microwave will use less energy to cook certain items than will the conventional oven. Other appliances use a great deal of energy. The dishwasher, for example, should be run only when it is full. As meal manager, though, you must decide if using the food processor to do your slicing is worth the time and personal energy it saves you. Don't forget the time and energy needed to clean the appliance after use, as well as the electrical energy needed to run it.

## Money

Money is also an important and limited resource. Using it wisely is an important skill to learn. You should be aware that saving money in one place often results in spending more in some other place. For example, buying a cheaper but

Does using a food processor add to your efficiency? Time is saved using it, but it takes electricity to run it, and you must spend time cleaning it.

less energy-efficient appliance results in larger monthly energy bills. Saving money on less tender cuts of meat may result in higher energy costs for the longer cooking time needed to tenderize the meat.

Have you ever heard the expression "Time is money"? Often, when you buy a more expensive food product, you are not buying extra quality—you are buying extra time. Purchasing instant, prepared, or frozen foods often costs more at the grocery store but saves food-preparation time in the kitchen. As the meal manager, you must decide first if you can afford many of these convenience foods, and second, if they are worth the extra cost. You must weigh the value of money against the value of time.

# Planning for Food Buying

Most people shop for a week at a time. They try to buy the ingredients they will need both for the week's meals and to restock their supply of "staples" (basic ingredients such as sugar, salt, and flour that are purchased for general use). They also try to keep up with other kitchen needs by buying napkins, toweling, foil, and detergent before they run out. Very often, they stock up on sale items or "specials" if they have the storage space and if the foods are sure to be used before they spoil. Most people find, however, that they do have to return to the store for a particular item or to resupply perishables, such as milk, before their next scheduled shopping trip. The better you plan your weekly shopping, the fewer extra trips to the store you will have to make and the better value you will get for your shopping dollar.

## Menu Planning

In order to plan for food buying, you must really plan for food preparation. Before you begin, ask yourself some important questions about your family members: What are the food needs of your family for the week? What are their preferences? Are there any medical restrictions on what particular family members can or should eat? Is anyone trying to lose or gain weight? How much does each person usually eat? Who will be home for each meal you are planning?

Spending some time to plan meals is worthwhile in time saved shopping and cooking and in the quality, nutrition, and enjoyment of serving and eating well-planned meals.

Ask yourself some questions about resources, too. What equipment is available in your kitchen? What is the level of your skills? Will someone be helping with food preparation? What is your budget? What produce is in season? What is on sale this week? What ingredients do you already have at home that can or should be used up?

When you have answered all of these questions, you have begun the first important step for food shopping: menu planning.

Planning menus does not have to be exact. You can decide, for example, that you will bake a chicken one day this week and make spaghetti and meatballs another day. Whether you make these meals on Monday and Tuesday or on Thursday and Friday, you will still need the same basic ingredients. However, if you plan the spaghetti and meatballs for the day you pass the bakery on the way home, you can pick up a fresh loaf of Italian bread to complement the meal.

When you plan meals, think about the whole meal, main course first. A green salad will go well with your pasta dish; what vegetables complement the baked chicken? What desserts and appetizers are suitable? What special ingredients do you need that you don't usually keep in the house? Do you have Parmesan cheese for the pasta? Croutons for the salad? Remember how variety in taste, color, texture, temperature, and cooking method makes food more interesting (see pages 102-105), and plan accordingly. Make sure you choose a balance from the Daily Food Guide (see Chapter 3).

Also consider the busy schedules and special needs of those who will be eating the meals. Babies and older people sometimes need special consideration. So do teenagers going through growth spurts or those who are engaged in vigorous exercise programs. They will eat larger portions, while those on weight-loss diets will eat less. Is there someone in your family who comes home late for dinner and needs an easily reheatable meal? Are there days when no one seems to be home at the same time? Perhaps individual heat-and-serve meals or a cold salad would be best for those days. Could you use any leftover baked chicken for that salad?

## The Shopping List

If prepared carefully, a shopping list is a valuable tool for planning meals, saving time, and saving money. It is a good idea to keep a "running list" in a handy spot in the kitchen. Add to it whenever you realize that something is needed. Writing down "noodles" as you empty the last box into boiling water or jotting down "onions" when you see there is only one left is better than hoping to remember them when you write your final list three days later. A list is important not only for remembering what you need; it also prevents impulse buying of things you don't need.

There are three sources for your shopping list. The first is the meal planning discussed above. You need all the ingredients for the dishes you plan to prepare. The second source is closely related to the first. For example, you do not need to buy a chicken if you already have one in the freezer, so the second source for your shopping list is "research" in your cabinets, refrigerator, and freezer. This home research should also include a look at all your staples to see if any need replacing. Don't forget to check condiments and spices.

The third source for your shopping list also involves research. This investigation is conducted in the advertisements in your newspaper. If veal, which is usually expensive, is on sale, you may want to change your baked chicken dish to a veal dish this week. If canned peas are on sale, you may want to stock up. If there is a cents-off coupon for an item that is usually beyond your budget, this would be a good time to make the purchase. This research may affect your meal planning, and your list may need to be revised.

Use a "running shopping list" posted conveniently in your kitchen to jot down items as you find you need them. This way, seldom-used items won't slip your mind when you organize your final list.

How much time do you think you have spent standing on line at supermarket checkouts? Try to shop when markets are least likely to be crowded, or use a smaller store to pick up just a few items.

Once you have a list of things you need to buy, rewrite it to group similar foods, such as dairy products, meats, or cereals. If you know the layout of your grocery store well, organize the list to reflect that arrangement. Having the listed items in the same order as they are available in the store can save you time and energy. Finally, if you are taking cents-off coupons, clip them to your list in the order they will be used. Note on your list which items will be purchased with coupons so that you will be sure to select the correct size and form of the product.

As you shop, check off the items on your list. You will be less likely to forget something that way. Use your list to prevent impulse buying of items that are attractively displayed, but that you never use. On the other hand, don't become too tied to your list. If you planned to buy fresh green beans and they look brown and wilted, switch to a vegetable that is fresher. Take advantage of unadvertised specials, too, or of a new shipment of a hard-to-find item, such as your favorite fresh fish.

## Amount and Form

Suppose you know that you need fruit and meat or chicken, noodles, and vegetables. What form of these foods will you buy? What amounts do you need? Should you buy exactly the amount of pasta you need for one meal? Should you buy frozen, canned, or fresh vegetables? What about a complete, frozen, prepared chicken dinner? Some of these decisions can be made as you plan your menus and your shopping list. Other decisions will be made in the store as you comparison shop for quality, freshness, and price.

**How Much Should You Buy?** Obviously, you need to purchase at least enough of each ingredient to make the meals you have planned. If the food is perishable, do not buy more than you will use before it spoils—no

How do you decide what size package of cheese to buy? Besides price and your home storage space, what else should you consider?

matter how much of a bargain it seems at the time. Check the dating codes on packages to help determine how long you can safely keep a product (see page 193).

Less perishable foods can often be purchased in large quantities at better prices. Check your storage space—cabinets, refrigerator, and freezer—before you stock up. Consider how often you use the food; just about everything spoils eventually. The large sizes of many products are usually bargains, but they may not be the best choice. For example, if only one

person in your family drinks orange juice, buying the two-gallon container would be wasteful. Also, if the giant-size ketchup or two-liter soda does not fit in your refrigerator, you have not found a bargain—you have created a problem.

**What Form Should You Buy?**  Here is where your decision-making role as meal manager comes into play. You must consider time, personal energy, appliances and equipment, skills, and budget. Usually, the more effort, time, and skill a product saves you, the more you have to pay for it. Occasionally, however, this is not the case. For instance, a single-serving frozen dish may cost less than buying all the ingredients needed to prepare the same amount at home.

The form you select may also depend on the time of year. Fresh fruits and vegetables are of better quality and at lower prices when they are in season. Apples from storage are usually available all year, but they do not taste as good or cost as little as they do in the fall and winter. Again, sales and coupons can affect which form of a food you choose. Stock up on canned corn when it is on sale; buy it fresh and inexpensively when the local crop comes in during the summer; try the frozen variety when you have a cents-off coupon. Of course, if you and your family like only corn on the cob, you will never buy the canned corn; it would only go to waste.

Anytime you select packaged foods, read the labels carefully (see pages 191-194). Check to see what has been added to the basic food. Do you want vegetables in butter sauce or packaged without it? Do you need to limit salt or saturated fats? "Frozen diet dinners" often contain a lot of salt. Check the list of ingredients. Are you trying to lose weight? Peaches canned in their own juice are less fattening than those in heavy syrup. Choose as economically as you can without sacrificing quality. There is no need to spend extra money on the whole form of a canned fruit or vegetable if you are going to chop or purée it in your recipe. Also check to see how much time a convenience food takes to prepare, whether it needs to be defrosted first, if any ingredients need to be added, and what appliance or equipment is needed to finish its preparation. Make sure you have everything needed to complete a dish—including time—before you decide to prepare it.

## When and Where to Shop

Many people go to several stores and go on several different shopping trips to purchase all of their food supplies. Usually, a once-a-week, one-stop trip to a well-stocked market with good prices should meet most of your needs. Some special items may require trips to specialty shops such as fish markets, fruit stands, or bakeries. It may save time to buy some perishables at a higher-priced convenience store when you run out of them. Occasionally, you may want

Its many specialty food stores make the South Street Seaport a wonderful place to browse and buy.

to purchase take-out food from a restaurant or delicatessen.

**When to Shop** Try to schedule all grocery shopping trips when you are neither tired nor hungry. If you are tired, you probably will not take the necessary time to evaluate quality and compare prices. If you are hungry, you are likely to overbuy.

Try to shop when your market is well stocked and least crowded. Often on Monday mornings and late evenings, the shelves have not been restocked with new deliveries. Items may be sold out, or produce may look "old" and picked over. The best selection can usually be found midmorning on weekdays; weekends are often most crowded. Of course, you must schedule shopping around your work, school, and other responsibilities. Try to leave enough time to shop carefully.

**Where to Shop** There are several types of stores to choose from for your basic grocery shopping. Be sure to choose markets that are clean and where perishables are fresh and kept at the right temperature. The market should also be well organized with helpful personnel and efficient service or check-out. You should be satisfied with the quality and variety as well as the prices you find there. Also consider the store's location. Remember that time is one of your resources. The use of fuel for the car, and ease of parking are also considerations. The fewer stores you have to visit, the more traveling time, energy, and expense you save.

Food markets can be grouped into several categories. *Supermarkets* are large, high-volume stores. They carry many varieties, forms, sizes, and brands of food in large quantities. This high volume—and the fact that they are basically self-service—should keep prices low. Many larger supermarkets contain small "specialty shops," such as bakeries and delicatessens, where you are waited on individually. Other services and products are sometimes offered, including check-cashing, health and beauty products, car-care products, plants, magazines, and others. Supermarkets are usually centrally located with large parking lots. Because many are owned and managed as "chains" (groups of stores treated as one business), they can often afford to run special sales and promotions.

*Neighborhood and convenience stores* are much smaller than supermarkets. Before supermarkets became popular, most people bought their groceries from smaller neighborhood stores where they knew the staff and often were given personal service. The lower prices and greater selection in supermarkets have driven many of these stores out of business. Those that remain usually have higher prices than supermarkets, but they make up for that with service, sometimes including delivery, and location in or near residential areas.

Large supermarkets often contain specialty shops or departments selling nongrocery items.

Convenience stores are often run as chains, like supermarkets, but they are smaller and offer primarily basics, perishables, and the kind of "emergency supplies" people tend to run out of at night or on weekends. Their prices are often higher than supermarkets, but they are usually open well into the night and on holidays. They are usually conveniently located near residential areas or in town centers.

*Specialty shops* are small food markets that are becoming more popular again after having declined when people began to shop in supermarkets. Butcher shops, bakeries, and fish markets are traditional food specialty shops, as are fresh produce markets and farm stands. These stores offer a wide variety within their specialty, and their products are often fresher than those in supermarkets. Delicatessens, which offer a variety of cooked meats and prepared salads and sandwiches, have also been around a long time. Newer specialty shops include cheese stores, health-food stores (which stock organically

No-frills, or discount, markets display goods in their original packing cases. Customers are usually willing to "bag their own" in order to take advantage of the lower prices.

grown, unprocessed, and other specialized foods and vitamins), and gourmet take-outs (which prepare fancy main dishes, salads, or whole meals to be reheated at home).

*Discount markets* follow the trend toward no-frills or warehouse-style shopping. Discount markets offer less variety and few services. Food is often displayed in the original packing cartons, and customers must "bag their own" at the checkout. By cutting down on these frills, discount markets can charge lower prices. An occasional trip to a warehouse market to stock up on canned goods and other nonperishables can be a good way to save money.

*Food cooperatives* require that you be a member; you cannot just "stop in" and benefit from their low prices. In food "co-ops," groups of people join together to do their shopping and get lower prices because they are buying in large quantities. Co-ops buy wholesale—the way a public store would—reflecting the needs of the members. Since the idea is to buy in bulk, there usually is not much variety. Some groups set up cooperative markets in which members buy a share and often do some of the work. The co-op market then buys wholesale and sells to the members without a profit. The selection is usually quite limited. Once you have joined or "bought into" a co-op, you probably will not want to spend money in other food stores, so think carefully before you make the commitment. There are limited co-ops, too, that specialize in only one type of food, usually meat.

## Using Advertisements, Coupons, and Refunds

Not every food product is the same price all the time—even in the same store. There are various ways to save money buying your favorite brand of tuna, for example. One way is to shop in a store that generally has lower prices, such as a discount market. Shopping for "specials" and using coupons and refund offers are other ways to save.

**Advertised Specials**   As you read on page 181, one thing you should do as you make your shopping list is check your local newspaper for advertised specials or sales on particular items. Some sale prices start with the manufacturer; most are promotions by individual markets or chains of stores. Most supermarkets advertise weekly specials; the types of products vary. If you keep track of these promotions, you can probably estimate how often your favorite brand of tuna will be put on sale. Since canned tuna has a long shelf life, you can buy enough each time to last at least until the next sale. Some of these price reductions are substantial, and buying this way can save a lot of money.

What if a store you don't usually shop in has an advertised special for something you use often? Ask yourself several questions before you rush to take advantage of this "bargain." Does your favorite store ever sell the item at this low price? Do you need the item immediately, or can you wait until your market puts it on sale? How far away is the store with the special? Are the other prices and quality in that store worth doing your weekly shopping there this time? If not, would you spend more time and gasoline (two important resources) than the savings in money (also an important resource) is worth? Would you buy enough of the product to make the trip worthwhile? How perishable is the product? Do you have room to store it? Remember that stores advertise one bargain to get you to spend money on other items while you shop.

**Coupons**   Along with the ads for specials in your newspaper, you will find cents-off coupons. A coupon reduces the price of a particular product (usually limited to brand, size, and type, and sometimes by date) by the amount printed on the coupon. Most coupons are offered by manufacturers and can be redeemed in any store. Others are store coupons and can only be used at the market making the promotion. Coupons can also be found in magazines, on the labels or in the packages of the products, or in promotional items received in the mail.

Some supermarkets offer *double coupons* as a sales promotion. These stores give you twice the face value of the coupon as a discount. This, too, is an effort to get you to do your major shopping in their store. Double coupons can give substantial savings, but be sure you are not using up those savings by paying higher prices for other items in that market. Also be sure you really need the item you are buying with the coupon. Cut out coupons only for those items you use and the brands that you prefer. Then clip them to your shopping list when you need that item. Be sure to check the expiration dates; it may be worthwhile to buy canned goods or paper products before you really need them in order to take advantage of the savings.

You can save money using cents-off coupons. Have them ready when you make your list, and choose the correct product sizes and types.

**Refunds** These are the most difficult money-saving offers to take advantage of, but they can be worth the most money. Refunds, sometimes called *rebates,* are offers of money back (or cents-off coupons) by mail from the manufacturer when certain conditions are met. Many people will buy a product with the intention of sending for the refund, and then will forget. Refunds offers usually require a certain number of box tops, labels, or other proof that you have bought the product. It's easy, however, to throw out the cereal box before remembering to cut out the proof-of-purchase label. Don't choose a product because of refund offers unless you really like the item and will follow through on the refund requirements.

## For Review

1. Why should you plan menus before making your shopping list?
2. What are the three sources for your shopping list?
3. In what order should you group the items in your shopping list? Why?
4. What factors should you consider when deciding what form and amount of a food to buy?
5. Briefly describe the advantages of shopping in each type of food store.
6. Briefly describe four ways to save money on your favorite brand of canned tuna. Which do you think is the best way? Why?

# Comparison Shopping

You have already seen how to compare food stores for price, variety, and quality. Once you have chosen your market, you continue **comparison shopping** by comparing brands and cost per unit or per serving.

## Comparing Brands

The surest way to find out which brand you prefer is to try the product. This method, however, can use—or waste—a lot of time and money. Another good way is to look for the brand or manufacturer whose other products you like. Price is also a consideration, of course. There are times when you will feel that several products are so similar in quality and taste that price is the most important consideration. Other times, you will have a strong preference and be willing to spend a little more to get exactly what you want. There are three basic groups of brands at three different price levels. All must meet quality and safety standards, but their quality may differ.

National brands usually offer greater variety in size and style of canned foods than either store or generic brands. "Lite" fruits, for example, are often found only in brand-name products.

# Computer Food-buying and Planning

Do you need help planning menus and ordering food? Maybe a computer can help you.

In recent years, the food industry has turned to computers for help with inventory, cost control, purchase orders, and menu planning. For institutions, such as schools and hospitals, that prepare large quantities of food, the computer has become especially useful.

Inventory can now be kept on the computer so that staff members of an institution know instantly what food is in storage and what food needs to be ordered. Before ordering, the computer can figure out the projected costs of various recipes and menus. In addition, it can analyze the nutritional value of menus by investigating the kinds and quantities of foods to be served. Thus, computers make it possible to base menu decisions on detailed cost and nutritional analyses.

For the home kitchen and small food-business owner, personal computers can be helpful. Software packages are being developed specifically for planning meals. This will make menu planning easier for homemakers.

In the meantime, some people have developed computer programs for themselves. One enterprising chef developed a data base of recipes that helps him make better use of leftover food. If, for example, he has leftover pasta, he can consult a host of recipes listed under "pasta" in his home data base.

Few people have computers in their personal kitchens . . . yet. Who knows how we will use computer technology in the future?

**Name brands** represent a particular manufacturer. Many of them are available and advertised nationally. Brand-name foods may be available in different grades and styles at different prices. Of the three types of brands, these are usually the most expensive.

**Store brands** on food products carry the name of the store or chain that sells them. Very often they are produced at the same plants that put out the brand-name products. Usually, store brands are not advertised, and some distribution costs are also saved, so their prices are usually lower than name brands. It is worth trying these foods to see if you like them as much as the more expensive varieties.

**Generic brands** are plain-label, or "no-name," products. The labels carry only the generic, or general, name of the product, such as "sweet peas," the ingredients, net content, and the name of the manufacturer or distributor. A store may carry between 25 and 50 or more generic items. Most generic items are displayed together. This may make it more difficult for you to compare prices. Generic items are lower in price than name brands or store brands. The reduced cost of generic items is due to somewhat lower quality (for example, USDA Grade C, and some Grade B), little advertising, and inexpensive packaging and labeling. The selection of generic-brand products is usually limited to only one size for each product.

## Unit Price

Once you have chosen the brand and variety of food to purchase, what size package is the most economical? This is not exactly the same as asking what *amount* to buy because you could purchase two 4-ounce jars or one 8-ounce jar and end up with the same amount. While it is easy enough to find the most economical way to purchase those jars (just double the price for the 4-ounce jar to see if it is more or less than the price of the 8-ounce jar), package sizes are not always in exact multiples of each other. How would you decide which is a better buy, the 5-ounce size at $1.29 or the 9-ounce size at $2.25? The answer is to refer to the unit price.

**Unit price** tells you the cost for each standard unit of measurement, such as an ounce (gram) or quart (liter). Most stores post the unit price on the shelf. That way you can compare, for example, the large box price-per-ounce of corn flakes and the small box price-per-ounce of the same item. Usually the larger box costs less per unit, but not always. Particularly when one of the sizes is on special, it is wise to check the unit price before you buy.

Another unit to compare in terms of cost is the serving. You will have to determine this yourself, but you can refer to the servings-per-package or serving-size information on the package label. A box of frozen vegetables may serve

Unit prices are usually posted on the edge of the shelf under the product. Note the item price on the right and the unit price on the left.

Consider price per serving for some foods. There is less waste in boneless chicken, so you get more servings per pound.

four, while the canned variety serves only three. Trial and error will tell you if this serving information really reflects the way your family eats. If you divide the 85-cent price of the frozen vegetables by 4, you will get a price-per-serving of about 21 cents; if you divide the 55-cent price of the canned variety by 3, you will get about 18 cents per serving, definitely a better buy. However, if you need to serve four people, not three, it would still be more economical to purchase one frozen package than two cans.

When you are shopping for meat, try to determine the cost per serving rather than the cost per pound. Remember that chicken bones, for example, add to the weight even though they are not eaten. The higher price per pound for a boneless portion may turn out to be more economical.

## For Review

1. Why can store brands be sold at lower prices than name brands?
2. What are the advantages and disadvantages of buying generic foods?
3. How should you use unit pricing when you comparison shop?

## Consumer Aids

Generations ago, shoppers had to judge the quality of food products themselves. In some ways this was easier: food was usually displayed unpackaged, and shoppers could see all the produce, whole chickens, or entire sides of beef. In some ways, it was more difficult: shoppers had only their senses of sight and smell and the seller's reputation to judge how fresh a fish was or how long milk had been in the store. Today, much consumer information is required by law for health and safety reasons. Other information is provided by manufacturers and retailers in an effort to create good will among the public.

### Labels

Much of the information you need to know in order to be a good shopper is found on food-product labels. There is often other useful information as well, such as serving suggestions, directions, recipes, and money-saving coupons. The basic label requirements are the name of the product, the net contents or net weight, and the name and address of the manufacturer.

**Ingredients** Food-product labels must name the product accurately. They may not call

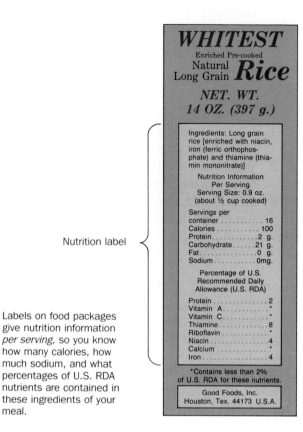

**WHITEST**
Enriched Pre-cooked
Natural *Rice*
Long Grain

NET. WT.
14 OZ. (397 g.)

Ingredients: Long grain
rice [enriched with niacin,
iron (ferric orthophos-
phate) and thiamine (thiamin mononitrate)]

Nutrition Information
Per Serving
Serving Size: 0.9 oz.
(about ½ cup cooked)

Servings per
container . . . . . . . . . . 16
Calories . . . . . . . . . . . 100
Protein . . . . . . . . . . .2 g.
Carbohydrate . . . . . .21 g.
Fat . . . . . . . . . . . . . .0 g.
Sodium . . . . . . . . . . .0mg.

Percentage of U.S.
Recommended Daily
Allowance (U.S. RDA)

Protein . . . . . . . . . . . . .2
Vitamin A . . . . . . . . . . . .*
Vitamin C . . . . . . . . . . . .*
Thiamine . . . . . . . . . . .8
Riboflavin . . . . . . . . . . .*
Niacin . . . . . . . . . . . . .4
Calcium . . . . . . . . . . . .*
Iron . . . . . . . . . . . . . .4

*Contains less than 2%
of U.S. RDA for these nutrients.

Good Foods, Inc.
Houston, Tex. 44173 U.S.A.

Nutrition label

Labels on food packages give nutrition information *per serving*, so you know how many calories, how much sodium, and what percentages of U.S. RDA nutrients are contained in these ingredients of your meal.

a product "juice" if it is only ten percent juice. If a product is not as nutritious as the one it is a substitute for, its label must carry the word "imitation." An example of an **imitation food** is imitation butter. If the product is just as nutritious (but still not "the real thing"), it does not need to be labeled "imitation," but is given a new brand name. Egg substitutes, for example, are known by their brand names.

Labels must also give the variety (albacore tuna or cling peaches), style (french-cut green beans or whole tomatoes), and material in which the food is packed (vegetable oil or water). For most combinations of food, ingredients must be listed in order of proportion. That means the ingredient in the largest amount is listed first, and so on. When you check ingredients on a label, look for several versions of the same or similar substances: sugar may be listed as sugar

or as dextrose or fructose; salt and monosodium glutamate both contribute sodium. Also check to see that the food you wish to purchase is present in a large proportion and that the product is not mostly water or filler.

Additives, such as food coloring, preservatives, and sweeteners, are also listed as ingredients (see pages 24-25). The Food and Drug Administration (FDA) tests additives to be sure they are safe. They publish a **GRAS list** of ingredients "Generally Recognized As Safe." Items on this list can be used in food products without special permission of the FDA. Substances not on the GRAS list are "regulated," and the manufacturer must get special permission to use them. The food processor must prove to the FDA that the ingredient is safe in order to get that permission.

Some standardized foods are not required to list their ingredients. These foods must meet FDA **standards of identity** by containing certain ingredients for the product. Catsup, mayonnaise, and ice cream are among these foods. Often, the manufacturers list the ingredients anyway in order to aid ingredient-conscious consumers.

**Nutrition Labeling**   Only two kinds of foods are required to provide nutrition labeling: those with nutrients added (such as vitamin-D milk and enriched bread) and those that make a nutritional claim (such as low-fat or low-calorie). Many other foods provide nutrition labeling, too, because it has become important to consumers. The particular format required for all nutrition labeling helps you to compare different products. The **nutrition label** must list: the serving size; the number of servings in the package; the number of calories per serving; the amounts of protein, carbohydrate, and fat per serving; and the percentage of the U.S. RDA for protein, vitamin A, vitamin C, thiamin, riboflavin, niacin, calcium, and iron. Information about other ingredients, such as sodium and cholesterol, is optional. Some labels give nutrition information about the food after it has been prepared with other ingredients.

**Open Dating**　The four kinds of dates found on food packages help you judge how fresh a product is and how long you may safely and successfully use it. This is known as **open dating.** Open dating is not required by law, and not all products have it. You should know how to use the four different types of dates when they do appear.

The *expiration date* is the last day the food can safely be used. It is most often found on baby food and yeast. The *pull* or *sell date* is the last day the store should sell the product. The date allows for some home-storage time at the proper temperature. The sell date is often found on dairy products and cold cuts. The *freshness date* is the last day you can expect top quality and

freshness. It does not mean the product will be "spoiled" after that date, but you may not get the best possible results when you use it. Packaged grain products often have these dates. The *pack date* is usually found on products with a long shelf life. It indicates the day the food was packaged. You must be the judge of how long the food will stay fresh.

**Grading and Inspection Labels**　Some foods carry USDA grades, such as A, B, and C. These are determined by the U.S. Department of Agriculture according to taste, texture, size, and appearance. They do not reflect nutritional value. You will read more about grading and inspection in Chapters 18 and 19.

**Control Numbers**　Food manufacturers and processors produce many packages of the same product. In order to keep track of them, these companies put control numbers on the packages. These numbers are important to consumers if something goes wrong with a particular batch of food. You have probably heard media announcements of recalls of particular batches of contaminated or improperly processed or packaged food. When you hear such warnings, you should immediately check the numbers on the packages you have at home (on canned goods, the numbers are stamped on the bottom end) and return or discard any of the questionable product.

**Irradiated Foods**　The FDA allows the irradiation of spices, but the labels on the spices must indicate that the product has been irradiated. Irradiation is the exposure of the food to gamma radiation to extend its shelf life. There is a great deal of controversy over irradiation since it is thought to cause chemical changes in the food. Irradiation of pork and fresh fruits and vegetables has recently been approved by the FDA, but the foods are not required to be labeled as such. If you are concerned about

Different kinds of foods use different kinds of dating. You should not use a product past the expiration date (A) or buy it past the pull or sell date (B). The freshness date (C) shows when quality will begin to decrease, while the pack date (D) indicates when these foods were canned.

buying irradiated food, ask the store manager what foods in the store have been irradiated.

**UPC** Another symbol found on food packages is the **UPC,** or Universal Product Code. As you read in Chapter 1, the UPC is a grid or arrangement of lines that can be read only by an electronic scanner and interpreted by a computer. The scanners are located at the checkouts of supermarkets. They read the UPC and post the price on the register tape. Checkout is usually faster and more accurate using the UPC and scanner than it is by hand. This system also helps markets keep track of stock and saves them money. These savings can then be passed to consumers in the form of lower prices.

## Consumer Protection

In addition to your own good sense and careful comparison shopping, there are individuals and organizations who can aid you in making good food-shopping decisions. Trained home economists and dieticians, medical professionals, and local government agencies are good sources of information about products and stores. Many health organizations, such as the American Cancer Society, and federal government agencies, such as the Food Safety and Inspection Service, put out pamphlets or have telephone "hot lines" that provide information at no cost.

No matter how carefully you shop, however, you are bound to have a complaint now and then. Some complaints can be more serious than others. The first place to take your complaint is to the store where you purchased the product. If the lettuce you bought yesterday is brown inside today when you open it, or if the cookies were smashed when you opened the box, return the item to the store. You should get a replacement or a refund. If you are dissatisfied with the quality or performance of a product, write to the manufacturer. That is one reason that the company's name and address must appear on the product label. Be sure to give complete information to identify the product, the store, and your problem, as well as your address and telephone number. Food companies depend a great deal on consumer good will, and are often anxious to "make good" when someone has a legitimate complaint.

If you don't get satisfaction from these sources, there are agencies of the federal government to help you. As you know, the FDA regulates food products. Contact your nearest FDA office (look in the phone book under "United States Government" or "U.S. Department of Health and Human Services"), or write to their Washington office:

Food and Drug Administration
5600 Fishers Lane
Rockville, MD 20857

For complaints about meat, poultry, and eggs, notify the Food Safety and Inspection Service (FSIS) of the U.S. Department of Agriculture (USDA). Again, refer to your phone book for the local office, or write:

U.S. Department of Agriculture
Washington, D.C. 20250

For complaints about local stores, contact the main office of the store chain or the owner of a small store. If the problem relates to health, call your local health department or consumer-protection agency. Also notify your local Better Business Bureau or Chamber of Commerce. These organizations provide information about businesses of good reputation, and they keep track of complaints against local firms.

Finally—and very importantly—if you believe you have discovered a serious public health hazard, notify the police. Food products that have been tampered with can be lethal. Batches of food that have been accidentally contaminated are also very dangerous. Quick action to remove these foods from store shelves, to warn consumers who may already have purchased them, and to find the source of the problem is critical.

## Food-assistance Programs

There are a number of reasons why some people cannot provide nutritious meals for themselves or their families. Some of these reasons are financial; some relate to poor health or disability. Various government and private organizations provide aid to people in these circumstances.

**School Lunch Program** Low-cost, nutritious lunches in public schools are supported by federal government funds. In certain circumstances, breakfast is also provided. Low-cost or free milk is also made available in schools, camps, and day-care centers.

**Food Stamps** Some low-income people qualify for the federal Food Stamp Program. Food stamps can be used like cash for food items (but not on other products), and the cost of buying the stamps is much less than their face value. Therefore, a person gains food-purchasing power by participating in the program. It allows those with very limited income to get proper nutrition at low cost.

**Food Pantries and Soup Kitchens** These are usually operated by local governments and private or religious groups. They often depend on donations. Pantries give away food products to the needy. The kitchens prepare hot, nutritious meals without charge, as well as a place to eat them.

**Group Meal Programs** These are designed particularly for older adults. They provide low-cost, nutritious meals and companionship at mealtime.

**Home-delivered Meals** Also designed for older adults, these programs deliver hot, nutritious meals to those who can neither prepare the meals nor leave home. The best-known of these programs is Meals on Wheels.

Home-bound senior citizens appreciate the companionship and the meals provided by programs such as Meals on Wheels.

**Shopping Assistance** This program offers transportation and nutrition advice to older adults who want to keep their independence and do their own shopping.

### For Review

1. In what order are the ingredients of a food product listed on the label? Why is this important to you as a consumer and meal manager?
2. How can you use nutrition labeling to compare and choose food products?
3. List eight food products with open dating that your family buys regularly. Next to each product, write the kind of open dating found on that product.
4. Whom should you notify with a complaint about a "spoiled" food product? About unsanitary conditions in a food store? About a food product that has been tampered with?
5. What food-assistance programs are specifically for older adults? For low-income individuals or families?

# 8 Chapter Review

## Summary

A food manager carefully considers the best use of all resources. These resources include the ingredients and their use, time, energy, and money. Before shopping for food, plan the week's menus, prepare the shopping list by determining the amount and form of the food you need, and decide the most convenient time to shop and which store offers the best selection and lowest prices. Reading the advertisements of the weekly specials can help plan a menu to take advantage of products with lower prices. Coupons and refunds are other procedures that can reduce the grocery bill. At the market, compare the brands and the unit prices to purchase the products that meet your needs and that are the most economical. Also, much of the information needed to be a good shopper is included on food-product labels. In addition, consumer protection agencies can help consumers with their food-shopping decisions. For people who need assistance with their meals, there are government and private organizations that provide nutritious foods.

## Vocabulary

comparison shopping
generic brands
GRAS list
imitation food
name brands
nutrition label
open dating
standards of identity
store brands
unit price
UPC

To be a wise shopper, you need to do __(1)__ by comparing price, variety, and quality as well as brands and cost per unit or per serving. __(2)__, __(3)__, and __(4)__ are the three basic groups of brands at three different prices. In addition to comparing brands, you should check the __(5)__ to make sure that you are paying the lowest cost for each standard unit of measurement. Then look at the label of the food product, where the ingredients are listed. When a product is a substitute for a more nutritious one, it is considered an __(6)__. Additives are also listed on the label, and these can usually be found on the FDA's __(7)__ of ingredients that are generally recognized as safe. Although some foods, such as catsup and ice cream, are not required to list their ingredients, they must meet FDA __(8)__ by including certain ingredients for the product. Foods that have nutrients added or that make a nutritional claim must carry a __(9)__ that gives such information as the serving size and the number of servings in the package. You will also want to check to see if the product has __(10)__ to see how fresh it is and how long you may safely use it. Many products also have a grid or arrangement of lines that is referred to as the __(11)__, or Universal Product Code, which makes checkout faster if your market has an electronic scanner.

## Chapter Questions

1. What is the most important time-saving strategy for kitchen cleanup?

2. What are four kinds of food to help you save cooking time?

3. What should you consider before purchasing instant, prepared, or frozen foods?

4. What are at least four things you should consider when planning a menu for a week?

5. Why should you be neither tired nor hungry when you food shop?

6. Briefly describe the five kinds of food markets.

7. If you were to do the food shopping for your family, what are at least four ways you could save time and money?

8. When you shop for groceries, how can you use food-product labels and nutrition labels to make wise purchase decisions?

9. What kinds of help are available from consumer protection and information agencies?

10. What are the values of food-assistance programs?

## Skill Activities

**1. Critical thinking** In your food journal, evaluate the food markets that are in your area. Write the date of your evaluation, and then down the left-hand side of your notebook, list these headings: "Name of market"; "Kind of market"; "Types of products sold," (leave three lines after this heading); "Price for one gallon of whole milk"; "Price for one dozen large white eggs"; "Price for one dozen oranges"; "Price for 75% lean ground beef"; "Brands, sizes, and prices for canned beans"; "Special Services"; "Days and Hours Open for Business." After each heading write your findings. For "Types of products sold," tell whether the store sells canned and frozen goods, fresh fruits and vegetables, fresh meat, bakery items, dairy products, baking supplies, pet food, paper goods, and cleaning supplies. If a store does not sell an item that you are price checking, leave the space blank. Under "Special services," include such items as double coupons, delivery, check cashing, and nongrocery products. Now decide where you would prefer to shop, and tell which factors led to your decision.

**2. Social studies** Fold a piece of lined paper in half. At the top of the paper and then just below the fold, write one of these headings: "Expiration date," "Pull or sell date," "Freshness date," and "Pack date." (Use both sides of the paper.) Visit a market, and find examples of the four kinds of dating. Record the names of the food products under the appropriate heading.

**3. Human relations** Write an invitation to a home economist from your county extension agency to speak to your class. With your class prepare questions for the home economist. Include questions about the kinds of services provided by the agency, the kinds of recipes for nutritious low-cost meals, and the variety of responsibilities a home economist has with a county extension agency.

# The Recipe

## 9

## As you read, think about:

- why recipes are important.
- why exact measurement is important to good recipe results.
- why understanding the terms of cookery techniques is important in following a recipe.
- how to modify recipes.
- how to make and use a time-work plan.

**Vocabulary**

recipe
yield
standard
  system of
    measurement
metric system
  of measurement
liquid
    displacement
    method
time-work plan
dovetailing

*338 KITCHEN REFERENCE*

n 1 teaspoon of sugar from the cup onto a piece of wax
e the remaining sugar and the flour in a mixing bowl
tir in the orange juice and rind and almond extract. Bea
in first the melted butter, then the half-and-half, then
e and reserved teaspoon of sugar to stiff, glossy peaks
ixture until no streaks of white or orange remain. Pour
in a moderate oven (350°F. or 175°C.) for 35 to 40 m
browned. Remove the pie from the oven and coo
tting. The filling will fall slightly, but that is as it s
d serve.

*ARIATIONS*

tard pie: Prepare exactly as directed, but substi
d) lemon juice and rind for the orange and omit t

Prepare as directed, but substitute 3 tablespoons
lime juice and 1½ teaspoons freshly grated lime
omit the almond extract.

### *Open-face Dutch almond-apple pie*

*MAKES A 9-INCH (23 CM) PIE*

*T*his is a good recipe. And such an easy one, too,
particularly if you have a processor with which to buzz up the almond cream
filling. The best apples to use are super-tart ones because of the richness of the
almond cream.

| | | |
|---|---|---|
| *4 pounds* | *tart green apples* | *2 kg (scant)* |
| *2 tablespoons* | *lemon juice* | *2 tablespoons* |
| | *marzipan, cut into small pieces* | *60 g* |
| | *unsalted butter* | *2 tablespoons* |
| | *ly packed light brown sugar* | *105 g* |
| | *aten* | *2 tablespoons* |
| | *on* | *1 large* |
| | *h a high fluted edge* | *240 ml* |
| | | *A 23 cm* |

ectly into a large bowl. Sprinkle with
oment. Cream the marzipan, butter,
a food processor fitted with the metal

*1 tea*
*1 cup*
*table*
*¼ pound*
*5 large (abo*
*pounds)*
*1 large*
*¼ teaspoon*

The **recipe** is a tool of cookery, a blueprint or pattern to follow in preparing food. There are as many different recipes as there are ways to prepare food. Some are complicated and some are simple, but all recipes tell you what ingredients to use and how to put them together. You already know some simple recipes by heart, without even thinking of them as recipes. When you beat eggs with a little salt and milk and then scramble them in the skillet to "create" scrambled eggs, you are following a recipe just as surely as when you go through the steps listed in a cookbook for the creation of a soufflé.

## The Importance of Recipes

Recipes are important to good results in cookery. They allow those good results to be shared by many cooks, and they insure the same good results each of the many times they are used. Recipes are a way to expand your cookery skills. You can collect recipes from many sources: from cookbooks both old and modern as well as local and foreign, and from friends, relatives, and the media. Some recipes are handed down in families; others are newly created. Standard recipes, tested recipes with exact measurements, are best for the beginning cook. As you gain experience, you will probably want to try to create your own recipes or combine the elements of several recipes you already know.

Whatever its source or origin, a recipe has two important parts: (1) a list of ingredients and (2) directions for combining the ingredients to make a specific food product. When you read a recipe, you should know what ingredients, equipment, and skills you need, as well as how much time will be required to create the dish. You should also know how many servings the recipe will produce. Then you can decide—as

*Plumb Pudding*
Take a Pound of best Flour, sift it and make it up before Sunrise-with six Eggs beaten light -a large Spoonfull of good Yeast and as much Milk as will make it the Consistance of Bread-let it rise well, knead into it half a Pound of Butter, a grated Nutmeg, one Pound of Raisins, stoned and chopped up, mix all together, wet the Cloth, flower it, tie loosly, so the Pudding may have Room to rise. The Raisins should be rubbed in Flower.

Recipes have not always been as precise. Would you have any trouble following this early American recipe? Why?

A recipe gives the ingredients and equipment you need, as well as the measurements and procedures required to make a dish. To ensure perfect results, follow the recipe exactly.

meal manager—whether it is a recipe you want to use.

## Scientific Principles of Cookery

The ingredients called for and the directions given in a recipe for a particular product follow special rules or principles that are based upon science. From science we learn what nutrients are in food and how the nutrients will react to certain cooking procedures. For example, science tells us that protein will coagulate, or become firm, when heated, and at high temperatures it will toughen due to loss of water. We also learn that eggs contain protein. By applying this information to egg cookery, we know that heat will cause egg protein to become firm, and that low temperatures should be used to prevent toughening of egg protein. All good recipes are based on sound cookery principles like these. Always pay close attention to times and temperatures as well as to ingredients in recipe directions.

## Recipe Formats

There are three different styles or formats for recipes. They list ingredients and directions differently. No matter what style or order they are in, however, all recipes should have:

1. A list of ingredients in the exact form and measurement they are needed. To be most useful, the ingredients should be listed in the order they will be used.
2. The size and type of cookware or specialized tools that are needed.
3. The temperature at which foods should be cooked. This may be given as degrees Fahrenheit or Celsius of oven temperature or as the condition of the food, such as "simmer" or "rolling boil."
4. The length of time for cooking or other procedures, such as chilling or marinating.

This is sometimes also represented as the condition you wish the food to reach, such as "until lightly browned, about ten minutes."
5. Step-by-step directions, in order, for all procedures involved.
6. The **yield,** or number of servings the recipe will make.

**Standard Recipe Format**  The most widely used recipe format is the standard form. It first lists all ingredients, in order. Measurements are given for the ingredients in their final or usable form. (In other words, the recipe will say "½ cup diced onion"; not "½ cup onion, diced." That way you know to measure the onion *after* it is diced, not before.) The directions for preparation follow the list of ingredients. They may be in paragraph form or in numbered steps. This recipe format is the one usually found in cookbooks and is the easiest to follow.

**Action Recipe Format**  This format emphasizes the activities the cook performs. The ingredients are listed as they are used. Ingredient measurements are given in their final form, as they are in the standard format. The action format is also easy to follow, but it usually takes up more space on a cookbook page or recipe card.

**Narrative Recipe Format**  This format is best used for short, simple recipes with few ingredients. It combines the ingredients and directions in narrative paragraphs or "story" form. Since it takes the least space, the narrative format is often used in newspapers and magazines as well as on food-product labels.

## Selecting Recipes

When there are many recipes for the same dish, which one should you choose? Recipes that

**The Standard Recipe Format**
This is the most common form for recipes and the easiest to follow.

### Coleslaw

3 c (750 mL) finely shredded cabbage
½ grated carrot
¼ c (60 mL) diced green pepper
¼ c (60 mL) cooked salad dressing or mayonnaise

1. Wash all vegetables and place into refrigerator to crisp.
2. Shred cabbage and prepare carrot and green pepper.
3. Add dressing and mix to coat vegetables.
4. Serve immediately.
Yield: 4 servings

**The Action Recipe Format**
This recipe form emphasizes the actions taken in preparing a dish. The ingredients appear as they are needed.

### Coleslaw

Wash 1 cabbage, 1 carrot, and 1 green pepper.
Place vegetables into refrigerator to crisp.
Place into bowl 3 c (750 mL) finely shredded cabbage, ½ grated carrot, and ¼ c (60 mL) diced green pepper.
Add ¼ c (60 mL) cooked salad dressing or mayonnaise.
Mix to coat vegetables.
Serve immediately.
Yield: 4 servings

**The Narrative Recipe Format**
Short, simple recipes can be written in this form. It is often used where space is limited.

### Coleslaw

Wash and place into refrigerator 1 cabbage, 1 carrot, and 1 green pepper. Place into bowl 3 c (750 mL) finely shredded cabbage, ½ grated carrot, and ¼ c (60 mL) diced green pepper. Add ¼ c (60 mL) cooked salad dressing or mayonnaise, and mix to coat vegetables. Serve immediately. Yield: 4 servings are selected with the following points in mind will be most satisfactory. Be sure that the selected recipe: (1) fits into your needs for the menu you have planned; (2) gives complete directions and measurements that you can easily understand; (3) uses ingredients and equipment that you have available; (4) does not call for skills that you do not have; (5) can be made in the time you will have available; and (6) is within your food budget.

Carefully selected recipes help you to use time and energy to the best advantage and to avoid food waste.

## Using Recipes

Carelessly used recipes can result in failure and waste of time, effort, food, and money. The following steps will help you use a recipe so that the results will be satisfactory. First, read the entire recipe. This will give you a complete picture of how the dish is prepared. If you are confused, reread the recipe until you understand each step and every cookery term. Assemble the ingredients and equipment. Measure the ingredients carefully. Follow directions exactly. Leave enough time to perform all preparation tasks completely and in the correct order. Finally, enjoy the results!

### For Review

1. In what order are ingredients listed in a good recipe?
2. What six elements should all recipes contain?
3. How is the standard recipe format different from the action format? From the narrative format?
4. Why is it important to read a recipe all the way through before you decide to use it, and again before you begin to prepare the food?

### For Perfect Results

Read the recipe carefully before you start! Every word of it!

Check to see that you have all the ingredients you need.

Check to see that you have all the utensils you need to prepare the recipe.

Complete the preparation of ingredients such as chopping nuts, melting chocolate, dicing onions, or sifting flour.

If the oven is needed, set it so that it can reach the proper temperature. If cookware needs to be pretreated, such as greasing a pan, do so carefully.

Measure exactly.

Mix carefully, following each direction.

Bake or cook for the time and at the temperature directed.

# Exact Measurement— The Key to a Recipe

One of the most useful things about a recipe is precise measurement. "A little of this and little of that" does not produce the same, reliable results time after time for different cooks in different kitchens. Another reason that different cooks can get the same results from a recipe is the widespread use of standardized measuring equipment. The proper use of this equipment ensures that your "teaspoon of this and half cup of that" is the same every time you use the recipe.

For convenience and efficiency, many recipes list all the dry ingredients first and then list all of the liquid ingredients. Because of this type of listing, you can use the same measuring utensil more than once without having to wash it. For instance, you do not want to put a dry ingredient into a wet or sticky measuring cup, and you do not want to insert a damp or sticky spoon into a container of dry ingredients. Even if a recipe does not list them that way, measure your dry ingredients first whenever possible. It will save the time and effort of rewashing utensils over and over.

## Systems of Measurement

No doubt you have already noticed that the measurements in this book are given two ways. The standard measurement is given first. The metric equivalent, what the standard measurement equals in the metric system, is then given in parentheses. You have probably also noticed that many food-product labels carry both measurements, too. So do some recipes, but many use either one system or the other. You should be able to understand how to use both systems of measurement and have measuring equipment available for both, too.

**Standard Measurements** It is the **standard system of measurement** that is customary in the United States. The measurements you will use most often in cooking are those of volume: gallon, quart, pint, cup (and fractions of a cup), tablespoon, and teaspoon; and those of weight: pound (and fraction of a pound) and ounce. It is worthwhile to learn how the most commonly used standard measures relate to each other; in other words, how many

Many of the recipes you will use list the dry ingredients first. What is the advantage of this type of listing?

## Equivalent Measures

| Standard Measure | Standard Equivalent Measures | Approximate Metric Measure |
|---|---|---|
| 1 gallon | 4 quarts | 3.8 liters |
| 1 quart | 4 cups, 2 pints | 946 milliliters or 0.95 liter |
| 1 pint | 2 cups | 470 milliliters or 0.47 liter |
| 1 cup | ½ pint, 16 tablespoons | 240 milliliters |
| ¾ cup | 12 tablespoons | 180 milliliters |
| ⅔ cup | 10⅔ tablespoons | 160 milliliters |
| ½ cup | 8 tablespoons | 120 milliliters |
| ⅓ cup | 5⅓ tablespoons | 80 milliliters |
| ¼ cup | 4 tablespoons | 60 milliliters |
| ⅛ cup | 2 tablespoons | 30 milliliters |
| 1 tablespoon | 3 teaspoons | 15 milliliters |
| 1 teaspoon |  | 5 milliliters |
| ½ teaspoon |  | 2.5 milliliters |
| ¼ teaspoon |  | 1.25 milliliters |
| ⅛ teaspoon |  | 0.5 milliliter |
| 1 pound | 16 ounces | 450 grams or 0.45 kilogram |
| ½ pound | 8 ounces | 225 grams or 0.23 kilogram |
|  | 1 ounce | 28 grams |

of the smaller units it takes to equal a larger unit. You probably know that 16 ounces make 1 pound and that 4 quarts make 1 gallon, but what about the number of teaspoons in a tablespoon? Most cookbooks include an equivalency chart like the one above. You might want to keep a similar chart handy wherever you keep your recipes. Be sure to make note of the standard abbreviations, too. It is easy to mix up *tsp* (for *teaspoon*) and *Tbs* (for *tablespoon*) if you are not careful.

**Metric Measurements** Most other countries use the **metric system of measurement** in their everyday speech as well as in their technical measurements. The metric measurements you will use most often in cooking are those of liquid volume, based on the liter, and those of solid weight, based on the gram. The metric system uses multiples of ten, just as we do in our money system. The multiples of ten are identified by prefixes that are added to the basic unit. For example, you will use the prefixes

| Prefix | | | | for Weight | for Volume | for Length |
|---|---|---|---|---|---|---|
| milli- | is | 0.001 | basic unit or | milligram | milliliter | millimeter |
| centi- | is | 0.01 | basic unit or | centigram | centiliter | centimeter |
| deci- | is | 0.1 | basic unit or | decigram | deciliter | decimeter |
| deka- | is | 10 | basic units or | dekagram | dekaliter | decameter |
| hecto | is | 100 | basic units or | hectogram | hectoliter | hectometer |
| kilo- | is | 1000 | basic units or | kilogram |  | kilometer |

*milli-* (for one thousandth), *centi-* (for one hundredth), *deci-* (for ten times), and *kilo-* (for one thousand times).

**Cup Measurements** Although the standard measurement for a cup is based on the quart, and the metric cup is based on the liter, they are very close in size. Some measuring cups show the standard measure on one side and the metric measure on the other side. Both cups have a similar volume so that the difference in measurement with either cup falls within the tolerance-permitted variance of plus or minus 5 percent set by the American Standard Association Institute for household measuring cups. The difference in position of markings on the two cups is very little. Look at the markings on the cups shown below. Note that the metric cup is 500 milliliters, or ½ liter, and that it equals 2 standard cups plus 2 tablespoons. Use whichever cup measurement is consistent with the system of measurement in your recipe. If the recipe uses standard measures throughout, use the standard cup. If it uses metric measures, use the metric cup.

Many recipes today provide you with both the standard and metric measurements of ingredients. Liquid measuring cups often have markings for both systems of measurement.

## Measuring Equipment

Measuring cups and spoons are essential for following a recipe correctly. Fortunately, while they are among the most useful tools, they are also among the least expensive.

Liquid measuring cups come in glass or transparent plastic. Always place the cup on a flat surface and read the measurement at eye level when measuring. Dry measuring cups and measuring spoons may be plastic or metal, and often come in "nesting sets" in which the smaller utensils fit neatly inside the larger ones. See Chapter 7, pages 169 and 172, for more information on basic measuring equipment.

## How to Measure Accurately

Whenever you measure ingredients, you want to be sure your measurements are accurate. In other words, you want to use the exact amount the recipe calls for so that the results will be predictable and successful. Different ingredients require slightly different measurement techniques.

**How to Measure Liquid Ingredients** Liquid ingredients are measured in a liquid measuring cup with a rim above the top measuring line. Place the cup on a level surface, and fill it to the desired mark. Bend or stoop to check the measurement at eye level.

**How to Measure Dry Ingredients** Dry ingredients such as baking powder, baking soda, salt, cornstarch, cream of tartar, and spices should be stirred first to break up lumps. With a measuring spoon, scoop up an overflowing spoonful and level it with a straight-edged spatula.

**How to Measure Flour** Flour will pack on standing. For measuring, flour should be sifted once onto paper and then lightly spooned

## Measuring Techniques for Different Ingredients

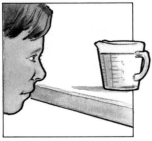

Measuring liquid at eye level, on flat surface.

Leveling dry ingredients with a straight edge.

Sifting flour onto waxed paper.

Packing down brown sugar into a measuring cup.

Packing solid shortening into a measuring spoon.

Using liquid displacement to measure shortening.

Cutting the correct measurement of shortening.

Beating eggs before placing them into a measuring cup.

Lightly pressing soft bread crumbs into a measuring cup.

Weighing small amounts of food on waxed paper, or larger amounts in a container, on a kitchen scale.

into a dry measuring cup to overflowing. The excess should be leveled with a straight-edged spatula. The cup should never be tapped to level the flour; tapping packs down the flour and results in more than the required amount.

Presifted, no-sift, or instant flours were developed to eliminate the need to sift flour. It was then found that some adjustment in the amount of flour must be made when the presifted flour is used for regular recipes. The weight of a cup of presifted, spooned flour can be adjusted to the approximate weight of a cup of sifted flour by removing 2 level tablespoons (30 mL) from each cup.

When your recipe calls for flour, not sifted flour, use the following spooning method. Spoon flour into a graduated dry measuring cup to overflowing. Level the cup with a straight-edged spatula.

**How to Measure Sugar** Sugar does not require sifting before measuring unless it is lumpy. White sugar should be spooned into a dry measuring cup and made level with a straight-edged spatula. If brown sugar is lumpy, crush lumps with a rolling pin or press it through a coarse sieve. Brown sugar, free of lumps, should be packed firmly into a dry measuring cup so that it will retain the shape of the cup when it is turned out. Use a straight-edged spatula to level the cup.

Confectioners' sugar tends to lump and may require sifting before measuring. It should be lightly spooned into a dry measuring cup without tapping, and the measure made level with a straight-edged spatula.

**How to Measure Shortening** Shortening should be at room temperature when measured. Solid shortenings should be pressed firmly into a dry measuring cup so that air spaces will be avoided. The measure should be made level with a straight-edged spatula. Remove the shortening carefully from the cup so that none is left clinging to the sides. For measures less than ¼ cup (60 mL), use a measuring spoon. Pack shortening into the spoon, but hold your finger under the bowl of the spoon to prevent breaking it.

Another way to measure solid shortening is the **liquid displacement method.** In this method, the amount of shortening is judged by how much water it displaces, or moves out of the way, in a liquid measuring cup. To use the liquid displacement method, subtract the amount of shortening you need from the full amount the measuring cup holds. Say your recipe calls for ¼ cup shortening. Your cup holds 1 full cup. That leaves ¾ cup. Fill the cup with ¾ cup cold water. Then spoon in shortening until the water rises to the "full," or one-cup, level. Pour out the water; the shortening remaining in the cup is the correct (¼ cup) amount.

Shortenings such as butter, margarine, and lard are usually sold in 1-pound (454 g) packag-es. Butter and margarine are often packed four sticks to a pound and their wrappers marked with tablespoon or fractional cup measurements. When only approximate measures of butter or margarine are required (to use in a white sauce or to season vegetables, for example), the portion may be cut through the wrapper. The equivalent measures are:

4 sticks = 1 pound (454 grams) = 2 cups (500 mL)
1 stick = ¼ pound (114 grams) = ½ cup (125 mL)
½ stick = ⅛ pound (57 grams) = ¼ cup (60 mL)

Liquid shortenings such as salad oil or cooking oils should be poured directly into a liquid measuring cup up to the desired level.

**How to Measure Eggs** Eggs vary in size from small to large; because of this, some recipes call for cup or milliliter measurements of egg. Eggs are then measured in a liquid measuring cup, and only the quantity called for should be used. Other recipes give the number of eggs required; most recipes were developed to use large or medium eggs.

When measuring eggs, beat them with a fork or a wire wisk until the white and yolk are blended. Then pour the beaten eggs into a liquid measuring cup to the desired mark. Remember to look at the cup at eye level.

On average, the following approximate equivalencies for eggs hold true:

2 medium eggs = ⅓ cup = 80 milliliters
2 large eggs = ½ cup = 125 milliliters
3 medium eggs = ½ cup = 125 milliliters
3 large eggs = ⅔ cup = 160 milliliters

**How to Measure Other Ingredients**
Ingredients such as shredded coconut, nuts, chopped dried fruits, and soft bread crumbs

should be lightly pressed into a dry measuring cup until level with the top of the desired graduated dry measure.

**How to Weigh Ingredients** Two scales, pounds-ounces and grams-kilograms, are used to weigh all dry ingredients and solid fats. To weigh a small amount (ounces or grams) of food, place waxed paper on the scale. Place the food directly on the paper until the desired weight is reached.

Large amounts (pounds or kilograms) of foods are often weighed in a lightweight container. You should: (1) weigh the container, (2) add the desired weight of food to the container weight, and (3) place the food in the container until the desired combined weight of the food and the container is reached. Foods to be weighed do not require sifting or packing as for cup measurement.

## For Review

1. Why should you measure dry ingredients before liquid ones?
2. What is the metric equivalent of a standard cup?
3. What special precautions should you take when measuring flour? Why?
4. Which type of sugar should be packed firmly in a dry measuring cup? How should brown sugar and confectioners' sugar be measured?
5. What kinds of shortening can be measured (approximately) by using the marks on the wrapper? What measurements are used on these wrappers?
6. What size eggs should you use when a recipe calls for a certain number rather than a liquid measurement of egg? Why?

# Cookery Terms—The Language of the Recipe

Tested recipes and good measuring techniques alone do not guarantee good results in food preparation. What to do with the ingredients must also be understood and followed exactly. It is important to become familiar with the cookery terms used in recipes for they, too, are important tools of the cook. There are many cookery terms, and each has its own specific meaning. You must understand the meaning of such terms as *cut in, fold, blend, beat,* and others so that you know exactly what procedures to follow. The most common recipe terms, referring to the techniques used in preparing, mixing, cutting, and cooking, along with their definitions are listed below and on the following two pages. Always use exactly the technique your recipe calls for to achieve the best possible results.

## Terms Used— Techniques of Preparation

**Bread:** To cover a food with a coating of crumbs made from bread, crackers, or cereal. The food is often dipped in a liquid such as milk or egg before coating.

**Brush:** To spread a liquid coating on a food, using a pastry brush or paper towel.

**Dredge:** To cover a food with a dry ingredient such as flour or sugar. The food may be rolled in, sprinkled with, or shaken in a bag with the dry ingredient.

**Flute:** To form a standing edge on pastry, such as pie crust, before baking. Press the dough with your fingers to create this scalloped edge, or use a fork to "crimp" the edge.

**Grease:** To rub shortening, fat or oil, on the cooking surface of bakeware. Use waxed paper or paper towel to spread a thin, even layer.

## Cookery Terms

Bread

Dredge

Flute

Beat

Cream

Cut in

Fold in

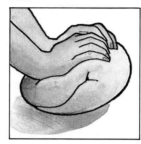
Knead

Whip

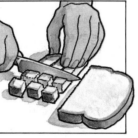
Cube

Dice

Julienne

Mince

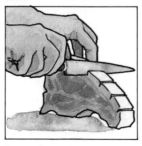
Score

Trim

Baste

Deep-fat fry

Poach

Steam

Stir-fry

**Marinate:** To soak in a seasoned liquid, called a marinade, to add flavor and/or to tenderize.

**Sift:** To put dry ingredients through a sifter or a fine sieve to incorporate air.

## Terms Used— Techniques of Mixing

**Beat:** To mix with an over-and-over motion, using a spoon or a rotary or electric beater.

**Blend:** To combine thoroughly two or more ingredients.

**Combine:** To mix together, usually by stirring, two or more ingredients.

**Cream:** To soften and blend until smooth and light by mixing with a spoon or an electric mixer.

**Cut in:** To mix solid shortening with flour by cutting the shortening into small pieces and mixing until it is completely covered with the flour mixture. Use a pastry blender, two knives, or a fork.

**Fold in:** To combine a delicate mixture, such as beaten egg white or whipped cream, with a more solid material. Insert the edge of a spoon or rubber scraper vertically down through the middle of the mixture, slide it across the bottom of the bowl, bring it up with some of the mixture, and fold over on top of the rest. Continue slowly and gently, turning the bowl often, until all is evenly mixed.

**Knead:** To work dough by folding, pressing, and turning, until it is smooth and elastic. Place dough on a floured board, fold it in half, and press firmly with the heels of your hands. Turn the dough about a quarter turn, and repeat the folding and pressing.

**Mix:** To combine two or more ingredients, usually by stirring.

**Stir:** To mix with a circular motion of a spoon or other utensil.

**Whip:** To beat rapidly with a rotary beater, an electric mixer, or wire whisk; to incorporate air and make light and fluffy, as whipped cream or egg white.

## Terms Used— Techniques of Cutting

**Chop:** To cut into small pieces.

**Core:** To remove the core of a fruit with a corer or paring knife.

**Cube:** To cut into small squares.

**Cut:** To divide foods into small pieces with a knife or scissors.

**Dice:** To cut into very small cubes.

**Grate:** To rub food, such as lemon or orange peel, against a grater to obtain fine particles.

**Grind:** To cut by putting food through a food chopper or grinder.

**Julienne:** To cut food into long, thin strips.

**Mash:** To crush food until it becomes smooth. Use a potato masher or fork.

**Mince:** To cut into very small pieces with a sharp knife.

**Pare:** To cut away the skin or a very thin layer of the outside of fruits or vegetables. Use a vegetable peeler or knife.

**Score:** To make thin, straight cuts through the outer edge of fat on meat to prevent the meat from curling during cooking.

**Scrape:** To rub a vegetable, such as a carrot, with the sharp edge of a knife in order to remove only the outer layer of skin.

**Shred:** To tear or cut into thin pieces or strips.

**Slice:** To cut food into flat pieces.

**Sliver:** To cut in long, thin pieces.

**Trim:** To cut away most of the fat from the edges of meat.

### Practical Tip

- Write your own observations and suggestions on a recipe after you use it for the first time.

# Computerized Recipes

The personal computer makes the kitchen of the future a possibility today. In recent years, software companies have developed several programs for personal recipe files and computerized cookbooks. These software packages facilitate organizing your recipes and locating new recipes. Usually these packages take one of three forms.

**Personal Recipe Files** These packages do not include any recipes. They were created to aid you in computerizing your recipes. With these programs, you can organize your recipes into categories such as appetizers and meats. Some programs will even convert the recipes for larger or smaller yields.

**Recipe Index** Many popular cookbooks are not yet available on computer diskettes. You can, however, obtain a computerized index of recipes from popular cookbooks. Some of these programs allow you to include your recipes in the index. How the recipes are organized varies —ingredients, preparation time, and kind of cuisine are among the various categories. Some of these programs can be used with computerized cookbooks.

**Computerized Cookbooks** A recipe-index program is needed to gain access to computerized cookbooks. Sometimes the index program and the cookbook come together; sometimes they are separate. Some computerized cookbook packages allow you to input your recipes; others do not. Some of the programs will convert the recipes for larger or smaller yields. Currently over 25 cookbooks are available on computer disks.

The quality and the potential uses of these recipe software packages vary widely. If you decide to take a step into the future, carefully consider your needs and research the available software to make sure the software you purchase will suit your needs.

Recipe software for personal computers can provide ease in menu planning.

## Terms Used—
## Techniques of Cooking

**Bake:** To cook in an oven or oven-type appliance in a covered or uncovered pan.

**Barbecue:** To cook meat or poultry slowly over coals on a spit or in the oven, basting it often with a highly seasoned sauce.

**Baste:** To spread, brush, or pour liquid (such as sauce, drippings, melted fat, or marinade) over food while it is cooking. Use a baster, brush, or spoon.

**Boil:** To cook in liquid, usually water, in which bubbles rise constantly and then break on the surface.

**Braise:** To cook meat slowly, covered and in a small amount of liquid or steam.

**Broil:** To cook under direct heat or over coals.

**Brown:** To make the surface of a food brown in color by frying, broiling, baking in the oven, or toasting.

**Deep-fat fry:** To cook in hot fat that completely covers the food.

**Dot:** To place small particles of a solid, such as butter, on the surface of a food.

**Fry:** To cook in hot fat.

**Pan-broil:** To cook uncovered in an ungreased or lightly greased skillet, pouring off excess fat as it accumulates.

**Pan-fry:** To cook in an uncovered skillet with a small amount of fat.

**Poach:** To cook gently in a hot liquid below the boiling point.

**Preheat:** To set the oven to cooking temperature in advance, so that it has time to reach the desired temperature by the start of cooking.

**Roast:** To cook by dry heat, uncovered, usually in the oven.

**Sauté:** To cook uncovered in a small amount of fat in a pan.

**Scald:** To heat a liquid to just below the boiling point; or to pour boiling water over food or to dip food briefly into boiling water.

**Sear:** To cook meat quickly at a high temperature until it becomes brown. Use a skillet with a small amount of fat, or the oven at a high temperature.

**Simmer:** To cook in liquid just below the boiling point. The tiny bubbles that form should break before they reach the surface.

**Steam:** To cook over steam rising from boiling water.

**Steep:** To cover with boiling water and let stand without additional heating until flavor and color are extracted, as for tea.

**Stew:** To cook slowly and for a long time in liquid.

**Stir-fry:** To fry small pieces of food very quickly in a small amount of very hot oil while stirring constantly. Use a wok or skillet.

**Toast:** To brown by direct heat in a toaster or in the oven.

## Abbreviations in Cookery

Most recipes in cookbooks, magazines, or newspapers use the abbreviations for measurements and various other cooking terms in order to save space. In order to understand and follow recipes correctly, you must learn the accepted abbreviations listed below or have a list handy for reference every time you cook.

### Abbreviations and Symbols in Cookery

| | |
|---|---|
| few grains—f. g. | hour—hr |
| teaspoon—tsp or t | minute—min |
| tablespoon—tbsp, Tbs, or T | inch—in |
| cup—c | gram—g |
| pint—pt | kilogram—kg |
| quart—qt | milligram—mg |
| gallon—gal | liter—L |
| ounce—oz | milliliter—mL |
| pound—lb | deciliter—dL |
| dozen—doz | centimeter—cm |
| square—sq | millimeter—mm |

## For Review

1. List three cookery terms that were unfamiliar to you before you read this section. Define them.
2. What two preparation techniques do you think you will use most often? List at least two dishes for which you would use them. Do the same for cutting techniques, mixing techniques, and cooking techniques.
3. Which two abbreviations do you think are the easiest to confuse? Suggest a good way to remember the difference.

## Modifying a Recipe

There will be times when you will want to prepare a particular dish, but your recipe yields too many or too few servings, or calls for an ingredient you don't have available. Rather than giving up the idea of making the food, or guessing at another way to prepare it, you can use some accepted methods of modifying the recipe.

### Increasing or Decreasing Recipes

When it comes to quantity or size, many recipes provide enough food for six to eight servings. Because of this, it may be difficult to find recipes that will give the exact number of servings you need at a particular time. If you are cooking for only two people, you would not want to use a recipe that would serve six or eight. When friends come for dinner or the size of your family increases, you may find that the recipe yield is too small. By using multiplication and division, however, you can increase or decrease the size of the recipe to meet your needs.

Large dinner parties will require you to increase many if not all of the recipes you have chosen. Why is it important for you to have a table of equivalent measures?

To halve a recipe, use exactly one-half the amount of each ingredient. To do this, you will need to know the equivalent measures listed on page 204. Also, the food equivalents listed in the table on page 621 may help you in dividing or multiplying ingredients.

If divided recipes call for less than one egg, beat up a whole egg and measure it with a measuring spoon into two equal parts. The leftover egg may be used in making another dish, such as scrambled eggs, sauces, batter coating, or french toast.

Baking pans used for half recipes of cakes or pies should measure about half the area or size of those that would be used for the whole recipe. The oven temperature will be the same, but the baking time may be shorter.

To double a recipe, use exactly twice the amount of each ingredient listed in the recipe. For doubling recipes for cakes, an extra minute of beating is then necessary. If the increased recipe calls for uneven amounts of ingredients, you will find that the table at the top of this page can be helpful.

When you double a recipe for a cake, you will need to use twice as many pans of the same size as called for in the original recipe, or a pan double in area, so that the batter will be of the same depth. The baking temperature and the time will remain constant.

## Food Equivalents

Food equivalency tables help you determine the quantity of foods in terms of cups. The cup measures are often used in recipes, but pounds (kilograms) and ounces (grams), and units (such as a loaf of bread or a box of crackers) are used when foods are purchased. Suppose you wish to make peanut cookies and the recipe calls for 1 cup (250 mL) of peanuts; how many peanuts would you need to buy? The *Table of Equivalents*

For many recipes, you may substitute certain ingredients for those listed. For these brownies, what is being used instead of chocolate?

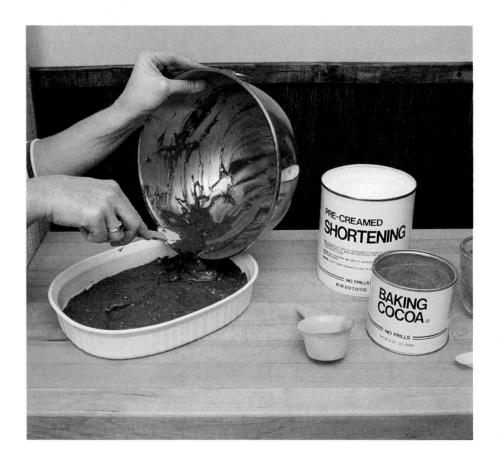

on page 621 shows that 5 ounces (141.75 g) of peanuts will measure 1 cup (250 mL), the amount indicated in the recipe. Use this table as a reference whenever you are uncertain about food equivalents.

## Food Substitutions

There may be times when you do not have on hand the ingredients listed in a recipe. Suppose that you want to make brownies, but you have no chocolate. You can substitute cocoa for chocolate if you know how to make the substitution. The *Table of Substitutions* on page 622 shows that instead of one square of chocolate, you can use 3 tablespoons (45 mL) of cocoa plus 1 tablespoon (15 mL) of shortening. This table of substitutions is helpful in meeting emergencies, but it is best to use the exact ingredients listed in a recipe whenever possible. When you substitute one ingredient for another, the results may not be perfect.

### For Review

1. When you divide a cake recipe in half, what changes do you need to make in ingredients? In pan size? In baking time? In baking temperature?
2. How do you divide an egg in half?
3. In what situations will you need to use the *Table of Equivalents?* The *Table of Substitutions?*

# Using a Recipe—A Time-Work Plan

Food preparation begins with planning. The steps in preparing food are to: (1) decide which dishes you want to make; (2) find the recipes; (3) check your supplies; (4) prepare a grocery list; (5) get the ingredients and equipment you need; and (6) establish a time-work plan.

Earlier in this book, you looked at how to create balanced meals, how to select suitable recipes, and how to shop wisely (see Chapters 3, 5, and 8). Now look at the details of preparing individual recipes.

## The Time-Work Plan

A **time-work plan** is a step-by-step guide to preparing a particular recipe. As you can tell from its name, it includes all the activities you must perform and how long they will take.

Make your time-work plan before you need to begin actual food preparation. Always read each recipe for your menu all the way through, and be sure you understand every term. On your time-work plan, list the foods you wish to prepare, the food supplies needed, the steps or activities in preparing the foods, the utensils and equipment needed, the order in which you will perform the activities, and the time required to do them. Note activities and preparation steps that can be done in advance, and decide when to do them. For instance, you may wish to prepare a sauce in advance, refrigerate it, and then heat it just before serving. Also note shortcuts, if any, that might save time or energy. Before you decide to use shortcuts, consider whether they will affect the quality or nutritional value of the meal. For example, you might consider using bottled garlic powder or flakes instead of crushing fresh garlic, or to use canned mushrooms instead of preparing the fresh product.

Also consider **dovetailing,** or fitting several tasks together so they are done at the same time. Foods that bake or roast for a long time must be started well in advance of mealtime, but they usually do not require constant attention. You can be washing, peeling, slicing, and cooking the accompanying vegetables while the meat

## Time-Work Plan

| | |
|---|---|
| Foods to Prepare: | Cocoa Drop Cookies |

| | |
|---|---|
| Food Supplies Needed: | All-purpose flour 1¾ cup (435 mL) |
| | Soda ½ tsp (2.5 mL) |
| | Salt ½ tsp (2.5 mL) |
| | Cocoa ½ c (125 mL) |
| | Shortening ½ c (125 mL) |
| | Sugar 1 c (250 mL) |
| | Egg 1 egg |
| | Buttermilk ¾ c (185 mL) |
| | Vanilla 1 tsp (5 mL) |

| | | |
|---|---|---|
| Utensils Needed: | Set graduated measuring cups | Wooden mixing spoon |
| | Glass measuring cup | Metal spoon to lift flour |
| | Set measuring spoons | and pack shortening |
| | Flour sifter | Teaspoon to drop cookies |
| | Spatula and rubber scraper | 2 cookie sheets |
| | 2 sheets paper for sifting | 2 racks to cool cookies |
| | Medium mixing bowl | Container to store cookies |

Time in Minutes

| Order of Work: | | Time in Minutes |
|---|---|---|
| | 1. Assemble utensils and ingredients. | 3 |
| | 2. Measure all ingredients. | 5 |
| | 3. Set oven at 400° F (200° C); check rack position. | 1 |
| | 4. Mix cookies | 5 |

    a. Soften shortening in bowl with wooden spoon.

    b. Add sugar and egg and beat thoroughly.

    c. Add milk and vanilla and stir.

    d. Sift flour, soda, salt, cocoa into bowl with shortening and stir to blend.

5. Bake cookies

    a. Drop rounded teaspoonfuls of dough on cookie sheet 2 inches (5 cm) apart. Bake 8 to 10 minutes.

    b. As cookies bake, drop dough on second cookie sheet and begin to clean up.

    c. Bake second sheet of cookies. Remove baked cookies to cooling rack. Continue cleanup.

    d. After cooling, store baked cookies in covered jar or container.

| | |
|---|---|
| Approximate Yield: | 50 cookies |
| Total Time: | 39 minutes |

Dovetailing allows you to accomplish several tasks during the same time period. You can keep an eye on a simmering sauce while you cook the pasta, and stir the pasta occasionally while making the salad.

roasts. Dovetailing also works for foods cooked on top of the range. While your sauce is simmering, you can boil water, add salt, add pasta, and stir to prevent sticking. Dovetailing does not mean leaving some foods to cook unattended. Since you will be nearby, doing another food-preparation task, you can keep a watchful eye on the roast or sauce, too.

After you have decided on the time requirements for different preparation tasks, include some time at the beginning of your time-work plan for gathering your equipment and supplies. If you have counter space, it is a good idea to gather all the things you will need before you begin. List times for prepreparation and cooking. Don't forget such things as measuring, slicing, bringing ingredients to room temperature, and preheating or cooling, if necessary.

An example of a time-work plan for making cookies appears on the opposite page. Note that cleanup is included in step 5b, before the cookies are finished. Cleaning up as you work is a good example of dovetailing.

**For Review**

1. What are the six steps in the preparation of food?
2. What are three reasons for reading a recipe all the way through before preparing your time-work plan?
3. What tasks that are not written into recipes should you allow for on your time-work plan? Why?

# 9 Chapter Review

## Summary

Although recipes come in three different styles, they are all based on scientific principles of cookery. Therefore, it is important to follow exactly the directions in a recipe to get perfect results each time. The keys to achieving good results are to measure the ingredients properly and accurately and to follow the techniques called for in the recipe. When it is necessary to substitute an ingredient or to increase or decrease the number of servings, you may need to refer to the Table of Substitutions for ingredients and the Table of Equivalents for measurements. To thoroughly understand all that is called for in a recipe, read it through first and develop a time-work plan before actually preparing the food. A good food manager always plans ahead.

## Vocabulary

dovetailing
liquid displacement
  method
metric system of
  measurement

recipe
standard system of
  measurement
time-work plan
yield

1. A _____ tells you what ingredients to use and how to put them together.
2. In order to know how many servings a recipe will serve, you need to know the _____.
3. A good food manager develops a _____, which gives all the activities that must be performed and how long they will take.
4. When several food preparation tasks can be done at the same time, it is called _____.
5. The _____ uses cups, tablespoons, and teaspoons to measure ingredients.
6. Liters and grams are used for ingredients in the _____.
7. A method of measuring solid shortening by the amount of water it moves out of the way is the _____.

## Chapter Questions

1. How can you be a good cook and have good results from following recipes?
2. Why are recipes important?
3. When you read a recipe, what are five things you should know?
4. Why should you pay close attention to the cooking times and temperatures given for ingredients in a recipe?
5. Determine which format of the recipe for coleslaw on page 201 you would find easiest to follow. Support your decision.
6. When you find several recipes for the same food, what are six things you should consider before selecting the one to follow?
7. Why are exact measurements important to good recipe results?
8. What is the correct way to measure one cup of liquid?
9. Why is it important to understand the terms of cookery techniques in following a recipe?
10. What is the proper term used in recipes for each of these techniques?

a. to mix with an over-and-over motion using a spoon
b. to mix with a circular motion using a spoon
c. to cook under direct heat
d. to tear or cut into thin pieces
e. to cook in an uncovered pan in a small amount of fat

**11.** Make a time-work plan for preparing cole-slaw according to the recipes on page 201.

# Skill Activities

**1. Critical thinking** The next time you plan to follow a recipe, write in your food journal the date and then the time-work plan you will follow. After you have prepared the food, record how you applied the principles of good cookery when you followed the recipe. For example, tell how you read the recipe carefully, assembled the equipment and ingredients before hand, measured the ingredients, used the cooking techniques called for, and cooked the ingredients according to the recommended times and temperatures.

**2. Resource management** Practice using flour, shortening, sugar, and water using the recommended measuring techniques. Use the 1 cup (250 mL), ½ cup (125 mL), and 1 tablespoon (15 mL) for each ingredient. If metric measures are available, measure sugar and flour in grams and deciliters and water in milliliters and deciliters.

**3. Math** Determine how you would modify this recipe to feed two people:
Waldorf Salad
Wash 2 medium-sized apples and 4 celery stalks. Quarter, core, and cut apples into bite-sized pieces. Then place them into a bowl. Add ¾ cup (185 mL) diced celery, ¼ cup (60 mL) coarsely chopped walnuts, and 3 tablespoons (45 mL) cooked salad dressing or mayonnaise, and toss gently with a fork to mix. Arrange salad on 4 lettuce cups.

**4. Reading** In a file box or in your food journal, make a collection of different recipes for sugar cookies, chocolate cake, and roast beef. Examine cookbooks, magazines, newspapers, and other publications to find these recipes. How do the styles of writing for the recipes differ? How do the ingredients for the same kind of recipe differ? Do the yields differ? What cookery terms are used? Which recipes would you choose to follow? Why?

**5. Communication** Write to the Consumer Information Center, P.O. Box 100, Pueblo, Colorado 81002 for a catalog that lists the many publications about food and nutrition that are available from the U.S. government. Or, if a federal bookstore is located in your area, visit it and report your findings to the class.

# 10 Microwave Cookery

## As you read, think about:

- how microwave cooking is different from conventional cooking.
- what techniques and utensils should be used in microwave cooking.
- what factors affect cooking time.
- how to use the microwave for several foods on a menu.
- what special precautions and care are required for microwave ovens.

## Microwave Magic

Today's microwave cooking — speedy, cool, clean, and energy efficient — opens up a new world of excitement and challenge. That's not to say short cooking times inhibit a relaxed, creative approach to cooking; and don't think you have to forget what you already know about cooking. You're simply adding another dimension.

### WHY COOK WITH MICROWAVES?

Microwave cooking saves time — when you're cooking from scratch, when you're thawing frozen foods, and when you're reheating previously cooked foods. Many foods cook by microwaves in about a quarter of the time it would take conventionally. But not all foods cook well in the microwave. Very large quantities, foods that need time to absorb water (like rice and pasta), and foods that need to simmer a long time to become tender are best left to conventional methods.

Not only do many foods cook faster in the microwave, but they also retain more color, flavor, and texture. You'll especially appreciate the way the microwave cooks vegetables — they emerge bright, flavorful, and tender-crisp. Moreover, there's a greater retention of nutrients, especially water soluble vitamins, in microwave cooking.

Since the ov[...]
minimally fro[...]
blast of hot ai[...]
to check or rer[...]
won't have ar[...]
mer day.
Cool cookin[...]
don't burn on [...]
any) doesn't h[...]
most foods are[...]
there are rare[...]
as an added [...]
save energy [...]

### HOW DOES [...]

To understand [...]
to know how it [...]
wave oven is t[...]
verts ordinary [...]
frequency micro[...]
ignated by the F[...]
mission for use i[...]
megahertz. This [...]
2½ billion times p[...]
When the microw[...]
they're distributed [...]
These waves are eit[...]
through, or absorbed[...]
Metal reflects microwa[...]

material and stirrer fan are made [...]
Glass, pottery, paper, plastic, and [...]
[...] through —

4  Introduction

Throughout history, people have cooked foods by placing them directly on or near heat sources. Improvements—from pots, pans, and rotisseries to ranges and ovens—have always used this process. For example, the range burner or coil gets hot itself and heats the pan and the food, or the oven is made hot and the food is heated by being placed inside it. Until the development of microwave ovens, the basic procedures of cookery remained much the same.

As you will see in this chapter, microwave cooking is different. Food gets hot and is cooked by a completely different process in a microwave oven. Thus, microwaving requires different techniques and utensils, special precautions, and different considerations in meal planning. Many people use and enjoy microwave cookery. However, as with any new process, you should be sure you understand its similarities to and differences from conventional cooking before you decide if, when, how often, and for what foods you want to use the microwave method.

From ancient bonfires, to cooking hearths (above), to ranges, food has been cooked by placing it on or near a heat source.

## Microwaving—A Revolution in Cooking

Food requires much less time to cook in a microwave oven than in or on a conventional range. In a conventional range, the heat from a hot burner or a hot oven is transferred to the food. In microwave cooking, the heat is produced directly within the food by microwaves. The **microwaves** are a form of electromagnetic energy much like that of heat, light, or radio waves. A magnatron tube within the oven produces the microwaves, and a stirrer or a fan distributes the microwaves throughout the oven. The microwaves penetrate the food and cause the molecules of the food to vibrate rapidly, thus creating heat. (A **molecule** is the smallest particle of a substance that retains the proper-

ties of the substance.) A microwave oven does not get hot while it is in use. Any heat you notice inside the oven or in a baking dish comes from the food. The microwave cooking process is very quick. Some foods are cooked in several minutes; others in only a few seconds. One cup (250 mL) of liquid at room temperature, for example, heats in about one minute and comes to a boil in about two minutes in a microwave oven.

### Microwave Ovens

Microwave ovens that meet federal standards and are operated according to manufacturer's directions are safe. Most microwave ovens come with a recipe book which includes the same kinds of recipes as other recipe books, but it gives the required microwave cooking time

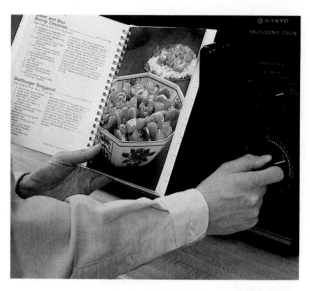

For best results, always follow the cooking as well as use-and-care directions for your particular model microwave oven.

instead of the temperature setting and cooking time for a conventional oven.

The first microwave ovens had a rotating timer and a single power level. All foods were cooked with high power. Foods such as breads, cakes, meats, and casseroles cooked, but they did not brown as they do in a conventional oven.

Today some ovens combine conventional electric elements and microwave units. This makes it possible to have the advantage of fast cooking and browning, too.

**Microwave Oven Features** We now realize that high power is not suitable for all microwave cooking. Several power settings are now available on almost all microwave ovens. You can select the recommended power setting by pushing a button, rotating a dial, or selecting a numbered setting. Computerized controls allow you to select a number of complex processes or operations.

When microwave ovens were first developed, time was the only variable in microwave cookery. A number of microwave ovens now come with a temperature probe. The probe is inserted into the food to be cooked and then connected to the electrical system of the oven. The probe senses the internal temperature of the food. When the preselected temperature is reached, the microwave power is turned off. Some microwave ovens have a humidity sensor that measures the level of moisture being given off by the food as it cooks. Other ovens may have microwaves enter from both sides of the oven cavity. This gives more cooking area and also permits several foods to be cooked at the same time.

## Microwave Cookery Terms

Microwaves give you a new way to cook foods. They also require a new vocabulary. You should be sure you understand the terms used to describe particular microwave procedures in order to make successful microwave meals.

**Arcing:** a spark caused by a discharge of static electricity. This occurs between separated particles of metal (metal trim on dishes or metal twists for plastic bags).

**Bursting:** a buildup of steam in foods, causing the outer surface or skin to break open. This may occur in foods that are enclosed in a skin, membrane, or shell (such as fruits, vegetables, poultry, and eggs).

**Cooking Time:** the time required to heat or cook foods to serving temperature.

**Overcooking:** cooking foods for so long that they become dried out or toughened. Hard spots may form, and some sauces may separate.

**Puncturing:** breaking the skin or membrane of foods or a plastic bag or cover to allow steam to escape.

**Reheating:** bringing cooked food to serving temperature.

**Rehydrating:** replacing water or liquid removed from food.

Microwave cooking requires some special procedures and precautions. One procedure is puncturing this plastic cooking bag in its safe-to-microwave foil-type container. What is the reason for puncturing the bag?

transfer the microwaves to the food. If this does not happen, the food will not be cooked.

**Materials for Microwave Utensils**
Metal reflects microwaves. The walls of a microwave oven are metal to reflect the microwaves toward the oven cavity where the food is placed. Metal utensils should not be used in microwave cooking because they reflect the microwaves, preventing them from both reaching and cooking the food.

**Practical Tip**

• To restore crystallized honey to its liquid state, put it in the microwave for 30–40 seconds on the high power setting.

**Rotating:** turning a container or a whole food one-quarter to one-half turn for more even cooking.
**Resting or Standing:** the time suggested to allow the heat in the food to spread to the center of the food, either during or after cooking.
**Turning:** turning over or inverting a food such as meat during cooking.
**Trivet:** an inverted cover or dish to elevate foods above the cooking liquid (used with meats or poultry).
**Undercooking:** cooking food to a less-than-done stage and using standing time to complete the cooking.
**Utensils:** any dishes or containers used to hold food in a microwave oven.

## Utensils for Microwaving

Microwaves have a distinct nature. Some materials absorb microwaves; others transfer or reflect them. Foods absorb microwaves and are cooked by them if the cooking utensils you use

Some traditional cookware is not suitable for microwaving, but the types below are. Name some of these materials.

Glass, paper, and some plastics transfer microwaves. China or pottery containers can be used if they have no gold or silver trim, design, or printing anywhere on them. It is best to test any ceramic utensils before using them for microwave cooking. You can easily check the suitability of a utensil by measuring 1 cup (250 mL) of water into a glass measuring cup and then placing the cup into the dish, casserole, or other container to be tested in the microwave oven. Heat the oven on full power for 1 minute and 15 seconds. At the end of that time, only the water should be warm. The dish should be cool. If the dish is slightly warm or is hot in spots and the water is cool, do not use the container in the microwave oven.

Several materials and types of utensils can be used in the microwave. Glass and glass-ceramic containers, trivets, and covers are used for microwave cooking. The containers can also be used in a conventional oven. Food may be cooked and served from them.

Paper serves as a light cover to hold in steam, avoid spatter, and absorb grease during microwave cooking. Plastic-coated paper products may be used for juicy foods.

Foam cups and plates are good for thawing and heating foods, while heavy-duty plastic film serves as an adjustable cover. Both cooking and freezer bags hold in steam and moisture. They should be pierced with a knife to permit release of steam. Some plastic containers change shape with high heat or high-fat foods.

## How to Select Microwave Utensils

Utensils can influence the results of microwave cooking. When you select utensils for microwave cooking, consider the following points.

1. **Material.** The material of which the container is made should be sturdy and durable. Of course, the material should be suitable for microwave use.

2. **Shape and design.** Utensils in which meat loaf, casseroles, and quick breads are baked should be round and deep enough to contain the vigorous activity within the food that is being cooked. Deep wells at the sides or ends of utensils (in trays and racks) catch drippings that attract the microwaves. The length of time required to cook the food in such containers will be increased, since the microwaves enter the food from the sides, top, and bottom. Therefore these utensils should not be used.

3. **Versatility.** Utensils should generally be useful in preparation of several different foods.

4. **Ease of handling.** The utensil should be easy to handle when filled with food or when it is hot. The handle on the utensil should make it easy to move the utensil about.

5. **Microwave label.** Look for labels that indicate that the utensil is approved for microwave cooking. Be sure to follow the manufacturer's recommendation for the use of each utensil.

### Covers for Microwave Cooking

Foods cooked in a microwave are often covered to retain steam, or to avoid drying or spattering. Porous, light, tight utensil covers should be used. A cover may be used during both cooking and standing time. Paper towels or napkins are porous covers that permit steam to escape. They may be used to warm sandwiches and to cover bacon. A light cover such as waxed paper holds in steam and may be used to cover meats (such as poultry, hamburger, and roasts) and fruits. A tight cover holds in steam and is used when vegetables or fish are cooked. A plastic film cover can be turned back slightly or pricked to permit venting (escape of steam). Utensil covers hold in steam and are used for vegetables, saucy casseroles, and meats that require moisture and heat to tenderize.

In order to retain steam and to avoid spattering or drying out, many foods are covered when cooked in a microwave. What materials make suitable covers? Why?

**Microwave Thermometers** A thermometer is the best way to judge the doneness of meat. Microwave thermometers are now available and can be inserted into foods to be cooked by microwaves. Most regular cooking thermometers contain mercury, which may cause arcing in the microwave oven. Therefore, do not use a regular cooking thermometer in a microwave oven.

## Uses of Microwaves

You may use microwaves for cooking, reheating, and defrosting foods. Microwaves produce instant heat within foods, but many times this heat penetrates only a portion of the food. The rest of the food is heated by **conduction** (heat moving from the outside to the center). Conduction can occur in any of the three uses of microwaves.

**Cooking** The heat of cooking changes the flavor, texture, consistency, and appearance of foods. Microwaves easily produce the desired degree of doneness in quick-cooking foods. How-

ever, when a food requires a long period of cooking due to its size and density, it may be difficult to control the rate of cooking for the quality of product you want. For some of the long-cooking foods, you may prefer to use a conventional range in which it is easier to control the speed of cooking.

**Heating** Foods that have been cooked previously become hot but do not change in texture or appearance. You will find microwaves generally satisfactory for heating foods and reconstituting convenience foods. The porous foods (such as breads, cakes, and pastries) and those with a high fat or high sugar content heat through very quickly. Dense foods heat through more slowly than do porous foods. You may need to help distribute the heat throughout dense foods by stirring, rearranging, or allowing such foods to stand for a short time at the end of cooking to permit the heat to move from the outside toward the center of the food. In this way you avoid overcooking the edges.

As you increase the volume or amount of

Many people find microwave ovens especially useful for quick reheating of leftovers or home-prepared frozen foods as well as for preparing store-bought frozen items.

kg) portion of ground beef will defrost in about 5 minutes, and most of the juices will be retained. Large pieces of meat (over 5 pounds (2.25 kg)) require standing time after defrosting to assure even cooking.

### For Review

1. When a microwave oven is on, which of these should get hot: the inside of the oven, the utensils, or the food? Why?
2. How does a microwave probe work?
3. What material(s) should be used as microwave utensils? Why? Which material(s) should not? Why?
4. What are four types of covers used for microwave cooking, and what are their specialized purposes?
5. Why shouldn't you use a regular cooking thermometer in a microwave oven?
6. Why is a microwave oven particularly good for defrosting?

food, the time required to cook or reheat the item also increases. Twice as much food takes nearly twice as much time to cook.

**Defrosting**   When frozen food is defrosted, microwaves change ice to water. The frozen food is defrosted slowly so that the food does not become hot and begin to cook on the outside before the center has thawed. Most microwave ovens have low power settings (10 percent of total power) to allow quick defrosting. Alternating heating and standing times permits the heat to be conducted to the center of the food without any cooking at the outer edges. Many microwave ovens now include an automatic defrost feature.

Porous items such as breads, cakes, and pastries thaw quickly. Dense items such as meats or casseroles require a longer time for the center to defrost. A standing time is needed to defrost the center without outer-edge cooking. If cooking begins, decrease the microwave time and increase the standing time. A 1-pound (.45

## Cooking Successfully in a Microwave Oven

Microwave cooking techniques and directions differ from those of conventional cookery. For example, microwave cooking depends on power level and time, while conventional cooking depends on temperature and time. In addition, some foods require special procedures during microwave cooking in order to turn out successfully. Many foods that must be stirred, turned, covered, or rearranged during microwaving would not require this special attention in a conventional oven. On the other hand, microwaving almost always takes much less time than conventional cooking.

# Caution! Microwave Cooking and Pork

Caution! The U.S. Department of Agriculture advises that microwaving pork may not effectively destroy trichinae, the roundworm that causes the illness trichinosis. Trichinosis is a food-borne illness characterized by respiratory and digestive problems, pain and swelling in the muscles, and fever.

Live trichinae are found in 1 out of 800 hogs in the United States. A recent USDA study showed that the trichinae can survive quick-cooking methods including microwaving, char-broiling, and deep-fat frying. In order to destroy the trichinae, all parts of the pork have to reach a temperature of 170° F (77° C). The problem in a home kitchen is that it is hard to tell if the heat has distributed evenly throughout the meat. For this reason, the USDA suggests cooking pork by other methods.

However, the National Livestock and Meat Board and other experts suggest that if proper cooking procedures are followed, microwave cookery of pork is safe. Follow these guidelines for microwaving boneless pork roasts:

1. Cook a roast that is evenly shaped and no more than 3.5 pounds (1.6 kg) in weight or 4 inches (10 cm) in diameter.
2. Put the roast into a 10 × 16 inch (25 × 40 cm) cooking bag, and place it in a microwave-safe baking dish.
3. For proper browning, sprinkle the roast evenly with gravy mix.
4. Tie the bag loosely with a string, and cook the roast 22 minutes for each pound at medium-low power.
5. Turn the roast over halfway through the cooking time, and rotate the dish one-half turn; then continue cooking.
6. Leave the roast in the bag, cover it tightly with foil, and allow it to stand for 10 minutes before serving.

Although the USDA suggests cooking pork by conventional methods, pork, such as this boneless roast, can be microwaved if certain precautions are taken.

## Regulating Cooking Time

The power level and the time that you select will control the cooking that occurs. Although the specific power settings vary among the microwave ovens, they range from high to low. When your microwave oven is set on high, it is using full power, or about 650 watts. A medium-high setting uses 75 percent of full power; a medium setting uses 50 percent; a medium-low setting, 30 percent; and a low setting, 10 percent.

## Factors Affecting Cooking Time

Remember, microwaves penetrate only to a depth of 1 to 1 1/2 inches (2.5 to 3.8 cm), and the distribution of heat to the rest of a large amount of food is by conduction. Thus, the cooking time that a food will require is determined not only by the starting temperature of that food but also by its volume, density, moisture content, fat and sugar content, and shape.

**Starting Temperature** Foods at room temperature need less cooking time than do those at refrigerator temperature. Frozen items require the most time. In other words, the colder the food, the longer it will take to cook or to heat.

**Volume** The larger the size or quantity of food, or the number of food items, the longer the cooking, heating, or defrosting time will be in a microwave oven. In other words, the time increases in proportion to the number of pieces and the size or volume of the food.

**Density** The internal structure of foods varies according to how many molecules occupy a given space. The more molecules there are per square inch of food, the more dense, or compact, the food is.

Microwaves penetrate dense or solid foods more slowly than they penetrate porous foods,

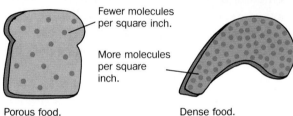

Fewer molecules per square inch.

More molecules per square inch.

Porous food.                    Dense food.

Dense foods have more molecules per square inch than porous foods. Therefore, it takes longer for microwaves to penetrate to the center of dense foods, such as meats, than it does for them to penetrate porous foods, such as bread.

which have fewer molecules per square inch. Therefore, the cooking, heating, and defrosting times are greater for denser foods. Light, porous foods such as cakes, pastries, and breads absorb microwaves faster than do more compact, moist foods of the same weight. The porous foods require only a few seconds to heat or to thaw.

Because the density of various foods is different, it is very difficult to state definite cooking times. To speed the cooking, heating, or defrosting of dense foods, you can help to distribute the heat within the food by stirring or rearranging it, or by including a short standing period at the end of cooking. This allows the heat to reach the center of the food. Always remember to consider the density of a food when you estimate the cooking time.

**Moisture Content** Water and foods with a high water content require more energy to reach the desired temperature than do similar amounts of foods with a lower moisture content. In other words, the higher the moisture content, the longer the cooking time will be.

**Fat and Sugar** Fat and sugar are heated quickly with microwaves. Foods that contain a high proportion of fat or sugar require less time to heat than do foods without fat or sugar. For example, the frosting on a sweet roll becomes hot before the roll is heated, and the side of the meat next to the fat heats more quickly than the side away from the fat. For these reasons, always consider the fat and sugar content of a food when determining the cooking, heating, and defrosting times.

**Shape** Flat, thin foods heat faster than thick, chunky foods. Before microwaving, you should make the pieces of a food as uniform as possible in size and shape. Whenever possible, arrange the foods in a circular shape, or form them into a rounded shape. Use round-shaped utensils whenever possible to avoid the overcooking that occurs in the corners of rectangular utensils.

## Techniques Affecting Cooking Time

In order to produce quality foods by microwave cookery, you should understand the proper techniques to follow when cooking foods by this method. Several of the techniques you will use are the same ones that you use in conventional cooking, but some are particular to microwave cookery. Many of these techniques are used either to speed cooking or to promote even cooking. They include stirring or rearranging, covering food, and using standing time. It is important to use these special techniques when microwaving in order to achieve the best results in the finished product. If you use your microwave oven as though it were merely a fast conventional oven, you will be disappointed in the results.

**Stirring and Rearranging** Stirring is necessary in microwave cooking to redistribute the heat within some foods. Nearly all microwave recipes tell you when and how many times to stir. Stirring or rearranging moves the warmer food from the outside toward the center, and the colder food from the center to the outside. In this way, the heat is distributed more evenly. Casseroles, puddings, and sauces are foods that require stirring. If you are using less than full power level, less stirring is necessary. Foods that cannot be stirred should be rearranged for even heating. Whole vegetables, pieces of chicken, baked potatoes, and cupcakes are examples of foods that require rearranging. Foods that are cooked covered or at less than full power settings require less rearranging.

**Turning** Turning is the technique to use when foods cannot be stirred or rearranged. Meats and poultry, for example, can be turned over to redistribute the heat within the food. Cakes, pies, and soufflés (soo-FLAYZ) are often repositioned by rotating or turning the dish a quarter or half turn. If less than full power is called for, then less turning—or rotating and repositioning—is necessary.

**Covering** Covering is necessary for many foods to retain steam and to speed cooking, heating, or defrosting. It also helps to prevent dehydration (drying out) and spattering. A lid, an inverted plate, or plastic wrap can be used to provide a tight cover that retains both moisture and heat. Plastic covers, however, should not touch the hot food. Paper napkins and towels provide a loose cover and permit moisture from the food to escape. They are absorbent and can help prevent food from spattering on oven walls. A cover can be used during cooking as well as during standing time, since the food continues to cook after removal from the oven.

Many foods must be rearranged to heat or cook evenly in a microwave. Casseroles can be stirred (top), baked potatoes or other single items can be rearranged, and pies or cakes can be rotated.

**Standing Time** Standing time after the food is removed from the oven allows the heat from the outside of the cooked food to reach the center of the food without overcooking the outer edges. It is most useful for dense foods because they retain heat longer than porous foods.

## Cooking Foods Together

When more than one food is to be prepared in the microwave oven, heating time must be carefully considered. Select foods with the same moisture content. Plan to use the same quantity of each food so that all foods can be successfully heated at the same time. If the foods are somewhat different, you must consider placement, size and shape, use of a cover, and the initial temperature in order to heat such combinations successfully. Here are some suggestions that you can apply when you are trying to heat foods and combinations of foods. Attention to these rules means better results.

1. **Placement.** Place the foods with the shortest heating time (low moisture, high fat, high sugar) in the center of the utensil, with the smallest parts of the food nearest the center.
2. **Size and shape of portion.** Flat and thin foods heat more quickly than chunky, thick foods. Flat, doughnut-shaped foods heat most uniformly. Try to slice foods into similar shapes. Reduce the size of portions; make two portions out of one.
3. **Cover use.** Most foods should be covered to avoid drying. Breaded and crisp products may be left uncovered to avoid sogginess. All foods should stand about 1 minute before removing the cover.
4. **Initial temperature.** Allow more heating time for refrigerated foods than for room-temperature foods.
5. **Additions.** To make up for the somewhat longer cooking time of a particular food, add other foods later in the cooking period. Put them in the plate or container with the food that requires a longer heating time, or place them on separate side dishes.

Adjustable shelves are available for microwave ovens. The use of such shelves can make it easier to prepare several foods or to prepare complete meals at one time. This helps conserve both electrical and personal energy.

## For Review

1. What characteristics of a food determine the length of time needed for it to cook, heat, or defrost?
2. Which foods cook more quickly in a microwave: dense or porous foods? Moist or dry foods? Foods high in fat or sugar, or foods low in fat or sugar?
3. Are round utensils or rectangular utensils better for microwave cooking? Why?
4. Why do many foods cooked in microwave ovens require stirring, rearranging, or turning? What does standing time accomplish?
5. What are three benefits of covering foods during microwaving?
6. What shape foods heat most uniformly?

Cooking with a microwave oven does not mean giving up your favorite recipes. With planning and thought, conventional recipes can be adapted for use in the microwave.

# Special Considerations for Microwaving

Because a microwave oven uses a completely different method of cooking, you will have to make certain adjustments in the way you cook and plan meals when you microwave. You will also have to take special precautions in using your microwave oven, and care for it differently than a conventional oven.

## Adjusting Recipes

While there are more and more microwave recipes available, it is also possible to adapt conventional recipes to microwaving. When you do decide to adapt a recipe for microwave preparation, you must consider the nature and density of the food to be prepared, as well as its moisture, fat, and sugar content; initial temperature; and volume. Then you must apply the appropriate microwave techniques of stirring, covering, and standing time.

When you cook any of your adapted conventional recipes, set the timer for somewhat less than the time you believe is needed. You can always cook a food a few seconds or minutes longer to complete cooking, but you cannot change a food once it has been overcooked. Microwaved foods are generally cooked in about one-quarter of conventional cooking time.

## Convenience Foods

Some convenience foods may give instructions for microwave cooking. Follow these directions, but plan to undercook when you prepare the food for the first time. Allowing a few extra seconds or minutes to complete the cooking process can give you a perfectly cooked—not overcooked—product.

Although all microwave ovens operate on the same basic principles, there are specific characteristics for each brand. For this reason, it may be difficult to give one optimal cooking time for all microwave ovens.

A number of foods are packaged in materials that are not suitable for microwaving. These foods should be removed from their packaging and cooked in approved utensils. Because of the popularity of microwave cooking, more and

Many convenience foods give directions for microwave preparation as well as for conventional cooking. There are even convenience products made especially for microwave ovens.

more foods are being packaged in microwave-approved containers. Read labels on all packages, and look for microwave cooking instructions.

## Menu Planning

As with any other menus, menus for microwaving should be nutritious, colorful, and pleasing in texture and flavor. Best results are achieved when you observe the rules of microwave cookery. Energy is also used to the best advantage when these rules are followed.

You will probably develop preferences for certain foods prepared by microwave and others prepared by conventional means. Your preferences can be organized into meals that use both cookery techniques.

Time is always an important factor in cookery. You have to consider time carefully even when you microwave. Microwave cookery is fast. Although several foods may be cooked together in the microwave oven, the heating may not be even. Some foods attract more microwaves than others. Microwave meal preparation in most ovens requires **sequential cooking;** that is, cooking one food item after the other. Cooking in sequence requires careful planning. You have to consider serving temperature, cooking times, how long foods will remain hot, and how easily a particular food reheats.

Foods that are usually cooked first include large cuts of meat, casseroles, and foods that have been partially cooked. Small meat items, eggs, vegetables, and sauces are usually cooked near serving time. Breads and foods cooked previously but which have to be reheated before serving are cooked last because they require only a short time.

Complete meals can be prepared easily in the microwave oven when they are well planned. Begin with simple meals for breakfast or lunch. As you gain skill, you can plan and prepare more complicated meals in the microwave oven.

## Precautions with Microwaves

Although microwave ovens are designed to be safe and reliable, as with all appliances, you must know how to operate a microwave oven if you are to use it successfully. There are certain precautions or safety tips that you must also know. As you use a microwave oven, put these safety rules into practice.

1. Pierce skins of whole fruits and vegetables such as apples or potatoes before cooking. This permits steam to escape during the cooking and keeps the fruits or vegetables from bursting.
2. Do not cook or reheat eggs in the shell. Always pierce the yolk with the tip of a knife or fork before cooking to avoid bursting. Finely chop cooked eggs before reheating.
3. Pierce or open plastic and other airtight containers before heating to permit the escape of steam during cooking.
4. Liquids should be stirred or poured just before heating to mix in air and avoid eruption in the oven.

5. Extreme overcooking in both conventional and microwave ovens can cause foods to catch on fire. Should this happen in a microwave oven, push the stop button and leave the door closed until the fire is extinguished.

6. Do not use or prepare certain items in a microwave oven.

**a.** Do not pop ordinary popcorn. Special popcorn in bags designed for microwave use is available.

**b.** Do not use containers with restricted openings, such as baby food jars or syrup or catsup bottles. Rapid expansion could cause the containers to burst.

**c.** Metal cookware increases cooking time, decreases microwave efficiency, causes uneven cooking and arcing, and can damage the magnatron tube. Avoid all metal objects, including decorations on cookware.

**d.** Microwave canning is not recommended. The metal lids reflect microwaves. This interferes with the uniform heating of the food in the jars and leads to food spoilage.

**e.** Newspapers and recycled paper should not be used in a microwave oven. Some printer's inks absorb microwaves and may cause the paper to burn. Recycled paper products may contain small pieces of metal which could cause

the paper to catch fire. Paper toweling, which is sometimes reinforced with manufactured fiber such as nylon, is also likely to burn.

## Care of Microwave Oven

The microwave oven requires little care. Any spatter on the stainless steel sides is easily cleaned with a mild detergent in warm water and a cloth or soft sponge. Abrasives should never be used for cleaning a microwave oven. Cooking vapors and spattered foods do not bake onto the oven surface since the microwave oven interior is never heated like that of the conventional oven.

The glass tray on the oven bottom is easily removed. Wash it in warm water and detergent. The drip tray must be put back in place correctly. Never operate the oven without the drip tray in position.

The use-and-care manual contains the best advice for the operation and care of your particular microwave oven. Proper care means longer service and better cooking results. Always follow directions carefully when you use and clean the appliance.

Microwaves are easy to clean; their interiors do not get hot so spills do not bake on. Follow the manufacturer's directions.

## For Review

1. Microwaved foods are generally cooked in approximately what fraction of conventional cooking time?
2. Why is it better to estimate too little cooking time rather than too much?
3. What factors must you consider for sequential cooking in a microwave?
4. What foods should be pierced before being microwaved? Why?
5. What should you do if a fire starts in your microwave oven?
6. Why don't cooking vapors and spattered foods bake onto the inside of a microwave oven?

# 10 Chapter Review

## Summary

For centuries, people cooked food on or near a source of heat. However, the development of the microwave oven has made it possible for food to be heated quickly by a completely different process. When a microwave oven is operating, the microwaves cause the molecules within the food to rub against each other and thereby produce heat. When the microwave oven is used for cooking, it is important to follow certain procedures and techniques and to use the recommended utensils. Starting temperature, size and shape, density, and content of the food as well as the kind of cooking technique desired are important considerations by a meal manager prior to cooking food in a microwave oven. Microwave ovens meet federal standards, are safe to operate when the manufacturer's directions are followed, and provide reliable service and better cooking results when they are maintained properly and kept clean.

## Vocabulary

Use the vocabulary words below to fill in the blanks in the sentences that follow.

conduction          molecule
microwaves          sequential cooking

1. In microwave cooking, the heat is produced directly within the food by _____, which are a form of electromagnetic energy very much like that of heat, light, or radio waves.

2. The microwaves penetrate the food, which gets heated by the action of each food _____ vibrating rapidly.

3. However, because microwaves do not go deeply into food, the distribution of heat from the outside to the center of a large piece of food is by _____.

4. Since some foods attract more microwaves than others, it is often not practical to cook foods together; instead _____, which means cooking one food item after the other, is preferred.

## Chapter Questions

1. Why is high power not right for all microwave cooking?
2. What is the proper term for each of the following microwave procedures?
   a. breaking the skin or membrane of foods or a plastic bag to allow steam to escape
   b. turning a container or a whole food one-quarter to one-half turn for more even heating
   c. the time required to heat or cook foods to serving temperature
   d. the time suggested to allow the heat in the food to spread to the center of the food, either during or after cooking
3. How can you tell if a utensil is suitable for use in a microwave oven?
4. If you have, or could have, a microwave oven in your family, what would you pri-

marily use it for, and what kinds of food would you cook in it?

5. How can utensils influence the results of microwave cooking?
6. Why is standing time often required with dense foods?
7. Why is it better to cook a 10 pound roast beef in a conventional oven instead of a microwave oven?
8. Why do you need to stir, rearrange, or allow food to stand for a short time at the end of cooking when you use the microwave oven?
9. Why do breads and cakes thaw more quickly than meats or casseroles?
10. How do microwave cooking techniques and directions differ from those of conventional cookery?
11. When you use a microwave oven, why should you consider the density of the food when you estimate cooking time?
12. What kinds of adjustments should a food manager make to the cooking and planning of meals when a microwave oven is used?

## Skill Activities

**1. Decision making** In your food journal or in a card file box, start a collection of recipes that use the microwave oven. You can find recipes in magazines and newspapers, on the packages of convenience foods, and on the display boards in supermarkets. Organize your collection into sections that cover beverages, soups, meats, fish, poultry, casseroles, vegetables, fruits, and desserts. You may also wish to have a special section for low-calorie foods.

**2. Decision making** Visit the appliance section of a large department store where the microwave ovens are on display. Look at the EnergyGuide labels and compare prices and features of the models. What is the range of prices? How much more does the most expensive model cost than the lowest priced model? What features are offered on the most expensive model? On the lowest priced model? Which model or models are the most energy efficient? If you were to purchase a microwave oven for your family, which model would you choose? Give reasons to support your decision.

**3. Reading** Visit a supermarket and read the labels of convenience foods that require cooking. Find at least 3 products that give directions for microwave cooking. Write the name of each product and the directions for microwaving.

**4. Math** Place a cup of water in a microwave oven, and pour a cup of water into a pot on the stove. Bring the water to boiling. How long did it take the water to boil in the microwave oven? How long did it take on the stove?

# 11 Table Service

## As you read, think about:

- how to choose and care for table linens, dinnerware, tableware, and glassware.
- how to set a table.
- when to use the different kinds of meal service.
- how to wait on table.
- how to practice good manners at the table.

### Vocabulary

place setting
tableware
flatware
holloware
cover
meal service
plate service
family service
modified English
  service
compromise
  service
buffet service
formal service
table etiquette

You participate in some of the different aspects of table service each time you eat a meal. You need to know the proper way to use the implements and how to practice good table manners. Often, you will need to set the table for company, for your family, or even just for yourself. Occasionally you will wait on table, and you should know how to do this smoothly and comfortably. Actually, all the "rules" in this chapter are designed to make dining a pleasurable experience for everyone involved. When each individual at the table understands the principles of table setting, the styles of meal service, and the rules of table etiquette, no one is made to feel uncertain about what to expect or what to do. Then everyone can relax and enjoy the good food and the good company.

# Table Setting

Mealtime pleasure begins when you serve a well-prepared meal on an attractively set table. Whether you set a table for a family meal or for dinner guests, the principles of table setting are the same. They are based upon the comfort and convenience of those dining.

In order to create an attractive and comfortable setting for a meal, all implements that diners will use are neatly arranged on a table covering. This covering adds to the decoration as well as the protection of the table. The implements, including dinnerware, tableware, holloware, and glassware, are arranged to be reached easily, to be used conveniently, and to contribute to the appeal of the overall table setting.

## Table Linens

Since the table covering provides the background upon which you arrange the dinnerware, tableware, and glassware, it should always be clean and wrinkle-free. You can choose a table covering from among place mats, full-length tablecloths, and runners. These coverings now come in a variety of materials, from traditional lace and linen to easy-care plastic, paper, and no-iron, stain-resistant fabric. These are all referred to as "table linens" because, until recently, only linen was considered proper for table coverings. Today, however, you have many styles and materials to choose from in order to create the kind of atmosphere you want for a particular meal.

Traditions of table service and etiquette differ from culture to culture. Would you feel comfortable dining in this Tibetan tent? How might the Tibetans react to dinner at your house?

Rectangular place mats should be placed about 1 inch (2.5 cm) from the edge of the table.

For the most attractive table setting, use a smoothly pressed cloth of the correct size. The overhang should be 12–15 inches (30–38 cm) on each side. An ironed-in center crease is acceptable. A table pad under the cloth will protect your table.

A round place mat may touch the table edge. Leave enough room between mats so diners will be comfortable.

**Types of Table Linens**   Tablecloths are the most traditional coverings for a table. When you use a tablecloth, the hem should be straight and parallel with the floor. The cloth should be centered so the total overhang of 12–15 inches (30–38 cm) is even on both sides and ends. A tablecloth without any creases gives the best appearance, but you may use a cloth with a lengthwise center fold ironed in. It is a good idea to use a silence cloth or table pad under the tablecloth to protect the table.

Place mats are used without a silence cloth and are placed in the center of the space allowed for each person. Put rectangular mats about 1 inch (2.5 cm) from the table edge, or even with it. Place round mats so that the bottom of the circle is even with the table edge. Arrange the dishes and flatware on the mat. You may use place mats for family meals, informal guest meals, and entertaining.

Runners are long, narrow pieces of fabric that are arranged to "run" the length of a table. They do not cover the area of the place settings, so place mats are often used with them.

Napkins can be coordinated with any of the table covers. They are often sold in sets to match a tablecloth, runner, or set of place mats. Choices range from formal white linen napkins to colorful wash-and-wear fabric types to paper napkins, which are thrown away after being used.

**Selecting and Caring for Table Linens**   There are several factors to consider when you select table linens. One is the "look" or atmosphere you wish to create. Linens should coordinate attractively with your dinnerware, tableware, and glassware, as well as with the furnishings and decorations already in the room where they will be used. Color and pattern are not the only considerations. The level of formality is important, too. Heirloom bone china, sterling, and crystal will look all wrong on a vinyl tablecloth, while lace will look just as out of place with melamine plates in the kitchen.

Second, consider the care a particular kind of table covering requires. Formal tablecloths often require special laundering; many people

You can use a runner and coordinating place mats to set a beautiful, formal table. Notice how the dishes and glassware complement the linens.

have them done professionally. Other fabric tablecloths or place mats may stain or may require ironing. Are you willing to care for them on an everyday basis? Flannel-backed vinyl cloths and mats are often used for family meals because they can be wiped clean. Even people who are willing to care for a fabric tablecloth on a regular basis prefer to use disposable paper napkins rather than fabric napkins for all but the most special occasions.

Also consider your table. If you eat casual family meals in the kitchen, you can probably just sponge the table clean. Dining-room tables,

however, often need protection from liquid and heat, so place mats, which leave bare spaces between settings, may not be suitable. Even a tablecloth may not offer enough protection, so use a table pad under the cloth, and trivets for hot dishes. There may be times when you wish to create a particular theme for a special occasion by using paper goods, including throw-away tablecloths. Be particularly careful to protect your table when using these kinds of table settings.

The size and shape of your table determine the size cloth or runner you will need. Measure your table (length and width, or diameter) and allow for a 6- to 7½-inch (15- to 19-cm) overhang on *each* side.

In addition to the usual materials for table linens, there are other choices available, particularly for place mats. These include straw, cork, bamboo, lucite, and even pewter. These materials can add visual interest and texture to your table settings whether they are used alone, with a runner, or over a tablecloth. Before you decide on one of these materials—or on any of the more traditional ones—consider their price, how often you will use them, and their care requirements. There are many inexpensive and practical table coverings available that can help turn even the simplest meal into a more pleasurable dining experience.

### Dinnerware

Dinnerware refers to dishes for all meals, including plates, bowls, and cups and saucers. It is sometimes called "china," but china is only one kind of dinnerware. Both the material and pattern determine how formal your table will look and what flatware, glassware, and linens will create a complementary appearance. Dinnerware also varies greatly in practicality and expense. Many families have several sets, including one for everyday use and another for more formal service.

**Dinnerware Materials** Several dinnerware materials are made of clay coated with a decorative and protective glaze. *China* is the most formal and most expensive of the fired (baked) clay-and-glaze dinnerware materials. It is thin and shiny, but strong enough to resist scratching and chipping. China is often made with painted decorations, from informal floral designs to gold-leaf borders. *Stoneware* has a less formal look than china and is much heavier. It also comes in attractive patterns and wears well. *Earthenware* is more likely to chip than china or stoneware, but it is less expensive. *Glass-ceramic* dinnerware is durable and lightweight, and goes from freezer to oven to table and then into the dishwasher. Another durable dinnerware material is the plastic called *melamine.* It comes in bright colors and is lightweight. While melamine doesn't usually break, it does scratch. It is good for casual dining and for use by children.

Occasionally, sets of dinnerware are made of silver. Usually, though, sterling silver, silver plate, stainless steel, pewter, glass, and wood are all reserved for special pieces or for serving dishes rather than for a whole set of dinnerware. For instance, wooden salad sets are popular special pieces, as are metal steak platters and glass dessert dishes.

**Selecting and Caring for Dinnerware** When selecting dinnerware, consider your real needs, not just what looks beautiful in a store display or catalogue. You will probably need durable everyday dishes before you have much use for the more expensive and formal fine china. Some patterns of stoneware can be used for company or informal parties, as well as for daily meals. Also consider color and design. Ask yourself how the pattern will look in your dining room and with food. Inquire about any special care required for dinnerware. Even if the material is dishwasher-safe, some decorations may be damaged by the dishwasher or by scouring. Try to find serving pieces that can go from oven to table. If the set you like doesn't have these extra pieces, look for a complementary pattern, and mix-and-match.

Dinnerware is sold in place settings, complete sets, or open stock. A **place setting** includes the dishes needed for one person at one meal. Some place settings include the more formal bread-and-butter plate and the dessert plate in addition to the usual dinner plate, salad plate, soup bowl, and cup and saucer.

*Complete sets* of dishes provide place settings for eight or twelve people, as well as the serving pieces. *Starter sets* usually contain only four place settings. The extra serving pieces are then usually offered *open stock,* or individually. When you buy dinnerware, it is a good idea to choose an open-stock pattern in case you wish to replace a broken piece or add individual items later.

Be careful handling and stacking clay-based or glass dinnerware. China or other fine dishes should be stored in racks or with layers of paper towel or cloth between the pieces to prevent chipping. Always wash fine dinnerware in hot, soapy water, and be careful not to chip it in the dishpan or drying rack. If you use the dishwasher, be sure pieces will not bang against each other during washing.

## Tableware: Flatware and Holloware

**Tableware,** which includes **flatware** and **holloware,** is metal utensils, serving pieces, and decorative accessories for dining. Flatware is sometimes referred to as "silverware," but it can be made of other materials as well. Flatware includes knives, forks, spoons, and serving utensils. Holloware pieces are usually used to hold something within their hollow shapes. They include bowls, teapots, pitchers, vases, and candlesticks. Flat trays are also often referred to as holloware.

Placing sheets of paper towel between pieces of fine china protects them from scratching and chipping when they are being stored.

**Materials for Tableware** The three metals used most often for flatware and holloware are sterling silver, silver plate, and stainless steel. Pewter and copper are occasionally used for decorative pieces. Plastic or wood is sometimes used on the handles of flatware.

*Sterling silver* is the finest and most expensive material for tableware. In order to be called sterling, a piece must contain at least 92.5 percent silver. Sterling is heavy in the hand and often comes in beautiful patterns from elegantly simple shapes to ornate and complicated designs. *Silver plate* refers to the process of covering, or plating, another metal with a thin layer of silver. Silver plate is lighter weight and less expensive than sterling, but it, too, comes in a wide variety of attractive patterns. The silver can wear off some silver-plate items. More expensive silver plate is "triple plated" with silver to prevent this. Both sterling silver and silver plate tarnish, or turn dark from a chemical reaction to air and other substances, and must be polished.

*Stainless steel,* as its name suggests, does not tarnish, but it usually does not give as formal an appearance as silver. Depending on the quality and design, stainless steel can range from a very reasonable to a quite expensive price. You can set a very attractive table with stainless steel flatware and holloware. It is not usually a good idea to use stainless with silver, however, since sterling and silver plate are much shinier than stainless steel.

### Selecting and Caring for Tableware

As with dinnerware, you should think carefully about your tableware needs before you buy. Even if you can afford silver plate instead of stainless steel for informal use, will you be willing to polish it? Do you really need sterling silver flatware for formal entertaining, or will silver plate do? Perhaps you can afford some

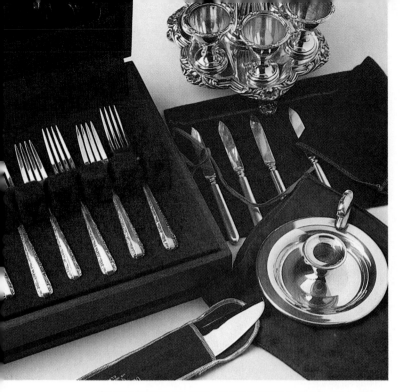

Storing silver in specially designed flatware chests or specially treated cloth bags can help prevent tarnish.

special, individual sterling pieces to go with a set of silver plate.

Also consider how many items you really need. Holloware is not really essential, but it is certainly nice to have. You may want to save up for a special piece and use ceramic or glass bowls and pitchers until then.

You do, of course, need enough flatware for family and company meals. Sterling is sold by the single piece or in sets. The place setting usually includes a knife, fork, teaspoon, soup spoon, and sometimes a salad fork. Sets of sterling and silver plate come in service for 4, 8, 12, or 24, and often include extra teaspoons and serving pieces. Stainless steel may come only in sets of 40 or 50 pieces.

Once you have decided on a material within your price range, look for a pattern that is not only attractive but also one that complements your dinnerware. Make sure flatware will be comfortable in the hand and easy to use. Then decide which of the methods of purchase is most economical for you. Don't buy sets if they contain more than you will ever use. On the other hand, it is usually less expensive per piece to buy a set than to buy individually from open stock.

While stainless steel does not tarnish, it —like silver—will scratch. Store flatware in compartmentalized drawers to prevent scratching. Silver should be stored in tarnish-preventing chests or sacks. Even so, it will have to be polished periodically. All tableware should be washed in hot, sudsy water and then dried with a towel to prevent water spots.

### Glassware

There are two types of glassware. *Stemware* has a stem, or post, between the bowl (which holds the liquid) and the base. *Tumblers* do not have a stem and look less formal. Both kinds of glassware come in various materials and sizes.

**Materials for Glassware**   The finest and most expensive materials for glassware are lead crystal and hand-blown glass. These two types of glass can be made into beautiful and delicate stemware. The more ordinary pressed glass is made into less expensive stemware and tumblers. It is not as fragile as crystal, but all glassware is likely to break or chip if not handled carefully.

**Selecting and Caring for Glassware**
Stemware is suitable for a formal table setting and can be purchased in sets or by the piece. Be sure to coordinate the style and "look" of all elements of your table setting. Many formal patterns of stemware come in graduated sizes. The largest is usually used for water, while smaller glasses of the same pattern can hold various types of beverages. If you plan to set a table with several glasses, the size of the pieces will also be a consideration. Because stemware is so fragile, be sure to select a pattern that can

There are many glassware designs—for both stemware and tumblers—that can add to the beauty of a formal table setting. What linens and tableware go with fine crystal?

be "filled in" from open stock, should you need to replace broken pieces. Tumblers can also be bought in sets, and most are sold open stock. Many are very attractive and almost as fragile as stemware. Others are thicker and more durable but are attractive on an informal table.

When you select glassware, look for a clear, sparkling quality as well as a design you like. Handle stemware to see if it is well balanced. It should be heavier at the base so it will not tip when being filled. Make sure glassware is com-

### Safety Tip

- To keep wooden serving pieces, such as salad bowls, from cracking, rub them with mineral oil several times a year. Cracks can harbor old food and bacteria.

fortable to use. Fine glassware is a major investment. Think carefully about your needs before you make a selection.

Be very careful storing, washing, and handling all glassware. Wash it in hot, sudsy water, and towel dry it to prevent water spots. Don't let glasses bump into one another in the dishpan or drainer; they can chip or break easily. Do not wash fine glassware in the dishwasher. You should not stack most tumblers inside one another for storage. They may get stuck and be difficult to separate without damage. Be especially careful of stemware. Very fragile pieces can be stored in the compartmentalized boxes they came in or in special racks designed for stemware. When you handle stemware, hold the base of the bowl, not the fragile stem.

### The Place Setting

The place setting for each person is known as the **cover.** It includes all the flatware, dinnerware, glassware, and linen required for one person. Allow 20–24 inches (50–60 cm) of space for each cover. The principles of table setting are designed for the comfort and convenience of each diner. Note the position of each item in the illustrations on page 244. Then follow these step-by-step directions for correct table setting. Use the same format when you set trays for tray meals.

1. Place the plate in the center of the cover, or reserve this space for the plate if it is not to be placed immediately. Place flatware to the right and left of the plate or the space that has been reserved for the plate. Arrange the flatware in order of use. The flatware to be used first is at the outside of the cover, and that used last is next to the plate.

2. Arrange the forks to the left of the plate with the tines pointing up. Place the dinner fork and salad fork in order of their use and the dessert fork nearest the plate. When

## The Place Setting

1.

2.

3.

4.

5.

6.

7.

8.

9.

10.

11.

12.

the salad is eaten as a separate course before the main course, place the salad fork on the outside (to the left of the dinner fork). When salad is to be served with the main part of the meal, place the salad fork nearer the plate (to the right of the dinner fork). You may use the dinner fork for the salad and eliminate the salad fork.

3. When a knife is not used, you may place the dinner fork at the right of the plate.

4. You should always place the small cocktail fork to the right of the spoons.

5. Place the dinner knife to the right of the plate, with the cutting edge facing the plate. Place the butter spreader or knife across the top of the butter plate with the handle to the right, or along the right side of the plate vertically, never diagonally.

6. Arrange the spoons, bowls up, to the right of the dinner knife. Place the teaspoons to the right of the knife, and the soup spoon to the right of the teaspoons.

7. Place the napkin (folded into a rectangle or square) to the left of the forks, 1 inch (2.5 cm) from the table edge, and with the hemmed edges next to the plate and the edge of the table. In this way, you can easily pick up the napkin, unfold it, and place it on your lap.

8. Place the water glass at the tip of the knife, and any other glass to the right of the water glass and slightly below it. Place an iced beverage glass on a plate or a coaster to collect the moisture.

9. At breakfast, place the juice glass to the right of the water glass and a little below it.

10. When you serve juice as an appetizer, place the glass on a small plate in the center of the cover.

11. Place the cup and saucer to the right of the teaspoon, with the cup handle parallel with the table edge.

12. Place the bread-and-butter plate at the tip of the dinner fork. If a salad plate is used, place it to the upper left of the napkin. When you do not use a bread-and-butter plate, place the salad plate at the tip of the dinner fork.

**Table Accompaniments**  Other table accompaniments—such as butter, jelly, and relish dishes, or salt and pepper shakers—should be placed so they are within easy reach for passing and so the table will look well balanced. If you use individual salt and pepper shakers, place them at the top of each cover, or one pair between each of two covers.

A centerpiece adds beauty and gives color to your table setting. It is often placed near the center of the table, but may be placed at one

Even casual family meals can be made more attractive if you use attractive table settings. These dishes, glassware, and cloth are all easy to care for and not easy to damage.

side or end of the table when convenient. The centerpiece should harmonize in color with the room, food, and dishes. It should be low enough (about 10 inches (25 cm) high) so that diners can see each other across the table. Flowers, plants, fruits, fresh vegetables, and ornamental glass and pottery are often used for centerpieces.

When you set a table, you need to include only the items required for the meal you are serving. When you plan the setting for a meal, consider what is appropriate and which items look good together. Your choice of color, pattern, and design in table appointments can contribute to making mealtime enjoyable.

---

## For Review

1. For a formal atmosphere, what type of table linens should you use? What type of dinnerware? Flatware? Glassware?
2. What type of linens, dinnerware, flatware, and glassware are best for casual family meals served in the kitchen?
3. What are the three ways in which dinnerware is sold? What is an advantage of each?
4. How much space should you allow for each cover when you set a table? Why?
5. What is the basic principle of arranging flatware?
6. How do you decide which individual items you need to set the table for a particular meal?

---

# Meal Service

The term **meal service** refers to the way in which foods are served at the table. The rules of meal service have evolved over a period of time. The way in which you serve a meal should be suited to the menu and table appointments, and meal service should be attractive and convenient. The styles of meal service can be classified as informal and formal.

## Informal Service

When meals are served informally, members of your family or group take part in serving the meal. Informal meals can be served in five ways: plate service, family service, modified English service, compromise service, and buffet service.

**Plate Service** For **plate service,** plates are filled in the kitchen. They may then be placed on the table by one person or carried from the kitchen to the dining room by individual diners. Plate service is quick and has the added advantage of requiring no serving dishes that will need to be washed. Restaurants usually use a form of plate service, too.

**Family Service** Sometimes called country service, **family service** is self-service at the table. Serving dishes are placed on the table with the serving flatware beside them. Individual plates are placed at each cover. The serving dishes are passed at the table so that individuals can serve themselves.

**Modified English Service** For **modified English service,** the food is brought to the table in serving dishes and then is served. One person serves the main dish. Therefore, place the main dish, such as a meat platter, above the place setting for this person, and place the vegetable dish to this person's right or left. Place the appropriate flatware beside each dish, and warmed plates in front of the person who is to serve. Usually, a second person at the table serves the vegetable. As each plate is served, it is passed to the person for whom it was prepared. The first plate is usually passed to the

# Dinner Time

Different customs about how to eat and when to eat evolve in different cultures to meet the needs of the culture. For example, large breakfasts became a tradition in the United States because most Americans were farmers and needed many calories (energy) to perform their chores.

Around the world, dinner time is not the same as it is in the United States. In Europe, outside of the cities, dinner is often eaten in the afternoon. In other places, customs differ more dramatically from our own. The customs of three such places are described below.

### China

Lunch and dinner are almost identical meals in China. People sit at a table set with a rice bowl, soup bowl, soup spoon, small sauce dish, a large dish for main dishes, and a tea cup for each person. All dishes are served at the same time. The soup is placed in the middle of the table. Four main dishes surround it. These usually include pork, chicken, fish, and a vegetable. The Chinese eat with chopsticks. They lift their bowls from the table and use a shoveling motion with the chopsticks.

### India

In India, middle-class families enjoy rice or lentils, vegetable dishes, and bread for their main meal. If they are not vegetarian, they might also enjoy a fish or meat dish. All the food is served at the same time—even sweets are eaten with the rest of the meal. Usually the serving dishes are arranged on a large metal tray called a thalis. The rice is placed in the center of the thalis and is encircled by yogurt, chutneys, and pickles. Main dishes surround these condiments at the edge of the tray. People serve themselves with their fingers.

After the meal, people are required to wash their hands and rinse their mouths. Then they chew paan, chopped betel nut wrapped in a betel leaf and lime paste.

### Eastern Africa

In Eastern Africa, hand washing often occurs before and after meals. If the family is wealthy, a servant will bring a pitcher of water and a basin to the table. Otherwise, a member of the family brings the water and basin, pours water over each person's hands, and provides a towel for drying.

People sit at low tables on the floor, on pillows, or on carpets. Food is served on one large tray placed within reach of everyone at the table. People serve themselves with a spoon or with their fingers. Instead of using knives and forks, Eastern Africans use small pieces of unleavened bread to pick up their food.

Soup is the center of a typical Chinese dinner.

Family Service

Modified English Service

person at the end of the table, and then the next plates are passed to people along one side of the table and then to those on the other side. When all people at the table have been served, it is all right to begin the meal.

A person at the table may serve the salad, or it may be in individual portions at each cover before the meal begins. This person may also serve the beverage and the dessert. Other accompaniments of the meal, such as rolls, butter, relish, and gravy, are passed. One course is served at a time. The table is cleared before the next course is served. This adds dignity and a pleasant note of importance to meal service. The modified English service is often chosen for holiday meals or special celebrations.

**Compromise Service** As the name suggests, **compromise service** is a combination of English and formal service. The main course of the meal is served at the table (as in modified English service), and the remainder of the meal (such as salad and dessert) is served in individual portions from the kitchen. The accompaniments (such as bread and butter) are passed, as in modified English service. The beverage may be served at the table or from the kitchen. Compromise service may be used for any meal and is an easy way to serve.

**Buffet Service** For **buffet service,** the food and necessary table appointments are attractively arranged on a table, or buffet, in order of the meal pattern. The guests help themselves to all of the food, or the person who is entertaining may ask particular guests to serve the main dish, salad, and beverage. The dessert may be served to each guest from the kitchen, or it may be placed on the buffet table after the main course is cleared, so that guests may help themselves. When you serve the dessert from the kitchen, you may ask a guest to help you remove the used dishes. When the dessert is served from the buffet table, you may indicate to the guests where to take the dishes they have used in the first courses of the meal. Then they can go to the buffet table for dessert.

For buffet service, guests sit either at tables or in chairs, with the plate or a tray on the lap. If guests are not seated at tables, you should plan foods that can be served on one plate and eaten with a fork. Foods that can be prepared ahead of time, and those that keep well and stay hot (casseroles, for example) are good choices for buffet meals.

Individual plates for guests and then the main dishes are usually first in line on a buffet table; the flatware and napkins, if placed on the buffet table, are the last. When guests are to be

Buffet Service

seated at tables after serving themselves from the buffet table, the flatware is arranged on the tables at which they sit. Tumblers and glasses are better suited for buffet service than stemware is.

Buffet service is convenient for entertaining a large number of guests. Since your guests wait on themselves, it gives you more free time with them. Also, you may use buffet service for simple as well as elaborate meals, including breakfasts, brunches (a combination breakfast and lunch), parties, teas, and receptions.

## Formal Service

**Formal service** requires the assistance of someone to wait table. It is the most elaborate style of meal service and is sometimes called *Continental* or *Russian service.* It is used for formal luncheons and dinners. Restaurants and hotels often use formal service from the kitchen. Food may be served on individual plates and placed before you. On particularly elaborate occasions, the food may be served from serving dishes to the individual guests, or the guests may serve themselves while the person who is serving holds the serving dish.

In strictly formal service, place cards are used, and stemware and service plates are required. The service plate is a beautifully deco-

rated large plate. The first-course foods with their underlining plates may be placed on the service plate, but no foods are placed directly upon it. When the service plate is removed, it is replaced with a plate of food for the next course. When the plate for the food course is cleared, it is replaced with the service plate. This procedure is followed until the table is cleared for the dessert course, at which time the service plate is no longer required.

During formal service, food does not appear on the table until guests are seated. Because many pieces of flatware are used, dessert flatware is placed before the dessert is served. Finger bowls are sometimes used, and strong black coffee (demitasse) is often served in the living room as a separate and last course.

You probably will not use formal service because it requires someone to wait table. However, knowing formal style of service will make you comfortable when you are being served at a banquet or in a formal restaurant.

## Selecting the Style of Meal Service

You can select any of the informal styles of meal service for your family meals. Because breakfast and lunch tend to be hurried meals, you may choose to use plate or country service. For dinner and special meals, you may select

When you wait on table, serve from the left side of the diner, and use your left hand.

Clear dishes from the left, using your left hand. Then place larger plates in your right hand as you continue clearing with your left.

Stand to the right of the diner when you refill a glass. Do not lift the glass, but hold it steady on the table.

When offering a serving dish, stand to the left. Hold the plate at a convenient height for the diner. Use a napkin to protect your hand from a hot serving dish.

compromise or modified English service. When you select the style of meal service, be sure that you consider the menu. Simple menus are usually served informally. Elaborate meals are usually served formally. You should also consider the dining space, available table appointments, time available for serving and eating a meal, the number of persons, and the occasion. Select the style of service that can be conveniently and easily performed. It should be one that is most suitable for your situation, and one that will contribute the most to a pleasurable meal.

### Waiting on Table

When you wait on table, move quickly and quietly and remain calm even though an emergency may develop. Your responsibility before the meal may be to see that the dining room is comfortable, the table is set correctly, and the chairs are in place.

During the meal, remove dishes and place all foods, except beverages, from the left side with your left hand. The water glass and beverage cup are on the right; you should refill and place them with your right hand from the right side. At times you may serve bread or desserts.

After the main course, you first remove all serving dishes. Then remove the used plates and flatware from the left of each person with your left hand.

You will be able to clear all of the dishes from one cover at a time when you first remove the dinner plate and flatware with your left hand from the left side. Place the salad plate on the dinner plate in your right hand, and next remove the bread-and-butter plate and butter spreader with your left hand. Take the dishes to the kitchen, or place them on a portable cart until all the covers are cleared. When you remove extra pieces of flatware or small articles (such as salt and pepper shakers), or when you are placing flatware for the next course, use a small tray.

Use a folded napkin to brush crumbs from the table onto a plate. Clean each cover from the left side with the folded napkin in your left hand and the small plate in your right hand. Follow the same order around the table as you used in removing main-course dishes.

When you refill glasses, stand to the right of the person and use your right hand. You should not lift the glass from the table, but you may move it to the edge if necessary. Grasp it from the bottom. Use a napkin in your left hand to catch any drops from the pitcher.

Before you serve dessert, place additional flatware, if needed. Then serve the dessert.

When guests serve themselves from a dish you are serving, offer the food from the left side with your left hand. Hold the dish at a height convenient for each guest. If the dish is hot, place a napkin under it to protect your palm.

All styles of meal service require some waiting on table. Even though it may be as limited as in country service, it should be done well.

## For Review

1. Which type of meal service is best for large parties? For hurried family meals? For special family occasions or holidays? For formal banquets? Why?
2. What is a service plate? What is its purpose?
3. What type of menu should you plan for a buffet meal?
4. When you wait on table, from which side should you serve the food and remove the dishes? From which side do you serve beverages?

# Table Manners

Table manners reflect part of your personality to others, and you will want your table manners to reflect nice things about you. As you practice good manners, they become a part of you, and you become relaxed and poised at mealtime.

## Using the Eating Implements

Earlier in this chapter, you learned how to set an individual cover on the table. Make sure you know how to use the eating implements.

1. Use a fork to eat all food, except finger foods, served on a plate. The fork has three basic uses: to carry food to the mouth, to cut soft foods (such as waffles, meat loaf, and cooked vegetables), and to hold foods when cutting them with a knife. You should hold the fork as you do a pencil, with the tines up when you carry food to the mouth. To cut soft foods with a fork, hold the fork so the tines are turned sideways; after the food is cut, turn the tines upward to carry the bite of food to your mouth. When not in use, place the fork on your plate, tines up. At the end of the meal, place the fork across the center of the plate, tines up.

2. When you cut foods with a knife, hold the knife in your right hand so that the handle rests in the palm of your hand and your forefinger is on the back of the knife blade. Hold the fork in your left hand (in the same way as the knife), tines down, and cut only one or two bites of food at a time. Place the knife on the edge of your plate with the blade facing you, transfer the fork to your right hand, and, with tines up, lift the food to your mouth. Perhaps you have seen the fork kept in the left hand after the food had been cut, and the food carried to the mouth with the tines down. This is the European or Continental style. The American style is to keep the tines up.

3. Use your knife for spreading butter and jelly when a butter spreader is not provided. Break the slice of bread in half, and then break the half to form two pieces. Spread only one-quarter of a slice of bread at a time, and break the remaining half of bread when you are ready to eat it. You may butter a whole slice of hot toast, and a hot roll may be broken apart and buttered while it is still hot. As you either break or butter bread, hold it over the plate to avoid getting crumbs on the table. Always keep the buttered roll or bread on your plate, never on the tablecloth. Keep

In the American style of using eating utensils, the fork is placed in the right hand, tines up. After cutting, the knife is placed on the plate.

In the European style, the knife is kept in the right hand after cutting, and the fork is kept in the left hand, tines down.

the butter spreader and the knife across the edge of the plate when not in use. Do not use the spreader or the knife to help yourself to butter or jelly, but use the provided service flatware (butter knife and jelly spoon). At the end of the meal, place the knife across the center of the plate with the cutting edge of the blade toward you and the fork beside it, tines up.

4. Spoons are used for foods that you cannot eat with a fork. You use a teaspoon for stirring sugar or cream into a beverage and for tasting beverages. The used teaspoon is placed on the saucer; it never remains in the cup. You also use the teaspoon to eat soft foods such as soup, cereal with milk, and pudding. The teaspoon is dipped toward you, and the food is eaten from the tip of the spoon.

Soup spoons are larger spoons than teaspoons and are used for eating soup. When eating soup, dip the spoon away from you, fill it about half full, and sip from the side of the spoon. Never lift the soup dish from the plate; you may tip it slightly away from you when it is nearly empty.

5. Use a napkin to protect your clothes, to blot your mouth, and wipe your fingers. Let the napkin unfold as you remove it from the table to your lap. Place a large napkin only half unfolded on your lap, with the fold facing you; a small napkin may be unfolded completely. During the meal, use the napkin inconspicuously when needed. Leave it on your lap until the end of the meal. After the meal, leave the napkin unfolded beside your plate.

In addition to these basic rules for handling eating implements, you should also follow the basic rules of table courtesy.

## Table Courtesy

Table manners can also be called the rules of table courtesy, or **table etiquette.** They represent the rules of eating that have been developed through use over a period of time. These rules are based upon consideration for others before, during, and after the meal.

1. Before you enter the dining area, make sure that you are well groomed and appropriately dressed. You will show your consideration for the hosts when you arrive for a meal a few minutes before the scheduled time. When you are unavoidably detained, be sure to let your hosts know that you will be late.

2. You should not go to the table until the meal is announced. Sit down from the left side of

When you finish eating, leave your cover neat. Place the knife and fork on the plate and your napkin to the left.

your chair. When the chair is properly placed, you do not need to move it to seat yourself.

3. You should sit straight with your shoulders back, your arms close to your sides, and your feet flat on the floor. Keep your hands in your lap when you are not eating. Always keep your free hand in your lap as you eat.

4. Take cues from others at the table as to mealtime procedure. Remember not to put too much food in your mouth at once. Chew with your mouth closed, and do not talk with food in your mouth.

5. Take your turn with conversation at the table. Keep it pleasant, and include topics that are of general interest to the group.

6. Assist with passing food, but do not help yourself first unless the person to whom you are offering the food suggests it. Foods are generally passed to the right.

7. When the meal has ended, place your napkin at the left of your plate and rise from the right side of your chair.

The table manners that you have just reviewed are basic to all meals. You will have occasion to use them every day with every meal. Occasionally, you will need to know the following special rules. Knowing them may avoid embarrassment for you.

Whenever a special accompaniment or a garnish is served with meat (such as apple rings with roast pork, mint jelly with lamb, or raisin sauce with ham), you should place it on your plate with the meat.

A few foods are considered finger foods. Bread, tacos, crackers, most raw fruits, celery, radishes, potato chips, pickles, olives, salted nuts, or cookies may be eaten from your fingers. Chicken should be cut from the bone, not picked up with your fingers, except in the privacy of your own home or at picnics.

Bread with gravy, and creamed food over bread are eaten with a fork, and a knife is used for cutting when necessary. You should eat salads with a fork, but you may use a knife when necessary to cut lettuce or other salad greens. Cream puffs, éclairs, and ice cream on cake or pie are eaten with a fork.

When you use a spoon to eat fruit with seeds (such as prunes or canned cherries), remove the seed from your mouth with the tip of your spoon. If possible, it is better to avoid taking the seed into your mouth. Olives or other fresh fruits with seeds are eaten from the fingers, and therefore the seed is removed with the fingers. Occasionally a small piece of bone may be taken with fish or chopped meats; you may remove this with your fingers and place it on the edge of your plate.

When you spill water or a beverage, or drop a piece of flatware, make a sincere but brief apology. Offer to help clean it up. The dropped flatware will need to be replaced with clean flatware.

Your study of table manners will help you avoid awkward situations and embarrassing moments. You will be showing your good manners when you handle eating implements properly and are considerate of others.

## For Review

1. In the American style of good table manners, in what hand should you hold your fork when you cut with a knife? When you bring food to your mouth, should the tines be up or down?

2. When you are finished with your meal, where should you place each implement of flatware and your napkin?

3. Where should you keep your free hand while you are eating?

4. What foods are always considered finger foods?

# *11* Chapter Review

## Summary

The principles of table setting, the styles of meal service, and the rules of table etiquette are designed to make dining a pleasant experience for the participants so that they can relax and enjoy the good food and good company. When a table is set properly, the linen, dinnerware, tableware, glassware, and centerpiece look appropriate together and convey the intended atmosphere. The style of meal service, which can range from formal to informal, depends upon the number of people attending the meal, the occasion, the menu, the table appointments, and the dining space. Basic to all meals are the proper use of eating utensils and the practice of polite table manners to make dining a pleasurable time for everyone.

## Vocabulary

Match each numbered vocabulary word with its definition.

1. buffet service
2. compromise service
3. cover
4. family service
5. flatware
6. formal service
7. holloware
8. meal service
9. modified English service
10. place setting
11. plate service
12. table etiquette
13. tableware

a. The dishes that are needed for one person at one meal.

b. Metal utensils, serving pieces, and decorative accessories for dining.

c. Sometimes referred to as "silverware"; the knives, forks, spoons, and serving utensils used for a meal.

d. The decorative accessories for dining that include bowls, teapots, pitchers, vases, candlesticks, and flat trays.

e. The place setting for one person that includes all the flatware, dinnerware, glassware, and linen.

f. The way in which foods are served at the table.

g. The style of serving food where the plates are filled in the kitchen.

h. The style of service where the dishes are arranged on the table in the order of the meal pattern and the guests help themselves to the food.

i. Sometimes referred to as "country service"; the style of service where the serving dishes are passed at the table so that the diners can serve themselves.

j. The style of service where the main course is served at the table, and the remainder of the meal is served in individual portions from the kitchen.

k. The style of service that requires someone to wait on the table; may be used in a formal restaurant or at a banquet.

l. The style of service where the main course is served at the table with one person serving the main dish and another person serving the vegetable.

m. Table manners, or the rules of table courtesy.

# Chapter Questions

1. Name the three kinds of table coverings.
2. What kind of dinnerware and what pieces are used for everyday dining in your family?
3. Why is it important not to wash fine glassware in a dishwasher?
4. What is the proper way to set the table with flatware for everyday dining?
5. Describe and tell the name for the kind of meal service used in your family for everyday dinner and for special occasions.
6. Describe the proper way to clear the table when the main course is over.
7. Why should you show good table manners?
8. How should you use a napkin at the table?

# Skill Activities

**1. Communication**   In your food journal, write a menu for a spaghetti dinner that includes a salad, garlic bread, beverages, and dessert. Determine the meal service to be followed. Draw a diagram of the place setting you would have for each diner.

**2. Human relations**   With your classmates, practice setting the table for a dinner that includes a juice appetizer, a salad, a main course, dessert, and beverages. Then practice the steps for removing the dishes, flatware, and other table accompaniments when the main course is completed.

**3. Social studies**   Make a chart or display of the various kinds of serving pieces. Either show the server or draw its shape. Beside each serving implement, include a caption that tells its particular use. For example, a gravy ladle is used to serve sauces, gravies, or dressings from either bowls or boat-shaped dishes. Information about the different uses of serving implements may be found in books that describe the care and use of flatware.

**4. Social studies**   For special occasions, you may wish to fold a fancy napkin. Napkins can be folded as a bishop's hat, buffet fold, candle, lobster, and fleur de lys and in other shapes as well. Napkins should be about 17 inches square, although there are some that are a little larger or a little smaller. Fold the napkin out and iron it smooth. Then fold the napkin according to the directions, using your fingers or the iron to press in the folds.

The following are directions for a buffet fold napkin: (1) Fold the bottom half of the napkin up over the top half. (2) Fold back the half just folded up, so that there are now 3 layers to the bottom section. (3) Turn the napkin around. Now fold the top right and left corners down diagonally to meet at the center. (4) Fold the corners of the back layers down, so the napkin is in the shape of a triangle. (5) Fold the 2 lower points of the triangle to meet in the center. (6) Then fold the left and right sides to meet at the center, forming pockets for the flatware. Display your fancy napkin to the class.

# Unit 4

# THE WORLD OF COOKERY

# 12 Spices, Herbs, and Garnishes

## As you read, think about:

- how to use spices, herbs, and other condiments.
- how to buy and store seasonings.
- how garnishes enhance foods.

It is likely that the first use of seasonings came when primitive people wrapped meat in leaves before cooking it on hot coals. The leaves not only protected the meat from dirt but also gave it a good flavor. This was also perhaps the first instance of the use of a garnish.

Centuries ago, a flourishing spice trade developed between the East and the Mediterranean region. Spices were brought from India and taken to Damascus, Athens, and Rome. Spice cookery became more complex and extended to vegetable dishes and even puddings. Today, a wide variety of seasonings is available. Although spices, herbs, and other seasonings have little or no nutritional value, they can make the difference between an ordinary dish and one that is highly praised.

# Spices

**Spices** are aromatic flavorings of plant origin. Spices are dried seeds, buds, fruit or flower parts, or the bark or roots of tropical plants.

## Types of Spices

You can choose from a variety of spices to enhance just about any food you prepare. Ranging from the ordinary to the exotic, they truly "spice up" any food by adding not only flavor but also texture and color.

**Allspice** The flavor of allspice resembles a blend of cloves, cinnamon, and nutmeg. Allspice is the nearly-ripe fruit or berry of an evergreen tree. The berries are dried to a dark reddish-brown color and are available whole and ground. You may use whole allspice for pickling, and in beverages, soups, stews, sauces, pot roasts, and preserves; and ground allspice in baked products (such as apple pie and spice cakes), puddings, and sauces.

The 13th century saw the rise of the spice trade. Caravans, such as the one shown here, traveled long land routes to bring spices to Europe from such faraway places as Ceylon, Malacca, and the Malabar Coast.

**Cinnamon** Cinnamon is mildly pungent, distinctively sweet, and spicy. It is made from the dried inner bark of an evergreen tree. It is reddish brown in color and is available in stick and ground forms. You may use cinnamon stick for pickling, and in certain fruit and vegetable dishes, and beverages. Ground cinnamon is used in cakes, breads, pies, some fruit and vegetable dishes, puddings, and custards.

**Cloves** The flavor of cloves is sweet, pungent, and almost hot. Cloves are the dried unopened bud of an evergreen tree. The nail-shaped buds are available whole and ground. You may use whole cloves to stud ham and glazed beef, pork, fruit, and onions; and to add flavor to stews, pickled fruits, and meat gravies. Ground

Allspice, cloves and cinnamon all come from an evergreen tree but each spice comes from a different part of the tree. Which spice comes from the bark? The berry? The bud?

is available whole and ground. Whole ginger is used for pickling, and in syrups, beverages, and stewed fruits; ground ginger is used in baked goods, fruit or steamed puddings, sauces, soups, appetizers, punches, meats, and poultry. Often it is combined with other spices.

**Mace and Nutmeg** Mace and nutmeg have a similar aroma, but nutmeg is more delicate in flavor. They are the only spices found on the same fruit of a tropical evergreen. Mace forms the lacy covering around the nutmeg seed. Unground mace is used for pickling and preserving. Ground mace is a yellow-orange color, blends with other ingredients, and brings out their flavor. You may use it in cakes, puddings, sauces, and meat stuffings. Nutmeg is available both whole and ground. You may want to use it in baked goods, rice, custards, puddings, sauces, vegetables, and beverages.

cloves are used in baked goods, puddings, pie fillings, and fruit desserts. For a delightful treat, you may want to try cloves on squash, sweet potatoes, beans, and beets.

**Curry Powder** Curry powder is a blend of many spices, which vary with the type of curry powder. It is golden yellow to yellow-brown in color and is hot in flavor. Until you develop a taste for curry powder, you should use it sparingly for enhancing the flavor of food. Curry powder is used to make curried beef, lamb, seafoods, rice, chicken, and casseroles. You may want to try it as a seasoning in salad dressings, some vegetables, marinades, dried beans, and breads.

**Ginger** Ginger is light brownish yellow in color and has a hot, spicy, sweet flavor. It is the dried and peeled root of the ginger plant and

Both mace and nutmeg come from the same fruit of a tropical evergreen tree. The nutmeg seed is surrounded by a lacy film that is mace. What are some uses for unground mace? For ground mace? For whole and ground nutmeg?

**Pepper**  Pepper is a widely used spice. It has a hot, biting, pungent taste. White pepper has a slightly musty flavor and is milder in flavor than black pepper. Pepper grows on a vine and, when harvested, looks like a cluster of red currants. The berries turn black and shrivel when dried in the sun. White pepper comes from berries allowed to ripen before harvesting; the outer shell is removed to leave a grayish-white kernel.

Whole black peppers are ground in pepper mills. You can buy ground black pepper in three grinds—fine, coarse, and cracked. You can use pepper in many dishes, but you may prefer to use white pepper in light-colored foods to avoid black specks. You may substitute white pepper for black pepper in any recipe.

**Poppy Seed**  Dried poppy seeds have a pleasant, nutlike flavor. The slate-blue seeds come from the pod of cultivated poppies. You may use poppy seeds as a tasty topping for rolls, breads, pastries, and cookies; or in a poppy-seed filling for cakes, coffee cakes, and cookies.

**Turmeric**  Turmeric has a brilliant yellow color and a slightly bitter flavor. It is the root of a plant in the ginger family, although ginger and turmeric are very different in flavor. The cleaned roots of the plant are dried and usually ground. Turmeric is an important ingredient in prepared mustard and curry powder. When you use turmeric, you add color, flavor, and aroma to foods. You may use it for pickling, and in relishes, cream sauces, mayonnaise, salad dressings, soups, and prepared chicken and fish.

**Vanilla**  Vanilla has a delicate, subtle flavor. Vanilla is the long pod (bean) of an orchid plant. It is picked green and is then cured and dried. The cured pods are dark brown in color and have a rich flavor and aroma. You can use vanilla to flavor sweet foods such as cakes, desserts, and candies; and to enhance the flavor of dessert mixes.

**Extracts**  Extracts are a blend of alcohol and the oils pressed from aromatic plants. Extracts give foods a specific flavor. Vanilla, lemon, and almond are popular pure extracts, but a variety of imitation extracts is available. Pure extracts are more expensive than imitation products, but the amount you use is so small that the difference in cost may not be important. When you use extracts, keep in mind that uncooked foods containing the extract will have a more pronounced flavor than after they are cooked.

### Buying and Storage

Spices and seasonings tend to lose their flavor, aroma, and color with prolonged storage. You should purchase them in small amounts and write the date of purchase on the container. Always keep the container tightly closed when not in use, and store spices in a cool, dry, dark place.

Using spices and herbs creatively adds individuality to recipes.

**For Review**

1. List three spices that can be used in the making of pickles. Three spices that can be used in sauces.
2. What should you remember when cooking with extracts?
3. How should spices be stored? Why?

# Herbs

**Herbs,** used for seasoning foods, are the aromatic leaves and sometimes the flowers of plants. Most recipes call for dried herbs, which have a more concentrated flavor than fresh herbs. You need about 3 teaspoons (15 mL) of a fresh herb to equal the flavor provided by 1 teaspoon (5 mL) of the dried herb.

## Types of Herbs

The many types of herbs available make it possible for you to serve food that has variety,

Many people like to grow their own herbs in order to have a ready supply of a variety of fresh seasonings. Some herbs that are easily grown in the home are chive, dill, and parsley.

an appetizing aroma, and a unique flavor. One well-seasoned dish can make your meal outstanding. However, remember not to use the same herb in several dishes in the same meal, and do not serve heavily seasoned foods in every course.

**Basil** Basil, also known as sweet basil, is aromatic and gives food a mildly pungent flavor. It is an annual plant of the mint family. The leaves and tender stems are used either fresh or dried. Basil gives a great flavor to most tomato-rich dishes. Use it in soups, stews, sauces, and salad dressings. Try adding it to vegetables or sprinkling it over lamb chops before cooking.

**Bay Leaves** Bay leaves have a distinct, strong, pungent, almost bitter flavor. They are usually removed from foods when cooking is completed. The evergreen sweet-bay or laurel tree, native to the Mediterranean, provides bay leaves. These leaves are indispensable for pickling and in the manufacture of vinegars, and are an important ingredient in mixed spices. For a pleasant flavor, use bay leaves when you cook vegetables or simmer any stew or any less-tender cut of meat.

**Caraway Seed** Caraway seed has a distinct flavor with a slightly sweet accent. Caraway seed is the fruit of a plant in the parsley family. These seeds give rye bread its distinctive flavor and are used in rolls, biscuits, and cakes. You can create an intriguing flavor when you add caraway seed to mild cheeses or coleslaw or when you cook it with asparagus, cabbage, or sauerkraut.

**Chervil** Although chervil leaves slightly resemble parsley, the flavor is more distinctive and sweeter. The French use chervil in their famous herb omelettes. Use this herb, as you would parsley, in soups, sauces, salads, and stuffings.

Throughout history, people have attributed healing properties to some plants, especially herbs. Many plants were first used as medicine and later took their places in stews or soups or were used with meats as flavorings and condiments.

Recent medical research upholds a few ancient claims about the healing power of plants. However, most folk remedies either have not been investigated or have been discounted by scientific research. Described below are the histories of four somewhat unusual plants thought of as both medicine and food. It is important to note that the medicinal properties of the plants have not been proven.

**Scorzonera** This root vegetable comes from the Mediterranean. The root is covered with a black rind that gives it much of its flavor. One of the most important vegetables in Europe during the Middle Ages, scorzonera was given to people who had smallpox. Some people believed it to be an antidote for snake bites and a cure for indigestion.

By the 18th century, this plant was well-known throughout Europe and the English-speaking world. During the 19th century, Victorian cooks peeled the "dirty" skin off and robbed the vegetable of its flavor. The vegetable became less popular. In Europe today, scorzonera is grown in small gardens—and it is working its way back to the United States. It is served in soups, or is baked or fried.

**Salad Burnet** This herb has scalloped leaves and a white, pink, or purple flower. The leaves taste like cucumbers and are used as salad greens or for seasoning.

People may have cultivated this herb since ancient times. Anglo-Saxons used the leaf in ointments, and Europeans of the 15th–16th centuries used the herb as protection against the plague and as a remedy for wounds. The colonists brought salad burnet with them to North America.

**Burdock** Burdock is a plant that, when left to grow in the wild, produces burrs. The Japanese who have cultivated burdock call it gobo. It is said that gobo purifies the blood and alleviates arthritis, gout, and skin diseases. To use gobo, roots are dried and stored. Then the skin is scraped off the root until the white fiber is exposed. This part is cut into fine pieces and can be used to flavor vegetables or soups. It can also be used as a condiment for rice and fish.

**Horseradish** Horseradish originated in Eastern Europe and the Middle East, but is now grown in regions of the world with cold winters and temperate summers. Its medicinal uses can be traced to ancient times, and it has been eaten as food in Europe since the Middle Ages. European settlers brought it to North America in the 1600s. Mixed with vinegar, horseradish can be served as a condiment with meat and fish. It is supposed to help cure rheumatism, and, with honey, relieves coughs and congestion.

Herbs for foods are often ground with a mortar and pestle.

**Chives**   Chives have a mild onion flavor. They are most often used fresh or frozen because their flavor and bright-green color is lost when dried. You may use chives both as a garnish and seasoning in salads, omelets, cheese dishes, dips, and sauces. Their mild flavor combines nicely with fish, chicken, potatoes, rice, fruits, and other herbs.

**Coriander**   Coriander has a mild, fragrant odor and an aromatic flavor somewhat like a blend of lemon peel and sage. It is the dried ripe fruit of a parsleylike plant. It is used commercially in frankfurters and many meat products. Whole coriander is used for pickling and in Spanish rice. Ground coriander is added to curry blends, rolls, pastries, and cakes, or sprinkled in applesauce, cookies, and gingerbread. Coriander is used in many Spanish and Mexican rice, bean, and meat dishes.

**Cumin**   Cumin has a distinctive, slightly bitter taste. It is the dried, yellowish-brown fruit or seed of a plant in the parsley family. It is used commercially in the preparation of meats, pickles, cheeses, sausages, curry and chili powders, and chutneys. You may purchase cumin whole or ground and use it to give an exotic flavor to soups, stews, breads, rice, and tomato sauce. Add a dash to meat loaf or to bean and lentil dishes for a tangy flavor.

**Dill**   Green dill is delicate in flavor, while dill seed has a warm, aromatic, slightly sharp taste. Dill is a plant of the parsley family. It is best known as a flavoring for pickles and for rye and pumpernickel breads. Commercially, it is used in processed meats. For a delightful aromatic touch, add green dill to salads, sauces, egg dishes, vegetables, breads, salad dressings, cottage or cream cheese, and stuffings. Add dill to green beans, cauliflower, or cabbage while these vegetables cook.

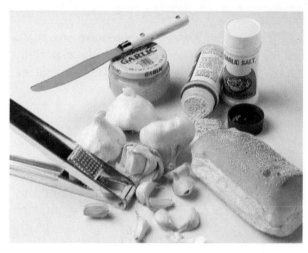

Your market probably carries garlic in various forms, both fresh and prepared. You can separate and crush fresh cloves yourself or buy a number of packaged varieties of garlic.

**Garlic**   Garlic has a strong, pungent flavor. It is a member of the lily family, and its root, made of small sections called "cloves," is the edible part. It is available in cloves, in liquid or powder forms, or mixed with salt. You may use garlic products in soups, dips, sauces, gravies, salads, salad dressings, some vegetables, some cheese dishes, stews, marinades, and for garlic bread. Remember, just a little garlic goes a long way and does wonders for many foods.

**Horseradish**   Horseradish has a very sharp taste. It is prepared from the root of the thick white horseradish plant. Horseradish adds zest to seafood, meats, poultry, sauces, and sour cream.

**Marjoram**   Marjoram has a distinctive, slightly bitter flavor. It is a plant of the mint family, and its gray-green leaves are available dried or ground. It is an ingredient in poultry seasoning and in processed meats. Add it to lamb, roast beef, or veal before cooking for a specially pleasing flavor. You may use marjoram in almost any dish except sweet foods.

A corned-beef-and-cabbage meal just wouldn't be complete without horseradish. You can choose either the red or the white variety. Note the horseradish root on the lower left of the picture.

**Oregano**   Oregano is a type of marjoram and is somewhat similar in flavor and aroma. Commonly used in spaghetti sauce, oregano also adds flavor to chili con carne, pizza, pork, hamburger, stews, vegetables, and cheese dishes.

**Parsley**   Parsley has a mild scent and a pleasant flavor. Some describe the taste of parsley as fresh, piney, with a faint taste of onion, and a hint of licorice. One variety of parsley has a flat leaf; another has a curly leaf. The flavor of parsley blends nicely with foods and other seasonings. You can make pale foods attractive with parsley and enhance their flavor as well. Use parsley both in and on food. Try it with soups, salads, potatoes, noodles, cheeses, stuffings, meats, fish, and poultry.

### Practical Tip

- Make your own flavorful basting brushes for meats and poultry by tying long, fresh sprigs of rosemary and basil together.

**Rosemary**   Rosemary has a fresh, sweet, piney flavor with a hint of ginger. Some describe the flavor as a true hot mint. Rosemary is the leaf of an evergreen shrub of the mint family. This fragrant herb enhances the flavor of meats, vegetables, and fruits. You will enjoy the fragrance of rosemary when you add it to the liquid used in cooking vegetables. For a delicious flavor, sprinkle it on meats before cooking, or add it to scrambled eggs, corn muffins, or corn-bread batter.

**Saffron**   Saffron has a clean, pleasantly bitter flavor and is prized for its color. Saffron comes from a plant in the crocus family. Add saffron to rolls, breads, and cakes for a distinctive flavor and a golden color. A pinch of saffron added to boiling water gives rice a sunny richness and delicious flavor. You can also use saffron in chicken dishes, seafood dishes, soups, and sauces.

Saffron added to rice offers not only a subtle, unusual flavor but also a rich yellow-orange color. Only a pinch of this very expensive spice is used to provide a deep color.

## Onion Relish  Yield: 8 servings

| | |
|---|---|
| 1 c (250 mL) vinegar | 1½ c (375 mL) chopped |
| 2 Tbs (30 mL) confection- | fresh mint leaves |
| ers' sugar | 2 c (500 mL) thinly sliced |
| | small onions |

1. Combine vinegar, sugar, and mint; let stand 30 minutes.
2. Add onions. Cover and refrigerate for 24 hours.

Approximate nutrition information per serving: calories–25; protein–1 g; fat–trace; cholesterol–0; carbohydrates–7 g; sodium–6 mg.

**Sage**  Sage has a tart, fragrant flavor. It is the dried leaf of a plant in the mint family. Sage is available ground or in whole-leaf form, and is an important ingredient of poultry seasoning. Sage is a perfect accompaniment for meats, fish, and poultry. Use it in stuffings, salad dressings, chowders, vegetable soups, creamed vegetables, and cottage cheese.

**Tarragon**  Tarragon has an aromatic, intriguing, and somewhat sharp licorice flavor. It is the slender dark-green leaf of a shrublike plant. Tarragon is used to flavor vinegars, pickles, and prepared mustards. To develop an interesting taste treat, use tarragon with green salads, seafood salads, meats, poultry, fish sauces, and egg and tomato dishes.

**Thyme**  Thyme has an aromatic, warm, slightly pungent flavor. Thyme is the grayish-green leaf of a plant of the mint family and is available either ground or as dried leaves. You may use thyme to season meats, poultry, fish, stuffings, tomatoes, and cheeses. Also try it in sauces, stews, cheese dishes, and fresh salads.

### Buying and Storage

Fresh herbs often have a better flavor than those that are dried at home, or those that are packaged and sold in stores. Whole herbs retain their flavor longer than when ground, powdered, or crumbled. Purchase herbs in small amounts so that you can use them before they become stale.

Remember that dried herbs are more compact than the fresh form, and you need only one teaspoon of a dried herb to contribute the flavor equivalent of about three teaspoons of the fresh herb. For this reason, you need to purchase dried herbs in smaller quantities than fresh herbs.

Because they contain volatile oils, which give them their characteristic flavor and aroma, herbs lose their valued flavor and aroma if exposed to air. Fresh herbs can be stored in a refrigerator for about two weeks when you place them upright in a closed container with a little water in the bottom. Most herbs can be preserved by drying or freezing. For freezing, wash the herbs and pat them dry; spread them in a single layer on freezer paper and roll up the paper. Seal the ends with freezer tape. Although the flavor of frozen herbs is good, the leaves become limp and begin to darken soon after they have thawed. Store dried herbs in airtight containers away from heat and light, and remember to close the containers securely after each use.

### For Review

1. What do you have to keep in mind when cooking with dried herbs instead of fresh herbs?
2. List three herbs that can be used in sauces. Three herbs that can be used with vegetables.
3. How should fresh herbs be stored? Dried herbs?

# Other Condiments

**Condiments,** which include herbs and spices, enhance the flavor of foods. Some condiments, such as catsups and mustards, are made from several ingredients. If foods are saturated with these condiments, the natural flavor of the food is masked or lost. However, when condiments are used appropriately, the flavor of the food is enhanced and enriched. It takes experience to choose the most desirable condiment for a particular food in order to achieve the desired effects.

### Prepared Mustard

*Prepared mustard,* a blend of ground or whole mustard seeds, vinegar, and herbs and spices, has a tangy, spicy bite and a pleasant flavor. The most popular use of prepared mustard is on processed meats such as hot dogs and bologna. Prepared mustard is also used to flavor many other meats and can be used as an ingredient in a variety of sauces and salad dressings.

Condiments such as these are popular in our culture. If they are overused, however, they can drown out the flavor of the food. How should condiments be used?

Extra spicy, Dijon-style, and whole-seed mustards are just a few of the many available mustard condiments.

### Catsup

*Catsup* is a blend of tomatoes, vinegar, and herbs and spices. Most often used to enhance the flavor of meats, such as hamburger, catsup can also be used in sauces, salad dressings, and vegetable dishes.

### Relish

*Relish* is a food or a combination of foods that are pickled by a preservation process. Pickle relish is used most often on hot dogs and hamburgers, while other relishes, such as corn relish, can serve as a side dish or as a condiment for other foods. Because of their tart, zesty flavor, relishes add a pleasing zip to many foods.

## Sauces

*Soy sauce* is an oriental brown sauce that is made from soy beans that have been fermented. Soy sauce can be used as an ingredient in both meat and poultry dishes, in soups, stews, and casseroles, and in rice dishes. It can also be used by itself as a condiment for many Japanese and Chinese dishes.

*Worcestershire sauce* is a pungent sauce that is made from vinegar and molasses and from a variety of herbs and spices. Often used as an ingredient in both meat loaf and hamburgers, it can also be brushed on steaks and chops before they are broiled or just before they are served.

*Tabasco sauce* is a pungent condiment that is made from hot peppers and vinegar and from herbs and spices. Tabasco sauce is often used as an ingredient in spaghetti sauces, gravies and soup. It can also be added as an ingredient to tomato juice, hamburgers, and eggs for an added pungent taste.

# Garnishes

When you garnish, you decorate a food to make it attractive. **Garnishes** add flavor, texture, color, and interest to foods. A garnish harmonizes with the food it decorates. You should anticipate how a prepared food will look and how you might garnish it. Attractive foods do not just happen, so you must plan the use of the color, size and shape, and arrangement of garnishes.

The red color of a tomato wedge, the orange of a carrot curl, or the bright red or

Various sauces can enhance the flavor of foods. Soy sauce adds to oriental dishes, tabasco sauce to tomato juice, and Worcestershire sauce to hamburgers.

With garnishes, ordinary sandwiches become works of art (left), bay leaves provide a floral design (above left), and a red pepper becomes a handy serving dish (above right).

## Practical Tip

- To have fresh parsley always available, put chopped fresh parsley into divided ice cube trays with water and freeze. Then just drop individual cubes in soups and sauces as needed.

green of an apple peel can enhance a salad. A sprig of crisp, leafy greens, slices or wedges of cheese or hard-cooked egg, pickle fans, and radish roses all add colorful interest to main dishes. Large vegetables and fruits can be carved into interesting shapes to use as garnishes. Small whole fruits and tender vegetables are attractive garnishes when carefully placed to complement the food served.

You can add colorful accents to cold beverages and punch with citrus fruit slices, mint leaves, or a scoop of sherbert or ice cream. Use a sprinkle of spice, a twist of lemon or orange, or a dab of whipped cream to enhance hot beverages.

Carefully chosen garnishes for sandwiches add pleasing contrasts to their flavor, texture, and color. Select sandwich garnishes from a variety of crisp greens; sections, slices, and creative cuts of fruits and vegetables; or relishes, pickles, and cheeses. You may arrange these garnishes so they can be added to the sandwich.

The careful arrangement of foods, along with attractive garnishes, offers an added pleasure to dining. Food is not just to be eaten—but to be enjoyed.

## For Review

1. What is the purpose of garnishing foods?
2. List four garnishes that can add to the attractiveness of food.

# 12 Chapter Review

## Summary

For centuries, herbs, spices, and some condiments have been used to flavor and add zest to meals. Herbs, spices, and condiments are used to enhance the flavor of meats, stews, soups, beverages, vegetables, fruits, salads, baked products, and other foods. Herbs, spices, and condiments should be used sparingly to achieve the desired results. As with herbs, the use of spices and condiments makes it possible to serve a meal that has variety, an appetizing aroma, and a unique flavor. Another way to create an outstanding dish, is to use a garnish. Garnishes add contrasts of flavor, texture, and color to make a meal more pleasurable.

## Vocabulary

Match each numbered vocabulary word to the lettered examples and definitions. Each vocabulary word has three or more matches.

1. condiments
2. extracts
3. garnishes
4. herbs
5. spices

a. Catsup
b. Aromatic flavorings that are dried seeds, buds, fruit or flower parts, or the bark or roots of tropical plants
c. Carrot curl
d. Lemon
e. Clove
f. Aromatic leaves or flowers of plants that may be used fresh or dried
g. A blend of alcohol and the oils pressed from aromatic plants
h. Soy sauce
i. Sage
j. Turmeric
k. Radish rose
l. Thyme
m. Almond
n. Decorations to make food attractive
o. Herbs and spices and sometimes other ingredients
p. Basil
q. Cinnamon
r. Relish
s. Scoop of sherbet

## Chapter Questions

1. What are five spices and two herbs that may be used in baked products?
2. Why might a person want to purchase and use an imitation product instead of a pure extract for cooking?
3. What spices are in your family's kitchen and what types of foods are they generally used for?
4. How are herbs and spices alike and how are they different?
5. What herbs are in your family's kitchen, and what foods are they generally used to flavor?
6. Why do you need to purchase dried herbs in smaller quantities than fresh herbs?
7. What are the steps to follow for freezing fresh herbs?

8. Why should herbs, spices, and condiments be used in small quantities?
9. What are three uses for prepared mustard?
10. What are two condiment sauces and how are they used?
11. What are some garnishes you can use to enhance a platter of meat?

## Skill Activities

**1. Communication**  In your food journal, write about your experience preparing a food using an extract, an herb, a spice, a condiment, or a garnish to enhance a meal. Write the name of the food and the names of the spices, herbs, condiments, or extracts you used. If you used a garnish, describe what it was, how you made it, and how it enhanced the food.

**2. Human relations**  With your classmates make a display of garnishes. Directions for making garnishes are printed in many cookbooks. In your display try to include examples of beet or turnip pompons, beet or lemon, orange, or lime rind roses, radish roses, carrot curls, frosted grapes, cucumber cartwheels, and lemon, lime, or orange twists. Decide with which kinds of foods these garnishes would best be used.

**3. Reading**  Select an herb or spice, and write a report about it. In your paper, try to include information about where it is usually grown, how long it has been used, the history of its use, and other interesting facts about the herb or spice. Also include two recipes that use the herb or spice as an ingredient.

**4. Social studies**  Chives, basil, mint, sage, and parsley are herbs that grow well in plant pots, brighten up a kitchen, and may be used to prepare foods. Select several herbs to grow in pots in your kitchen. Then make a display of fresh herb leaves to show their shapes and fragrances. Tell how you plan to use the herbs in your cooking.

**5. Resource management**  The Japanese use many garnishes with their meals, and they also cut the vegetables into many interesting shapes. Read and follow the directions in a Japanese cookbook for cutting and slicing vegetables. Make a display of your work and demonstrate to your classmates the steps you took to create each particular garnish.

**6. Food science**  All spices have distinct aromas and flavors that are caused by particular chemical compounds. Use encyclopedias or other library reference books to find out which aroma and/or flavor-producing substance is present in two of the following spices: cinnamon, cloves, allspice, and nutmeg.

# 13 Fruits

## As you read, think about:

- how to identify, select, use, and store fruits.
- what nutrients fruit provides for you.
- how to prepare and serve fruits.
- how cooking affects fruits.

**Vocabulary**
fruits
protective foods
scurvy
ascorbic acid
enzyme
canning
storage
collagen
carotene

**Fruits,** seed plants used for food, are called **protective foods** because they contribute vitamins, minerals, and cellulose (bulk). The experiments of James Lind, surgeon to the British navy in the 18th century, and his successors in the 20th century have established the protective value of fruits.

During long voyages, sailors developed **scurvy,** a disease of the joints, teeth, and blood vessels, caused by a severe lack of vitamin C. In 1747, Lind chose 12 sailors who showed similar symptoms and grouped them into six pairs. These sailors ate the food prepared in the ship's kitchen but were given different remedies to cure them of scurvy. Each day, two of the sailors drank a quart of cider; two others received 25 drops of dilute sulfuric acid three times a day; a third pair drank two spoonfuls of vinegar three times a day; a fourth pair drank sea water; a fifth ate nutmeg three times a day; and a sixth pair ate two oranges and a lemon daily.

Only the sailors who ate the oranges and lemons improved and were able to report for duty by the sixth day. Later the British navy gave a small amount of lime juice to every sailor to prevent scurvy. Because of this practice, the British sailors were nicknamed "limeys." The **ascorbic acid,** or vitamin C, in oranges and limes was the substance that prevented the sailors from contracting scurvy.

Modern transportation, packaging, and refrigeration make it possible to have fresh fruits the year round. The varied sizes, shapes, aromas, colors, and flavors of fruits add pleasure to eating.

# Fruit Groups

The many varieties of fruits can be divided into groups or classes according to their shape, structure, and botanical nature. One such grouping includes the following: pomes, drupes, berries, citrus fruits, melons, and tropical fruits.

This farmer from the early 1900s proudly displays hand-picked apples on his horse-drawn sled.

## Pomes

Pomes are characterized by a smooth-skin covering and an enlarged fleshy area that surrounds the core. The most common pomes are apples and pears; others include quince and kiwi fruit.

## Drupes

Drupes contain a single seed, or pit, surrounded by a fleshy, juicy edible portion. Peaches, nectarines, apricots, cherries, and plums are all drupes.

## Berries

Berries have a fragile, highly perishable cell structure. Berries are pulpy and juicy, with tiny seeds embedded in the flesh. Common berries are blackberries, blueberries, cranberries, strawberries, and grapes.

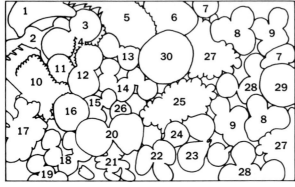

1. Bananas
2. Red pears
3. Grapefruit
4. Cranberries
5. Pineapple
6. Watermelon
7. California avocado
8. Peaches
9. Plums
10. Blueberries
11. Orange
12. Navel oranges
13. Lemons
14. Tangerines
15. Limes
16. Granny Smith apple
17. Strawberries
18. Fresh figs
19. Dried figs
20. Red delicious apples
21. Dates
22. Kiwi fruit
23. Anjou pears
24. Bosc pear
25. Ribier grapes
26. Seckel pear
27. Cherries
28. Nectarines
29. Cantaloupe
30. Honeydew melon

## Citrus Fruits

Citrus fruits are grown in warm regions and are characterized by their firm rind and pulpy flesh. Good sources of vitamin C, citrus fruits include oranges, grapefruits, tangerines, lemons, limes, kumquats, citrons, tangelos, and ugli fruit.

## Melons

Melons have a hard outer surface, smooth or netted, and juicy flesh. Melons include the cantaloupe, honeydew, watermelon, muskmelon, casaba, Persian, and crenshaw.

## Tropical Fruits

Grown in very warm climates, most tropical fruits are available fresh in the United States. Some of the most popular are bananas, pineapples, avocados, dates, and figs. Other tropical fruits include plantain, mangos, pomegranates, and papayas.

## For Review

1. List the six groups of fruits, and give an example of each.
2. Why are fruits considered to be protective foods?
3. What group of fruits contain only a single seed?

# Forms, Selection, and Storage

There are many factors to consider about the use of fruit. For instance, do you want fresh, crisp apples to be used for snacks? Do you need frozen blueberries as an ingredient in a dessert? How can you prevent spoilage of fruit? Choices of form, selection, and storage should be considered with each purchase of fruit.

## Forms of Fruit

Not only are there many varieties of fruits from which to choose, but many fruits are usually available in several forms: fresh, frozen, canned, and dried. Fresh fruits spoil or deteriorate rapidly and must be used shortly after purchase. Frozen, canned, and dried fruits, specially treated, keep longer.

**Fresh Fruit** Usually, only ripe fruit is good for use. Ripening enhances the overall eating quality of the fruit. Several changes take place during ripening: the fruit develops to its full size, the edible tissue becomes soft, the color changes, the flavor becomes mildly sweet, and the characteristic aroma of the fruit develops. These changes are brought about by enzymes found in the fruit tissue. **Enzymes** are substances that cause chemical reactions. Enzymes will continue to function even after the fruit is ripened, and will cause eventual spoilage and an undesirable texture and flavor. The softening of fruit can be slowed down by proper refrigeration.

Late in the season, some Valencia oranges tend to turn from a bright orange to a greenish color. This color change affects only the outer skin. The oranges are fully ripe inside and may have certified food color added to the skin to improve its appearance. Oranges so treated must be marked "color added." This color treatment has no influence on the interior.

Some fresh fruits are packaged in plastic bags. The prepackaging cuts down on loss of moisture from the fruit and reduces contamination by dirt and insects. The plastic bags have small holes to prevent softening of the fruit due to an accumulation of carbon dioxide.

Large fruit is generally more expensive than average-size fruit of the same variety. The largest fruit is not necessarily the best; its flavor and texture could be less desirable than that of the smaller fruit. The color and size of fruit rather than its flavor and quality tend to determine its cost and salability.

It is no longer necessary to live in the tropics to have fresh fruit the year round. Even though some fruits tend to be seasonal and other fruits are grown only in certain areas, some types of fresh fruit can be purchased the year round. Improved transportation, refrigeration, storage, and packaging have made available a constant supply of fruits from the many areas of our country and from distant lands. However, the fresh fruits which are grown locally may be somewhat lower in price and they may also be fresher.

**Processed Fruit** For longer periods of storage, fruits are processed by freezing, canning, and drying. These fruits are readily available regardless of season. The basic purpose in all three methods of processing is to control the action of spoilage organisms and enzymes.

Many kinds of *frozen* fruits are available. Small whole fruits such as cherries, raspberries, strawberries, and sliced or cut large fruits such as peaches, apples, and pineapples are frozen. There are also frozen mixed fruits and fruit juices. Most fruits are sweetened and then frozen quickly at a very low temperature. The low temperature prevents the action of spoilage organisms. The color, flavor, and nutritive value of frozen fruits tend to be like that of the fresh fruit.

Most common fruits are available in the *canned* form. Fruits may be canned whole, in halves, sliced, cubed, and as a sauce or juice. Fruits are usually sweetened before canning. During **canning,** the fruits in containers are exposed to high temperatures which destroy spoilage organisms and enzymes so that the fruits are preserved and will not spoil.

Fruits that are commonly *dried* include plums (prunes), apricots, dates, figs, grapes

(raisins), currants, and mixed fruits. As a result of drying, a large portion of the water is removed from the fruit, and the keeping quality of the fruit is extended considerably.

## Selection of Fruit

Most cultivated fruits are available in many varieties. One variety may be especially valued for its flavor, such as the red or yellow Delicious apples, while another may have better cooking qualities, for example, the Rome Beauty or McIntosh apples. When it comes to oranges, the two most common varieties are the navel, which is seedless and best suited for eating raw, and the Valencia orange, which may contain seeds and is known as the juice orange.

When purchasing fruit, it is important to consider the intended use. Fruits that will be cut, sliced, or cubed in preparation for the table need not be the largest in size. Small-size fruits such as apples and peaches are excellent for stewing and for pastry. The medium to large-size fruits may be more attractive to serve whole. They may also be cut into slices or chunks and served in salads.

**Selecting Fresh Fruits** The United States Department of Agriculture has established grades for fresh fruits, but these do not always appear on the fresh fruit labels. When they are used, grades are a good guide for purchasing fruits. The grades used for fresh fruit are the premium grades, U.S. Extra Fancy,

What methods of preserving the taste and nutritional value of fruit are shown in the picture below? Which is your favorite?

U.S. Fancy, U.S. Extra No. 1, and the basic trading grades, U.S. No. 1 and U.S. No. 2.

Fruit prices are not a reliable guide to either the quality or the nutritive value of fruits. Fruit that is in season is generally cheaper and of better quality than fruit that is sold out of season. When poor growing conditions limit the supply of any particular fruit, it may be of inferior quality yet high in price.

Since fresh fruits deteriorate rapidly after they have ripened, buy only the quantity which can be used before spoilage sets in. Color is an excellent indication of ripeness in many fruits. Most fruits lose their green color as they ripen; peaches and apricots turn yellow; cherries turn pink or red. A characteristic fruit fragrance can also be a guide to the selection of ripe cantaloupes and pineapples.

Some fruits are sold by the pound, such as apples, pears, grapes, peaches, and plums; berries are sold by the pint or quart; others are sold by units, such as one avocado, lemon, or melon; oranges are usually sold by the dozen.

Because fresh fruits are perishable, it is necessary to be able to recognize good quality when buying them. Good quality fruits are sound (free from blemishes, bruises, and mold), crisp (not wilted or limp), and firm (not overripe or soft). When looking for any fruit, the words *sound, crisp,* and *firm* are the important keys to their freshness.

**Selecting Frozen Fruits** Even though the United States Department of Agriculture has established some standards and grades for frozen foods, these seldom appear on the labels. You must rely on the brand name as a guide in the selection of frozen fruits. After you have used a brand, you will know its quality. Avoid buying frozen fruits in packages that are stained or not hard frozen. These signs indicate that defrosting and deterioration have taken place and quality is spoiled.

**Selecting Canned Fruits** Canned fruits and fruit juices are packed in cans and jars of different sizes. Knowing the can sizes and number of servings in each can will help you to avoid waste.

Most fruits are canned in a sugar syrup, but some are packed in fruit juice or water. The label gives information about the quality and contents of the can. Every label should include the name of the fruit, the net contents in weight or fluid ounces, and the name and address of the processor. It may include a letter grade or a descriptive word, or both, to indicate quality: Grade A, or Fancy; Grade B, or Choice; Grade C, or Standard.

The largest and most perfect of each kind of fruit is Grade A. Grade B is used for good fruit not so large as Grade A, and Grade C for good fruit less uniform in size and shape. Graded

Grades can be helpful when selecting fresh fruit, what other factors should you consider?

U.S. Extra Fancy
U.S. Fancy
U.S. Extra No. 1
U.S. No. 1
U.S. No. 2

## Usual Dried Fruit Package Sizes

| | |
|---|---|
| Raisins: | 1 ½ oz (42.5 g) Snack-Packs<br>15 oz (425 g) pkg = 3 c (approx.)<br>1 lb (454 g) transparent bag = 3¼ c (approx.) |
| Prunes: | Prunes are graded and sold according to size in 1 and 2 lb (454 and 900 g) cartons and transparent bags.<br><br>Usual sizes are:<br>Jumbo Imperial. . . . .26 to 30 per lb<br>Extra Large. . . . . . . .38 to 43 per lb<br>Large. . . . . . . . . . .48 to 53 per lb<br>Medium. . . . . . . . .62 to 67 per lb<br>Breakfast. . . . . . . .75 to 85 per lb<br><br>Also sold vacuum-packed in 1 lb (454 g) jars and cans. |
| Apricots: | Sold in 11 oz (312 g) cartons and 8 and 12 oz (227 and 340 g) transparent bags. Medium and large size fruits. |
| Peaches: | Sold in 11 oz (312 g) cartons and 12 oz (340 g) transparent bags. Medium and large size fruits. |
| Mixed Fruits: | Assorted prunes, apricots, peaches, and pears. Sold in 11 oz (312 g) cartons and 12 oz (340 g) transparent bags. |

Adapted from *Your Guide to Buying, Storing, Cooking, Dried Fruits and Raisins* Leaflet by Del Monte Foods, San Francisco.

canned fruits are packed under the supervision and inspection of a government official.

Packers may set their own standards of quality for fruit and may use their own brand names. Each grade would have a different brand name. Choose the grade that is satisfactory for your use. Avoid cans with dents or bulging ends. These are signs of spoilage or a broken seal.

**Selecting Dried Fruits** Dried fruits come in handy protective cartons and in clear bags. Quality grades are not usually listed on packages of dried fruit, but their labels give valuable information about the size and type or types of fruit. The common dried fruits and their package sizes are listed in the table on this page.

# Delicious Sources of Nutrients

Calorie for calorie, fruits provide us with a rich source of nutrients. They are low in calories and high in some essential minerals and vitamins, especially vitamins A and C. They supply us with dietary fiber. Composed of 80–95% water, fruits offer an additional benefit: they are thirst-quenching.

Fruit is an ideal food for the weight-conscious. The high water content combined with high fiber content make us feel full. The fructose can satisfy a longing for sweets. Most fruits contain no fats.

Of the 13 known vitamins, two types exist: fat soluble and water soluble. Fat-soluble vitamins can be stored by the body. Vitamin A, a fat-soluble vitamin, is stored in the liver. Fat-soluble vitamins can withstand high temperatures. Thus, cooking does not adversely affect the storage of these nutrients.

Vitamin C is a water-soluble vitamin. The body cannot store water-soluble vitamins. It uses the amount of vitamins it needs and excretes the extra. For this reason, fruits with vitamin C should be eaten daily. They should also be eaten raw or as juice whenever possible. Vitamin C and other water-soluble vitamins cannot withstand prolonged cooking or high temperatures.

## Common Fruits and Their Nutrients

*Apples* are available year round. Over 7,000 kinds are grown in the United States, but the most common varieties sold in produce departments include Cortland, Granny Smith, Jonathan, McIntosh, Red and Golden Delicious, and Rome. Apples contain some potassium and vitamin A. They are a rich source of dietary fiber, and supply pectin, the ingredient used to make jams and jellies. Pectin has recently been linked to lower blood cholesterol levels.

*Bananas* are actually berries. They are picked green to achieve the best flavor and to prevent the seeds from becoming too large. Easily digested, bananas are popular with all age groups from infants to the elderly. Bananas are rich in potassium and contain some vitamin A, iron, niacin, and protein.

*Oranges* have become popular in the United States within this century, although they have been grown in eastern Asia for thousands of years. Oranges are Americans' main source of vitamin C. They are also a rich supply of potassium and a fair amount of vitamin A. Ironically, frozen orange juice can be a better source of vitamin C than fresh-squeezed.

*Peaches* are another favorite fruit, apparently enjoyed as much as 4,000 years ago by the Chinese. Once picked, peaches do not ripen well. For optimal flavor and nutrition, buy ripe peaches. When ripe, they are rich in vitamin A and potassium and have a fair amount of niacin and some iron and vitamin C.

*Pears* also go back some 4,000 years. Today, 5,000 different kinds are grown. Pears ripen best off the tree. They are good sources of dietary fiber and potassium.

Fruits provide vitamins A and C and dietary fiber.

## Storage of Fruit

To preserve and protect the quality, nutrient value, color, flavor, and general appearance, fruit should be stored properly. Proper **storage** requires placing the fruit in a container or space that will protect the fruit.

**Fresh Fruit Storage**  Ripe fruits are perishable and should be stored in the special fruit and vegetable drawer of the refrigerator in order to prevent rapid loss of moisture. Fruits may be washed before storage, except for berries, which spoil quickly after being washed. Fruits should be handled gently to avoid bruising. If fruits such as peaches, pears, plums, and bananas are slightly green, they may be ripened at room temperature and then stored in the refrigerator. The skin of bananas may darken, but the flesh will remain flavorful and firm. Fruits with strong aromas, such as pineapples, cantaloupes, or apples, should be carefully wrapped before they are stored so that their fragrance will not be absorbed by any of the other foods in the refrigerator.

**Frozen Fruit Storage**  Frozen fruits should be stored immediately in the freezer. They should not be thawed until they are to be used. Once the fruit has been thawed, it should not be refrozen.

**Canned Fruit Storage**  Canned fruits should be stored in a cool, dry place. After the can has been opened, the fruit becomes perishable and should be transferred to a plastic or glass container. It should be stored covered in the refrigerator.

**Dried Fruit Storage**  Dried fruits are stored in a cool, dry place in their original sealed carton or clear bag. After opening, close the box tightly, or fold the bag tightly. Cooked dried

Unused portions of fresh fruits should be wrapped and refrigerated to prevent spoilage.

fruits are perishable and should be covered and refrigerated.

When properly stored, fruits can add much to the pleasure of eating. Proper storage of all fruits will preserve color, texture, flavor, aroma, and nutrient values. It is because of their nutrient values that fruits are important protective foods.

### For Review

1. Describe at least three changes that occur as fruit ripens. What causes these changes?
2. What are three forms of processed fruit? Why are fruits processed?
3. What are some characteristics to look for when selecting fresh fruit? Frozen fruit? Canned fruit?
4. Describe three ways to prevent spoilage of fresh fruits.
5. Explain one way to prevent spoilage in frozen fruit. In canned fruit. In dried fruit.

## Applesauce     Yield: 4-6 servings

6 medium cooking apples    ⅓ c (80 mL) sugar, or
½ c (125 mL) water              more if desired

1. Wash, pare, quarter, and core apples; place in saucepan.
2. Add water, cover, and simmer over low heat until tender, 15 to 20 minutes.
3. Mash with potato masher or press through coarse sieve.
4. Stir in sugar (sweeten to taste) and heat until sugar dissolves, 1 to 2 minutes.
5. Serve hot or cold, or store in refrigerator.

Approximate nutrition information per serving: calories–90; protein–trace; fat–trace; cholesterol–0; carbohydrates–24 g; sodium–trace.

## Nutrient Contributions

Nutrients are the building blocks of food, and the same building blocks that make up food are used to make up your body. These nutrients are divided into six groups: Carbohydrates, fats, protein, vitamins, minerals, and water. Your need for each of the nutrient groups will be studied along with the foods in which they are found most abundantly. Most foods are made of more than one nutrient. Fruits, for example, are made chiefly of vitamins, minerals, water, and carbohydrates.

### Vitamins

Most fruits contain generous amounts of vitamins, but all vitamins are not present in the same amounts in all fruits. Fruits are the best sources of vitamin C (ascorbic acid); they are good sources of vitamin A; and they provide moderate amounts of the B vitamins.

The citrus fruits—oranges, grapefruits, lemons, limes—as well as cantaloupes and strawberries, supply *vitamin C* in the largest amounts. The citrus fruits are our most depend-able common food sources of vitamin C. Oranges in some form—fresh, frozen, or canned—usually give more vitamin C per dollar spent than other foods. Most fruits contain vitamin C; some in abundance, as in citrus fruits, cantaloupes, and strawberries; others in lesser amounts, as in pears and apples.

The high levels of vitamin C in pills, advocated by some, have no special curative powers, and could be harmful. Food can supply your body with all the vitamin C it needs.

Although scurvy is not a problem for us today, many people do not get as much vitamin C as they need for good health. Many students have diets that are low in vitamin C. Does your diet measure up to your vitamin C needs? It probably does if you include one serving of citrus fruit with the other fruits and vegetables in your daily food intake.

Your body needs vitamin C to form a cementlike material called **collagen,** which holds the cells together in much the same way mortar holds brick together. When vitamin C is lacking, collagen cannot be formed and then several things happen: (1) the bones become

Oranges grow in warm regions, such as this grove in Florida. Occasional cold snaps can damage the fruit; very cold weather can even endanger the orange trees themselves.

## Fruits: United States Seasonal Availability and Nutrient Qualities

| Fruit | Season | Vitamins | Minerals |
|---|---|---|---|
| apples | fall, winter, spring | E | potassium |
| apricots | summer | A | |
| avocados | year-round | A, C, niacin, $B_6$ | potassium, zinc, phosphorus |
| bananas | year-round | $B_6$ | magnesium, potassium |
| blackberries | summer, early fall | C | |
| cantaloupe | summer, early fall | A, C | |
| cherries | spring, summer | A | |
| cranberries | fall | C | |
| dates | fall | niacin | potassium, iron, magnesium, calcium |
| grapefruit | fall, winter, early spring | C, A (pink) | |
| grapes | summer, fall | C | |
| lemons | year-round | C | |
| limes | summer, early fall | C | |
| nectarines | summer | A | |
| oranges | winter, spring | C, A, folacin | magnesium |
| peaches | spring, summer | A, niacin | potassium |
| pears | summer, fall | A | |
| pineapple | year-round | C | |
| plums | late summer | A | |
| raisins | year-round | | potassium, phosphorus, magnesium, iron |
| raspberries | summer | C | |
| strawberries | winter, summer | C, A | iron |
| tangerines | winter, early spring | A, C | |
| watermelon | summer, early fall | C | magnesium, potassium, iron |

fragile and break easily; (2) gums become soft and can bleed easily; (3) walls of blood vessels and muscle cells become weak, less elastic, and frequently rupture, causing small pinpoint hemorrhages; and (4) wounds and broken bones do not heal properly.

When vitamin C is adequate, blood vessels are more elastic, gums are firmer, and bones are stronger. The body is made of many types of cells, and all of these cells require vitamin C to form the collagen which binds them together. You will need vitamin C, or ascorbic acid, as long as you live.

Your body cannot store or manufacture vitamin C, so your supply of it will need to come from the food you eat each day. Therefore, it is important to include in your daily diet at least one food that is high in vitamin C.

Along with vitamin C, some fruits, recognized by their yellow to red color, can also contribute vitamin A to your diet. A yellow pigment in plants (fruits and vegetables) is called **carotene.** This pigment can be converted by the body into vitamin A. The yellow melons, pineapples, apricots, and peaches are special sources of vitamin A because they contain carotene. Most fruits supply some vitamin A, but the fruits that are deeper yellow supply more carotene than those that are pale yellow or white. You will learn more about the foods that contain vitamin A in the milk and vegetable chapters.

Vitamin A is important for good vision. In areas of the world where diets are low in vitamin A, severe eye disease is a problem. In our country, most of us get enough vitamin A to prevent a serious eye disease. How quickly do your eyes adjust when you go from a well-lighted lobby into a dark theater? Vitamin A helps your eyes adjust quickly from light to dark. It prevents "night blindness" so that your eyes can adjust to the dark. You also need vitamin A for good growth and healthy skin and hair. When vitamin A is missing from the diet, hair becomes dry and coarse, and its growth slows. Foods that contain vitamin A should be included in your diet each day.

In addition to vitamins A and C, most fruits contain the B vitamins; however, other foods, such as milk and cereals, are more important sources of the B vitamins.

## Minerals

In addition to vitamins, fruits supply an added bonus by contributing minerals to the diet. Two minerals, *iron* and *calcium,* are found in fruits in important amounts. Fruits such as oranges, strawberries, cantaloupes, and the dried fruits such as figs, dates, raisins, prunes, and apricots are good sources of iron and calcium. You need iron for red blood and calcium for strong bones and teeth.

## Other Nutrients

*Sugar* and *cellulose* are carbohydrates found in fruits. Ripe fruits contain more sugar, which gives them a pleasant sweet flavor. Fruit sugar supplies the body with energy. The skin and pulp of fruits contain cellulose, which the body cannot digest, but which serves as a natural laxative and helps to maintain body regularity.

Fruits, as a group, contain very little protein and fat. These nutrients are provided by other foods. Fruits make their most important contribution to the diet through their generous supply of vitamins, minerals, and cellulose.

### Practical Tip
- Store unused tomato paste for later use by first freezing it by individual teaspoonfuls on a cookie sheet and then wrapping it in moisture-proof wrap and freezing.

Fresh fruits combined with lettuce and other vegetables provide extra nutrition to salads.

## Preparation of Fruits

Most ripe fruits are delicious and enjoyable when eaten raw. Raw fruits need only a thorough washing to remove any dirt or remaining spray before eating. Fresh fruit may be served whole, cut, or sliced. Fruits are popularly served for breakfast, but they can and should be included at other meals. Fresh fruits served as appetizers, salads, and desserts give a pleasing contrast to the soft foods of the meal.

Most raw fruit is more palatable and has a higher nutritive value than the cooked or processed fruits. Cut raw fruits such as banana, apple, and pear, which have a low acid content, turn dark on exposure to air. This discoloration can be prevented by sprinkling the cut surface with an acid fruit juice such as lemon or orange.

Fruits may be cooked for variety in eating and to soften the cellulose of hard fruits. Fruit cookery involves two important principles: (1) a change in texture, form, or consistency of the fruit due to cooking; and (2) the preservation of nutrients or food values.

The method of cooking will determine the texture of the cooked fruit; that is, whether the fruit will break apart or retain its shape. When fruits are cooked in moist heat, the cellulose in them becomes soft and the fruit breaks apart. This effect is desirable when fruits are used for

Many Chinese main dishes make use of fruit, such as pineapple, to add flavor and color to the meal.

making sauces such as applesauce or rhubarb sauce. When fruits are cooked with sugar, they will retain their shape because the sugar strengthens the cellulose structure and keeps the fruit from coming apart. When preparing cinnamon apple rings or stewed apples or peaches, for example, the fruit is cooked with sugar or in a syrup. Fruits cooked in a sugar syrup will retain their shape and firm texture, while fruits cooked without sugar will soften and break apart. The texture desired in the cooked fruit product will determine whether sugar is to be added before or after cooking.

Another principle of fruit cookery and preparation involves the preservation of the food values or nutrients. Some vitamins, especially vitamin C, can be destroyed by exposure to the oxygen in the air. If fruits and fruit juices are prepared just before serving, vitamin loss from air can be reduced. Cooked fruits and canned fruits should be stored after opening in a covered container in the refrigerator. Use a proper sized jar for leftover fruits and juices so that oxygen will have less chance to destroy vita-

mins. Also, when fruits are cut, more surface is exposed to air and vitamin loss will be greater. When preparing fruit juices, do not strain them because this brings the juice into greater contact with air and results in greater destruction of vitamin C.

Fruits should be cooked in as little water as possible so that vitamins and minerals will be preserved. Some vitamins, like vitamin C for which fruits are important, can dissolve in water, as sugar does. The amount of water used to cook fruit depends on its cellulose and water content. Juicy fruits, such as berries and rhubarb, contain less cellulose and more juice or water; they can be cooked in their own juice without adding water. Other fruits, such as apples and peaches, may require a very small amount of water. The liquid in which fruits are cooked will contain dissolved vitamins and minerals, and it should be served with the fruit.

In many fruits, vitamins and minerals are concentrated just under the skin. You will have the advantage of all of the nutrient values when

Many desserts are nutrient-poor and high in kilocalories. Using fresh fruits, such as in this orange tart, increases the vitamin, mineral, and cellulose content of a dessert.

fruits are eaten with their skins. For example, unpeeled apples in Waldorf salad will not only retain the nutrients, but will add color appeal as well. When you wish to remove the skins from fruit, peel thinly so that nutrient loss will not be great. Large whole fruits, such as apples, pears, and apricots, can be cooked in their skins. The skin preserves the shape of the fruit and helps retain more of the vitamins and minerals.

Special care is required to protect the nutrients in fruits. Vitamin C is the most easily destroyed of all vitamins. To avoid unnecessary loss of vitamin C, remember that it is easily destroyed by oxygen and heat, and it dissolves in water.

## Methods of Cooking Fruits

To provide interest and variety in the use of fresh fruit, the fruit may be cooked. The appearance, texture, and flavor will be changed by cooking. Fruits are most often cooked by *simmering, stewing,* and *baking*. To simmer, fruits are cooked covered in their own juices or in a small amount of added water. Simmered fruits are often mashed to give a fruit sauce of uniform consistency, as with applesauce. Stewing is another way to cook fruit. Stewed fruit is usually cooked in a small amount of liquid with added sugar, and each piece of fruit retains most of its original shape. Fruits with heavy skins are good for baking because the skin serves as a cover; it holds in the steam needed to soften the cellulose and protects the nutrients and fruit flavors. Fruits such as peaches, plums, rhubarb, and bananas may be baked in a covered baking dish.

Many people enjoy eating dried fruits without cooking them; others prefer the plump, soft texture of cooked dried fruits. Much of the moisture lost when fruits are dried is replaced during cooking. Dried fruits may be soaked in hot water for a short time and then cooked in the same water. The fruit is cooked at a simmering temperature (below boiling) in a covered pan. However, most dried fruits do not require soaking before cooking. If you use sugar, add it near the end of the cooking period, after the fruit is plump and soft. Sugar can interfere with the absorption of water by the fruit and keep the cell walls from softening.

Fruits may be used in a variety of other ways. Occasionally fruits are used to make fritters. Fruit fritters are made from such fruits as apples, bananas, and pineapples. The cut or dried fruit is dipped into a batter, deep-fat fried until golden brown, and served hot with powdered sugar or syrup.

Some baked products are made with fruit. Date, orange, cranberry, and blueberry quick breads are popular. Canned, frozen, fresh, mashed, or candied fruits may be used for these special breads.

Pies to please every taste can be made from fresh, canned, frozen, or dried fruits. Cream pies often include a layer of fruit such as banana, peach, or strawberry. Fruit-flavored sherbets and ice creams are always popular. The variety of fruit desserts includes exotic cherries jubilee or a gourmet fruit soufflé!

## Microwaving Fruits

Because of their high sugar and moisture content, fruits will cook very quickly in the microwave, so special care must be taken in timing. So all fruit will cook at the same rate, select whole fruits or cut pieces of a uniform size. Always cover fruit sauces to retain moisture, but leave any fruit desserts containing pastry uncovered to prevent soggy crusts.

## Tips for Microwaving Fruits

- To increase fruit yield, microwave citrus fruits 20–30 seconds on HIGH.
- To dry lemon and orange peels, place the grated peel in a glass bowl, and cook on HIGH for 30–60 seconds.
- To soften dried fruits, sprinkle with water and heat 30 seconds on HIGH.
- To toast coconut, cook on HIGH for 1–1½ minutes.
- To defrost frozen orange juice, heat on LOW for a few seconds, stirring once or twice.
- Do *not* use the microwave for preparing fruits for canning.

## Convenience in Fruits

Canned, frozen, and dried fruits offer a convenience. First, they have been processed so that the fruit can be kept without spoilage long after the growing season ends. Preparation procedures such as washing and cutting are done by the packer, and even sugar is added to most fruits except the dried fruits. All forms of fruit can be served directly from the package except for the partial thawing of frozen fruits.

Canned and frozen fruits are prepared in the same forms—whole, half, sliced, sauce, or juice—as are commonly used for fresh fruits. Fruit pie fillings are available and are ready for the pastry as soon as the can is opened. Juices which have been frozen, canned, or packed as a dry mix eliminate the need to squeeze the fruit. Canned juices need only to be chilled before serving; frozen juices and powdered fruit concentrates require only dilution with water for serving.

All of these convenience items have been designed to use time, effort, and energy well.

However, these convenience items have not eliminated the need to make decisions. Because of the wide variety of fruit products available, decision making has become more complicated. The decision is yours when it is time to select which item to use. Will you use fresh, frozen, dried, or canned fruit? What will help you make the decision? Will you consider time available, quality of food, and cost? How will such factors as the color, flavor, size, shape, texture, and nutrient value of the prepared food product fit into your meals? Will the convenience fruit item add interest, contrast, and attractiveness to your meal? If the food is not packed in glass, how will you learn what quality and kind of food is in the package?

Your answers to these many questions can help you decide which food product is best for your meals. In deciding which fruit product to purchase, you should also consider your values and standards. Products that measure up to your values and standards will provide greater eating pleasure and satisfaction for you. You will be pleased with your accomplishments.

## For Review

1. Describe at least three ways that fruits can be served.
2. What happens to fruit cooked in moist heat? Why is this sometimes a desired effect?
3. Why is it important not to expose fruits to air?
4. Describe two advantages of cooking apples in their skins.
5. Why are plums a better fruit for baking than blueberries?
6. What are three advantages of using convenience forms of fruits?

# *13* Chapter Review

## Summary

During the mid 1700s, fruits became recognized for their nutritious value in preventing disease. Today, fruits with vegetables comprise one of the groups in the Daily Food Guide. Fruits are an important food source to include in the diet because of their minerals, vitamins, and cellulose. There are several ways of categorizing the many kinds of fruits. One way is to group them as pomes, drupes, berries, citrus fruits, melons, and tropical fruits. Although most fruits are available as fresh, frozen, canned, or dried, the form purchased should be determined by its intended use. In the preparation of a fruit, consideration needs to be given to the method of cooking as well as the preservation of nutrients. To protect its nutritive value and flavor, proper storage is necessary.

## Vocabulary

Use these vocabulary words to complete the statements below.

ascorbic acid             fruits
canning                   protective foods
carotene                  scurvy
collagen                  storage
enzymes

1. Seed plants used for food are called _____.
2. One experiment found that sailors who were given small amounts of lime juice were able to prevent _____, which is a disease caused by the lack of vitamin C.
3. Another name for vitamin C is _____.
4. Our bodies need vitamin C to form a cement-like material called _____, which holds the cells together.
5. Because fruits contribute important minerals, vitamins, and cellulose, they are known as _____.
6. Some fruits have a yellow to red color, and this yellow pigment, which can be converted by the body into vitamin A, is called _____.
7. Because fresh fruits spoil quickly, proper _____ is needed to protect their nutritive value, color, flavor, and appearance.
8. _____, which are substances that bring about chemical reactions, cause fruits to ripen, but they are also one of the reasons why fresh fruits spoil quickly.
9. _____ is one method of preserving fruits for later use by exposing the fruits in containers to very high temperatures.

## Chapter Questions

1. Name the group to which each of these fruits belongs:
   a. cantaloupes     d. kiwis
   b. papayas         e. tangerines
   c. apricots        f. grapes
2. What kinds of fresh fruit do you eat in your family and to which group does each kind of fruit belong?
3. Why are prices not a reliable guide to the quality and nutritive value of fruits?
4. How should you store left-over canned pineapple and fresh pineapple? Why?

5. What are three uses for canned peaches?
6. Why should fresh fruit be washed before eating?
7. What is a way to prevent slices of fresh apple from turning brown?
8. Why is the preservation of food nutrients an important principle of fruit cookery and preparation?
9. Compare fruits cooked in a moist heat and fruits cooked in a sugary syrup.
10. When you prepare fruits, how can you preserve vitamin C?
11. What are the various forms that are available for purchasing canned and frozen fruits?

## Skill Activities

**1. Decision making** In your food journal or card file box of recipes, add recipes that use a fruit from each fruit group. For example, a recipe for apple pie would be appropriate for pomes and peach cobbler for drupes. You can find recipes in books, magazines, and newspapers, and on the backs of canned and frozen fruit containers.

**2. Decision making** Make a chart to compare the price, color, texture, and nutritive value of fresh fruits. Divide a piece of lined paper into six columns. Down the left-hand side, on every other line, write: "Kind of fruit," "Price," "Color," "Texture," "Nutritive value," and "Fruit groups." Visit a grocery store and select fruits to compare, trying to include at least one example from each fruit group.

**3. Communication** Research and report on how to dry fruits. Include two ways fruit can be dried and the methods to follow, the benefits of dried fruits, uses of dried fruits, and two recipes that use dried fruits as ingredients.

**4. Critical thinking** Make a chart to record the fruits that you eat in a week. List each day of the week down the left-hand side of a sheet of paper. Across the top, make four columns and write one of these headings above each column: "Kind of fruit," "Fruit group," "Fruit form," and "Ingredient in another food." Then write the kind of fruit you ate, the fruit group to which it belonged, its form, and if it was an ingredient in another food, what that food was.

**5. Food science** The tartness of fruits is usually directly related to the acid content of the fruit tissue. First, taste at least three fruits, such as apple, orange, tomato, or grape, and rank them according to tartness. Next, use litmus paper to compare the acidity of the fruits you tasted. Place a small piece of the tissue (pulp) of each fruit on a separate piece of litmus paper. Compare the color change of the litmus paper with the pH chart provided; the lower the pH, the higher the acid content. How do your taste-test results compare with the litmus test?

# 14 Grains

## As you read, think about:

- how to identify, select, use, and store grain products.
- what nutrients grain products provide.
- how cooking affects grain products.
- how to prepare grain products.

**Vocabulary**
grains
staple foods
beriberi
thiamin
riboflavin
amino acids
enriched
restored
cereal

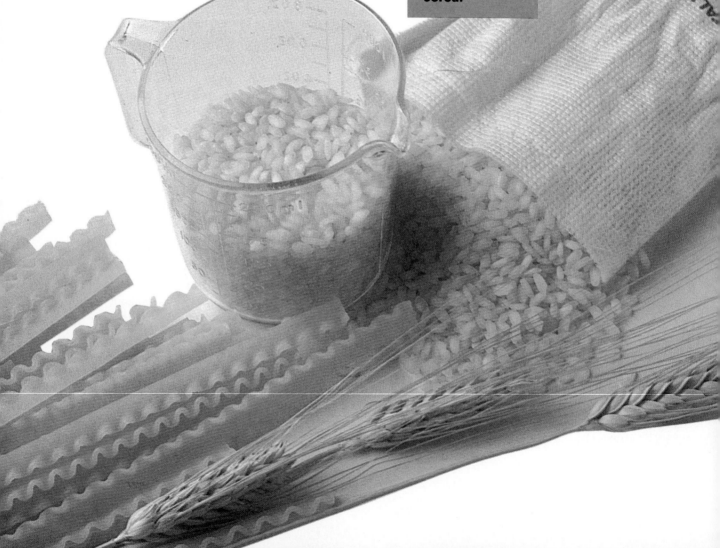

**Grains** are the edible seeds of certain grasses. In most parts of the world, a good diet centers around a grain food. The principle grains include barley, buckwheat, corn, oats, rice, rye, and wheat. Rice is still the most common food in many parts of the Orient and India. In Latin America, corn is used in porridge and in a thin, flat bread served at every meal. Wheat is the chief grain in the United States. Wheat, the most important of the grains, provides nourishment for more nations of the world than any other food. Wheat is basic in the diets of people in Europe, Africa, North America, South America, Australia, and a part of Asia. Grains and their products are considered to be **staple foods** because of their good keeping quality, their high energy value, and their relatively low cost.

Long ago, corn was ground by hand into flour or meal (below) directly from the corn plant (above right). The wheat plant (above left) and the barley plant (below right) were also manually ground. Today, machines quickly perform the milling process, providing various types of flours and cereals.

# Types of Grains

*Wheat,* like most grains, is used to make flour, breakfast cereals, and pastas (macaroni products). *Corn,* second to wheat as the most popular grain in the United States, is often used as a vegetable, but it is also made into breakfast cereals, grits, and hominy.

Wheat

Corn

Barley

*Oats* are used in breakfast cereals and as an ingredient in baked products and in some desserts. The cereals made from oats are usually made of the whole grain with only the outer husk removed. Because of this process, oat cereals are rich in nutrients.

Three other types of grains—rye, barley, and buckwheat—are used for flour. *Rye* is used mainly for bread flour, while *barley* is used for the flour in baby foods and for the production of malt. *Buckwheat* is used for pancake flour, although some buckwheat groats are used as a breakfast cereal. No matter what the use of a particular grain, each type shares the same structure.

### Parts of Grains

Each grain has three basic parts: bran, endosperm, and germ. The *bran* is the outside covering of the grain and consists of several layers. It protects the grain kernel until it is planted or milled. The *endosperm* is the inner white portion. The *germ,* found at one end of the kernel, is the sprouting part from which a new part grows. The grain kernel illustration shows the location of the three parts of a grain.

The bran and germ may be separated from the endosperm in the milling process, leaving only the white endosperm for use as flour or as refined cereals.

Whole-grain flour and cereals contain the finely ground bran, germ, and endosperm of the whole kernel. Whole-grain products have a dis-tinctive flavor and coarser texture than those made from white flour. Because of the higher fat content of the germ, whole-grain flour is more difficult to keep and sometimes develops an unpleasant flavor under poor storage conditions.

### For Review

1. List the four types of grains and a use for each.
2. List and describe the basic parts of a grain kernel.
3. What is the difference between refined flour and whole-grain flour?

## Nutrient Contributions

The grain kernel is a storehouse of nutrients needed and used by people since civilization began. The nutrients provided by cereals include carbohydrates, vitamins, minerals, fat, and protein. The nutrients are not equally distributed throughout the three parts of the grain. The bran and germ are rich sources of minerals, vitamins, and cellulose; the endosperm is a rich source of starch but lacks vitamins, minerals, and cellulose.

All cereals and grain products are rich sources of energy, but their vitamin and mineral values will depend upon which parts of the grain

Note the proportions of bran, endosperm, and germ in each of the four types of grain shown.

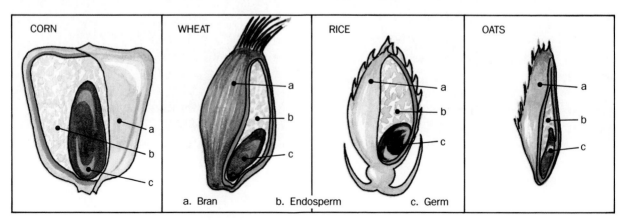

CORN  WHEAT  RICE  OATS

a. Bran  b. Endosperm  c. Germ

are used. Cereals and breads that have high vitamin and mineral value are those that contain all three parts of the grain. The refined cereal products are made from the endosperm, which is rich in starch but lacks vitamins and minerals.

## Carbohydrates

The nutrients supplied by grains serve many functions in the body. Two forms of carbohydrates are found in grains: *starch* for body energy and *cellulose* for regularity. Three-fourths of the grain is made up of starch and is an excellent source of energy. Cellulose is found abundantly in the bran, and although it cannot be digested by the body, it supplies roughage (bulk or fiber). Because cellulose is not digested, it acts as a natural laxative and sometimes is called the "scrub brush" for the intestine, helping to keep the body regular.

The bran of whole grains is a concentrated source of fiber in your diet. For this reason, fiber from whole grains is a more effective laxative than that from fruits and vegetables. The fiber of whole grains absorbs water and thus enlarges in bulk and keeps fecal materials soft. If your diet includes little fiber-rich foods, an increased intake of whole-grain products, fruits, and vegetables could overcome most constipation problems. The skin, peelings, and pulp of fruits and vegetables and the hulls (bran) of grains will furnish the fiber you need.

Some recent research also suggests low-fiber diets may contribute to an increase in diseases of the intestinal tract. Some native Africans consume an unrefined diet and take in six times more fiber than people of developed Western countries. They do not develop intestinal diseases.

High-fiber diets are now used to relieve the pain and bowel irregularity associated with diverticulosis (pouches or sacs in the intestinal membrane). Liberal intake of fiber-rich foods will help you avoid constipation as well as diverticular disease.

It is generally believed that dietary fiber increases fecal bulk. Although some have proposed other benefits for dietary fiber, at this time no other general agreement has been reached concerning the role of fiber for humans. Some people assume that dietary fiber causes fecal substances to move quickly through the intestinal tract before bacterial decomposition of intestinal materials occurs. Other people say that dietary fiber may combine with some possibly harmful substances and prevent their absorption into the body.

Although dietary fiber serves an important function in contributing to bowel regularity, in excess it can reduce the digestibility of other food nutrients. Fiber in your diet should come from the generous use of fruits, vegetables, and whole grains rather than from high-fiber breads or other purchased fiber supplements. An excessive intake of fiber can interfere with absorption of calcium and trace elements such as zinc.

Whole grains, fruits, vegetables, nuts, and legumes (peas, beans) are fiber-rich foods. Wheat bran is the richest source of fiber; refined grains (breads, cereals, pastas) have considerably less fiber than do whole grains; while fish, poultry, meat, eggs, sugars, and fats lack fiber.

Fiber is a necessary part of the diet. Foods can provide all of the fiber you need when you include liberal amounts of fiber-rich foods daily.

## Vitamins

The loss of many Japanese sailors because of the disease **beriberi** led to the discovery of another vitamin: *vitamin $B_1$,* or *thiamin.* This disease, caused by the lack of vitamin $B_1$, was so common among Japanese sailors that three out of every ten were likely to have beriberi, and some died from it.

## B Vitamins

| Name | Purpose | Deficiency |
|------|---------|------------|
| B₁ (thiamin) | Thiamin is needed for growth, good appetite, healthy nerves, and good body coordination. It helps the body release energy from carbohydrates. | *Beriberi Symptoms:* polyneuritis, fatigue problems, and lameness of the legs. |
| B₂ (riboflavin) | Riboflavin is needed for growth, nerve tissue, the digestive tract, and health. It helps the body to release energy from carbohydrates, fats, and protein. | *Ariboflavinosis Symptoms:* Cheilosis cracks at corners of mouth; lips become inflamed. Glossitis—smooth, purple-red tongue. |
| niacin | Niacin is needed for oxidation of carbohydrates in body cells. It is needed by all living cells to release energy from carbohydrates, fat, and protein. | *Pellagra Symptoms:* red rash on face and hands, scaly and dark pigmentation of skin exposed to sun, nervousness, irritability. |

Takaki, a Japanese navy physician, believed that the disease was due to diet. He studied two shiploads of men on a nine-month voyage. On one ship, the regular diet of white rice was served; on the other ship, the diet included meat, fish, and vegetables in addition to white rice. On the first ship, the sailors developed beriberi; the sailors on the second ship did not.

Dr. Eijkman, a Dutch physician, studied two groups of birds. To one group he gave white polished rice; to the other group he gave brown rice. The birds on white rice developed beriberi. Several years later it was discovered that vitamin $B_1$ was the nutrient that prevented beriberi.

Grains are important food sources of the vitamin B group, which is also known as the B-complex group. Whole-grain cereals are important sources of several of the B vitamins —$B_1$, $B_2$, and niacin. The chemical name for vitamin $B_1$ is **thiamin,** and for vitamin $B_2$, **riboflavin.** Your body needs vitamin $B_1$ for growth, good appetite, healthy nerves, and good body coordination, and to help the body release energy from carbohydrates. Vitamin $B_1$ prevents the disease beriberi. Some of the symptoms of beriberi are fatigue, dizziness, digestive problems, and lameness of the legs.

**Riboflavin** (RY-buh-flay-vin), or $B_2$, is needed for growth, nerve tissue, the digestive tract, and health. It helps the body oxidize, or "burn," sugars and starches to release energy.

**Niacin** (NY-uh-sin) is required for oxidation of carbohydrates in body cells, and it prevents pellagra. Niacin is required by all living cells to release energy from food.

The B vitamins, like vitamin C, are soluble in water and cannot be stored in the body. You need a new supply of these vitamins each day; therefore, it becomes important to include grains and grain products in your daily meals.

## Minerals

In addition to carbohydrates and the B vitamins, whole-grain and enriched grain products contribute minerals to your diet. The minerals *iron* and *phosphorus* are found in important amounts in grain or cereal products. You will recall that iron is needed for good red blood, and phosphorus for strong bones and teeth.

## Protein

Grains supply proteins, but some of the protein in grain products or in cereals lacks essential amino acids. The **amino acids** are the building blocks from which protein is made. The proteins that lack some of the essential amino acids are called incomplete proteins because they are unable to adequately meet the needs of your body for protein. However, the proteins of cereals do make a valuable contribution to the total amount of protein in your diet. Cereals are usually served with milk and, in this way, the milk protein supplements the cereal proteins. The milk protein contains the amino acids lacking in cereal, and the two foods, milk and cereal together, supply valuable proteins to meet the needs of your body.

## Enrichment of Grain Products

Whole-grain or enriched products add important nutrients to the diet. Grains which have been refined contribute only calories and incomplete proteins, since vitamins, minerals, and cellulose are removed in the refining process.

Many people prefer white bread to whole-grain bread products. To offset the loss of nutritional value, a bread enrichment program was started in 1943. The nutrients thiamin ($B_1$), riboflavin ($B_2$), niacin, and iron, lost in the refining process, were put back into the bread product. This bread is called **enriched** bread. These same nutrients are also added to some cereals and other grain products that are labeled **restored** or enriched. Many bakers and producers voluntarily enrich their bread and cereal products.

Today, more than 85 percent of cereals are fortified. Some cereals are fortified to provide greater than whole-grain amounts of vitamins, minerals, and protein. Most ready-to-eat cereals are fortified with B vitamins ($B_1$, $B_2$, and niacin) and usually iron. A one-ounce (30-g) serving of these cereals before the addition of milk provides about 20 percent of your minimum daily requirement for these vitamins. The whole-grain cereals and bread products contain *all* the nutrients, both known and unknown, while enriched products include only those that have been restored after refinement.

Rolling fields of rice are carefully cultivated to produce the thousands of grains from each single plant.

White rice in which nutrients have been preserved is known as "converted" rice. Before polishing, the brown rice is soaked and steamed under pressure and then dried. This parboiling treatment draws the vitamins into the endosperm where they will be retained during milling. No added nutrients are necessary because the natural vitamins of the rice are preserved.

## For Review

1. Which part of the grain kernel contains starch?
2. Why do refined cereal products have less nutrient value than the unrefined products?
3. What are three possible benefits of a high-fiber diet?
4. What disease results from a vitamin $B_1$ deficiency? A niacin deficiency?
5. Why is it important to have a daily supply of B vitamins?
6. In your diet, how can you make up for the lack of essential amino acids in grains?
7. Why are bread products often enriched? Fortified?

## Uses of Grains

The term *cereal* can mean any breakfast food made from grain, or it can mean any grain that is used as food. However, the term **cereal** often refers to specially prepared grain products used as breakfast cereals. Grain products can be used in a variety of ways in our meals. For convenience, their uses can be grouped into four general classes: the breakfast cereals, the pastas (macaroni products), rice, and flour.

## Breakfast Cereals

Breakfast cereals appear in many shapes and forms. They can be grouped into two major types: the ready-to-eat cereals, which have been cooked and are ready for the table, and the cereals that require cooking before serving.

Common uncooked cereals are made from corn, oats, and wheat and are purchased as cornmeal, rolled oats, and cream of wheat. Many of the uncooked cereals are available in a form for quick cooking such as quick rolled oats.

The variety of ready-to-eat cereals is almost endless. Ready-to-eat cereals are precooked and then rolled, flaked, puffed, or shredded. They are often made from corn, oats, wheat, and rice.

All forms of cereals served with milk are popular for breakfast. The combination of cereal, milk, and some fruit is an excellent source of nutrients and is a good way to begin the day.

In addition to their service as breakfast main dishes, cereals have other uses. The ready-to-eat cereals may be used as a topping on casseroles, or may be rolled into crumbs and

Because grain is such a basic food, drought-stricken areas of the world receive this staple from nations with a surplus.

Fiber is the stringy part of vegetables, fruits, and legumes. It makes carrots and lettuce crunchy, bean soup thick, and whole-grain bread heavier. Fiber gives form to vegetables and fruit. It is made up of many chemical compounds, but the most abundant is cellulose, the material that makes plant cell walls. Fiber cannot be digested, but it plays an important role in digestion.

For generations, folk wisdom held that fiber aided digestion. Until recently, even nutritionists tended to undervalue fiber, thinking it was nonessential to the diet.

The rediscovery of fiber's role in the diet began about 20 years ago. A British scientist noted that urban Africans experienced diseases unknown to rural Africans. The scientist speculated that the fiber content in the diets of the rural Africans helped guard against the diseases. Highly controversial, this research prompted others to investigate fiber's role in the diet. More recent investigations reveal some evidence (but no conclusions) that fiber may help regulate constipation, cancer of the colon, diabetes, and obesity. This recent research prompted the U.S. Department of Health and Human Services and the USDA to advise Americans of the possible consequences of a low-fiber diet. Fiber, once classified as a nonessential part of the diet, has become important again.

How does fiber affect digestion? Its effects begin with chewing. Fiber takes longer to chew than other foods. Chewing activates saliva production which, in turn, stimulates the stomach to produce digestive juices. Once in the stomach, fiber absorbs water and adds bulk to stomach contents. The contents swell and become thicker. This slows down the emptying of the stomach and the movement through the intestines. More nutrients can be absorbed when the food travels more slowly. However, fiber also binds calcium, zinc, copper, and other nutrients,

All of these foods are rich in dietary fiber. Although fiber cannot be digested, it serves an important role in the diet.

preventing the body from getting some important minerals.

Scientists speculate that fiber may help control obesity because many plant foods, which are rich in fiber, are low in calories and make you feel fuller. The slowing down of digestion that fiber causes may delay feelings of hunger. This and other properties of fiber may help control colon cancer and some forms of diabetes.

So, how much fiber should you eat? Experts suggest eating fiber several times a day from different plant sources. Try eating a healthful balance of fruits, vegetables, whole-grain breads, nuts, cereals, and legumes.

used for breading meats, poultry, and fish. They are used as an ingredient in cookies, quick breads, and desserts. The uncooked cereal may replace part of the flour in cookies and quick breads. Whenever whole-grain or enriched cereals are used as an ingredient, they increase the nutritional value of the product.

## Pastas or Macaroni Products

Pastas or macaroni products include spaghetti, vermicelli, and noodles, along with macaroni. They are made of durum wheat, a special kind of wheat that is high in gluten, a protein.

Grains take many different forms and can be used in a wide variety of dishes. What other grain foods can you think of?

Noodles are a macaroni product to which egg has been added.

Macaroni products are made in many different shapes and sizes such as tubes, solid rods, ribbon shapes, alphabet, seashells, spirals, and others. They can be used as a main dish (macaroni and cheese, chicken and noodles), as an accompaniment to meat instead of potato (spaghetti or noodles), and as an ingredient in a main dish, soup, or salad.

## Rice

The most common rice, *white rice,* contains only the endosperm of the kernel. *Brown rice* has more nutrients because it also contains the bran and the germ. However, most white rice sold has been enriched to provide the nutrients lost in processing. *Wild rice,* not truly a rice but the seed of a grass grown in Minnesota and Canada, has a strong, nutlike flavor.

Rice is available in three sizes—short grain, medium, and long grain. Long-grain rice is available in *instant,* or *precooked,* form that can be prepared quickly. *Converted,* or *parboiled,* rice has been treated to keep the nutrients, especially the B vitamins, of the original grain. Rice can be used as an accompaniment to meat and as an ingredient in puddings, soups, and salads.

## Flour

Another grain product, *white flour,* is used as the chief ingredient in many baked products. Usually called simply *flour,* it can be bleached or unbleached. While white flour consists mainly of the endosperm, *whole-wheat flour* also contains the bran and the germ to give it a coarser texture and a nutlike flavor. *All-purpose flour* is made from a blend of different wheats. *Instant,* or *quick-mix, flour* is a type of all-purpose flour that has been specially treated so that it blends into liquids easily, without lumping, and so is

## Spanish Rice    Yield: 3-4 servings

½ lb (227g) ground beef | 1 tsp (5mL) chili powder
2 Tbs (30mL) finely chopped onion | ½ tsp (2.5mL) salt
2 Tbs (30mL) chopped green | dash black pepper
  bell pepper | ½ c (125 mL) water
1 16-oz (454g) can tomatoes | 1 c (250mL) precooked rice

1. Brown ground beef, onion, and green pepper in skillet; pour off any grease.
2. Cut up tomatoes; add to meat mixture.
3. Stir in seasonings and water; heat to boiling.
4. Reduce heat to simmer; stir in rice. Cover and cook for 5 minutes, or until all liquid is absorbed.

Approximate nutrition information per serving:
calories–120;
protein–5 g; fat–4 g;
cholesterol–90 mg;
carbohydrates–15 g;
sodium–160 mg.

### Practical Tip

- To bring out extra flavor, toast wheat germ and sesame seeds before using.

good for making sauces and gravies. Another all-purpose flour, *self-rising flour,* contains added leavening (baking powder or baking soda) and salt in the right amounts for baking. *Cake flour* is made from soft wheat. It is especially good for making cakes and other baked products because it is lower in gluten and higher in carbohydrates than all-purpose flour.

### Starch

Starch, obtained from grains in the form of cornstarch and flour, is used to thicken gravies, sauces, puddings, and pie fillings. When starch in the form of cornstarch, flour, or tapioca is heated in water or another liquid such as milk or fruit juice, the starch granules will absorb water and swell. The swollen particles of starch require more space and crowd together, making the product thicker. The thickness of the product is determined by the amount of starch or flour used.

The starch particles in flour and cornstarch are very fine, and they lump together easily. Lumping can be prevented by separating the starch in one of the following methods: (1) The flour or starch may be mixed with a small amount of cold water or liquid. (2) The flour may be mixed with a small amount of melted or liquid fat before the liquid is added. This method is used when making gravy or white sauce. (3) The starch or flour may be mixed with sugar. This method is used for puddings and pie fillings.

After the starch grains are separated, the flour or starch mixture is combined with the remaining liquid or ingredients of the recipe. The mixture is usually cooked, with constant but gentle stirring, until the mixture thickens and becomes clear. Properly cooked starch loses its milky appearance and becomes clear.

**Methods of Separating Starch**

1.

2.

3.

**For Review**

1. What is the advantage of using whole-grain cereals as an ingredient?
2. What is one advantage of instant rice? Converted rice?
3. Why is it more convenient to use self-rising flour than all-purpose flour when baking?
4. What would you mix with flour when making a blueberry filling for a pie?

# Principles of Grain Cookery

Grain and cereal products come in a variety of forms: many require cooking; others, such as ready-to-eat cereals, are ready for the table when purchased; "instant" cereals require only the addition of boiling water. The goals of grain cookery are to improve flavor, soften the cellulose, gelatinize the starch, and produce a product free of lumps. The most abundant nutrient in grains is starch, which makes up three-fourths of the grain. It is the starch which determines the cookery procedures used for grains.

### Breakfast Cereals

In all cereals, the goal is to avoid lumps. Cereal granules must be separated from each other so that lumps will not form. Two methods

## Methods of Separating Cereal Granules

1.

2.

are used to separate cereal granules. (1) Cereals may be added slowly to rapidly boiling water while stirring. (2) Fine cereals such as cream of wheat and cornmeal may be mixed with a small amount of cold water before they are stirred into boiling water.

When cereal grains are placed in boiling water, the outer surface becomes sticky. To prevent the granules from sticking, continue stirring slowly until the water boils again. Several things happen when starch is cooked: (1) the starch absorbs water; (2) with heat and an excess of water, starch swells enormously; (3) with continued heating, starch becomes translucent; (4) thickness develops.

The term *gelatinization* refers to the soft gel that forms when starches are cooked. A proper amount of water and heat is required to produce gelatinization. Some cereals, such as cream of wheat, are able to absorb more water than others, such as rolled oats. The various cereal grains will use different amounts of water to form a gel of the right stiffness or consistency. Gelatinization, the thickening or formation of a starch gel, takes place quickly at the boiling temperature. Well-prepared cereals will have a pleasing flavor, will be free of lumps, will form a soft gel, and will not be pasty.

## Other Cereals

Regardless of the type of raw cereal product, the goal is to gelatinize starch without the formation of lumps. The basic principles of starch cookery—separation of cereal particles with cold water and application of heat to swell the starch grains—apply to all cereal products.

The whole-cereal grains such as rice, and pastas such as macaroni, spaghetti, and noodles are larger pieces than cereal granules and are more easily separated when stirred into water. The starch which they contain will swell during cooking. The granules will double in size (½ cup (125 mL) raw macaroni = 1 cup (250 mL) cooked). The starch will gelatinize, and the rice or macaroni product will become tender and easy to chew without breaking apart.

Cereal products are cleaned before packaging and do not require washing before use. Whole-grain or enriched cereal products contain the water-soluble B vitamins and minerals. Excess water should not be used to cook cereal

---

### Tips for Herbs and Spices

Herbs and spices to use in grain dishes are: basil, bay leaves, cumin, curry powder, dill, garlic, marjoram, oregano, pepper, poppy seed, rosemary, saffron, sage, tarragon, thyme, turmeric, and chives.

Fresh fruit, either added to or served with hot cereal for breakfast, offers color and texture along with added nutrients. The fruit provides nutrient-rich sweetness that added table sugar does not.

products so that dissolved nutrients will not be discarded with the excess water. The amount of water and cooking time will vary with the different cereal products.

Each cereal package provides recipes and instructions for the best use of a cereal product. The suggested amount of water is usually two to two and one-half times that of the cereal product. With this amount of water, none will remain to be discarded.

The practice of rinsing cooked cereal products such as spaghetti or rice with boiling water tends to prevent sticking of the cooked product, but it also tends to rinse away some of the water-soluble nutrients.

## Microwaving Grains

Preparing cereals or grains in the microwave is not a timesaver. If you do decide to cook grains in the microwave, first boil the required

amount of water on a conventional range. Then put the water in a bowl large enough to prevent boiling over in the microwave. Most grains

### Tips for Microwaving Grains

- Prepare breakfast cereal at night by conventional cooking, and reheat in the microwave in the morning.
- Undercook pasta slightly because reheating adds a bit of cooking time.
- For making popcorn, use only microwave-safe bags or containers sold for that purpose. Making popcorn in a paper bag may cause a fire during cooking.
- Rub oil on the rim of the bowl to prevent pasta from boiling over.

require several minutes of covered standing time after cooking. Pasta, rice, and other grains can be cooked ahead and reheated, covered and vented, for about three minutes. Stir well and cook one minute more.

## For Review

1. What occurs when starch is heated?
2. What is gelatinization?
3. What are the signs that cereals have been prepared properly?
4. Why is it easier to cook pasta on a conventional range rather than in a microwave?

# Buying and Storage of Grain Products

Since grain products are basic to almost every meal, it is important to have them ready for use at all times. Careful selection and proper storage of grain products such as flour, rice, pastas, and cereals will insure their ready availability and freshness.

## Buying Grain Products

Cereals and grain products are an economical source of energy. They are among the most widely used foods and can contribute important vitamins and minerals. The vitamin and mineral content of grain products is determined by the parts of the cereal grain used. Whole-grain cereals and breads include the bran, germ, and endosperm, and will provide the most nutrients for the money spent. The enriched, restored, or converted grain products may provide more than whole-grain amounts of some nutrients.

You will get the least nutrients for your money from refined grain products such as plain white bread or flour. Some kind of grain product usually appears in almost every meal; therefore, the nutrient values of these products should be considered when they are purchased. Read the label on all grain products before buying. The label will indicate whether the cereal is whole grain or enriched and will tell you the amount of nutrients in each serving. Whole-grain and enriched grain products can contribute valuable nutrients to all diets, especially when money is limited.

It is better to buy cereal products by weight and not by size of package or size of loaf. Puffed cereals may be in a box several times larger than a compact cereal, yet the small box may be greater in weight and provide more servings. Some big boxes may be only partly filled. The cost of cereal is best compared by determining the cost per serving or weight. Look for unit pricing, the cost per pound or unit of weight, to determine which product is the best buy. Ready-to-eat cereals are more expensive weight-for-weight than cereals that require cooking. Presugared cereals, individual multipacks of cereal, and instant cereals prepared directly in the serving bowl are usually the most expensive.

Check the label to note what other ingredients were used in bread, macaroni, and noodle products. The yellow of noodles is due to food color as well as egg yolk. The food color itself has no nutrient value, but the eggs are a rich source of nutrients. Bread products made with milk or milk solids will provide more nutrients than those that do not include milk.

All forms of grain products are made by several different food processors and are sold under different brand names. The personal experience that you gain through using different brands, along with the information on the labels, will help you select those that best meet your needs.

## Storage of Grain Products

The eating quality and nutrients can be preserved in grain products by proper storage. The cereal should be stored in a closed container which is kept in a cool, dry place. The boxes or packages in which cereals are purchased are suitable for storage. The opened package should be closed tightly so that the cereal will not absorb moisture from the air and lose its crispness. You can restore the crispness of ready-to-eat cereals by placing them in a preheated oven for a short period. Cereal and grain products properly stored have excellent keeping quality. However, whole-grain products stored for long periods of time may acquire an unpleasant flavor due to a chemical change in the fat contained in the germ.

## Sweetened Cereals

Cereal manufacturers recognized the consumer practice of adding sugar to cereals before eating them. They therefore developed presweetened cereals. The manufacturer fortifies the ready-to-eat presweetened cereal in the same way as the unsweetened cereal. Both the sweetened and unsweetened cereals contain the same amounts of added vitamins and iron. You, as the consumer, have a choice between presweetened or unsweetened cereals. Sugar added to cereals at home or by the manufacturer contributes four calories per gram. Learning to eat cereals without sugar would be a painless way to decrease your caloric intake (1 tablespoon (15 mL) sugar = 46 calories).

The starch in cereals is digested by your body into glucose, a simple sugar, and in this way contributes to your body's energy need. The chemical name for table sugar is *sucrose*. Two simple sugars, glucose and fructose, combine to form sucrose, the most common sugar in foods of plant origin. The sugar you use to sweeten foods and as an ingredient in food products has been extracted from sugar cane and sugar beets. Fruits, some vegetables, and milk contribute small quantities of sugar.

Each year most of us consume about 100 pounds (45 kg) of sugar, as a sweetener and as an ingredient in food preparation. This amount of sugar, as sucrose, contributes about 12 percent of our total daily caloric intake. Your body cannot distinguish between the sugar that comes from the sugar bowl or the sugar present in fruits and vegetables.

A healthful diet provides a balanced and varied selection of nutrient-rich foods and enhances your well-being. You should remember that sugar in any form (white, brown, honey, and all other forms) is nutrient poor but calorie rich. Regardless of the form of sugar you prefer, use it to enhance taste appeal, but do not go the extreme of eating large amounts of any sweetener. Sugar easily satisfies your appetite and, in this way, keeps you from eating other nutritious foods. You can handle the calories provided by sugar as long as your total energy intake meets your energy expenditure.

Any nutrient you consume in excessive amounts, including sugar, leads to a dietary imbalance and should be avoided. Sugar is a normal constituent of fresh fruits, vegetables, and milk—all nutrient-rich foods. The food groups continue to be very reliable guides to your dietary balance.

## Convenience in Grains

There was a time when cereal grains were grown in fields surrounding the home, and when the small hard kernels of cereal were pounded between stones to crack and pulverize the grain. Today, the growing, processing, milling, and even some of the cooking has been completed before the cereal products reach the home. Cereal may be flaked, puffed, shredded, or sugar-coated, and it can go directly from the package into the cereal bowl. It may be precooked so that only a few minutes of cooking time is required, or it may be instantized so that it can be placed directly into the cereal bowl, requiring only boiling water or milk.

The milling and packaging of grains signaled the first step in convenience which led to today's just-add-boiling-water-and-stir cereals. All of the convenience cereal items were designed to use time and energy to the best advantage.

When it comes to selection, you are confronted with an almost unlimited choice. Which will you select: whole grain, enriched, or refined? Will it be ready-to-eat, instant, or precooked? Will it be wheat, oats, corn, or rice? Will your decision consider nutrient values, palatability (taste), cost, your personal values, as well as saving time and energy? Your decision is most important because it will not only influence you and your food needs, but it also could influence others.

Convenience also tends toward a built-in monotony because of the sameness and exactness with which each product is produced. It is only with your creativity and imagination that this monotony can be overcome. Convenience items make it possible to use time and energy to advantage, but their use demands creativity and increased cost per serving.

## For Review

1. Why is it better to buy cereal products by weight and not by size of package?
2. Explain three things to look for when purchasing grain products.
3. What is the purpose of careful storage of grain products?
4. Does your diet require the eating of sweetened cereals? Why or why not?

Cereals are available in many convenience forms for either a hot or cold breakfast. Which is your favorite? Why?

# 14 Chapter Review

## Summary

Grains and their products provide nourishment for more nations of the world than any other food. However, in order for humans to benefit from the valuable nutrient contributions of grains, it is important that whole-grain foods as well as refined products that have been enriched, fortified, or converted be included in the diet. Grains are used for cereals, macaroni products, rice, flour, and starch. Some of these require cooking, but others are ready-to-eat or are instant. To maintain the eating quality and nutritious minerals and vitamins in grains, proper storage is necessary. The advances of technology have made it possible for many grain products to be packaged and sold as convenience foods. This allows the food manager to use time and energy to the best advantage.

## Vocabulary

Use the vocabulary words below to fill in the blanks in the paragraph that follows.

amino acids      restored
beriberi           riboflavin
cereal             staple foods
enriched         thiamin
grains

In the United States, many people begin the day with a bowl of a specially prepared grain product known as __(1)__. Grains contribute many nutrients to the diet. However, to make grain products, such as bread, grains are processed. During the processing, some of the essential nutrients are lost. When nutrients are put back into a bread product, it is called __(2)__ bread. When these same nutrients are put back into other grain products, such as cereal, they are called __(3)__. One of the important vitamins found in grains is vitamin $B_1$, which is also known as __(4)__. The lack of this vitamin in the diet can cause the disease __(5)__. Another vitamin found in grains helps the body burn sugars and starches to release energy. This vitamin is vitamin $B_2$, which is called __(6)__. Grains also supply protein, but some of the grain products lack __(7)__, which are the building blocks from which protein is made. Throughout the world, most people have a daily diet that centers around __(8)__, such as wheat, barley and other edible seeds of certain grasses. In addition to supplying important nutrients to the diet, grains and grain products have good keeping quality, high energy value, and low cost, and as a result are known as __(9)__.

## Chapter Questions

1. What products made from grains does your family use?
2. What are the five nutrients that grains and enriched grain products provide?
3. What are the two forms of carbohydrates that are found in grains and what is the function of each?
4. What are the B vitamins that grains provide and why are they important?

5. Why is it important to include grains and grain products in your diet?

6. How does milk interact with cereal to provide protein?

7. How are grain and grain products stored in your home?

8. Why is "converted" rice more nutritious than polished white rice?

9. What is the difference between whole-grain cereals and breads and enriched cereals and breads?

10. What cereals do you use in your family? Are they ready-to-eat, instant, or do they have to be cooked?

11. What can you do to prevent lumping when you use flour or cornstarch for making gravies and white sauces?

12. When you cook cereal, why should the water be boiling when you add the raw cereal?

13. Which of these—whole grain bread, enriched bread, or plain white bread—is the most nutritional purchase and why?

## Skill Activities

**1. Communication** In your food journal, keep a daily record of the grains and grain products you eat in a week. Divide your paper into three columns, and write one of these headings above each column: "Whole-grain products," "Enriched, restored, converted, fortified products," "Untreated processed grain products." For each day, write the date and the meal. Then enter the names of the grain products. What nutrients did you receive from the grain products you ate? Were your selections healthful? What portion of your total calories came from them?

**2. Resource management** Visit a grocery store and find the cereal aisle. Calculate the cost of 1 ounce (28 grams) of a ready-to-eat cereal, instant cereal, and a cereal to be cooked from the same grain. Which cereal is the most expensive? Which cereal is the least expensive? What are the different nutritive values among the cereals? Which cereal provides the most nutritive value?

**3. Decision making** In your food journal or card file box of recipes, add recipes that use whole-grain products and cereals as ingredients. For example, you may wish to include a recipe for granola, or a recipe for cookies that uses a cereal as an ingredient. You can find recipes on the backs of grain products as well as in magazines, books, newspapers, and on the display board in grocery stores.

**4. Food science** The cereal grains—oats, barley, wheat, rye, rice, and corn—are excellent sources of nutrition. Using diet and nutrition guides or other library sources, compare any two cereal grains on the basis of their protein, carbohydrate, fat, and vitamin content.

# 15　Milk

## As you read, think about:

- what nutrients dairy products provide for you.
- how milk is processed.
- how to select, use, and store milk products.
- how to prepare milk products.

**Vocabulary**
calcium
phosphorus
lactose
pasteurization
homogenization
fortified
fermented
curdling

Milk and milk products are so diverse that a wide variety of them can be easily included in any meal or snack. Milk is a highly nutritious food for which there is no substitute. It is used as a beverage by all age groups, and as the liquid ingredient in many recipes.

## Nutrient Contributions

Milk is one of the best foods for promoting and maintaining health because it contains so many nutrients needed by people of all ages. Milk is an excellent source of minerals, vitamins, and proteins.

### Minerals

Minerals are vital for life, health, and the regulation of all body processes. Milk is an abundant source of *calcium,* and calcium is present in the body in larger amounts than any other mineral. Most of this calcium is in the bones, a smaller part is in the teeth, and a very small amount is in the blood serum. Bones and teeth, like other body tissues, are living structures that are constantly changing. Although the amount of calcium in blood is small compared with that in the bones, it is necessary for normal bodily functions.

**Calcium** is a mineral that is needed by every body cell as it helps to: (1) build strong bones and teeth; (2) give strength or firmness to body cells; (3) aid in the clotting of blood; (4) regulate contraction and relaxation of muscles; (5) assist in regulating the action of the heart muscle; and (6) maintain normal nerve function. Because of its many functions in the body, calcium is important to adults and adolescents as well as growing children.

What happens when the food you eat does not supply the calcium your body needs? The body can draw calcium from the bones whenever

These milk wagons made daily deliveries—often before breakfast time—to insure the freshest dairy products for their customers.

the diet is deficient in this mineral, because the bones are a storehouse for calcium. At the same time, calcium strengthens the bones. A continuous loss of calcium from the bones will affect the soundness of teeth and bones. A calcium-poor diet will not permit you to grow to your full height. In fact, nutrition studies with animals show that the animals on a low-calcium diet do not grow well and remain much smaller than those on a calcium-rich diet. A calcium-poor diet can cause fragile bones and teeth, poor posture, and can interfere with normal nerve function, blood clotting, muscle contraction, and heartbeat. Milk is an important daily source of calcium. Without milk, it is difficult for both children and adults to meet the body's need for calcium.

Bone health is an important concern in early, middle, and advanced years. Several studies have found that the loss of bone mass is related to the consumption of large amounts of alcohol, caffeine, and protein, and to inactivity and smoking. *Osteoporosis* is a condition in which bone mass gradually decreases with age and the risk of fracture increases. Your calcium intake during early life has a great effect on your peak skeletal mass when you reach maturity. The skeletal mass you bring to your elderly years is extremely important to stopping calcium loss in the bones. If you get adequate calcium and regular exercise, and if you do not smoke, or drink alcohol or caffeine, you should be able to reduce both the risk of fractures and the loss of bone mass.

In addition to calcium, milk contains a high level of *phosphorus.* **Phosphorus** is needed for every body cell, and it combines with calcium to make bones and teeth. Phosphorus influences the oxidation of foods in the body cells to release energy to the body. Most of the compounds that release energy to the body from food contain phosphorus. From 80 to 85 percent of the phosphorus in your body is present in the bones, with smaller amounts in muscles and in body fluids.

Milk and milk products are excellent sources of phosphorus. Phosphorus is more widely distributed in foods than is calcium. Whole-grain cereals, meats, poultry, and eggs are also good sources of phosphorus.

## Vitamins

Vitamins aid the body in growth, maintenance, and repair. Because they keep the body operating in an efficient and orderly way, vitamins are often referred to as body protectors and regulators. Vitamin A is in the fat portion, or cream, of milk, and the B-complex vitamins are in the nonfat or liquid portion of milk.

Milk is the best food source of *vitamin $B_2$,* or *riboflavin.* It helps all of the cells use oxygen so that the carbohydrates, sugars, and starches which you eat can release energy for all your activities. Vitamin $B_2$ keeps the skin, eyes, and tongue in good condition and also promotes growth. It is needed for good health, vigor, and healthy appearance. It is also necessary for proper function of nerve tissues and the digestive tract. A common sign of vitamin $B_2$ deficiency is cracking of the lips, especially in the corners of the mouth.

Riboflavin is very easily destroyed by light, and that is why paper milk cartons or brown bottles, which light cannot penetrate, are used to help protect the milk against loss of vitamin $B_2$. All forms of milk are rich sources of riboflavin, or vitamin $B_2$.

*Thiamin* and *niacin* along with riboflavin belong to the B-complex or B group of vitamins. Thiamin and niacin are found in milk in fair quantities. You will remember that the B vitamins are found in whole-grain cereal products, discussed in Chapter 14. You will also recall that these vitamins assist in maintaining a normal appetite, a good digestive system, and proper nerve function. They help in releasing food energy for use by the body.

Whole milk is also a good source of *vitamin A.* When skim milk is made, this fat-soluble vitamin is removed with the cream. However, today it is possible to buy skim milk with vitamin A added. You will remember that vitamin A in the form of carotene is found in fruits. Vitamin A is important for vision, mucous membranes, and growth.

Another fat-soluble vitamin in milk is *vitamin D.* Whole milk does not contain very large amounts of vitamin D, but this vitamin is often added to milk to make it a rich source of vitamin D. It helps your body to use the minerals calcium and phosphorus in a way that builds sound bones and teeth. When vitamin D is lacking, a disease called rickets develops. *Rickets* is a disease of defective bone formation. The bones are weak and remain soft. The legs will bow because the bones are not rigid enough to support the weight of the body. Most milk is fortified with vitamin D and is a reliable source of this vitamin.

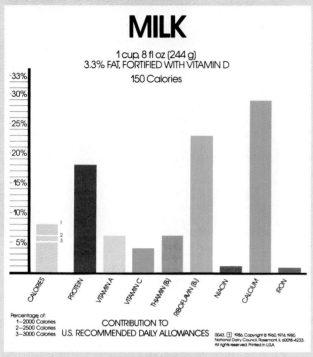

# MILK

1 cup, 8 fl oz (244 g)
3.3% FAT, FORTIFIED WITH VITAMIN D
150 Calories

Percentage of:
1—2000 Calories
2—2500 Calories
3—3000 Calories

CONTRIBUTION TO
U.S. RECOMMENDED DAILY ALLOWANCES

0043. 1986, Copyright © 1960, 1974, 1980.
National Dairy Council, Rosemont, IL 60018-4233.
All rights reserved. Printed in U.S.A.

# SOFT DRINK

1 cup, 8 fl oz (246 g) COLA
96 Calories

Percentage of:
1—2000 Calories
2—2500 Calories
3—3000 Calories

CONTRIBUTION TO
U.S. RECOMMENDED DAILY ALLOWANCES

0043. 1986, Copyright © 1960, 1974, 1980.
National Dairy Council, Rosemont, IL 60018-4233.
All rights reserved. Printed in U.S.A.

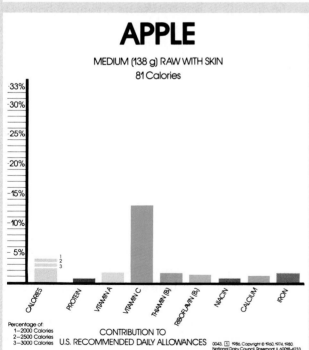

# APPLE

MEDIUM (138 g) RAW WITH SKIN
81 Calories

Percentage of:
1—2000 Calories
2—2500 Calories
3—3000 Calories

CONTRIBUTION TO
U.S. RECOMMENDED DAILY ALLOWANCES

0043. 1986, Copyright © 1960, 1974, 1980.
National Dairy Council, Rosemont, IL 60018-4233.
All rights reserved. Printed in U.S.A.

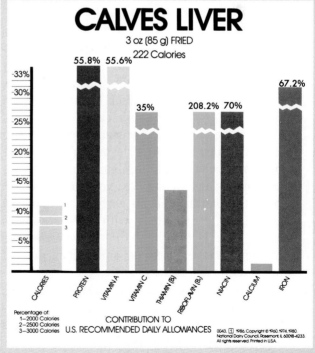

# CALVES LIVER

3 oz (85 g) FRIED
222 Calories

55.8% 55.6%    35%    208.2% 70%    67.2%

Percentage of:
1—2000 Calories
2—2500 Calories
3—3000 Calories

CONTRIBUTION TO
U.S. RECOMMENDED DAILY ALLOWANCES

0043. 1986, Copyright © 1960, 1974, 1980.
National Dairy Council, Rosemont, IL 60018-4233.
All rights reserved. Printed in U.S.A.

**Comparison Cards, courtesy of National Dairy Council.**

### Protein

Along with vitamins and minerals, milk contains high-quality protein. You need protein to help you grow, to make muscles, and to repair worn or broken tissues.

### Carbohydrates

**Lactose,** or milk sugar, is the carbohydrate found in milk. Lactose, like all carbohydrates, provides energy. When milk becomes sour, the lactic-acid bacteria change lactose into lactic acid, giving sour milk its characteristic flavor.

**Lactose Intolerance** Lactose, found only in milk, is a sugar that lacks sweetness. Some healthy individuals are unable to use lactose because their bodies cannot break the lactose down into its simple sugars (glucose and galactose). This is because a sugar-splitting enzyme, *lactase,* is lacking in the small intestine. Such individuals are unable to use lactose and, therefore, are identified as being lactose-intolerant. Lactose remains undigested in their intestinal tract and contributes to abdominal pain, diarrhea, and flatulence (gas). These individuals can usually tolerate fermented dairy products such as buttermilk, cottage cheese, and yogurt, and milk to which lactase has been added.

Lactose intolerance is usually found among Black Africans; Black Americans; Chinese; some South Americans; Alaskan, Canadian, and American Indians; and among Eskimos and Mexicans. Lactose intolerance begins early in life and may become more prevalent with age. Research studies show lactose-intolerant individuals have sufficient lactase to digest small quantities of milk (1 cup (250 mL)).

Should you be lactose-intolerant, include small quantities of regular milk and/or fermented milk products to be sure that your body has an ample supply of calcium.

Yogurt, a milk product, is an attractive and nutrient-rich accompaniment to many Middle Eastern main dishes. What nutrients does yogurt provide?

### Fats

Fats also supply energy for your body. The fat in milk is referred to as cream or butterfat. Milk fat is very special because it contains the fat-soluble vitamin A in large amounts and vitamin D in smaller amounts. Remember that whole milk and lowfat milk contain fat. Skim milk and nonfat milk do not contain fat. Because nearly all the fat has been removed from skim milk and nonfat dry milk, they provide fewer calories and can be used when necessary to reduce calories.

Whole milk contains minerals, vitamins, protein, carbohydrates, fat, and water. Because milk contains important amounts of most nutrients, it has been called the most perfect food. However, milk with all its goodness is very low in iron and vitamin C, or ascorbic acid, and is rather low in niacin. Milk is especially important in your meals because of its abundant supply of calcium, riboflavin, and protein. By including a generous supply of milk in your meals each day, you can eat well, look good, and feel good.

# Processing of Milk

Milk which is sold must be free of harmful bacteria, and therefore the production and sale of milk is controlled by local health departments. There are regulations designed to produce milk with a low bacterial count, good flavor, satisfactory keeping quality, and high nutritive value. Thus, people are assured milk that is safe to use.

## Pasteurization

To insure safety, most milk is pasteurized. Louis Pasteur, a French scientist after whom the process of pasteurization is named, is credited with developing the heat treatment of milk. Milk that has gone through the process of **pasteurization** (pass-chuh-ruh-ZAY-shun) has been heated at a temperature below boiling to destroy harmful organisms. Two methods are used to pasteurize milk: the flash method and the holding method. In the flash method, the milk is brought to 160° F (71° C) for a minimum of fifteen seconds. In the holding method, the milk is brought to a temperature no lower than 143° F (62° C) for thirty minutes and is then cooled rapidly.

## Homogenized Milk

Most whole milk today is homogenized. In **homogenization** (ho-moj-uh-nuh-ZAY-shun), milk under pressure is forced through small openings to break the fat particles so small that they will remain uniformly distributed throughout the milk and will not rise to the top. The protein in the milk forms a soft curd and is more easily digested.

In modern processing plants, the homogenization of milk is carefully supervised for quality control.

### Fortified Milk

The amount of vitamin D in fresh whole milk is small and variable. Most whole milk being sold is now **fortified** by adding vitamin D. Each quart (liter) of fortified milk contains 400 I.U. (International Units), or 10 micrograms (new unit for measurement of vitamin D level), of vitamin D. This amount of vitamin D will supply your body's need for this vitamin. Milk is fortified by exposing it to ultraviolet light (by the process of irradiation), which changes some of the fat components in milk to vitamin D. Milk can also be fortified by adding a vitamin D concentrate to it prior to pasteurization. Most of the milk sold today is pasteurized, homogenized, and fortified.

### For Review

1. What is the difference between the flash method and the holding method of pasteurization? What is common to both methods?
2. How does milk that has been both pasteurized and homogenized differ from milk that has been simply pasteurized?
3. What is fortified milk?

# Forms, Grades, and Uses of Milk

Milk is available in a number of different forms, and each form has its own special qualities. To aid the consumer even further in its selection, milk is graded. The consumer thereby has several choices when purchasing milk that is to be used either as a beverage or as an ingredient.

### Forms of Milk

Almost all milk available in the United States is *pasteurized milk*, milk that has been heated to destroy harmful organisms. *Homogenized milk* is pasteurized milk that has had its fat globules reduced to very small particles so that they are distributed evenly throughout the milk. This means that the cream will not separate from the milk and rise to the surface. Both pasteurized and homogenized milk are available as *vitamin D milk*, milk to which vitamin D has been added.

Several forms of milk are available for people with health or diet considerations. *Certified milk*, produced under very strict sanitary conditions, is used on a doctor's orders in cases of infant and invalid feeding. *Skim milk* has fewer calories than whole milk because much of the fat has been removed, yet it is still a good source of calcium, riboflavin, and protein. Because the fat-soluble vitamins A and D have also been removed with the fat, skim milk is usually fortified with these vitamins. *Lowfat milk* also has had some of the fat removed, but it contains between one-half and two percent milk fat, more than that in skim milk. Lowfat milk is also usually fortified with vitamins A and D and with milk solids. Both fortified skim and lowfat milk have a nutrient value comparable to whole milk, but with fewer calories. They are both suitable for fat-controlled and/or calorie-restricted diets.

Flavored milks include *chocolate milk*, whole milk with added chocolate flavor, and *chocolate drink*, skim milk with added chocolate flavor. Flavored milks are sweetened.

*Concentrated milk* is the result of reducing the water content of fresh fluid milk. It is available in canned or dried forms.

*Evaporated milk* is a canned concentrated milk from which about 60 percent of the water is evaporated. It is sealed in the can and heat treated so that it will not spoil. You may whip

Dried concentrated milk—either dry whole milk or nonfat dry milk—is added to chocolate and other ingredients to make hot cocoa mixes. The dried milk is reconstituted by adding hot water.

undiluted evaporated milk that has been chilled until ice crystals form. The milk can be *reconstituted*—returned to its original form—with an equal amount of water and used as whole milk.

*Sweetened condensed milk,* used as a thickener, is also a canned concentrate milk. It is made from sweetened whole milk from which about 60 percent of the water has been removed and to which about 45 percent sugar has been added.

Two dried concentrated milks have all of the water removed. *Dry whole milk* is whole milk without the water. Because the fat it contains easily develops an unpleasant flavor, it does not keep well. It is used for formulas for infants. *Nonfat dry milk* is skim milk without the water. It keeps well, is economical, and can be reconstituted with water and used in the same manner as fresh milk. It can also be partially reconstituted to liquid milk and then whipped to provide a low-calorie whipped topping.

**Fermented** milks have a sour flavor due to the breakdown of lactose (milk sugar) to lactic acid by bacterial action. Most *buttermilk* today is cultured buttermilk, made chiefly from pasteurized skim milk that has been treated with lactic-acid bacteria. Cultured buttermilk is mild in flavor and has a thick texture. *Yogurt* is a milk product with a custardlike consistency. It is made by fermenting partially skimmed milk with special acid-forming bacteria. Its nutritive values are similar to those of the milk from which it is made.

Cream is the fat of whole milk. Different types of creams vary in fat content. *Heavy whipping cream,* or *heavy cream,* contains a minimum of 36 percent fat, while *light whipping cream* contains 30 to 36 percent fat. *Coffee cream,* or *light cream,* contains 18 to 30 percent fat, and *half-and-half* (a blend of milk and cream) has 10 to 12 percent fat. *Sour cream,* with 18 percent fat, is cream that has been soured by lactic-acid bacteria.

## Grades of Milk

The bacterial count of milk is the basis for its grading. The highest grade, *Grade A,* has the lowest bacterial count and is the grade sold in retail stores. *Grades B* and *C* are safe and wholesome; however, in some areas only one grade may be available. The grade is usually indicated on the bottle cap or on the side of the milk carton. The grade of milk does not indicate its richness but applies only to its degree of sanitation. Butterfat content is usually indicated as a percentage, for example, "Standardized 3.5% B.F."

## Uses of Milk

Milk has two general and most popular uses. It is used as a beverage and as an ingredient in recipes. Either way, it is wholesome and filling.

**Milk as a Beverage** If milk is to be used as a beverage, it requires no preparation other than chilling. Because milk has a mild taste, it can be blended with a number of flavors. Flavored milk drinks, milkshakes, and eggnog are available in an endless variety to suit everyone's taste. Milk and milk beverages can be served hot or cold with meals, as snacks, and as party foods.

**Milk as an Ingredient** Milk contributes to the nutritive value, flavor, texture, consistency, and browning quality of food products. Milk in all forms can be used as an ingredient in a variety of recipes. It can be used in cream soups, chowders, sauces, gravies, casseroles, custards, puddings, breads, and cakes. As an ingredient, milk is used with a variety of foods such as vegetables, meat, fish, poultry, fruits, and cereals.

Constant stirring of a milk-based sauce insures a smooth product that can be used over vegetables, meat, poultry, and fish. What contributions does milk make when used as an ingredient?

Milk will greatly improve the nutritional value of any food or recipe with which it is used. It also promotes the browning quality of baked foods. A nice golden brown in certain foods and baked products adds a special taste and appearance which most people associate with attractive meals.

Evaporated milk may be used to replace fresh milk in a recipe. For general use in cookery, evaporated milk is diluted with an equal amount of water (½ c (125 mL) evaporated milk plus ½ c (125 mL) water = 1 c (250 mL) fresh whole milk) and can be used as a substitute for fresh whole milk. Only recipes developed for evaporated milk use this milk right from the can. For all other recipes, evaporated milk must be diluted with an equal volume of water.

Condensed milk contains added sugar and, therefore, requires special recipes for its use in food preparation.

# Yogurt

Yogurt originated in Turkey centuries ago. Throughout history as other people came in contact with the Turks through invasions or trade, the use of yogurt in cooking spread to the Middle East, Eastern Africa, and Asia. People from these areas adapted yogurt to their own cuisines, and a wide variety of yogurt dishes evolved.

In the United States, we usually eat yogurt mixed with fruit or other flavorings as a light meal or snack. In other cultures, however, yogurt serves as the basis for soups, salad dressings, appetizers, and sauces.

**Greece**   A popular appetizer called *yiaourti skordalia* is a creamed mixture of yogurt, cucumber, and lots of garlic. It is served with pita bread.

**Ethiopia**   A staple of this Eastern African nation is a large, soft, pancake-shaped bread called *injera.* Ethiopians tear off small pieces of the injera, and use them to pick up bits of very spicy stews. As a side dish also eaten with injera, yogurt provides cool relief from the hot sauces.

**Iran**   Iranians use yogurt for both hot and cold soups. One kind includes grated cucumber combined with yogurt and topped with raisins and mint leaves.

**India**   Curry is a group of main dishes in India. People from different regions prepare curry differently. The preparation of one type of curry involves cooking fruits and vegetables with spices and serving the sauce with chicken, fish, or lamb. A yogurt salad called *raita,* made of vegetables and seasonings, is served with curry. *Rayata,* a main dish, is made from potatoes, yogurt, tomatoes, cucumber, and spices. Indians also prepare a thick, creamy, sweetened yogurt for dessert.

Maybe this international look at yogurt has inspired you to try some ideas of your own. You can make your own yogurt by allowing 2–4 tablespoons (30–60 mL) of prepared yogurt to sit at room temperature for 2–3 hours. This serves as your yogurt culture. In a double boiler, heat 1 quart (1 L) of whole or skim milk with the culture until the temperature reaches 110° F (43° C). Turn down the heat, and maintain the temperature between 90–105° F (32–40° C) for 2–3 hours. When the mixture thickens, refrigerate immediately. (Be sure to put aside 2–4 tablespoons (30–60 mL) of the yogurt to serve as a culture for your next batch.)

Yogurt culture contains "friendly" bacteria. These bacteria can withstand the temperature of the human body. They settle in the intestines and there break down sugar into lactic acid. The presence of the acid prevents other, harmful bacteria from reproducing. Thus, yogurt can contribute to a healthy digestive system. Perhaps this accounts for the many uses of yogurt in so many cultures for so many centuries.

The bacteria in fruit yogurt, *raita,* plain yogurt, and *rayata* contribute to a healthy digestive system by breaking down sugar into lactic acid.

Whole or nonfat dry milk that is reconstituted with water can be used as a substitute for fresh milk in most recipes. Reconstituted dry milk is used as a beverage and as an ingredient in soups, custards, and sauces. For baked products, the dry milk solids are usually sifted with the other dry ingredients, and then water is added instead of the fluid milk.

**For Review**

1. What forms of milk are good for people on low-calorie diets?
2. List two types of concentrated milk and a characteristic of each.
3. What type of cream contains the most milk fat? What type of cream contains the least milk fat?
4. How is Grade A milk different from Grade B milk?
5. What are two reasons to use milk as an ingredient in recipes?

# Principles of Milk Cookery

Milk is an important protein food. It is the protein of milk that influences the principles of milk cookery. The objectives of milk cookery are to prevent: (1) film, or scum, formation; (2) boiling over; (3) scorching; and (4) curdling.

A thin film, or scum, may form when milk is heated at a low temperature. As the temperature is increased, a tough film forms; as soon as the film is removed, another will form. The protein in the milk is chiefly responsible for the scum.

## Prevention of Milk Film

One of the objectives in milk cookery is to prevent the formation of the film, or scum. Formation of the film on the milk surface can be prevented by using a covered container, by stirring the milk during heating, or by beating the mixture with a rotary beater to form a layer of foam on the surface. Hot cocoa, for example, is often beaten to form a layer of foam so that a film will not develop on the surface.

## Boiling Over

The formation of the film on boiled milk is the principal reason for the boiling over of milk. A pressure develops under the scum which forces the milk to break through the film and boil over the sides of the pan.

## Scorching of Milk

When milk is heated, some of its protein tends to settle out (coagulate) on the sides and bottom of the pan and can scorch easily unless the milk is heated on a very low heat. Stirring the milk while it heats helps to thin out the film, but a low temperature must be used to prevent scorching. The milk sugar, lactose, with protein also forms a brownish film on the pan when milk is heated. Milk can be heated over hot water to avoid scorching; however, with controlled low-heat settings on ranges, the use of water is not essential. Heating milk on low heat will take longer, but it will avoid scorching. Heating milk in this way is useful for scalded milk. When milk is scalded, it is heated to just below boiling.

## Curdling of Milk

Another objective of milk cookery is to prevent **curdling.** When acid is added to milk, the protein settles out in white clumps, or curds, and separates from a greenish-yellow liquid, or whey. The milk is then said to be curdled. For example, this can easily happen when cream of tomato soup is prepared. The acids in tomatoes and other vegetables can cause milk protein to separate.

Curdling of milk can be prevented in three ways. One way is to thicken with starch either the milk or the food to be added to the milk. For example, curdling of tomato soup can be prevented by thickening the milk with flour and then adding the tomato, or by thickening the tomato and then adding the milk.

Another way to reduce or prevent curdling is to use a low temperature for cooking. For instance, scalloped potatoes heated at a low temperature will show less curdling than if heated at a high temperature. Low-temperature cookery will also help prevent scorching, reduce scum formation, and avoid boiling over.

Using very fresh milk is the third way to prevent curdling. Milk with a high acid content will curdle when heated. Acid can develop in milk that has not been properly stored or has been stored for too long a time. The lactic-acid bacteria normally found in milk can change the lactose into lactic acid, which will result in curdling.

### Microwaving Milk

Milk, like eggs, mayonnaise, and sour cream, is delicate and can easily overcook or separate. A low power setting is required for proper cooking unless the milk is an ingredient in other dishes, such as casseroles or soups.

### Practical Tip

Mix 1 cup (250 mL) evaporated milk at room temperature with 1 tablespoon (15 mL) vinegar for a low-calorie sour cream substitute. Let the mixture stand until it thickens.

When heating milk by itself, use a large container (⅔ full) to prevent boiling over. Watch closely and turn off the power if the milk shows signs of foaming.

### For Review

1. What are three ways to avoid scum formation?
2. How does scum contribute to the boiling over of milk?
3. What are two ways to avoid scorching?
4. What are the two products of curdled milk?
5. What are three ways to avoid the curdling of milk?

## Milk Storage, Substitutes, and Convenience Forms

Proper storage of milk and its many forms is required to protect flavor and nutritive value. While many nondairy products are now available to the consumer, they do not provide the same nutrient value as fresh, dried, or canned milk. The intended use of milk and milk substitutes should be carefully considered before purchase.

### Fresh Milk Storage

Milk storage involves cleanliness, cold temperature, and prevention of contamination. The care of fresh milk begins as soon as it is delivered to the home. The first step is to wash or wipe off the outside of the milk container. This will prevent bringing any dirt and germs into the refrigerator. Milk is a very perishable food and should be kept in the coldest part of the

## Baked Custard    Yield: 6 servings

| | |
|---|---|
| 2 eggs | 2 c (500 mL) scalded milk |
| 1/3 c (80 mL) sugar | 1/2 tsp (2.5 mL) vanilla |
| 1/4 tsp (1.2 mL) salt | |

1. Set oven at 325°F (180°C).
2. Beat egg until well blended but not foamy.
3. Add sugar, salt, and vanilla; stir.
4. Stir scalded milk slowly into egg mixture.
5. Pour into custard cups and fill to about 1/2 inch (1.2 cm) from top.
6. Place cups in a baking pan; pour hot water into pan up to about 1 inch (2.5 cm) from top of cups.
7. Place into oven and bake at 350°F (180°C) for 40 to 50 minutes, or until knife inserted in center of custard comes out clean.
8. Remove cups from water immediately and cool.

Approximate nutrition information per serving: calories–340; protein–17 g; fat–27 g; cholesterol–70 mg; carbohydrates–7 g; sodium–490 mg.

refrigerator, that is, beside or below the cooling unit. It should always be stored in a covered container to protect it from absorbing undesirable flavors and odors. Allowing milk to stand on the doorstep or in a warm kitchen causes rapid growth of bacteria and hastens spoilage. Permitting milk to stand exposed to light destroys vitamin $B_2$, or riboflavin.

### Dry Milk Storage

Dry milk can be stored at ordinary room temperature in an airtight container. Once the package has been opened, it should be closed tightly and kept in a cool place. Since the fat has been removed from nonfat dry milk, it has a better keeping quality than dried whole milk. When dried whole milk is exposed to air and moisture, it develops an undesirable flavor. To avoid flavor changes, the dry whole milk package can be placed in a container with a tight-fitting cover. Reconstituted dry milk has a high water content and will spoil in the same way as fresh whole milk. If it is not to be used immediately, dry milk should be refrigerated as soon as it is reconstituted.

### Evaporated and Condensed Milk Storage

Unopened cans of evaporated and condensed milk may be stored at room temperature. The cans should be kept in a dry, well-ventilated place to prevent any rusting of the can. Once the can is opened, the remaining milk in the can must be stored, well wrapped, in the refrigerator.

Evaporated milk, a form of canned concentrated milk, is used as an ingredient in many dessert recipes that call for milk. What are the advantages of using evaporated milk?

## Milk Substitutes

Several imitation milk products are available on the market. Some of these are found on shelves near regular milk products, and others are found in frozen-food cases. An imitation milk product is made to resemble fluid whole milk by substituting a nondairy ingredient for one or more of the nutrients found in milk products. This product is not permitted for sale in all states. Nondairy ingredients included in the imitation dairy products are coconut oil, vegetable oils, monoglycerides, corn syrup solids, soy protein, and others.

The nutrient values of imitation products can be quite different from those found in milk. Milk and milk products are one of the best food sources of nutrients in the best proportion required for optimum health and body mainte-

nance. Earlier in this chapter, milk was designated as the best food source of calcium, rich in complete proteins and vitamins A, D, and B complex. The amounts of protein, vitamins, and minerals can be quite variable in imitation products. The nondairy foods are imitations of milk but not necessarily a substitute for milk. They do not provide the same nutrients found in milk.

The nutrient content of nondairy products is listed on the package. The nutrient content of

### Tips for Herbs and Spices

Spices which will add flavor to milk beverages are: allspice, cinnamon, cloves, nutmeg, and vanilla.

You can select from a variety of convenience milk products. Which of the products shown do not need refrigeration? Which can be used without being reconstituted?

these products should be considered carefully before purchase, since the nutrient content of nondairy foods and milk are not the same.

With such a variety of milk and nondairy products from which to choose, selection becomes the major problem. It is important to select the products which best meet your needs and nutritional requirements.

## Milk as a Convenience Food

The milk bottle has replaced the family cow as a source of milk. Milk in a bottle or carton is a convenience in itself which cannot be appreciated unless one has experienced the work involved in obtaining milk directly from the cow. Milk in a bottle is ready to be used as a food or as an ingredient in a recipe.

Convenience in the use and storage of milk has been increased by processing. Nonfat dry

milk and unopened cans of evaporated and condensed milk do not require refrigeration. Because they do not require refrigeration, an extra supply of milk can be on hand so that the milk supply will never run out, even in an emergency.

Both dry and evaporated milks can be easily reconstituted with water, and can replace whole milk in recipes. The dry or instant form of milk can also be combined directly with the dry ingredients without first being reconstituted. Then, only water is added as the liquid to provide the needed moisture. In this way, the milk becomes automatically reconstituted as the liquid (water) is added to the dry ingredients of the recipe. Nonfat dry milk can also be added to foods such as breads, gravies, soups, and beverages to supplement their food value.

Nonfat dry milk and evaporated milk can be whipped. Equal amounts of nonfat dry milk and cold water are beaten until soft peaks form. Evaporated milk is first chilled until fine ice crystals are formed, and then it is whipped. The foams formed by both milks make an acceptable topping.

Sweetened condensed milk adds to the convenience of dairy products. This milk is useful in desserts because it will thicken to the consistency of a pudding when an acid such as lemon juice is added to it. Heating the milk will also cause thickening. Many special recipes that can be made both quickly and easily use condensed milk.

Cream combined with sugar, stabilizers, emulsifiers, and an appropriate gas is available in pressurized cans. This is a convenience form of whipped cream. In addition, many whipped cream substitutes are now being marketed. These products generally have a protein base, vegetable fat, and stabilizers, but some are made without any dairy products. They may come as powders to whip with water, in pressurized cans, or prewhipped in containers. Because of their lack of fat, these items have fewer calories than whipped cream.

**For Review**

1. List three things to do to avoid spoilage of fresh milk.
2. Why should someone who needs extra calcium and vitamins *not* use milk substitutes instead of milk?
3. Describe three benefits of convenience milk products.

# 15 Chapter Review

## Summary

Popular as a beverage and as an ingredient, milk is often referred to as the most perfect food since it contains significant amounts of valuable nutrients. In fact, preservation of the nutrient protein is central to the principles of milk cookery. Without milk, it is sometimes difficult to supply the necessary minerals and vitamins that are needed daily by the body to remain healthy. Although there are milk substitute products, none equals the valuable nutritional content of milk.

In the United States, all milk is pasteurized and usually homogenized as well. It is available in a variety of forms, ranging from fresh, to canned, to dry. However, proper storage is needed for all forms of milk to protect the nutritional qualities as well as to prevent spoilage and the growth of bacteria.

## Vocabulary

Complete the following numbered sentences with one of these vocabulary words:

calcium
curdling
fermented
fortified

homogenization
lactose
pasteurization
phosphorus

1. Milk contains an abundant supply of _____, which is needed daily to prevent crippling bone diseases, such as osteoporosis.
2. _____ is a carbohydrate found in milk that provides the body with energy.
3. In the United States before milk is sold, it is heated to destroy harmful organisms through a process called _____.
4. Milk provides the mineral _____, which combines with calcium to make strong bones and teeth.
5. Most whole milk today has very small particles of fat evenly distributed throughout as a result of the process of _____.
6. Buttermilk and yogurt are examples of milk that has been _____ by adding special bacteria.
7. Most whole milk for sale today is _____ with vitamins A and D.
8. _____ sometimes occurs when an acidic food is added to milk, and the milk separates into white clumps.

## Chapter Questions

1. What nutrients does milk provide for you?
2. Compare a) skim milk, b) lowfat milk, and c) whole milk.
3. If your store is out of whipping cream, what are 3 things you could do to make a whipped topping?
4. If fresh milk is not available for use as an ingredient, what are two kinds of milk that may be used instead?
5. How can you make white sauce so that it does not develop a scum?
6. What forms of milk do you use in your family and what is the purpose for each?
7. If you have to heat milk, what temperature should be used and why?

8. When you bring fresh milk home from the market, what should you do to store it properly?

9. When evaporated milk is used in place of fresh whole milk as an ingredient, why should an equal amount of water be added to it?

10. What are the advantages of using milk in recipes?

11. Why is milk a more nutritious snack than a candy bar or a soft drink?

12. In what ways is milk a convenience food?

## Skill Activities

**1. Decision making** In your food journal, keep a three-day record of the milk, in any form, that you include in your meals or snacks. Divide your paper into two columns. Above one column, write "Liquid milk," and above the other, write "Milk in a food product." Write the date, and record the amount of fluid milk you drank and the food you ate that included milk.

**2. Resource management** Compare the nutritional information for one cup servings found on the nutrition labels of fresh whole, 2% milkfat, 1% milkfat, and skim milk. Down the left side of a lined piece of paper, write: "Calories," "Protein," "Carbohydrates," "Fat," "Sodium." After these, draw a line and write "% of U.S. RDA." Then list these nutrients: "Protein," "Vitamin A," "Vitamin C," "Thiamin,"

"Riboflavin," "Niacin," "Calcium," "Iron," "Vitamin D," "Vitamin $B_6$," "Vitamin $B_{12}$," "Phosphorus," "Magnesium," "Zinc," and "Pantothenic acid." Divide the paper into 4 columns, and write one kind of milk at the top of each. Go to a local grocery store, and find the four kinds of milk. Then record the information you find on the nutrition labels. What is the difference in calories among the four kinds of milk? What is the difference in the amount of fat in each kind of milk? Are the RDA percentages the same or different? If they are different, which kind of milk contains the highest percentages?

**3. Critical thinking** Visit the dairy and frozen food counters of a local grocery store. Read the ingredients and nutritional labels to find three foods that are suitable for people who have lactose intolerance. List these three foods and the ingredients. Compare these foods to those with milk or cream that they replace. How do the ingredients differ? Instead of adding cream to a beverage, what can be used? Instead of using ice cream, what can be used?

**4. Food science** To observe how the enzyme rennin causes milk to separate into curds and whey, use the rennin contained in rennet tablets (found in the cheese departments of specialty or health-food stores). Add the rennet to milk according to package directions. Leave the mixture at room temperature for several hours and describe what happens to it.

# 16 Cheese

## As you read, think about:

- how to identify, select, use, and store cheese.
- what nutrients cheese provides for you.
- how to prepare cheese products.
- how cooking affects cheese.

**Vocabulary**
casein
curd
whey
process cheeses
kilocalorie

Although the origin of cheese making is unknown, we do know that European immigrants brought the art of cheese making to America. The first step required to change milk into cheese is to warm the milk slightly and then add a starter of lactic-acid-producing bacteria. When the milk becomes slightly acid, *rennin,* an enzyme which causes milk protein to settle out, is added. The milk protein **casein** (KAY-seen) coagulates (settles out) to form the **curd.** The curd is then cut to separate the **whey,** the clear liquid that contains some of the water-soluble substances in milk. After the curd is cut to remove the whey, it is mixed with salt and packed into cheesecloth-lined hoops. At this stage, the cheese is called "green cheese."

The pressed green cheese is dried for several days and is then coated with hot paraffin to prevent moisture loss during curing. The cheese is placed in a ventilated room at a controlled temperature, about 50° F (10° C), to develop the desired flavor.

The ripening, or curing, causes desirable changes in the texture and flavor of cheese. Some cheese becomes softer and more tender so that it can be blended easily or mixed into other foods. The changes in texture will vary with the different types of cheese. During ripening, some cheeses become very soft, others become harder and even crumbly, and still others become porous or develop holes. In addition, a distinctive flavor is developed in each kind of cheese.

Until this century, much of the cheese eaten by American farm families was made at home. Above is a recreation of cheese-making techniques of the early nineteenth century.

## Kinds of Cheese

Cheeses are available in many varieties. They are made from cow's milk, goat's milk, reindeer milk, and many other sources. They can be conveniently classified according to their degree of hardness.

### Hard Cheeses

Hard cheeses are made principally from partially skimmed cow's milk. Parmesan is a very hard cheese of Italian origin, usually used as a grated cheese. It can be used in cooking or added as a topping by individual diners according to their own taste. Swiss cheese is identified by the large holes that develop during ripening when special bacteria produce a gas. Edam and Gouda are hard cheeses recognized by their bright-red wax coatings. A very popular hard cheese is Cheddar, or American, cheese. Food coloring is added to give some Cheddar cheese a yellow color.

## Semisoft Cheeses

Brick, Roquefort, and Muenster are examples of semisoft cheeses. Brick cheese is a popular semisoft cheese. It gets its name from its shape. Roquefort, Gorgonzola, and blue cheese have a characteristic blue-green color and a pronounced flavor, caused by a special mold that develops during the ripening of the cheese. Gorgonzola and blue cheese are made from cow's milk, while Roquefort is produced from sheep's milk. Muenster cheese that is sold in the United States is mild in flavor, while that sold in Europe has a sharper flavor. This distinctive flavor is due to longer ripening. Other cheeses are described in the chart on the opposite page.

## Soft Cheeses

Soft cheeses are made from skim milk or whole milk. Two popular soft cheeses are cottage cheese and cream cheese. The action of rennin and acid causes curds to form in the milk. The soft, unripened curds are sold as dry cottage cheese or, with added cream, as creamed

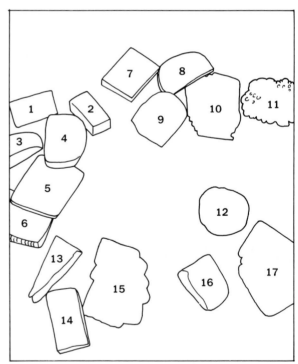

1. N.Y. Cheddar
2. Low sodium herb
3. Dried ricotta
4. Dill havarti
5. Fontina
6. Havarti with peppercorn
7. Romano
8. Gouda
9. Edam
10. Swiss
11. Ground Parmesan
12. Provolone
13. Brie
14. Cream cheese
15. Mozzarella
16. Blue cheese
17. Muenster

## Some Common Cheeses and Their Uses*

| Name | Color, Texture, Flavor | Use |
| --- | --- | --- |
| Muenster | Creamy white. Semisoft with tiny holes. Pungent. | Appetizers; sandwiches. |
| Romano | Yellow-white. Hard, granular. Sharp. | Grated for seasoning. |
| Parmesan | Yellow-white. Hard. Sharp. | Grated on soups, breads, spaghetti; in cooked foods. |
| Mozzarella, Pizza | White, Nonripened, soft. Stretchy, chewy. | Sliced; in cooked foods. |
| Provolone | Light yellow. Semisoft, smooth, and somewhat plastic. Mellow smoky. | Appetizers; sandwiches; in cooked foods; desserts. |
| Ricotta | White. Cottage-type, nonripened, soft. Sweet. | Appetizers; salads; in cooked foods; desserts. |
| Camembert | Creamy with edible white crust. Soft, surface ripened. Mild to pungent. | On crackers or with fruit; for appetizers; desserts. |
| Cheddar | White to orange. Hard. Mild to sharp. | Appetizers; sandwiches; salads; in cooked foods; desserts. |
| Blue | Blue-veined. Crumbly, semisoft to hard. Sharp, salty. | Appetizers; salads; salad dressings; in cooked foods; desserts. |
| Swiss | Light yellow. Large holes, hard. Nutlike, sweet. | Appetizers; sandwiches; salads; in cooked foods. |
| Brick | Creamy yellow. Semisoft with small holes. Mild to sharp. | Appetizers; sandwiches; salads; desserts. |
| Cream | White. Nonripened, soft and smooth. Mild, delicate. | Appetizers; sandwiches; salads; in cooked foods; desserts. |
| Gouda | Red wax on surface, creamy yellow interior. Semisoft. Nutlike. | Appetizers; salads; in cooked foods; sliced; desserts. |
| Edam | Red wax outer surface, yellow interior. Soft to hard. Nutlike. | Appetizers; salads; in cooked foods; desserts. |

*American Dairy Association.

cottage cheese. Cream cheese is a soft, uncured, smooth cheese made from whole milk to which cream has been added. Neufchatel is made with less cream and is similar to cream cheese.

## Process Cheeses

**Process cheeses** are produced from a blend of cheeses to develop a different texture and flavor. Process cheeses are made from selected cheeses with the desired flavor and texture characteristics. The cheeses are shredded and mixed together, and an emulsifier, such as sodium citrate or disodium phosphate, is added. The mixture is stirred and heated until the cheese becomes soft and well blended. This heating of process cheese stops bacterial and enzyme action so that no additional ripening can occur. Because of the heat treatment, this cheese may be labeled "pasteurized process cheese." Process cheeses have a mild, bland flavor and an excellent keeping quality. They blend easily and do not become stringy or tough during cooking.

## Process Cheese Foods

Pasteurized process cheese foods are similar to process cheese but contain less fat and milk solids and more moisture. In making cheese food, cream, milk, skim milk, or whey can be added to the cheese. They blend easily with other ingredients.

## Grades of Cheese

To assure a quality product, the United States Department of Agriculture (USDA) has defined quality standards for some varieties of cheese (Swiss, cheddar). The USDA inspection shield means the product was produced under sanitary conditions and is of good quality. The USDA grades are based on flavor, texture, appearance, and color. Cheese and cheese products not covered by a United States grade standard may be inspected and bear the USDA "Quality Approved" inspection shield on the container.

### For Review

1. Describe the roles of bacteria and rennin in the making of cheese.
2. List three categories of cheeses, according to their degree of hardness, and two examples of each.
3. List four common cheeses and a use for each one.
4. What are two advantages of using process cheeses?

# Nutrient Contributions

Cheese is a concentrated form of milk. A piece of cheese weighing 1 pound (454 g) contains the protein and fat of approximately 1 gallon (3.8 L) of milk. Cheese is a highly nourishing food containing protein and important amounts of several of the vitamins and minerals. It is an excellent source of calcium.

## Protein

Cheese is an excellent source of complete protein which is required for growth and body building. The milk protein, casein, is found abundantly in cheese.

## Vitamins

The cheese made from whole milk is an excellent source of *vitamin A,* a fat-soluble vitamin found in the fat of milk, the cream. Vitamin A is also needed for good vision, proper growth, and healthy mucous membranes.

Cheese can add to your intake of the B group of vitamins but not in as great quantities as milk. Since these vitamins are water-soluble, there is some loss of them in the whey that is pressed out from the curd in making cheese. Therefore, cheese is a fair source of the B vitamins *thiamin* and *riboflavin.* These vitamins are needed for growth, for nerves, and to help the body cells oxidize food for the release of energy.

## Minerals

The minerals in cheese are those found in milk, and, like milk, cheese is an important source of *calcium* and *phosphorus.* Do you recall your body's need for them? Calcium and phosphorus are needed for strong bones and teeth. In addition, calcium is required for blood clotting, muscle contraction, and nerve function; while phosphorus is also involved in the oxidation of foods to release energy to the body.

## Fats

Cheese will vary in fat content, depending upon the type of milk used to make it. Cheese

# "It all began with quiche"

Mary Brown has launched and run three successful food ventures—a catering business, a restaurant, and a wholesale food shop. "I never had any training," Mary explains. "I learned by reading."

Reading paid off for Mary. "It sounds funny, but I probably made the first quiche served in Boston. I read a recipe in the *New York Times*. For Christmas, I gave some quiche to my sisters-in-law, who were very social. People started asking me to make it. I asked them to pay for the ingredients, and then thought, 'Why not make them pay for it?' It all began with quiche."

By word of mouth, people learned of Mary's talents. Soon people were asking her to prepare dinners. She decided to try catering, and she rented space with a kitchen in a suburb of Boston. Mary Brown's Fine Foods was born.

Mary's quiche not only got her started in the business but also provided her catering business with its first big break. During this time, the Junior League sponsored an annual event called Show House. Needing food for the Show House events, the League invited several caterers to submit a quiche and a soup in a competition for the contract. Mary Brown's Fine Foods won the contract.

In the back of her mind, Mary had thought about opening a restaurant. She had cooked lunches in a friend's restaurant, and there was enough room in the space from which Mary Brown's Fine Foods operated. One day, "I finally bought tables and chairs for the restaurant," recounts Mary. The restaurant, Le Bocage, was first open only on Thursdays, Fridays, and Saturdays for dinner. "We were lucky," Mary goes on. "A local paper gave Le Bocage an excellent review the second week it was open. I can't remember anything the review said except the way it started, 'In the gloomy outskirts of Watertown . . .'" The successful restaurant now serves lunch and dinner on weekdays, and dinner on Saturdays.

As the restaurant business picked up, Mary began cutting back her catering business. Two years ago, Mary and her son switched from retail catering to the wholesale food business. They and a staff prepare foods made from pure and natural ingredients. In addition, they prepare specialty items, such as Cajun foods. Instead of selling directly to the public, they sell their foods to restaurants and retail food shops. They decided to retain the name, Mary Brown's Fine Foods, because people would recognize it.

Mary and her son enjoy running a wholesale business because "you can shut the door at five o'clock." Retail food shops place orders stating how much food they need and when they need it. As a result, Mary Brown's Fine Foods always knows exactly what and how much they have to prepare. On the other hand, Mary advises, "You have to sell more because the profit margin is less."

Selling more does not seem to be a problem for Mary Brown. With orders coming into their shop from towns 50 miles away, Mary sighs, "We need a bigger place."

An easily prepared quiche can launch a career.

Cheese making is an important industry in countries such as France, Italy, England, and Switzerland. Shops that sell only cheese are prevalent, even in the smallest towns. What types of cheeses are shown here?

made from skim milk, such as cottage cheese, will be low in fat, while cheese made from whole milk and added cream, such as cream cheese, will be high in fat. Most other cheeses are made from whole milk, and, therefore, are a rich source of fat.

Fats provide energy for play and work and also for basic body functions such as breathing and heartbeat. Fats provide a very concentrated source of energy. They contribute two and one-fourth times as much energy value as carbohydrates and proteins do.

The energy value of foods is measured in kilocalories, also known as kcalories. A **kilocalorie** (a unit of 1000 calories) is used to measure the energy value of foods in much the same way that a centimeter or an inch is used to measure a small object. Since fat contains more than twice as much energy as carbohydrates and proteins, it will also provide more than twice as many kilocalories. Each gram of fat yields nine kilocalories, and each gram of carbohydrate and protein will yield only four kilocalories.

## Tips for Herbs and Spices

Spices and herbs to use with cheese and cheese dishes are: basil, caraway, chives, dill, garlic, marjoram, oregano, parsley, pepper, rosemary, sage, tarragon, and thyme.

Besides energy, fats serve other important functions in your body. They are needed for the attractive appearance of your hair and skin. Too little fat in your diet may cause eczema and dry, rough skin. Fat cushions or protects vital body organs against shock of movement, and insulates the body against changes in temperature. Some foods such as cream, egg yolk, and butter, which contain fats, bring to your diet the fat-soluble vitamins A and D. Fats are found in all foods which are greasy, such as cheese, butter, nuts, meats, and oils.

Cheese and other foods which contain fats are popular foods. Because fats are an abundant source of energy and calories, it is easy to eat them in amounts greater than your body requires for energy. When energy supplied to the body exceeds the energy need, a gain in weight will occur. If you have a tendency toward overweight, avoid selecting too many foods that are rich sources of fats. You will learn more about fats in Chapter 27.

## Carbohydrates

The carbohydrate in milk is *lactose,* a sugar. Lactose is a water-soluble nutrient which tends to be lost in the whey when cheese is manufactured. Therefore, cheese is not a source of carbohydrate. Cheese, however, is a good source of many other nutrients already mentioned and should be included in a good diet.

---

**For Review**

1. Why is milk a better source of B vitamins than is cheese?
2. What determines how much fat content is in cheese?
3. What nutrient contributes the most energy value?
4. What are three functions of fats?

---

# Cooking Principles, Uses, and Storage of Cheese

Cheese has a high protein content, and it is the protein that influences the principles of cheese cookery. The use of cheese in recipes increases the nutrient value of the food and provides a flavorful addition. Proper storage of cheese is necessary to prevent molding and changes in flavor.

## Principles of Cheese Cookery

Cheese protein, like the milk from which it is made, coagulates when heated and becomes tough and rubbery when overcooked. The principles, or rules, of cheese cookery are: (1) cook at a low temperature to avoid a rubbery, tough consistency; (2) cook for a short time to avoid toughness; (3) when added to other ingredients, cut cheese into small pieces so that it will melt quickly and blend with other foods; and (4) use ripened cheese because unripened cheese may not blend with the other ingredients.

A high temperature and extensive cooking of cheese not only cause the cheese to become tough and stringy, but also may cause the fat to separate and drain from the cheese. Overcooking can be caused by cooking at too high a temperature as well as cooking for too long.

## Cheese as an Ingredient

When cheese is combined with other foods, the temperature should be low, and you should take care not to cook it any longer than necessary so that the cheese will remain soft and tender. For foods which require a hot oven temperature, such as pizza, the cheese may be covered with a sauce to protect it from the high temperature.

In some foods, the cheese is protected from the heat of cooking. Cheese in the center of a

## Welsh Rarebit Fondue    Yield: 4 servings

2 Tbs (30 mL) margarine     dash cayenne
2 Tbs (30 mL) flour     ½ lb (227 g) cubed cheddar
1 Tbs (15 mL) dry mustard     or American cheese
1 c (250 mL) milk
1 Tbs (15 mL) Worcestershire sauce

1. Melt margarine in the top of a double boiler.
2. Add the flour and dry mustard; mix well.
3. Gradually add the milk, stirring constantly, until cheese is melted.
4. Add remainder of ingredients; stir until cheese is melted.
5. Pour into a fondue pot or chafing dish; serve with cubes of French, rye, or whole-wheat bread.

Approximate nutrition information per serving: calories–340; protein–17 g; fat–27 g; cholesterol–70 mg; carbohydrates–7 g; sodium–490 mg.

### Practical Tip

• Grate cheese onto a wet plate to prevent the cheese from sticking to the surface.

grilled sandwich is protected and will remain soft and tender, while the cheese in an open-faced sandwich may become tough. Cheese can also be protected by the ingredients with which it is combined. Cheese added to pastry and biscuits is protected by the dough during baking. Cheese dishes are served hot, immediately after the cooking is completed.

Cheese that has ripened or aged will blend easily with the ingredients in a recipe. Ripened cheddars or process cheeses are popularly used in cooked cheese dishes because they do not form strings. However, all cheeses must be cooked carefully because they can become tough and rubbery if cooking temperature is too high or cooking time is too long.

## Uses of Cheese

Cheese adds variety and pleasure to any meal. It can be eaten alone, used as the chief ingredient in a dish, or grated and sprinkled on the top of a main dish.

Cheese is a favorite for sandwiches but is also popular on crackers. Crackers spread with cheese are pleasing accompaniments to soups and salads. Canapés (small pieces of bread with topping), cheese dips, and raw vegetables and crackers spread with cheese are served as appetizers and are party foods as well as before-meal taste-tempters.

Slices of cheese over grilled vegetables or hamburgers or on top of individual casseroles add flavor, variety, and nutrients. Bits of cheese can be added to cream sauces and soups for a flavor accent.

Cheese used in a main dish may be a bland or a sharp variety, depending on your own tastes. Nippy or strong-flavored cheeses are used in smaller amounts than bland cheeses. Mild cheeses are popular for sandwiches.

Cheese sauces are easily made by adding shredded cheese to a medium white sauce. Cheese sauces are excellent additions to vegetables. Foods cooked in a cheese sauce or sprinkled with grated cheese are listed as "au gratin" on restaurant menus. Cheese sauces are also used with pastas in main-dish foods such as lasagna.

Cheese may be used to improve the nutritional value of foods. When cheese is added to vegetables, pastas, and legumes, it improves the protein value of these foods so that they can be used as substitutes for meats. Cheese, like eggs and meats, is rich in complete protein and in fat. For this reason, cheese is best used to replace meat and eggs in meals rather than in addition to them. Cheese and foods containing cheese are low-cost replacements for meats.

Cheese can be combined with fruits and vegetables and made into salads. Cheese may be the major ingredient in a salad such as cottage cheese on pineapple or a peach. It may be cut into strips or cubes and used as one of the ingredients in a tossed or garden salad. It may also be used as a grated topping for fruit and meat salads or as a salad dressing ingredient in Roquefort or blue cheese dressing. Hearty cheese salads are used as the main dish of a meal, while lighter cheese salads are used as accompaniments to the meat or other main course.

Cheese pies, cakes, and fancy frozen or gelatin desserts are choice endings for meals. Cheese pies and cakes are made from soft cheeses such as cottage or cream cheese. Fruit and cheese trays are a popular Continental dessert custom. Because cheese is a concentrated food, a fruit-cheese tray could be served as a dessert for a light meal. Cheese is also a favorite accompaniment to a fruit pie such as apple pie.

Cheese, fruit, and bread make a nutritious light meal. What food groups are represented? What beverage would you add?

A cheese soufflé (right) or a cheese pie, known as a quiche, (below) are main dishes made with cheese. What cheeses are used in these dishes?

## Microwaving Cheese

Cheese is a delicate food that demands special attention to timing. Because of its high fat content, it cooks very quickly and even a few seconds can make the difference between proper melting or a tough, rubbery consistency. Cook cheese at a low power setting, or for a very

### Tips for Microwaving Cheese

- Shred cheese before melting it in the microwave.
- To soften cream cheese for easy sandwich spreading, remove the foil wrapper, place the cheese on plastic wrap or a glass dish, and microwave for a few seconds on a low power setting.

short time at the end of recipes. Higher power settings are permissible when cheese has been mixed into casseroles or soup, as the increased volume and density slow down cooking.

## Storage of Cheese

All cheeses should be tightly covered or wrapped and then stored in the refrigerator. Soft cheeses (cream, cottage) spoil more quickly than hard cheeses (Swiss, Parmesan, Cheddar). Cheese and cheese products such as spreads and dips are usually purchased in a protective package or container. Once the container has been opened, it should be closed carefully and the product refrigerated so that it will not dry out and deteriorate.

The flavors of strong cheeses can be picked up by other foods, and cheese can readily absorb flavor from other foods. This is another very good reason for keeping cheeses tightly covered.

Cheese improperly stored or stored for too long a time may develop mold on its surface. Cheese should be purchased in amounts which can be used conveniently without prolonged storage.

## Convenience with Cheese

Convenience in using cheese began when the art of cheese making was taken out of the home and put into the factory. Store cheese is available in many varieties and forms, and is packaged in many different containers. Sliced cheese comes in packages in which the slices can be easily separated for use or in which each slice comes individually wrapped. You may purchase cheese in a piece, grated, shredded, cubed, in pressurized cans, as spreads and dips in many flavors, and as a ball rolled in nuts. These convenience forms usually cost more than the same weight of cheese in a solid piece.

Cottage cheese comes in several varieties. It can be purchased as dry cottage cheese (no cream added) or creamed cottage cheese, or with added fruits, fresh garden vegetables, or chives.

Canned cheese soup or cheese sauces are available. The canned cheese soup is a ready-made cheese sauce for au gratin vegetables, casseroles, meats, and pastas.

With so much variety and convenience, you are forced to make your selection from among many. Will you select an unripened, ripened, or process cheese; will it be soft, semihard, or hard; will it have a mild or a strong flavor; will it be sliced, grated, a spread, or a dip; or will it be a canned cheese sauce? To complicate matters even more, in addition to the true cheeses, there are many food products containing cheese. These foods resemble process cheese but are not regular cheese foods. These products may be labeled "pasteurized process cheese food" or "pasteurized process cheese spread." They differ from the true cheese foods in fat content and moisture, and in other added ingredients, such as milk solids and *stabilizers* (ingredients that preserve a food's texture). Each product is identified by its label and the ingredients used; it is important to read this label in order to get exactly what you want.

### For Review

1. What are three principles to follow when adding Cheddar cheese to tomato soup?
2. Which type of cheese—ripened or unripened—combines more easily with other ingredients?
3. List three uses of cheese and an advantage of each use.
4. Why is it important to cover cheese tightly for storage?

# 16 Chapter Review

## Summary

One of the most popular milk products is cheese. There are several kinds of cheeses available in a grocery store, those referred to as true cheeses and those known as process cheeses and process cheese foods. In addition, cheese comes in a variety of forms and is packed in many different containers. As with other foods, cheese requires proper storage to preserve its quality and to prevent the growth of undesirable organisms. Although the nutrients found in cheese are similar to those in milk, the kind and amount vary since during the cheese-making process most of the water-soluble nutrients in milk are generally lost. However, cheese does contain a wealth of nutrients that are necessary for the maintenance of a healthy body. In fact, preservation of the nutrient protein is the consideration upon which the principles of cheese cookery are based.

## Vocabulary

Match the vocabulary words below to their lettered definition.

1. casein
2. curd
3. kilocalorie
4. process cheeses
5. whey

   **a.** The measurement for the energy value of foods.

   **b.** The part of milk thickened into a soft mass of white clumps from which cheese is made.

   **c.** A milk protein that is found abundantly in cheese.

   **d.** A clear liquid that contains some of the water-soluble substances found in milk.

   **e.** Food products that are made from a mixture of cheeses to create different flavors and textures.

## Chapter Questions

1. During the cheese-making process, at which stage is the texture and flavor of cheese established?
2. Which cheeses would be appropriate for the following? a) sandwiches, b) salads, c) with fruits for dessert, d) cooked foods.
3. Which nutrients are found in cheese?
4. If you planned to use cheese, but wanted to limit fat, what cheese could you use?
5. In what way are the principles of cheese cookery similar to those of milk cookery?
6. What kinds of cheeses and convenience cheese products are used in your family, and what is the purpose for each?
7. When cheese is added as an ingredient, why should it be cut into small pieces and then the mixture cooked at a low temperature for a short time?
8. How should you prepare the cheese and white sauce for making macaroni and cheese to have the best results?
9. What is the function of the white sauce, macaroni, and topping in a meal such as macaroni and cheese?

10. When a food is referred to as au gratin potatoes, what kind of a dish is it?
11. Why would serving a fruit and cheese tray for dessert after a heavy main course not enhance the meal?
12. What is the proper method of storage for cheese dips and spreads, and why?
13. In what ways is cheese a convenience food?

## Skill Activities

 **1. Decision making** In your food journal, or on several sheets of notebook paper, make a chart of the cheeses available at your grocery store and record purposes for which they may be used. At the top of each column, write one of these headings: "For appetizers," "For salads," "For sandwiches," "For cooking and toppings," and "For desserts." Now visit the cheese counter at your favorite grocery store. In the appropriate column or columns, write the names of the cheeses you find. When you are preparing a menu or shopping list, use this chart to help you determine the kind of cheese you might use and purchase, depending on your purposes.

 **2. Communication** During the cheesemaking process, whey was once discarded. However, today it is used for a variety of purposes. Write a report about the uses of whey and the food products that are made with whey.

 **3. Communication** Research and then write a report on the way cheese was made by the housewife during the early 1800s. Try to make cheese following this procedure, and display your results to the class.

**4. Human relations** Along with domestic varieties, cheeses imported from Western Europe are also available at the grocery store. Learn where some of them first came from. With your classmates, make a map of Western Europe that shows the countries of England, Belgium, Holland, Germany, France, Switzerland, Italy, Spain, and Portugal. Find out the country of origin for each of these cheeses: Bel Paese, Brie, Camembert, Cheddar, Edam, Emmental, Gorgonzola, Gouda, Gruyère, Limburger, Loreto, Mozzarella, Muenster, Neufchâtel, Parmesan, Port du Salut, Roquefort, Romano, Sapsago, St. Jorge, Stilton, and Swiss. In the appropriate country on the map, write the name of the cheese or cheeses that originated there.

**5. Food science** While sodium is necessary for the normal functioning of the body, excess sodium can be unhealthful for some individuals. Some sources of sodium are "hidden," making cutting down on sodium intake difficult. Read the labels of at least three types and/or brands of cheese and record the sodium content of each. Compile the data in table form.

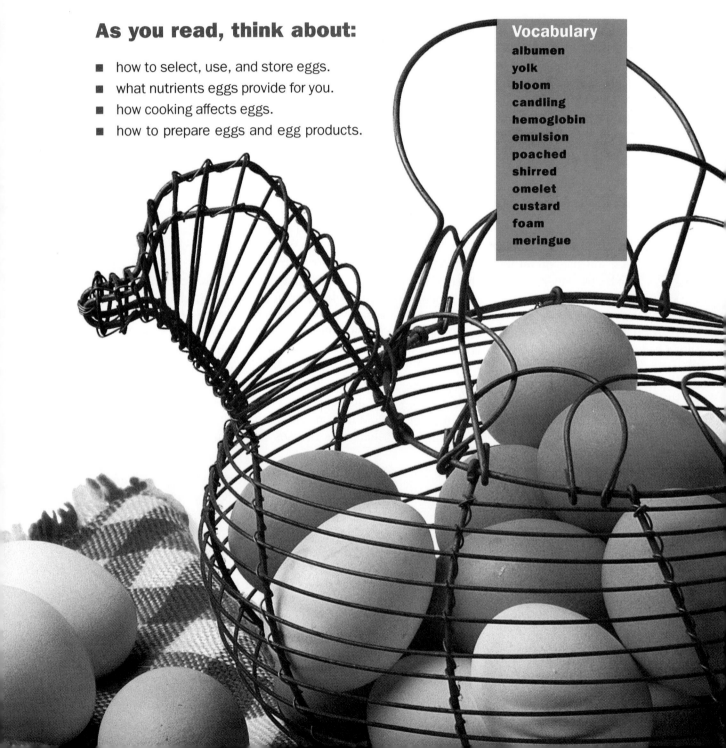

# 17 Eggs

## As you read, think about:

- how to select, use, and store eggs.
- what nutrients eggs provide for you.
- how cooking affects eggs.
- how to prepare eggs and egg products.

**Vocabulary**

albumen
yolk
bloom
candling
hemoglobin
emulsion
poached
shirred
omelet
custard
foam
meringue

The unique properties of eggs make them a versatile food. They are used in quiches, soufflés, custards, foam cakes, and hundreds of other dishes, as well as alone—on their own. Eggs are an important source of high-quality protein, vitamins, and a variety of minerals, including iron.

## The Structure, Grades, and Sizes of Eggs

One of the most versatile foods, eggs can serve as the main dish of a meal or in the preparation of other foods. An excellent source of protein, no matter what their grade or size, all eggs have the same structure.

### Egg Structure

You know that the egg is contained in a shell and consists of a white **albumen** (al-BYOO-min) and a yellow portion (**yolk**). In addition, eggs have several other parts.

The shell of the egg is porous, and it permits moisture and gases to pass through. On the outside of the shell there is a thin film called the **bloom** which helps to seal the pores and protect the egg from contamination. The color of the shell will vary from white to brown, depending upon which breed of chicken laid the egg. The color of the egg does not affect its cooking, eating quality, or nutrient value.

Between the shell and the egg white there are two membranes, the inner and the outer, which protect the quality of the egg. The white of the egg consists of the thin and the thick white. Fresh eggs will contain more thick white than older eggs. The thick white gives a high, rounded appearance to the egg when it is removed from the shell. Such an egg is more attractive when cooked than one in which the white spreads.

Egg gathering, now done by machine, was once done by hand.

The yolk membrane (the vitelline membrane) separates the yolk from the white. Attached to the yolk membrane on each side is a rope or cord called the chalaza which holds the yolk near the center of the egg. There is a light spot on the yolk known as the germ spot. This spot, on a fertilized and incubated egg, can develop into a baby chick. The yolk supplies the

The yolk, the albumen, and the shell are not the only components of an egg. What purpose do the egg membranes serve? What is the purpose of the chalaza?

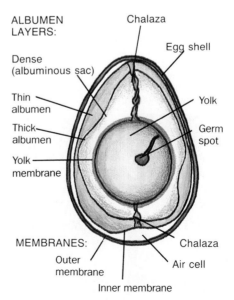

ALBUMEN LAYERS:

Dense (albuminous sac)

Thin albumen

Thick albumen

Yolk membrane

Chalaza

Egg shell

Yolk

Germ spot

MEMBRANES:

Outer membrane

Inner membrane

Chalaza

Air cell

food for the growing embryo. The color of the yolk depends upon the food the hen eats. In a fresh egg, the yolk is high, rounded, and centered in the thick white. The air cell is at the blunt end of the egg; its size increases as the egg ages.

## Grade and Size

Most eggs sold are graded for freshness and size. The standards for grading eggs were set by the United States Department of Agriculture. The freshness of an egg is graded by **candling,** which permits the grader to look inside the egg without breaking it. Long ago this was done by holding the egg before a candle. Today, most eggs pass on rollers over high-intensity lights that make the egg interior visible. Eggs are rotated so that all parts, including the outline of the yolk and the size of the air cell, can be seen. The freshest egg has a small air space and a thick white which supports the rounded, firm yolk.

The freshness of an egg refers to its quality and not its size. The freshest eggs are *Grade AA,* followed by *Grade A* and *Grade B.* The difference in grade is the firmness of the white and the yolk. The color of the shell has no influence on egg quality. Eggs are classified according to size and weight.

The egg carton has a label which indicates the grade (freshness) and the size of the egg. Although quality and size are both marked on the carton, one is not related to the other. That is, the largest eggs are not necessarily of the best quality. Eggs of any size may be in any of the three grades. For example, small eggs can be Grade AA, and jumbo eggs can be Grade B.

> ### For Review
> 1. What are the characteristics of a fresh egg?
> 2. What is the purpose of candling?
> 3. Describe a *Grade B* large egg.

# Nutrient Contributions

The nutrients in eggs are so well balanced that they can be rated with milk as a nutrient-rich food. Eggs make important contributions to the needs of your body. The yolk, rather than the white, is a rich source of nutrients. It contains some fat and more vitamins and minerals than the white. However, the yolk and the white are most often used together so that the nutrient values are usually considered for the whole egg, not for the yolk or the white alone.

## Protein

The egg contains a high-quality protein and can be used as a substitute for meat. Eggs, like milk, contain a complete protein which is needed for growth and replacement of worn body tissues.

## Vitamins

The yolk contains most of the vitamins found in the egg. The egg white contains only *riboflavin;* the yolk contains *vitamins A and D,* is a good source of $B_2$ (riboflavin), a fair source of $B_1$ (thiamin), and contains only a trace of niacin.

In the past, egg candling involved holding the egg before a candle (left). The modern process involves the eggs' passing over high-intensity lights (right).

Eggs are also important sources of *vitamin D* because most other common foods do not provide this vitamin. Fish-liver oils are the richest sources of vitamin D, but they are not usually eaten as food. Vitamin D was first found in cod-liver oil and then later in egg yolk and the cream of milk.

The sun can change some skin oils into vitamin D, and it is for this reason that vitamin D is called the "sunshine" vitamin. The sun must shine directly on the skin to convert skin oils into vitamin D. Window glass, clothing, and clouds prevent the ultraviolet rays of the sun from reaching the skin and forming vitamin D. Therefore, in cold climates and in areas where the sun isn't visible each day, very little vitamin D will be produced.

From your study of milk, you learned that vitamin D is added to milk and that vitamin D prevents a disease of the bones called rickets. Rickets is a disease caused by too little vitamin D in the diet or too little exposure to sunshine. Vitamin D is needed for the growth and maintenance of bones and teeth. It helps the body to absorb calcium and use it to build strong bones and teeth. Eggs and vitamin-D fortified milk will help you meet your body's need for this nutrient.

## Minerals

The most important minerals provided by eggs are *iron* and *phosphorus,* found only in the yolk. Iron is not widely distributed in foods, but it is found in meats and green leafy vegetables.

Iron is essential for the formation of **hemoglobin,** the red pigment of the blood. Hemoglobin carries oxygen to body cells and carries away carbon dioxide to be discarded from the body. When there are too few red blood cells, a condition called anemia develops. Since eggs are such an important source of iron and hemoglobin, they help prevent anemia. You will learn about another source of iron when you study about meats in the next chapter.

## Fat

Only the yolk of the egg contains fat. The vitamins A and D, because they are fat-soluble, are dissolved in the fat. The fat in egg yolk will also help to provide some of the body's energy needs. Any excess of these vitamins is stored by the body for future use.

## Egg Substitutes

The nutrient contribution of eggs makes them a valued food, even though some individuals must carefully control the kind and amount of fat they consume. The high cholesterol content of egg yolks is of concern to those who are on cholesterol- or fat-restricted diets. Especially for these individuals, food technologists developed egg substitutes. These products differ from eggs in that they are lower in fat, cholesterol, and calories. Several of these products are available in liquid, frozen, or dried forms.

The complete-egg and partial-egg substitutes are both available, although the partial-egg substitute appears to be preferred. The complete-egg substitute is made from soy or milk proteins. The partial-egg substitute retains the egg white but not the egg yolk. These egg substitutes have about one-half of the calories and fat of regular eggs and contain less sodium. The fat of eggs is replaced with vegetable oil (usually corn oil), giving the egg substitute a higher ratio of polyunsaturated fat to saturated fat. Unopened containers of egg substitute can be stored for ten weeks in the refrigerator and for two weeks after they have been opened.

Egg substitutes have a different flavor from real eggs, but they blend well with other ingredients in cooked foods. You can make acceptable omelets or scrambled eggs from these products. They may be substituted for eggs in recipes that call for whole eggs. Egg substitutes made of milk proteins do not have the thickening power of eggs and are not suitable in recipes, such as for custard, which use the egg as a thickener. Milk proteins do not coagulate (thicken) when heated, as do egg proteins.

Products prepared with egg substitutes are acceptable, but you may rate them somewhat lower than the product that you make with whole eggs. For example, the volume of cakes made with egg substitutes may be less than that of cakes which contain whole eggs. Egg substitutes are suitable for individuals who are on low-cholesterol or low-calorie diets.

### For Review

1. Why is it better to eat the whole egg and not just the white?
2. What is the importance of vitamin D in the diet? Besides eggs, where else can you get vitamin D?
3. What are some reasons a person would choose to eat egg substitutes rather than eggs?

# Principles of Egg Cookery

The principles of egg cookery are very much influenced by the egg's high protein content. As with all protein, high temperatures and overcooking cause toughening. Whether eggs are cooked alone or combined with other foods, the principles to observe are: (1) use low temperatures to prevent toughening, curdling, and discoloration; and (2) cook only until desired firmness is achieved. Overcooking also causes toughening, curdling, and discoloration.

## Functions of Eggs in Cookery

Eggs serve many important functions in cookery and are used in a variety of foods. Because of their color, flavor, viscosity (thickness), and ability to coagulate, eggs are valuable in various cookery processes. The functions of

eggs in cookery are: (1) to add nutrients; (2) to improve color, flavor, and texture of food products; (3) to thicken liquids; (4) to bind foods together or coat foods for frying; (5) to act as a leavening agent; and (6) to act as an emulsifying agent.

Eggs may be prepared alone or in combination with other foods. Either use will add to the nutrient value of the prepared food and the meal.

The color and flavor of most foods are improved when eggs are added. Eggs used in puddings, custards, and ice creams improve their color, flavor, and texture. In baked foods, eggs will improve the browning quality of the outer crust and can give a creamy or yellow color to the interior.

The protein in both the egg white and the yolk is a *thickening agent*. Because of the ability of protein in both egg white and yolk to coagulate, or clot, when heated, eggs can be used to thicken food mixtures. The coagulated egg will be firm. The coagulation of the egg protein will thicken custards; help to form the outer shell of cream puffs and the cell walls of cakes; bind together the ingredients of meat loaves; and hold crumbs together for a coating on breaded foods.

When eggs are heated, the protein will coagulate and become firm with a tender texture. However, if the heating is continued too long or if the temperature is too high, the protein will overcoagulate and become tough and rubbery. All protein, whether from cheese, meat, milk, or egg, will toughen when permitted to overcoagulate.

The *leavening action* of eggs is due to the air which can be beaten into them. Beaten egg white can hold a large quantity of air and form a foam. The air bubbles in the foam are surrounded by a film of egg white. When the foam is heated, the air bubbles expand and the egg white stretches. Then the egg coagulates to give a light, porous structure to the product. The

Eggs have a number of important functions in cookery, which is why they are considered such a versatile food. Among their purposes are (clockwise from top): (1) to add nutrients, as in a strawberry milk shake made with raw eggs; (2) to improve color, flavor, and texture, as in a custard pie; (3) to thicken liquids, as in a Hollandaise sauce; (4) to act as both a leavening and an emulsifying agent, as in cake; (5) to coat foods for frying, as for fried eggplant; and (6) to act as a leavening agent and to add attractiveness, as with bread brushed with an egg wash. What are the functions of eggs in other foods?

## Scrambled Eggs      Yield: 4 servings

4 eggs                      1 Tbs (15 mL) butter
¼ c (60 mL) milk
¼ tsp (1.2 mL) salt, and pepper if desired

1. Place eggs, milk, salt, and pepper in mixing bowl; beat with fork or beater until yolks and whites are blended.
2. Place butter in skillet; heat until slightly bubbly, but be careful not to burn.
3. Pour in mixture and lower heat. Cook slowly.
4. As mixture thickens on bottom and sides, lift cooked portion with spatula and turn gently. Do not stir, but permit the mixture to thicken in large portions. Do not overcook.
5. When eggs are thickened but still moist and glossy, quickly remove to heated platter and serve.

Approximate nutrition information per serving: calories–105; protein–6 g; fat–8 g; cholesterol–240 mg; carbohydrates–1 g; sodium–250 mg.

yolk forms only a small amount of foam and is not used for leavening.

An **emulsion** is a mixture of oil and another liquid, beaten together completely so that the oil is spread evenly throughout the mixture. The egg yolk acts as an *emulsifying agent* because the proteins it contains can surround tiny globules of oil and keep them from separating. Eggs act as an emulsifying agent in many foods, including cakes, popovers, and mayonnaise.

### Preparation and Uses of Eggs in Cookery

During cooking, eggs coagulate, and the degree of coagulation depends upon the cooking temperature and the length of cooking time. Sometimes eggs coagulate only slightly, as in

soft-cooked eggs, and at other times more completely, as in hard-cooked eggs.

Eggs are cooked in the shell or out of the shell, and they are used as an ingredient in many dishes. When cooking eggs alone or in combination with other foods, the best results are obtained when cooking temperatures are low and when cooking time is carefully controlled to give the desired degree of firmness.

When eggs are used alone or are the principal ingredient, it is important to use eggs of high quality. For your protection, use only clean eggs with no cracks in the shells.

### Tips for Herbs and Spices

Herbs and spices to use on eggs and in egg dishes are: basil, chives, dill, marjoram, oregano, parsley, pepper, sage, tarragon, thyme, and turmeric.

# The Versatility of Eggs

In many cultures, eggs—all different kinds of eggs—are a staple food and have been for centuries. At first, people probably collected the eggs of wild birds. Chickens were probably first raised in captivity around 2000 B.C. The Chinese started incubating chicken eggs about 1400 B.C. The practice of eating chicken eggs spread to Central Europe and Greece. When Columbus brought hens with him to the western hemisphere, both North and South Americans became chicken-egg eaters.

Today in the United States, each person eats an average of 27–30 eggs per year. Why are eggs so popular? Perhaps because they are so versatile. In the 18th century, one Frenchman said: "They know in France 685 different ways of dressing eggs, without counting those which [we] invent every day."

Eggs are used as the main ingredient for entrées, appetizers, and desserts. They are important ingredients in baking. Some of the ways that eggs are used in France and in China have been adopted and adapted by Americans.

## France

Following are some of the dishes that the French have developed for cooking eggs.

**Brioche**  Eggs added to breadlike dough make brioche a fluffy pastry.

**Soufflé**  Vegetables, fruit, or cheese are mixed with eggs and then baked to create a soufflé. This results in a light, fluffy dish that can be an appetizer, side dish, hors d'oeuvre, dessert, or entrée.

**Omelette**  Eggs are beaten, mixed in a frying pan, and then cheese, vegetables, and/or meat are added to create this popular egg dish. The eggs are folded over the filling. Omelettes are popular at any meal.

**Quiche**  Appropriate for breakfast, as well as for lunch or supper, quiche can be thought of as an egg pie. A pie crust is filled with a mixture of eggs, cream, cheese, vegetables, and/or meat.

## China

In China, eggs are added to some main dishes and soups. Some types of eggs are considered a delicacy.

**Egg Foo Young**  Sautéed vegetables are mixed with beaten eggs and cooked. The dish is then served with soy sauce.

**Egg-drop Soup**  An egg is beaten into a soup broth for a delicate taste. The egg solidifies in small pieces throughout the broth.

The versatile egg is used in such foods as (clockwise from top) egg foo young, an omelette, egg-drop soup, brioche, and quiche.

## Eggs Cooked in the Shell

Eggs cooked in the shell are correctly referred to as hard-cooked or soft-cooked rather than the more popular terms of hard-boiled or soft-boiled, since they are heated only to a simmering temperature. Boiling water causes overcoagulation and toughness. Eggs in the shell may be cooked by immersing them either in cold or hot water. The water should be heated only to simmering, which means that the water is just below the boiling point. The length of time eggs are cooked in the shell will determine the degree of coagulation or firmness. Cold eggs, taken directly from the refrigerator, require a longer time to simmer than do eggs at room temperature.

Sometimes the yolk of a hard-cooked egg may develop a dark green ring on the outer surface. This discoloration is due to a combining of the iron and the sulfur of the egg. The greenish color occurs when eggs have been overcooked or allowed to cook in boiling water. Cooling eggs immediately after cooking helps prevent discoloration.

Eggs that are soft cooked, hard cooked, or poached add little or no fat to the nutrients found in the egg itself. Why is it important to use eggs of the highest quality when using them alone?

## Eggs Cooked out of the Shell

*Fried* eggs are an American breakfast favorite. The shape of a fried egg depends upon the quality of the raw egg. A high-quality egg will result in the desired oval shape. Fried eggs are cooked in a small amount of fat over very low heat to the desired degree of firmness. To cook the top of the egg more quickly, the pan may be covered. If the fried egg is brown and the edges crisp, the pan and the fat were too hot.

*Poached* eggs are another favorite. It is important to use eggs of high quality so that the poached egg will be rounded with a film of coagulated white over the yolk. The egg to be **poached** is broken into a cup and carefully slipped into enough simmering liquid (milk or water) to cover the egg. A little salt or acid (vinegar) may be added to the cooking liquid to hasten the coagulation of the egg and minimize spreading. The liquid must be below the boiling point so that the egg will not toughen. The length of cooking time will determine the degree of firmness of the poached egg.

*Baked,* or **shirred,** eggs are very similar to fried eggs. The egg is placed into a lightly greased baking cup and is cooked in the oven at a moderate temperature—325°F (160°C)—to the desired degree of firmness.

Since eggs are usually beaten to blend the yolk and the white for *scrambled* eggs, eggs of a quality lower than AA or A can be used. A small amount of milk is added to the blended egg to produce a more tender product. The mixture is cooked in a pan containing a small amount of

### Health Tip

- When extra cholesterol poses a health problem, substitute two stiffly beaten egg whites for each whole egg needed.

Eggs that are shirred, fried, or used in an omelet require the use of added fat for cooking.

melted fat. A low temperature is used, and the eggs are stirred occasionally as they coagulate. Scrambled eggs should be tender, slightly moist, and in fairly large pieces.

An **omelet** may be either plain (French) or puffy. The plain, or French, omelet is made from beaten whole egg. For the puffy omelet, the yolk and white are beaten separately and then blended together by folding. Omelets, like scrambled eggs, are cooked on low heat in a skillet containing melted fat. The mixture is allowed to coagulate without stirring. Small areas of the coagulated portion are raised with a spatula to allow the uncoagulated egg to collect on the bottom of the pan. The omelet is a continuous disc of coagulated egg that is slightly moist on the upper surface. The disc, or circle, of coagulated egg is usually folded over when the omelet is served.

## Eggs as an Ingredient

As an ingredient, eggs are versatile because of their ability to form foams and to coagulate. Custards are thickened by coagulation of the egg protein, while angel food cakes, souffles, and meringues use egg foams.

A **custard** is a sweetened milk mixture thickened with egg. As the custard is cooked, the egg will coagulate, forming a protein network which can entrap liquids and cause the mixture to become a smooth, thickened product. Custards must be cooked at low temperatures so that the egg protein will not overcoagulate and squeeze out the trapped liquid to cause a watery or curdled custard.

The two types of custards are stirred, or soft, and baked. The ingredients used and the method of mixing are the same for both types of custard; only the method of cooking differs. The soft, or stirred, custard is cooked over hot water with constant stirring. It does not set firmly to form a gel like baked custard, but it is thick and velvety like heavy cream. A baked custard is cooked in the oven without stirring and will hold its shape when removed from the baking dish.

To avoid overcoagulation, soft custards are cooked with constant stirring over water that is simmering, not boiling. Cooking is stopped when the custard coats a spoon. Baked custards are set in a pan of hot water and baked in a moderate oven—350° F (180° C)—until a knife inserted near the center of one of the custards comes out clean.

Cooking custards for too long a time overcoagulates the egg protein. An overcooked stirred custard will be curdled or watery; an overcooked baked custard will have bubbles which can be seen through a glass baking dish, will be porous, and, when cut, its liquid will separate out.

Custards can be used in a variety of ways. A soft custard can be served alone or as a sauce over fresh or canned fruit, cake, or gelatin. A dessert called floating island is a soft custard garnished with spoonfuls of meringue.

Baked custards, too, can be varied. Before baking, a variety of flavorings or extracts can be added, or the top of the custard can be sprinkled with a favorite spice or coconut. Custard, pecan, coconut cream, and pumpkin pies are popular variations of baked custard.

Custard mixtures without sugar can serve as the basis for a main dish. Seasonings, grated cheese, corn, bread cubes, and other foods can be added, and the mixture is cooked as a baked custard. These custards make unusual main dishes. *Quiche* (KEESH) is an unsweetened, open-faced custard pie flavored with cheese and served as an entrée, or main dish. It often contains chopped vegetables, meat, poultry, or seafood.

A **foam** is formed when air is beaten into egg whites. The egg white surrounds the air bubbles in the foam. Egg-white foams are used in puffy omelets, souffles, meringues, angel cakes, and other foods. These foods use the egg foam as a leavening agent. The air in egg-white foams will expand when heated. This causes the batter or omelet to increase in volume until the heat coagulates the egg protein that surrounds the air bubble. This will give a light, porous structure to the product. Low temperatures delay coagulation of the egg white so that it can stretch with the expanding air and increase in volume.

Several things can affect the amount of air that can be beaten into egg whites: (1) egg whites at room temperature beat more quickly than those at refrigerator temperature and give a larger volume; (2) fat from any source interferes with the whipping of egg whites. Fat from egg yolk, milk, or a greasy bowl or beater will reduce the amount of air which egg whites can retain; and (3) a bowl with a small rounded

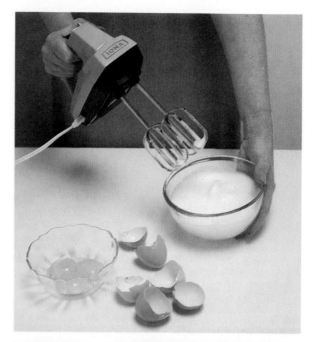

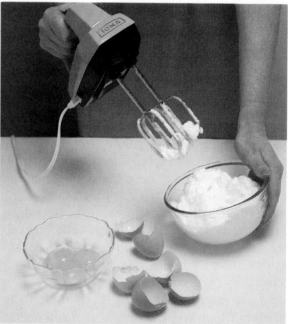

Egg whites beaten to the soft-peak stage (top) have larger air cells than egg whites beaten to the stiff-peak stage. What uses do soft egg whites have? What uses do stiff egg whites have? What happens when egg whites are beaten beyond the stiff-peak stage?

## Tips for Microwaving Eggs

- Avoid rubbery eggs by undercooking them slightly and then allowing some standing time.
- Stir finely chopped pieces of hard-cooked egg into sauces and then reheat in the microwave.
- When preparing eggs for scrambling, first mix them gently with a fork. Over-mixing will add too much air and will toughen the eggs.
- When adding ham, tomato, onion, and other foods to eggs, heat the add-ins first and then stir them into the eggs midway through cooking.
- If adding cheese to eggs, add it before cooking.

bottom and sides that slope out to a wider top permits eggs to beat to a better volume. The beater should fit the bottom of the bowl, and the size of the bowl should suit the amount of egg white.

For the best leavening action, the egg white should form a stable foam. A stable foam is one in which little liquid separates on standing. Some factors which influence the stability of the foam are: (1) cream of tartar added to egg white makes a more stable foam; (2) thick whites form more stable foams than thin whites; and (3) sugar increases stability but delays foam formation so that more beating will be required. It is usually best to beat the egg white to a soft-peak stage and then to add the sugar gradually.

The stiffness to which egg white is beaten is very important. After a little beating, the egg white looks frothy with large air bubbles on the surface. As beating is continued, the air cells become smaller and the foam becomes stiffer and white in appearance. The bubbles will become increasingly smaller as beating continues. The egg whites are suitable for folding into mixtures when the peak will just bend over as the beater is slowly lifted out of the foam. This soft-peak stage is also used for the beating of soft meringues which are to be spread on various kinds of cream pies.

Additional beating will cause the peak to stand up straight as the beater is lifted out of the foam. A stiff foam is difficult to fold into other ingredients. Hard meringues are beaten to stiff-peak stage.

Further beating produces a dry foam that breaks into pieces or lumps and does not blend well into other ingredients. At this stage, the pieces of egg whites are not useful for any food preparation.

A hard or soft **meringue** (muh-RANG) is egg-white foam to which sugar is added. Soft meringues are used as toppings for pies and as an ingredient in fruit whips and other desserts. The foam for hard meringues is beaten to the stiff-peak stage and contains twice as much sugar as the soft meringues. Hard meringues may be shaped into meringue shells or cookies, and baked at a low temperature—250°F (120°C). Meringue shells filled with ice cream and fruit are a very special treat.

### Microwaving Eggs

Eggs are a delicate food and should be microwaved on a low power setting. They can be cooked at a higher setting if they are ingredients in a casserole or soup.

Do *not* cook eggs in their shells in a microwave oven. The high fat content of the yolk causes it to cook faster than the surrounding white, causing the egg to explode. Instead, open the egg into a custard cup, and pierce the yolk with a toothpick. Cover the eggs tightly, and cook on a low power setting.

## For Review

1. What happens when eggs are either cooked at high temperatures or are overcooked? Why?
2. Why are eggs used as thickening agents?
3. How do eggs help create an emulsion?
4. Why do some hard-cooked eggs have a green ring around the yolk? How can this be prevented?
5. What are poached eggs? Shirred eggs?
6. How is a soft custard different from a baked custard?
7. Describe some precautions to take when making a foam.
8. What uses does an egg foam have?
9. Why should eggs *not* be cooked in their shells in a microwave oven?

# Egg Selection and Storage

Because eggs are such a basic food in our diet, their intended use should be considered before purchase. For recipes that call for beaten eggs, eggs of a lower quality can be used, while those of higher quality should be used in recipes calling for the whole egg. In both cases, eggs should be stored carefully and will therefore keep well for several weeks.

## Selecting Eggs

When buying eggs, the grade and classification standards set up for eggs are useful guides to egg quality and size. Along with grade, size, and the intended use of the egg, cost should be considered.

In high-grade eggs, the white is thick, and the yolk will stand up higher in the center of the egg than in low-grade eggs. Because of this, it is possible to have more attractive poached or fried eggs from Grade AA than Grade B eggs. However, the highest-grade eggs need not be purchased for all uses. All grades of eggs have acceptable uses. When eggs are served out of the shell alone, Grades AA and A may have a more delicate flavor and attractive appearance; but when eggs are combined with other foods, as in casseroles, salads, cookies, or muffins, Grade B may be used.

In addition to grade, eggs are sold on the basis of weight. You must consider both grade and weight in relation to the price of eggs. The highest grade and largest eggs are the most

As you can see, jumbo eggs are considerably larger than small eggs. Even if they cost less per dozen, are small eggs always a better buy than the larger sizes?

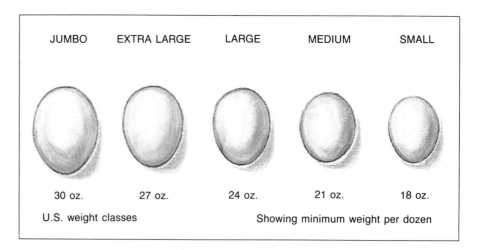

| JUMBO | EXTRA LARGE | LARGE | MEDIUM | SMALL |
|-------|-------------|-------|--------|-------|
| 30 oz. | 27 oz. | 24 oz. | 21 oz. | 18 oz. |

U.S. weight classes — Showing minimum weight per dozen

expensive. Grade and size are two separate factors; that is, Grade A eggs are of the same quality whether they are small or large. Generally, when there is less than seven cents difference between one size and the next smaller size of the same grade, the larger size will be more economical. Small eggs may cost less per dozen but may not be a better buy in terms of weight and actual quantity of egg.

The color of the shell may also influence cost. White-shell eggs may be in greater demand than brown-shell eggs and therefore cost more. You may save money by buying eggs with the shell color which is less in demand. The color of the eggshell does not influence nutrient value or eating quality of the yolk or white.

The size of eggs as well as their quality should be considered in relation to their use. The fact that jumbo eggs weigh almost twice as much as small eggs points out why uniform results in baking cannot be expected unless the recipe specifies the size of egg to be used. Most recipes were developed to use large or medium eggs rather than the jumbo or small sizes; some avoid variation in egg size by using a measured amount of egg.

## Storage of Eggs

An egg begins to deteriorate immediately after it has been laid, but this process can be slowed down by proper storage. As eggs deteriorate in quality, the white becomes thinner, the yolk flattens, and the air space increases in size. Purchase only eggs which are kept under refrigeration until they are sold. Place them immediately into the home refrigerator until you are ready to use them.

Because eggs can absorb odors through shell pores, they may be kept in the closed carton as purchased or in a covered container. Eggs are washed just before they are used rather than before they are stored. The protective coating on the shell helps to maintain egg quality during storage. Store eggs with the blunt end up to avoid movement of the yolk and the air cell. Leftover whites can be stored in a tightly covered container; leftover yolks, if the quantity is small, may need to be covered with a thin layer of milk or water and then tightly covered.

Raw eggs may also be stored—out of the shell—in the freezer for up to one year. The egg should be blended slightly before freezing, or the eggs can be separated and the yolks and whites frozen in their own airtight containers. When freezing yolks only, add ⅜ teaspoon (1.5 mL) of salt or 4½ teaspoons (24 mL) of sugar to every dozen yolks.

## Convenience and Eggs

Frozen and dried eggs are not usually sold in retail stores. However, frozen omelet mixtures and frozen cholesterol-free egg substitutes are available. Dehydrated egg products are used in some packaged mixes. For example, angel food cake mix contains dried egg whites, and a custard mix contains egg yolk solids. The use of egg solids in packaged mixes eliminates the need to add fresh eggs at the time of mixing. Because of the fat content of egg yolk, dried whole egg or dried yolk powders deteriorate and consequently do not keep well over long periods of time.

### For Review

1. Why may a lower-grade egg be used as an ingredient?
2. Under what circumstance might it be better to buy brown eggs instead of white eggs?
3. Why is it important to keep eggs covered when storing them?
4. Describe one advantage and one disadvantage of egg solids in packaged mixes.

# 17 Chapter Review

## Summary

Eggs are a versatile food as well as a nutritious one. They are a rich source of vitamin D, which is not usually found in other common foods, as well as protein. In fact, the high protein content influences the procedures to follow when cooking eggs. As an ingredient, eggs are used to thicken, emulsify, leaven, and improve the taste, texture, and color of many foods. Although eggs are sold in a variety of sizes, the determinant of their quality is not size, but freshness. Just as with the purchase of other foods, the intended use, cost, size and quality, or grade, of the eggs must be considered. Eggs must be stored in a closed container and refrigerated to protect them and to maintain their quality.

## Vocabulary

Use the vocabulary words below to fill in the blanks in the paragraphs that follow.

| | |
|---|---|
| albumen | hemoglobin |
| bloom | meringue |
| candling | omelet |
| custard | poached |
| emulsion | shirred |
| foam | yolk |

Before eggs are sold, they go through a process called __(1)__, which permits a grader to look inside the egg to determine its freshness. When the grader looks inside the egg, a thick white, called the __(2)__, and a round yellow portion, called the __(3)__, are visible. The eggs are sorted according to grades and then packed. They are not washed because this could destroy the __(4)__, which is the thin film on the outside of the shell that protects the egg from contamination.

Eggs are very nutritious. One of the most important minerals that eggs provide is iron, which acts together with __(5)__ to make red blood cells to prevent a condition called anemia from developing. Because of their high nutritious content, eggs are used as a main dish and as an ingredient. One way to cook an egg as a main dish is to put the egg into a lightly greased baking cup and cook it in the oven. This is called a __(6)__ egg. Similar to a scrambled egg, an __(7)__ is made by beating the whole egg, pouring the mixture into a skillet, and cooking it, without stirring, over low heat to form a circle of coagulated egg. A favorite of many people is a __(8)__ egg, which is cooked in just enough simmering liquid to cover it. An egg is also used to thicken a sweetened milk mixture to make a soft or baked __(9)__. When air is beaten into the white of an egg, a white mixture with bubbles, called __(10)__ is formed. When sugar is added to this white mixture, a __(11)__ is made, and this can be used as a topping on a pie or in other desserts. The yolk is also an important part of the egg. In fact, when eggs are beaten with other ingredients to make foods such as popovers and cakes, the eggs act to form an __(12)__ so that the oil is spread evenly throughout the mixture.

# Chapter Questions

1. What are the nutrients that eggs provide?
2. Compare eggs that have a white shell and those with a brown shell.
3. Why can eggs be a substitute for meat?
4. Why are there egg substitute products, and how do they differ from eggs?
5. How are the cooking principles for eggs and cheese similar?
6. What are the two procedures for making a hard-cooked egg?
7. What causes a custard to curdle?
8. In order to achieve success, what important factors should you understand about egg cookery when a recipe says to combine egg whites and cream of tartar and beat until the mixture turns foamy white and doubles in volume?
9. What is the difference between the soft-peak and stiff-peak stages for beating egg whites? When is each used?
10. When you purchase a dozen eggs, what considerations should you make?
11. How are eggs stored in your family? Will the way the eggs are stored give you the best cooking results? Why?
12. How are leftover whites and yolks stored?

# Skill Activities

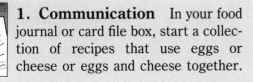

**1. Communication** In your food journal or card file box, start a collection of recipes that use eggs or cheese or eggs and cheese together. Frequently recipes call for a cheese or egg base, or a combined cheese and egg base. Examples of the kinds of recipes to include here are rarebit, macaroni and cheese, omelet, quiche, and souffle. Organize your collection into sections that cover beverages, main dish meals, breads, cakes, pies, and low-calorie foods. You can find recipes in books, magazines, newspapers, and on the display boards of grocery stores.

**2. Resource management** Eggs are used to emulsify, to leaven, to thicken, and to bind or coat. Use cookbooks to find at least one recipe for each function. Write the function, the name of the recipe, and then the recipe.

**3. Critical thinking** Compare the nutrients of a whole egg and egg substitute product. Down the left-hand side of a lined piece of paper, write: "Calories," "Protein," "Carbohydrate," "Cholesterol," and "Sodium." Now draw a line, and write "Percentage of U.S. RDA." Then list on a separate line: "Protein," "Vitamin A," "Vitamin C," "Thiamin," "Riboflavin," "Niacin," "Calcium," "Iron," "Vitamin D," "Vitamin E," "Vitamin $B_6$," "Folic Acid," "Vitamin $B_{12}$," "Zinc," and "Pantothenic Acid." Make two columns. Above one, write "Egg Substitute," above the other, write "One Large Whole Egg." From a foods value table, find the needed information about a whole egg. Read the nutritional label on an egg substitute, and record your findings. How does the substitute compare with a whole egg?

# 18 Meats

## As you read, think about:

- what nutrients meats provide for you.
- how to identify, select, use, and store meats.
- how to prepare meats.

The edible portion of animals is generally known as meat. To American pioneers, it meant buffalo, turkey, deer, bear, or whatever other animal they could find. To most Americans today, it means beef, veal, pork, or lamb. Our modern beef animal originated from the wild herds of aurochs that were domesticated in Asia centuries ago. Modern beef cattle produce larger quantities of meat than their forebears. Because meat is usually the most expensive item in a meal, it is most often the starting point for planning. Meat is a highly nutritious food with a satisfying flavor.

## Nutrient Contributions

Besides being a popular food, meat has outstanding nutritional value. It is an important source of complete protein, iron, and the B vitamins.

### Protein

Protein is made of small units or building blocks called *amino acids*. Meat protein contains all of the essential amino acids required by your body. When the diet does not contain enough complete protein, growth stops and muscles weaken.

Meat supplies a complete protein that is used by the body for growth and maintenance. Protein is needed by every body cell—muscles, red blood cells, skin, hair, teeth, bones, and nerves. You need protein constantly in order to repair and replace worn tissues and cells.

Each amino acid has its own special name and a particular job in building different tissues in your body. All amino acids need not be present in every food you eat. The body can make some of them if you eat the proper foods, but there are some which the body cannot make. The amino acids which the body cannot make are called the **essential amino acids.** They are

Thousands of years ago, animals were hunted, as shown in this ancient cave drawing. Today, animals are domesticated to provide protein-rich meat.

found in foods from animal sources which supply complete proteins. Milk, cheese, eggs, fish, and poultry, in addition to meat, come from animals and are *complete protein foods.* Complete protein foods promote growth and maintain the body.

Different foods contain different amounts and different kinds of protein. Cereals, breads, and vegetables lack one or more of the essential amino acids; therefore, they are *partially incomplete protein foods.* The partially incomplete protein from these foods can repair your body, but it cannot support growth. (See pages 43 and 56.) When eaten in the same meal, the protein in animal foods either balances or supplies the missing amino acids in the incomplete protein from plants. This is why it is important for you to eat a variety of foods.

## Minerals

Meats are important sources of the minerals iron, copper, and phosphorus. Minerals do not burn and do not give calories, but they are needed to repair and build cells and to maintain life processes.

Your body needs *iron* and *copper* to make red blood cells. Iron, which gives the blood its red color, is needed to make hemoglobin. The *hemoglobin* in red blood cells transports oxygen from the lungs to all body cells and removes waste. When the supply of iron is low, there will be too few red blood cells; this condition is known as **anemia.** In addition to fatigue it causes, anemia may also cause a lowered resistance to infection. Both girls and women are more inclined to be anemic than men because of the loss of blood, and therefore iron, during the menstrual period.

Iron is not widely distributed in common foods. Liver is the best food source. Lean meats, egg yolks, and green leafy vegetables are also important for their iron content. The iron and copper which meat contains help to build red blood cells.

Lean meats are also a good source of *phosphorus.* You will recall that phosphorus is needed to build bones and teeth and to help in the oxidation of foods (release of energy from food) in the body cells. Can you think of other foods that also contain phosphorus?

## Vitamins

Lean meats are a good source of the B vitamins *thiamin, riboflavin,* and *niacin.* Lean pork is the richest source of thiamin. Because these B vitamins are water soluble, some will dissolve in the cooking liquid. However, the juices from meat may be used to make gravy or soup, and in this way the vitamins in the juices are not lost. Can you recall what these vitamins provide for you? In what other foods besides meat are they found?

## Fat

The fat of meat does not provide vitamins, minerals, or protein. Fats, as you recall, are an abundant source of energy. Much of the fat in meat forms a thick layer around the meat muscle and is often removed before cooking or at the table. The lean which remains will contain some fat. In addition to energy value, fat will contribute to the flavor and palatability of meat.

Meats contribute important amounts of nutrients, but they are low in calcium and vitamins A and C. If you include milk, cheese, fruits, and vegetables along with meats in your meals, you will have a balanced diet.

### For Review
1. Why is meat a complete protein food?
2. Why are vegetables partially incomplete protein foods?
3. What is the importance of iron found in meats?

# Cuts, Forms, and Uses of Meat

Modern markets wrap fresh retail meats in transparent material and display them in open self-service refrigerated cases. Other forms of meat are available on the market shelves, in canned form, or in the freezer section. All meat-supplying animals are very similar in shape. The techniques of cutting meat are standardized so that similar cuts are available. Your knowledge of muscle and bone structure of animals in general will help you recognize specific cuts of meat from any animal. The shape of the retail cut from the same location on any animal will be the same; only the size of the piece and the color of the lean will vary.

## Wholesale and Retail Cuts

All cuts of meat are composed of lean or muscle tissue, connective tissue, and fat; some cuts contain bone. A carcass too heavy to be handled easily will be cut into smaller pieces called *wholesale cuts.* The wholesale cuts will be divided by the butcher into smaller cuts called *retail cuts,* which are offered for sale in display cases of markets. These cuts of meat come from beef, veal, pork, and lamb.

**Beef**  Meat from cattle over one year old is known as beef. It is bright red in color and has white or cream-colored fat. The beef carcass is first cut in half through the backbone to form two *sides* of beef. The side of beef is cut into two quarters and then into wholesale cuts which can be handled easily. Wholesale cuts are divided into retail cuts at each local store.

Only two wholesale cuts of beef, the rib and the loin, are tender; the other cuts are less tender. You will learn how to match the tenderness of meat cuts with cooking methods. The ability to recognize retail cuts is most helpful in selecting and cooking meat.

**Veal**  Veal is meat from cattle three to fourteen weeks old and is next in size to beef, but much smaller. Veal is fine grained, pink in color, lacks fat and marbling (flecks of fat in the meat), and has considerable connective tissue. The bones are pliable, porous, and red. It has a delicate flavor that blends well with other foods.

Because veal is from very young cattle, the cuts of veal differ somewhat from beef cuts. For example, the loin of veal and the rib section are used for chops instead of steaks, as in beef.

**Pork**  Pork comes from hogs or pigs usually not more than a year old. The color of young lean pork is grayish pink, changing to a rose color as the animal matures. The lean is well marbled and covered with a soft white fat. The cut surface of the bone is red. All cuts of pork must be thoroughly cooked to avoid the risk of **trichinosis,** a disease caused by a harmful parasite sometimes found in pork.

Bacon is usually made from pork sides that are treated with salt, sugar, certain chemicals, and often wood smoke. Meats treated in this manner are known as **cured** meats. They have a better keeping quality than fresh meat. Good bacon has liberal streaks of a dark-pink lean in a snowy-white fat.

Ham is the cured and smoked hind leg of a hog. The ham is injected with a curing solution and then smoked. A picnic ham is a pork shoulder that has been cured and smoked. The permanent pink color of ham is a result of the curing process.

**Lamb**  Lamb is the smallest animal used for meat; it is the flesh of sheep not more than fourteen months old. Mutton is the flesh of mature sheep. The lean of lamb is dark red, and the fat is white and firm. Mutton has dark-red flesh, firm bones, and creamy fat. The cuts of lamb are very similar to those of veal but smaller in size.

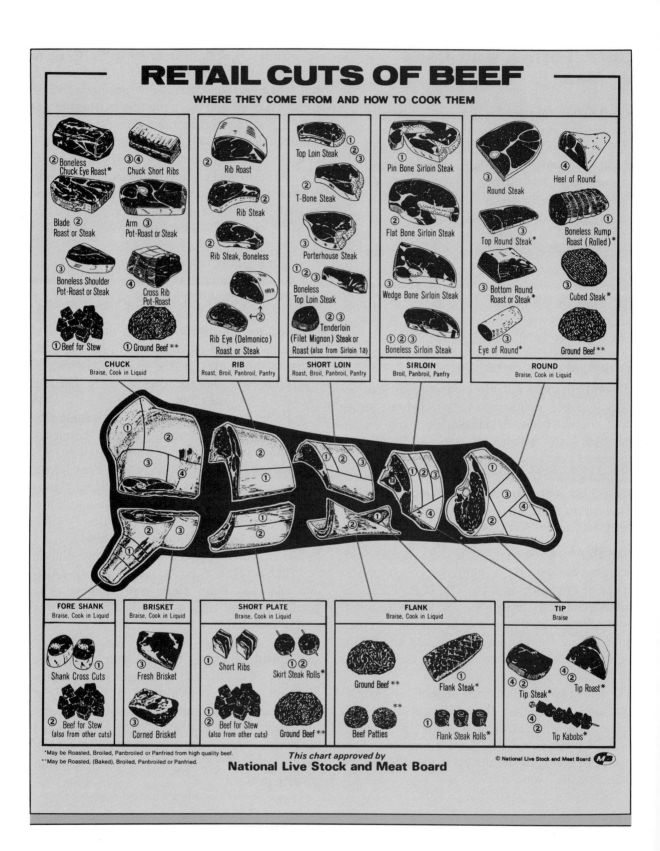

# RETAIL CUTS OF BEEF
## WHERE THEY COME FROM AND HOW TO COOK THEM

**CHUCK**
Braise, Cook in Liquid

② Boneless Chuck Eye Roast*
③④ Chuck Short Ribs
Blade ② Roast or Steak
Arm ③ Pot-Roast or Steak
③ Boneless Shoulder Pot-Roast or Steak
④ Cross Rib Pot-Roast
① Beef for Stew
① Ground Beef**

**RIB**
Roast, Broil, Panbroil, Panfry

② Rib Roast
② Rib Steak
② Rib Steak, Boneless
Rib Eye (Delmonico) Roast or Steak

**SHORT LOIN**
Roast, Broil, Panbroil, Panfry

①② Top Loin Steak ②③
② T-Bone Steak
③ Porterhouse Steak
①②③ Boneless Top Loin Steak
②③ Tenderloin (Filet Mignon) Steak or Roast (also from Sirloin 1a)

**SIRLOIN**
Broil, Panbroil, Panfry

① Pin Bone Sirloin Steak
② Flat Bone Sirloin Steak
③ Wedge Bone Sirloin Steak
①②③ Boneless Sirloin Steak

**ROUND**
Braise, Cook in Liquid

③ Round Steak
④ Heel of Round
③ Top Round Steak*
① Boneless Rump Roast (Rolled)*
③ Bottom Round Roast or Steak*
Cubed Steak*
Eye of Round*
Ground Beef**

**FORE SHANK**
Braise, Cook in Liquid

① Shank Cross Cuts
② Beef for Stew (also from other cuts)

**BRISKET**
Braise, Cook in Liquid

③ Fresh Brisket
③ Corned Brisket

**SHORT PLATE**
Braise, Cook in Liquid

① Short Ribs
①② Skirt Steak Rolls*
①② Beef for Stew (also from other cuts)
Ground Beef**

**FLANK**
Braise, Cook in Liquid

Ground Beef**
① Flank Steak*
Beef Patties**
① Flank Steak Rolls*

**TIP**
Braise

④② Tip Steak*
④② Tip Roast*
④② Tip Kabobs*

*May be Roasted, Broiled, Panbroiled or Panfried from high quality beef.
**May be Roasted, (Baked), Broiled, Panbroiled or Panfried.

*This chart approved by*
**National Live Stock and Meat Board**

© National Live Stock and Meat Board

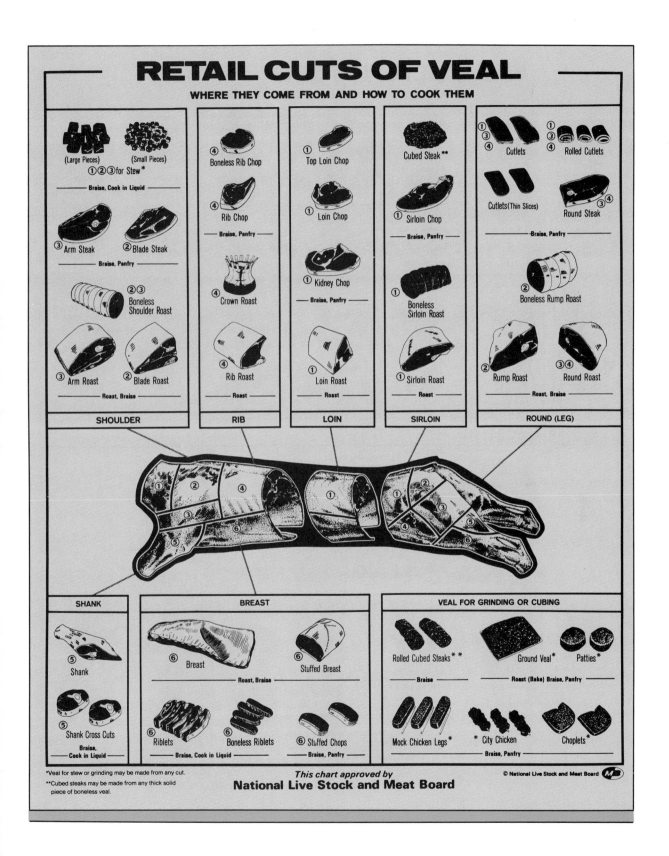

# RETAIL CUTS OF VEAL

**WHERE THEY COME FROM AND HOW TO COOK THEM**

## SHOULDER

(Large Pieces)   (Small Pieces)
① ② ③ for Stew*

— Braise, Cook in Liquid —

③ Arm Steak   ② Blade Steak

— Braise, Panfry —

②③ Boneless Shoulder Roast

③ Arm Roast   ② Blade Roast

— Roast, Braise —

## RIB

④ Boneless Rib Chop

④ Rib Chop

— Braise, Panfry —

④ Crown Roast

④ Rib Roast

— Roast —

## LOIN

① Top Loin Chop

① Loin Chop

① Kidney Chop

— Braise, Panfry —

① Loin Roast

— Roast —

## SIRLOIN

Cubed Steak **

① Sirloin Chop

— Braise, Panfry —

① Boneless Sirloin Roast

① Sirloin Roast

— Roast —

## ROUND (LEG)

①③④ Cutlets   ①③④ Rolled Cutlets

Cutlets (Thin Slices)   ③④ Round Steak

— Braise, Panfry —

② Boneless Rump Roast

② Rump Roast   ③④ Round Roast

— Roast, Braise —

## SHANK

⑤ Shank

⑤ Shank Cross Cuts

— Braise, Cook in Liquid —

## BREAST

⑥ Breast   Stuffed Breast

— Roast, Braise —

⑥ Riblets   ⑥ Boneless Riblets   ⑥ Stuffed Chops

— Braise, Cook in Liquid —   — Braise, Panfry —

## VEAL FOR GRINDING OR CUBING

Rolled Cubed Steaks **   Ground Veal*   Patties*

— Braise —   — Roast (Bake) Braise, Panfry —

Mock Chicken Legs*   * City Chicken   Choplets*

— Braise, Panfry —

*Veal for stew or grinding may be made from any cut.

**Cubed steaks may be made from any thick solid piece of boneless veal.

*This chart approved by*
**National Live Stock and Meat Board**

© National Live Stock and Meat Board

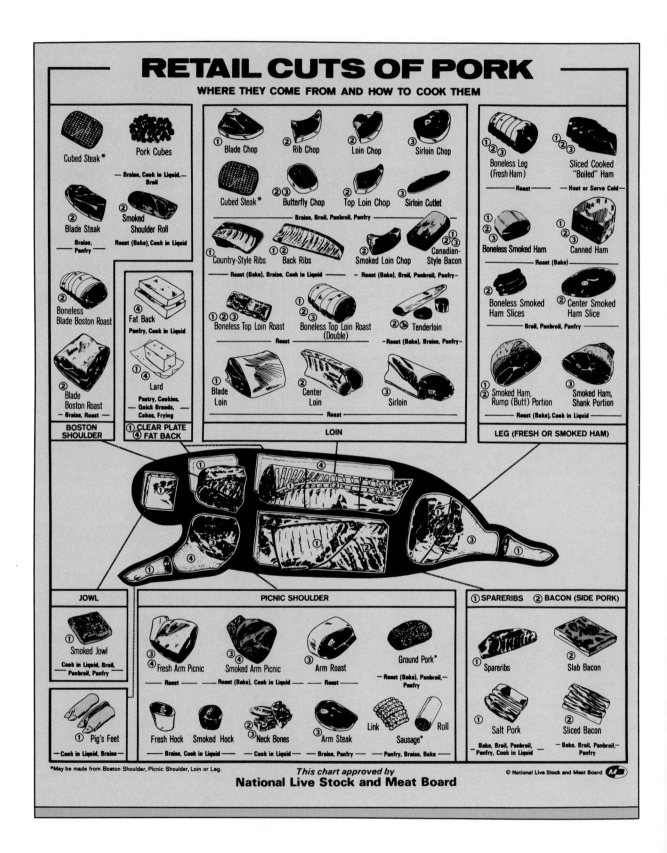

# RETAIL CUTS OF PORK

## WHERE THEY COME FROM AND HOW TO COOK THEM

**BOSTON SHOULDER**

Cubed Steak*

Pork Cubes

— Braise, Cook in Liquid. — Broil

② Blade Steak

② Smoked Shoulder Roll

**Braise, Panfry**

Roast (Bake), Cook in Liquid

② Boneless Blade Boston Roast

④ Fat Back

**Panfry, Cook in Liquid**

② Blade Boston Roast

— Braise, Roast —

① ④ Lard

**Pastry, Cookies, Quick Breads, Cakes, Frying**

**① CLEAR PLATE**
**④ FAT BACK**

**LOIN**

① Blade Chop

② Rib Chop

② Loin Chop

③ Sirloin Chop

Cubed Steak*

② ③ Butterfly Chop

② Top Loin Chop

③ Sirloin Cutlet

— Braise, Broil, Panbroil, Panfry —

① Country-Style Ribs

① ② Back Ribs

② Smoked Loin Chop

① ② ③ Canadian-Style Bacon

— Roast (Bake), Braise, Cook in Liquid — — Roast (Bake), Broil, Panbroil, Panfry—

① ② ③ Boneless Top Loin Roast

① ② ③ Boneless Top Loin Roast (Double)

② ③ ④ Tenderloin

— Roast — —Roast (Bake), Braise, Panfry—

① Blade Loin

② Center Loin

③ Sirloin

— Roast —

**LEG (FRESH OR SMOKED HAM)**

① ② ③ Boneless Leg (Fresh Ham)

① ② ③ Sliced Cooked "Boiled" Ham

— Roast — — Heat or Serve Cold—

① ② ③ Boneless Smoked Ham

① ② ③ Canned Ham

— Roast (Bake) —

② Boneless Smoked Ham Slices

② Center Smoked Ham Slice

— Broil, Panbroil, Panfry —

① ② Smoked Ham, Rump (Butt) Portion

③ Smoked Ham, Shank Portion

— Roast (Bake), Cook in Liquid —

**JOWL**

① Smoked Jowl

**Cook in Liquid, Broil, Panbroil, Panfry**

① Pig's Feet

— Cook in Liquid, Braise —

**PICNIC SHOULDER**

④ Fresh Arm Picnic

③ ④ Smoked Arm Picnic

③ Arm Roast

Ground Pork*

— Roast — — Roast (Bake), Cook in Liquid — — Roast — — Roast (Bake), Panbroil, — Panfry

Fresh Hock

Smoked Hock

② Neck Bones

③ Arm Steak

Link

Roll

Sausage*

— Braise, Cook in Liquid — — Cook in Liquid — — Braise, Panfry — — Panfry, Braise, Bake —

**① SPARERIBS**  **② BACON (SIDE PORK)**

① Spareribs

② Slab Bacon

① Salt Pork

② Sliced Bacon

— Bake, Broil, Panbroil, — Panfry, Cook in Liquid — — Bake, Broil, Panbroil, — Panfry

*May be made from Boston Shoulder, Picnic Shoulder, Loin or Leg.

© National Live Stock and Meat Board

*This chart approved by*
**National Live Stock and Meat Board**

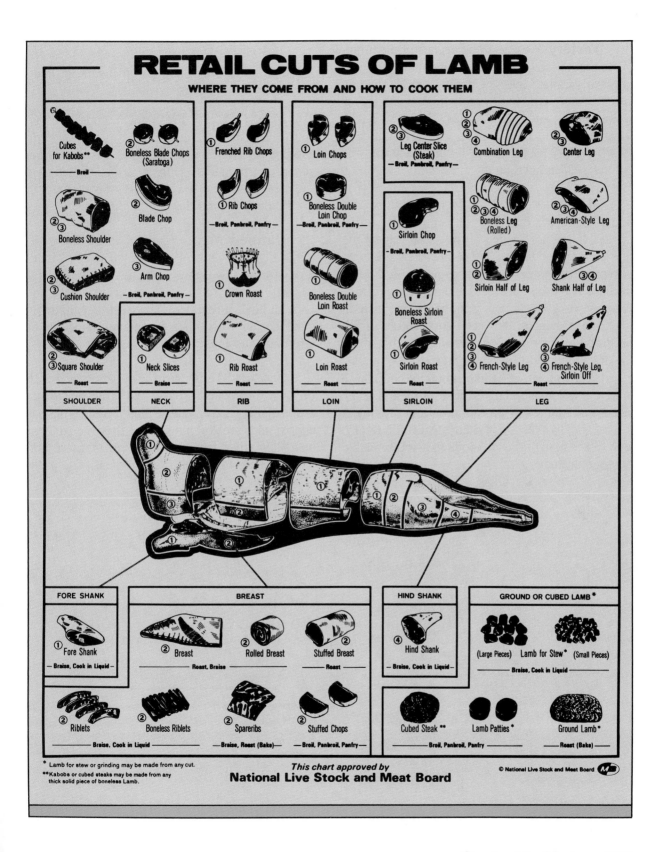

# RETAIL CUTS OF LAMB
## WHERE THEY COME FROM AND HOW TO COOK THEM

**SHOULDER**

Cubes for Kabobs**

② Boneless Blade Chops (Saratoga)

— Broil —

② Blade Chop

③ Arm Chop

— Broil, Panbroil, Panfry —

②③ Boneless Shoulder

②③ Cushion Shoulder

②③ Square Shoulder

— Roast —

**NECK**

① Neck Slices

— Braise —

**RIB**

① Frenched Rib Chops

① Rib Chops

— Broil, Panbroil, Panfry —

① Crown Roast

① Rib Roast

— Roast —

**LOIN**

① Loin Chops

① Boneless Double Loin Chop

— Broil, Panbroil, Panfry —

① Boneless Double Loin Roast

① Loin Roast

— Roast —

**SIRLOIN**

① Sirloin Chop

— Broil, Panbroil, Panfry —

① Boneless Sirloin Roast

① Sirloin Roast

— Roast —

**LEG**

① Leg Center Slice (Steak)

— Broil, Panbroil, Panfry —

①②④ Combination Leg

②③ Center Leg

①②③④ Boneless Leg (Rolled)

②③④ American-Style Leg

①② Sirloin Half of Leg

③④ Shank Half of Leg

①②③④ French-Style Leg

②③④ French-Style Leg, Sirloin Off

— Roast —

**FORE SHANK**

① Fore Shank

— Braise, Cook in Liquid —

**BREAST**

② Breast

② Rolled Breast

Stuffed Breast

— Roast, Braise —    — Roast —

② Riblets

② Boneless Riblets

— Braise, Cook in Liquid —

② Spareribs

— Braise, Roast (Bake) —

② Stuffed Chops

— Broil, Panbroil, Panfry —

**HIND SHANK**

④ Hind Shank

— Braise, Cook in Liquid —

**GROUND OR CUBED LAMB***

(Large Pieces)   Lamb for Stew*   (Small Pieces)

— Braise, Cook in Liquid —

Cubed Steak**

Lamb Patties*

Ground Lamb*

— Broil, Panbroil, Panfry —    — Roast (Bake) —

\* Lamb for stew or grinding may be made from any cut.

\*\*Kabobs or cubed steaks may be made from any thick solid piece of boneless Lamb.

*This chart approved by*
**National Live Stock and Meat Board**

© National Live Stock and Meat Board

**Variety Meats** The organs of meat animals are known as variety meats and commonly include brains, liver, kidney, heart, tongue, sweetbreads (thymus gland of veal, lamb, or young beef), and tripe (stomach lining of beef). Liver is one of the most popular variety meats. Many variety meats have a distinctive flavor, and all are rich in nutrients.

**Meatless Meats** Meat *analogs* are meatless meats that look very much like actual meats. They are cooked in the same way as the meats they represent. These meatless products are prepared from textured soy proteins. The oil is first removed (pressed) from the soybeans. The protein is shaped into fibers for use in meatlike products. Textured soy protein (TSP) in granular form may be combined with ground meats to get more servings from each pound.

Textured soy meatlike products contribute nutrient values similar to those of meats. They are good sources of protein, contain no cholesterol, and have less fat than meats. They also add to the many types of foods that are available to vegetarians.

## Forms of Meat

Canned, frozen, and cured meats, in addition to fresh meat, are available.

**Fresh Meat** Fresh meat undergoes no special treatment except that it may be aged in cooling rooms for a short time so that it becomes more tender. During aging, enzymes in the meat tissue cause changes that contribute to the tenderness and flavor of the meat.

**Canned Meat** Canned meat, however, is usually fully cooked and sealed in containers for storage without refrigeration. Popular canned meats include ham, dried beef, and corned beef. Meats are also often canned in combination with other foods such as stews or spaghetti and meat balls.

**Frozen Meat** Frozen meats may be either raw or cooked. Roasts and other large cuts are usually frozen raw. Smaller cuts such as chops and steaks may be either cooked or uncooked when frozen. There are many combination dishes made with frozen meat. The pack-

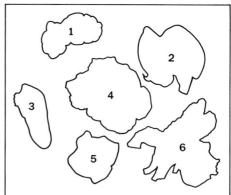

1. Kidney
2. Liver
3. Tongue
4. Brain
5. Heart
6. Tripe

age label indicates the contents and includes the cooking directions.

**Cured Meat** Fresh meats that have been treated with a mixture of salt, sugar, spices, and usually chemicals and/or wood smoke are called cured meats. Ham, sausages, lunch meats, bacon, Canadian bacon, and dried beef are examples.

## Uses of Meat

Meat or a combination meat dish is the center of interest in a meal and the starting point for planning the rest of the meal. All other foods, such as salad and vegetables, are chosen to enhance and go with the meat selected.

For lunch or supper, meats are usually served in combination with other foods. Foods such as macaroni, noodles, spaghetti, rice, or vegetables can be combined with meat for main dishes. Meats are used in casseroles, creamed dishes, main-dish salads, and sandwiches. Meats are filling, but they also add nutrients and variety to breakfast. Sausage, bacon, and ham are popular breakfast meats.

Because of their flavor, meats are used to enhance soups and to provide stock for soup-making. Meats such as bacon and ham are used to add flavor to green beans, scalloped potatoes, baked beans, salad greens, and other vegetables.

---

### For Review

1. Describe the meat of fresh beef, veal, pork, and lamb.
2. What are variety meats?
3. What might be some disadvantages of eating cured meats?
4. Why are meats considered so important to meals?
5. What are some advantages of meatless meats?

---

# Inspection, Grading, and Selecting

The purpose of meat inspection is to protect the consumer. According to federal law, meat sold between states subject to interstate commerce regulations must be inspected. This service is an assurance that the meat is from healthy animals slaughtered under sanitary conditions and is safe for consumption at the time of inspection.

## Inspection Stamp

Inspected meat is identified with a purple federal *inspection stamp*. The stamping is done with a safe purple vegetable dye on each wholesale cut. Because of the mechanized method of stamping, the stamp may not appear on all retail cuts. It is not necessary to cut the stamp off before cooking because the vegetable dye is harmless.

The Meat Inspection Act covers processed meats and canned meats in addition to fresh meats. The inspection stamp is found on the containers of processed meats. The ingredients used must be wholesome and listed on the label along with the net weight and the name and address of the processor. The grade of meat may also be listed.

## Grading

The grading of meat is not required by law, but most meat packers prefer to sell graded meat. The United States Department of Agriculture (USDA) has set standards for different grades of meat. The meat grades indicate the quality of the meat, while the inspection stamp indicates its wholesomeness.

Beef is graded for two factors: quality and cutability. Quality refers to the proportion of meat to bone, degree of marbling in the lean, firmness in texture, and normal color. Cutability

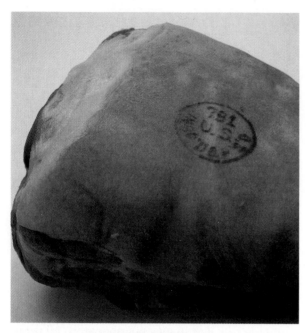

Meat packers often hire government graders to mark meat as approved by the USDA. The USDA imprint is made with a roller stamp, using a nonpoisonous dye.

refers to the proportion of edible meat: a greater amount of muscle in relation to a smaller layer of external fat. Beef that is graded for quality and cutability helps you choose high-quality beef without excess fat.

Although there are several grades of beef, only the higher grades are found in the retail store. The top grade, known as *Prime,* makes up only a small portion of beef and is usually purchased by restaurants. *Choice,* the second grade, and *Select,* the third grade, are usually available in markets. The lower grades, *Standard, Commercial,* and *Utility,* are not found in most markets. These grades are usually used in processed meats.

Packers hire government graders to grade meat. However, some packers use their own grading system, using such terms as *premium, select,* and others, instead of the grades of the USDA. The grade is marked on the meat with a roller stamp that leaves an imprint of the grade, and can be seen on most retail cuts.

*Beef* of high quality comes from a young animal. The lean is well-marbled, fine in texture, and normal in color (red). The texture becomes coarser and the color darker as the animal ages. *Prime* beef, the juiciest and most tender, is bright cherry red, well-marbled and fine-textured, with an outside layer of creamy-white fat. *Choice* beef is bright to deep red, has a smooth texture, is moderately marbled, and has a moderate layer of white to creamy-white fat. It is a very popular consumer grade. *Select* beef is light to dark red, has a moderately smooth texture, some marbling, and a thin outer layer of creamy fat. *Standard* beef is dark red, has an uneven, coarse texture, little marbling and a thin layer of slightly yellow fat. *Commercial* beef is light to dark red, has a coarse texture, very little marbling, may be somewhat soft and watery, and has a very thin covering of yellowed fat. *Utility* beef is light to dark red, has a coarse texture, lacks marbling, and has a very thin layer of grayish-white to yellow fat.

The USDA grades of *veal* are *Prime, Choice, Good, Standard, Utility,* and *Cull.* High-quality veal is rosy pink, fine in texture, and moist, with a very small amount of white fat. Poor-quality veal is dull pink, limp, very moist, and has no fat.

The USDA grades of *lamb* are *Prime, Choice, Good, Utility,* and *Cull.* Most of the lamb produced is either of Prime or Choice grade, and therefore may not often be graded, but it is inspected for interstate commerce. High-quality lamb is bright deep red, firm and fine-textured, and has a covering of firm white fat.

*Pork* does not usually carry a federal grade stamp, but it is inspected for interstate commerce. However, federal grades are used by some states and some meat packers. The grades of pork are *U.S. 1, 2, 3, Medium,* and *Cull.* The lean of high-quality pork is grayish pink and firm, and has a fine texture. The fat is medium-soft and snowy white. Pork of poor quality is deep red, flabby, and coarse.

## Selection and Buying

Standard names have been developed for cuts of meat by The National Live Stock and Meat Board. You will find these names on meat labels, including both the name of the primal cut (wholesale cut) and the standard name for the retail cut. The bones and muscles which make up the meats are similar, making it easy to learn to identify cuts of meat by the bones and muscles they have.

A large proportion of the food dollar is spent on meat. You, as the buyer, should rely on your own ability to judge quality and select the meat best suited to your wants and needs. Your selection should be based on factors such as quality, intended use, time available for preparation, and cost.

### Signs of Quality Meats

The first sign of quality is the official USDA stamp on meat which assures you of wholesome, inspected meat. The next clue to quality is the grade stamp or label. Prime is the highest quality and the most expensive. U.S. Choice and Select grades are most frequently available in the meat case. Grade influences flavor, juiciness, and ease of cooking—not nutritive value.

Other signs of quality meats include meat color, marbling, and bone color. High-quality meats will have a fine texture and a good characteristic color for the kind of meat; that is, beef will be a bright red, and pork a light or grayish pink. The color and firmness of the fat and the degree of marbling vary with the meat quality. A white to creamy-white fat that is firm to medium-firm, and liberal marbling throughout the lean are associated with high-quality meats. A coarse texture, very dark color in the lean, and a very yellow fat indicate poor-quality meat. The bone in meat indicates the age of the animal. The cut surface of the bone from a young animal is porous and pinkish in color; of an older animal, gray and flinty.

### Meat Tenderness

The location of the meat cut on the animal is a clue to its tenderness. The muscles which are used least are the most tender. Back, loin, and rib muscles receive little exercise and are found in the tender steaks, such as sirloin, porterhouse, T-bone, and club; and tender roasts, such as rib and standing rib. Leg and shoulder muscles receive more exercise and are found in the less tender steaks and roasts, such as round and chuck.

Higher grades of meat are usually more tender than the same cut of a lower grade. The tenderness of meat is related to the degree of marbling; meats with more marbling are more tender and of a higher grade.

Because beef comes from mature animals, all cuts of beef except the loin and rib sections are considered less tender. Even though veal is from a young animal, it is considered less tender because of the high proportion of connective tissue to muscle and because of the lack of fat. Lamb is slaughtered when young, so all cuts except the neck and shoulder are considered tender. Pork is generally classified as tender.

Bone shapes are also clues to tenderness. Cuts of meat from all animals that have either the rib, T-bone, or wedge bone are tender. The round bone indicates a tender cut from all animals except beef, in which it indicates a less tender cut. The blade bone indicates the least tender cut in all animals. The chart on page 368 identifies these bone shapes.

Meat can be made more tender by treating it with *enzymes* that split proteins. Meat tenderizers contain protein-splitting enzymes and may be sprinkled over meat before cooking to increase tenderness. The most commonly used enzyme is *papain,* from a fruit called papaya.

The protein-splitting enzymes can be injected into the veins of the animal a few minutes before slaughter. The enzyme is spread throughout the meat by the animal's circulatory system and causes tenderizing in all cuts. This meat is usually sold under special brand names.

## Meat Identification Chart

☐ Tender Cuts to Cook with Dry Heat
☐ Less Tender Cuts to Cook with Moist Heat

| | **Identify These Beef Cuts** | **Identify These Pork Cuts** | **Identify These Lamb Cuts** |
|---|---|---|---|
| **T-Bone**   | T-bone steak<br>Porterhouse<br>  steak<br>Strip loin*<br>Tenderloin* |  Loin chop†<br>Tenderloin†*<br>Center cut<br>  loin roast<br>  (rib and<br>  T-bone) |  Loin chop<br>English chop<br>Kidney chop<br>Loin roast<br>Rolled loin<br>  roast* |
| **Rib Bone**  | Rib steak<br>Club steak<br>Rib roast<br>Rolled rib<br>  roast* |  Rib chop†<br>Center cut<br>  loin roast<br>  (rib and<br>  T-bone)<br>Butterfly<br>  chop†*<br>Spareribs†† |  Rib (rack)<br>  roast<br>Crown roast<br>Rub chop<br>French chop<br>Riblets or<br>  Breast†† |
| **Wedge Bone**  | Sirloin steak<br>Sirloin roast<br>Top sirloin<br>  steak |  Loin end roast<br>  (wedge and<br>  T-bone)<br>Boneless loin* |  Rolled sirloin<br>  roast*<br>Sirloin chop |
| **Round Bone**   | Shoulder steak<br>Round steak<br>Chuck steak<br>Chuck roast<br>Rump roast* |  Ham<br>Picnic<br>Shoulder<br>Shoulder steak†<br>Cutlets†*<br>  SMOKED: Ham<br>  Ham Slice, Picnic<br>  Shoulder |  Leg roast<br>Leg steak<br>Roundbone chop††<br>Square cut,<br>  rolled* or<br>  cushion*<br>Shoulder roast††<br>Shank† |
| **Blade Bone**  | Chuck steak<br>Chuck roast |   Blade loin roast**<br>Boston butt**<br>Shoulder steak<br>SMOKED:<br>  Daisy††*<br>(Shoulder Butt) |  Blade bone chop††<br>Square cut,<br>  rolled* or<br>  cushion*<br>Shoulder roast††<br>Saratoga chop† |

*Cuts will appear boneless in store
**Cook with dry heat

†Cook with moist heat
††Cook with moist or dry heat methods

## Mechanical Methods of Tenderizing Meat

1. grinding

2. pounding

3. scoring

4. cubing

Meat can be tenderized by using mechanical methods to break up the connective tissue. Methods such as grinding, pounding, cubing, or scoring are used to make meats more tender. Hamburger is made tender by grinding. Swiss steak is tenderized by pounding, cube steak by passing through a cubing machine, and flank steak by scoring.

Now that you know how to judge the quality and tenderness of meat, it is important to learn how much meat you should buy to serve specific numbers of people.

**Amount to Buy** Meats are sold by pounds (grams). You must know how many pounds (grams) are needed to serve a given number of people. You will need to consider the amount of bone present in the meat when estimating the amount to buy. When meat contains bone, you will need to buy more than when the meat is boneless. The following table indicates the amount of meat, boneless and with bones, needed for one serving.

- ¼ lb (113 g) of boneless meat
- ⅓ to ½ lb (151 to 227 g) of meat with small amounts of bone (steak, roast)
- ⅔ to ¾ lb (302 to 339 g) of meat with large amount of bone (spare ribs, short ribs)

Multiply the quantity suggested for one serving by the number of servings desired to determine the amount that you should buy. However, with chops or slices of meat, you may only need to count the number of pieces needed.

**Cost** The cut or type of meat that is the best buy depends upon the cost per unit and upon the amount of waste in bone and fat. The prices of various meats are best compared by cost per serving.

The cost of meat is influenced by supply and demand. The tender beef steaks and roasts are in demand, and the supply is limited; therefore the price is high. The less tender cuts of meat are more plentiful and less in demand; therefore they cost less than the tender cuts. Similarly, lower grades of meat are less expensive than the higher grades. Lower grades contain less fat and thereby less waste, which can mean more servings at a lower cost.

The size of a cut of meat can influence cost per unit. For example, a pork loin roast will cost less per unit than pork chops from the same meat cut.

Most cuts of meat that can be cooked quickly cost more than those which require longer cooking. Select the cut and grade that is best suited for the cooking method you would like to use.

## Convenience in Meats

Ready-to-eat meats and canned meats were among the first convenience meat items. The variety and number of these items is steadily increasing. They may be canned, frozen, or refrigerated. Examples of canned meat products include beef stew, hash, ravioli, deviled ham, chili con carne, and spaghetti with meat sauce. Frozen meat products include meat pies, breaded chops, and frozen dinners. Meat products which require only refrigeration include lunch meats, wieners, and other sausages.

Many of the convenience meat items can be classified as meat products rather than as meat-alone products because they contain other ingredients in addition to meat. Examples of nonmeat items used in convenience products are cereal, starch, soya flour, and nonfat dry milk. Other convenience items, the add-to-meat variety, include a blend of seasonings and extenders (macaroni, noodles, rice) and granules of textured vegetable protein (TVP) to add to meats and meat combination dishes. When these products are added to meats, you get more servings than when the meat is prepared alone.

Convenience meat products, such as canned beef stew, can be uncomplicated, quick ways to provide nutritious meals.

Lunch meats often contain nonmeat products. Generally, the greater the amount of a nonmeat ingredient used, the lower the complete protein value of the food. The price of the lunch meat tends to be lower when nonmeat ingredients are used.

Some processed meats are relatively low in price and contain as much protein as higher-priced fresh meats. For example, bologna usually has as much protein as an equal amount of fresh meat. Other processed meats may have only a little over half as much complete protein as meat.

With meats, as with other food items, it is necessary to read the labels. All ingredients, including the nonmeat items, must be stated on the label. Locally processed meats do not require federal inspection as do the processed meats sold in interstate commerce. If you select meat products with USDA inspection labels, you can be assured that you are selecting a wholesome product with a limited amount of nonmeat ingredients.

Buying processed meat items, whether canned, frozen, or refrigerated, also requires a cost comparison based on the home-prepared product versus the convenience product. You may find that chili con carne costs about the same as homemade chili or that a frozen dinner costs twice as much as a comparable dinner prepared at home.

In addition to the label and the USDA inspection stamp, another guide to quality is the manufacturer. Well-known manufacturers will protect their reputations. Brand names usually can be reliable guides for selecting convenience meat items.

Convenience items make meal preparation less complicated, but they make food selection more complicated. It becomes your challenge to select the best convenience items for your use. What guides and criteria will you use in the selection of convenience items?

# Soybeans—Protein Source of the Future?

Subtle changes are taking place in the typical American diet. In 1985, people bought more poultry than pork for the first time in history. Poultry is expected to outsell beef sometime in the 1990s. Grocers prominently display lean cuts of meat. Pasta consumption has been steadily increasing. Consumption of whole grains and soybean products has also been rising. What is going on?

Concerned with warnings about the high risks of fat-rich diets, Americans are changing their eating habits. More people are seeking low-fat, low-cholesterol alternatives.

To reduce dependence on meat as the sole source of complete protein, some people are turning to incomplete plant proteins. They eat complementary proteins in order to supply their bodies with all the necessary amino acids. Complementary combinations of plant protein include: eating legumes with nuts, seeds, or grains; or eating any grain, legume, seed, or nut with small quantities of meat, fish, poultry, eggs, cheese, or milk.

For centuries, soybeans have served as a main source of protein in China and Japan. This protein-rich bean is just being "discovered" as a food in the United States.

Ironically, the United States is the world's leading producer of soybeans, and they are our biggest money-making crop. Over half the soybean crop is exported. The part reserved is used to make vegetable oil or to feed animals. Only a small percentage is used to produce soy foods.

Soybeans are the best source of protein among widely available beans. The fat in soybeans is highly unsaturated and has been connected with lower cholesterol levels in the blood. Soy products come in many forms for diverse uses. Soy flour, tofu, and soybean sprouts are just a few of these forms.

Soy flour is made by grinding defatted soybeans. It is used in bread and pasta.

Tofu is made from soybean curds. The beans are soaked and puréed. The purée is strained through a cloth and simmered. A solidifier is added, separating it into curds and whey. The curds are put into molds, pressed, and chilled. Tofu is easily digested and contains many minerals and vitamins, including B vitamins, vitamin E, iron, potassium, and sodium. One of its greatest assets as a protein source is its versatility. Tofu's bland taste makes it possible to combine with many other foods. It absorbs the flavors of accompanying foods, and can be used in pasta, vegetables, bread, and casseroles.

Soybean sprouts supply nutrients not in soybeans. Vitamins A and C are formed in the sprouts, which are rich sources of protein.

In the past decade, consumer demand for tofu and soy flour has increased steadily. The combination of high nutritional value and versatility just might make soybeans the protein source of the future.

A salad with tofu and soybean sprouts is rich in nutrients.

After you have found the best convenience foods, how will you fit them into your plan? All of the convenience meat items have in common the factors of improving the use of time and work, the fact that they may or may not be more expensive, and the fact that they may or may not provide the same food value as the home-prepared product. You should think of them as assistants and use them creatively.

**For Review**

1. Why might some fresh meat that you buy *not* be inspected?
2. List and describe the two factors on which beef is graded.
3. What are the USDA's top three grades of beef?
4. Describe some things to look for when selecting quality, tender meats.
5. How much ground beef should you buy to serve five people?
6. Why are lower grades of meat often a better buy than higher grades?
7. Describe two advantages of using convenience meats or meat products.

# Principles of Meat Cookery

Meat is cooked to improve its flavor, change its color, make it more tender, and to destroy harmful organisms. As with milk and eggs, the principles of meat cookery are greatly influenced by the high protein content. When meat is cooked, the protein of the muscle, or the lean, coagulates, and the protein of connective tissue is softened.

The long, tiny fibers of muscle tissue are held together by connective tissue. The connective tissue is made of a different protein than that in muscle tissue. A protein called **collagen** is tough and flexible and makes up the connective tissue that holds muscle fibers together. It can be softened by cooking. Another protein, *elastin,* makes up the connective tissue, but there is very little elastin in meat muscles. Some elastin is present in neck ligament. Elastin fibers stretch and are yellow in color in contrast to the pearly white of collagen.

Meats are classified into tender and less tender cuts. The tender cuts have less connective tissue than the less tender cuts, which come from muscles most frequently exercised.

The principles of meat cookery require the use of low temperatures. The low temperature will coagulate the meat protein and prevent toughening. Overcooking as well as high temperatures will cause toughening due to over-coagulation. Meat cooked at low temperatures will be juicy and flavorful.

Moisture, whether added or from the meat itself, is needed along with heat to soften collagen. Because protein coagulates more slowly at low temperatures, the muscle protein will not toughen before the collagen (connective tissue) can soften. For this reason, moist-heat methods are used to cook less tender cuts of meat. The tender cuts of meat contain little connective tissue and need to be cooked only long enough to coagulate the protein. Dry-heat methods are used to cook tender cuts of meat.

## Dry-heat Methods

Roasting, broiling, and pan-broiling are the dry-heat methods for cooking meat. The meat is cooked by direct heat, requires no added water, and is not covered. Dry-heat methods are used to cook tender cuts because they contain little connective tissue.

Large, tender cuts of meat are used for *roasting.* A shallow, open pan with a rack is used. The meat is placed on the rack in the pan with the fat side up. The rack elevates the roast

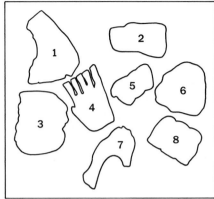

1. Beef standing rib roast
2. Pork arm roast
3. Rolled rib roast
4. Lamb crown roast
5. Lamb rolled loin roast
6. Pork blade loin roast
7. Veal rib roast
8. Veal loin roast

from the bottom of the pan so that heat can circulate around and under the roast.

A meat thermometer can be placed into the center of the thickest part of the roast, away from bone or fat. The thermometer shows the exact temperature at the center of the roast and in this way the exact doneness. A timetable for roasting meat (found in most cookbooks) can be used to estimate the cooking time required, but the meat thermometer is more accurate. The meat will continue to cook for a time after being removed from the oven.

Low oven temperatures—300 to 350° F (150 to 180° C)—are used to cook meat to the desired doneness. Beef can be cooked rare, medium, or well done. Veal, lamb, and pork are usually cooked until well done. Large, tender cuts of all meats may be roasted successfully. Some cuts of meat suitable for roasting are: beef standing rib roast, rolled rib roast; veal loin roast, veal rib roast; lamb rolled loin roast, lamb crown roast; pork arm roast, and pork blade loin roast.

*Broiling* is cooking meat above or below the direct source of heat from an oven unit or glowing coals. Meats to be broiled should be tender or made tender by the use of tenderizers and should be about 1 inch (2.5 cm) thick.

The meat is placed on the broiler rack, and the rack is usually placed 3 to 6 inches (7.5 to 15

Many forms of steak are suitable for broiling. Why is broiled meat salted *after* cooking?

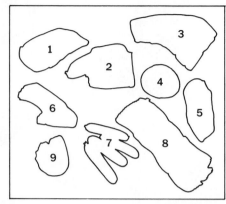

1. Sirloin rib steak
2. T-bone steak
3. Porterhouse steak
4. Beef patty
5. Top loin steak
6. Pork rib chop
7. Pork sausage
8. Bacon
9. Lamb loin chop

cm) away from the heat. A moderate temperature is maintained by regulating the distance of the meat from the source of heat. When the meat is half done (one side cooked), it is turned to cook the other side. Broiled meat is salted after it is cooked because salt retards browning.

Small, tender cuts of meat are suitable for broiling. Veal is not usually broiled because it lacks fat and will dry out. Cured ham and sausage, lamb, and the tender cuts of beef may be broiled. Some of the cuts suitable for broiling are: beef steaks (T-bone, porterhouse, sirloin rib), beef patty; lamb chops (loin, rib), lamb patty; bacon, and pork sausage.

*Pan-broiling* is cooking meat in a skillet without added fat. As the fat melts from the meat, it is poured off. Cook the meat slowly over low heat until it is brown on one side, and then turn. Never cover the meat or add water; to do so would be braising. Pan-broiling is used for small, tender cuts. All cuts which can be broiled are also suitable for pan-broiling.

## Moist-heat Methods

Moist-heat methods are used for the less tender cuts because of the large amounts of connective tissue in them. Moisture and heat are required to soften the protein of connective tissue. The moist-heat methods of cooking are braising and cooking in liquid.

**Braising** is using moisture (steam) from the meat itself or from added liquid. The meat

Less tender cuts of meat, such as a beef blade chuck roast, are suitable for braising. Long, slow cooking tenderizes the meat. What provides the moisture for cooking?

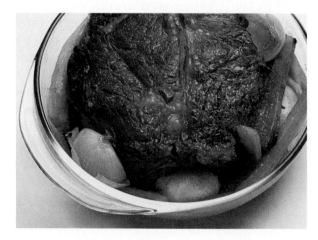

may be browned, if desired, before liquid is added or before the pan is tightly covered.

As the meat cooks, juices will be released to provide moisture, or a small amount of liquid such as water, vegetable juice, or stock may be added. Cooking may be continued over low heat on a range or in an oven at 300 to 325° F (150 to 160° C) until the meat is tender. A large cut of meat cooked by braising is often referred to as a pot roast.

Braising is used for all less tender cuts of meat, and it is used for the tender cuts of veal and pork. Both pork and veal should be cooked well done; pork to guard against trichinosis, and veal to develop flavor. Some of the cuts suitable for braising are: beef steaks (round, flank, chuck

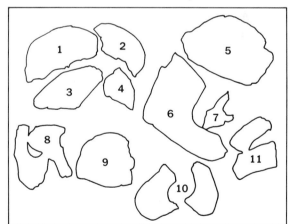

1. Beef round steak
2. Beef flank steak
3. Beef blade steak
4. Beef chuck steak
5. Beef chuck roast
6. Lamb shoulder
7. Lamb chop
8. Veal chops
9. Veal steak
10. Pork chops
11. Beef short ribs

blade), beef blade chuck roast, beef short ribs; veal chops (loin, rib), veal steaks (blade, arm); pork chops (loin, rib); lamb chops (shoulder arm, blade), and boneless rolled lamb shoulder.

Meats which require long, slow cooking to soften their large amounts of connective tissue are cooked in liquid. **Simmering** and **stewing** refer to cooking in liquid. Simmering refers to cooking large pieces of meat in enough liquid to cover them. When small pieces of meat are almost covered with liquid and then cooked, the process is called stewing.

For both stewing and simmering, the heat must be low so that the liquid remains at the simmering temperature and does not boil. Boiling overcoagulates the protein and causes toughening. Some cuts of meat suitable for cooking in liquid are: beef plate, beef short ribs, beef brisket, beef stew; veal breast, veal stew; pork smoked ham shank, pork spare ribs; and lamb riblets.

## Cooking in Fat

Two methods are used for cooking in fat: pan-frying and deep-fat frying. Frying is a quick method of cooking and is best suited for thin pieces of meat which have been made tender by cubing, pounding, or grinding. The meat may be rolled in flour or dipped in egg and then crumbs before frying. This gives the meat an attractive brown coating, contributes to flavor, and may help to retain meat juices. Meat prepared in this way is called breaded meat.

*Pan-frying* is cooking in a small amount of fat in an uncovered skillet. Pan-frying differs from pan-broiling in that the fat is not poured off as it collects. Moderate temperatures are used, and the meat is turned occasionally. High temperatures will cause the fat to smoke and to break down into an unpleasant-tasting substance. This method may be used for thin steaks and chops, and ground and cubed meat. Some cuts of meat suitable for cooking in fat are: beef steaks (T-bone, porterhouse, rib), beef patty; veal patty, veal liver (calf's liver); pork rib chops, pork fresh ham slice, Canadian bacon; and lamb chops (sirloin, loin, rib).

For *deep-fat frying,* enough fat is used to cover the food. Deep-fat frying is not considered a basic meat cookery method. It is best suited for meats that have been breaded or for cooked meat that has been combined with other foods and then breaded, such as croquettes. The temperature for deep-fat frying is higher than the temperatures recommended for meat cookery. However, the coating or breading may help to protect the meat from the hot fat.

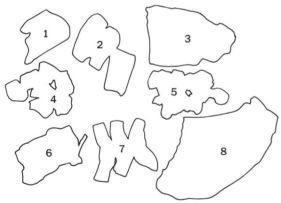

1. Beef shoulder steak
2. Beef short ribs
3. Beef brisket
4. Beef stew
5. Veal stew
6. Pork smoked ham shank
7. Pork spare ribs
8. Lamb riblets

## Cooking Frozen Meats

Commercially frozen products should be prepared according to the directions on the package. Frozen meat may be cooked satisfactorily by defrosting either before cooking or during cooking. When defrosting meat before cooking, the meat should be defrosted in its original wrapper, in the refrigerator. Once defrosted, it should be cooked in the same way as fresh meat. The tenderness of the cut will determine the appropriate method.

When meat is cooked from the frozen state, it is necessary to allow additional cooking time. Frozen roasts may require about one-third longer cooking time than defrosted roasts. However, completely defrosting large roasts before cooking will insure even cooking.

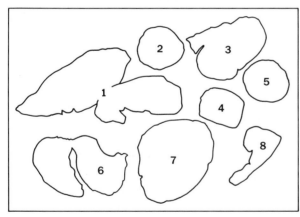

1. Beef steaks
2. Beef patty
3. Veal liver
4. Canadian bacon
5. Veal patty
6. Pork rib chops
7. Pork fresh ham slice
8. Lamb loin chop

## Cooking Variety Meats

Since variety meats are more perishable than other meats, they should be used soon after purchase. Liver is the most popular variety meat. You may braise or fry beef or pork liver; veal, lamb, and baby beef liver may be broiled, pan-broiled, or pan-fried.

The heart and tongue are less tender variety meats and may be braised or cooked in liquid. Tongue may be purchased fresh, pickled, corned, smoked, or canned. It requires long, slow cooking in liquid.

The kidney, brains, and sweetbreads are tender variety meats. The kidney is a delicacy and is served in several gourmet dishes. You may broil lamb and veal kidneys, but beef kidney

## Beef Stew  Yield: 4 servings

| | |
|---|---|
| 1 lb (454 g) beef (chuck or bottom round) in 1- or 2-inch (2.5- or 5-cm) cubes | 2 c (500 mL) water |
| 3 Tbs (4 mL) flour | 4 small whole potatoes |
| 1 tsp (5 mL) salt | 2 quartered carrots |
| 1 Tbs (15 mL) shortening or drippings | 4 small whole onions |
| | ½ c (125 mL) diced celery |
| | 1 Tbs (15 mL) flour |
| | ¼ c (60 mL) water |

Approximate nutrition information per serving: calories–615; protein–24 g; fat–39 g; cholesterol–110 mg; carbohydrates–43 g; sodium–730 mg.

1. Blend flour, salt, and pepper. Spread on waxed paper, and roll pieces of meat in seasoned salt.
2. Heat shortening in kettle; brown meat on all sides.
3. Add water, cover, and simmer until meat is almost tender (about 2 hours).
4. If necessary, add more water to replace any that has evaporated.
5. Add vegetables; continue to simmer until vegetables are fork tender.
6. If thicker broth is desired, place ¼ c (60 mL) water into jar, add 1 Tbs (15 mL) flour, cover, and shake to form smooth paste. Slowly stir into stew and boil for 1 minute.
7. Serve on preheated platter.

is less tender and should be braised or cooked in liquid. Brains and sweetbreads have a delicate flavor. They may be broiled, fried, braised, or cooked in water.

### Microwaving Meats

Meat cooked in the microwave shrinks less than meat cooked in a conventional oven. All visible fat on meat may be removed before cooking the meat in the microwave. The fat must be left on for conventional cooking because it protects the meat from high heat.

For roasts, use a dish just large enough to hold the meat and juices. Place roasts on a rack to keep them from stewing in their own juices. (Never cover tender cuts of meat during cooking; this would cause the meat to steam, rather than to roast.) Cook on a high power setting at first to brown the meat. Then cook on a lower setting to cook the inside properly, without overbrowning the outside. Choose meats with an even shape, and allow standing time after turning the power off in order to finish cooking and to allow the meat to absorb the juices.

A microwave thermometer is helpful for checking doneness, but if one is not available, press the meat and observe the color of the juices. Red signals a need for further cooking, pink indicates rare meat, and brown signals well-done meat.

### A Reminder

In all meat cookery, low temperatures are required to protect the protein of meat and avoid

## Tips for Microwaving Meat

- Make sure that roasts are completely defrosted before cooking in order to make correct timing possible. The purpose of defrosting is to thaw the food without cooking it. The microwave oven must be turned off before the temperature is reached at which cooking begins. This can be done by one of two methods. Either short cooking times can be alternated with resting times; or lower, continuous power can be used. Most microwave ovens have a special DEFROST cycle. If your oven does not have such a cycle, simply use the cooking/resting method for defrosting.
- Rotate meat one-half turn halfway through both defrosting and cooking.
- When microwaving stews, make sure that the meat is fully submerged in the liquid during cooking.
- Score fat on chops and steaks to prevent curling.
- Dip pork chops in flour before coating with an egg-and-crumb mixture in order to prevent the fat from soaking in during cooking.
- Cook meat loaf in a ring shape to shorten cooking time. Cook meat loaf with a sauce to prevent overbrowning.
- Cook bacon by laying strips on two thicknesses of paper towels. Put another piece of paper towel over the bacon to prevent spattering. Remove paper towels immediately after cooking, or the paper will stick to the bacon.
- Remove fat that accumulates during cooking; otherwise, the microwave will direct its power to cook the fat instead of the meat.

toughening. To develop the browned meat flavor, meats may be browned in a small amount of fat before they are cooked by moist-heat methods. At one time, meats were seared before roasting (browned quickly at high temperature) to keep in juices. We now know that searing does not prevent the escape of meat juices and there may actually be a greater loss of juices. A constant low oven temperature will give you the advantages of: (1) more evenly cooked meat; (2) less shrinkage of meat; (3) less spattering of fat; and (4) roaster pans that are easier to clean.

Proper cooking methods will retain the quality of the meat at the time of cooking, but the quality of the meat at the time of purchase can be preserved only by proper storage. Cooking cannot improve the quality of mistreated or poorly stored meats; it can only retain the quality present in the meat at the time. You will need to store meats properly to retain all of their flavor and quality.

## For Review

1. What determines the difference between the tender and the less tender cuts of meat?
2. Why are tender meats cooked by dry-heat methods?
3. What cuts of meat are most suitable for roasting?
4. What is the difference between broiling and pan-broiling?
5. Why is braising appropriate for less tender cuts of meat?
6. What is the difference between simmering and stewing?
7. Why are pan-frying and deep-fat frying suitable for thin, tenderized meats?
8. When microwaving a roast, why is it important to place the meat on a rack?

# Storage of Meat

All kinds of meat spoil quickly. To reduce spoilage, meat should be properly stored as soon as possible after purchase and after cooking. It is with proper storage that you can preserve the safety, nutritive value, and quality of meat.

## Fresh Meat Storage

Fresh meat not to be frozen should be stored in the coldest part of the refrigerator or in the meat storage compartment. The meat should be loosely covered, and storage should not exceed three days. Meat prepackaged for self-service may be stored in the original wrapping if used within two days. The wrapper may be loosened at both ends to permit circulation of air around the meat to preserve its red color. When the meat surface is deprived of oxygen, it will become dark.

Ground meats spoil very quickly because a larger area has been exposed to air and handling. If you plan to keep meat cuts and ground meat longer than two or three days, they should be wrapped for freezer storage. To prepare meats for freezer storage, first remove the original wrap and rewrap tightly in moisture-proof freezer wrap.

## Cured and Ready-to-eat Meat Storage

Cured and ready-to-eat meats such as cold cuts, ham, bacon, and frankfurters should be wrapped tightly to prevent drying. You may store the sealed, prepackaged cold cuts in their original wrap. Once the package is opened, it may require an additional wrapping to prevent drying. The flavor and quality of ready-to-eat meats are best when the meats are used within a short time.

## Frozen Meat Storage

You should store purchased frozen meats at $0°F$ ($-18°C$) in their original wrapping. Prepackaged, self-serve fresh meats should be overwrapped or rewrapped with moisture-proof material for frozen storage, separating individual servings by a double layer of wrapping material. Keep meat frozen until you are ready to thaw or use it. Use thawed meat immediately; do not refreeze it.

## Canned Meat and Leftover Meat Storage

Most canned meats, except canned hams weighing over 1½ pounds (681 g), can be stored in a cool, dry storage place. Large canned hams are perishable because they have not been completely sterilized. They must be stored in the refrigerator in order to prevent spoilage. You should also notice how these hams have been stored where you buy them.

All leftover meats, both canned or cooked, should be tightly wrapped or placed in a covered container and stored in the coldest part of the refrigerator. You should plan to use them within a short time.

---

**Safety Tip**

- When broiling fatty meats, place a slice of bread in the bottom of the broiling pan. The bread will absorb the grease and reduce spattering.

---

**For Review**

1. Why should fresh meat *not* be tightly covered when stored in the refrigerator?
2. Why might it be better to eat fresh meat just purchased than fresh meat that has been stored for several days in the refrigerator?

# *18* Chapter Review

## Summary

To most people today, meat means beef, veal, pork, or lamb. The center of interest in a meal, meat is highly nutritious as well. It is one of the foods that has complete protein, and the preservation of that protein is central to the principles of meat cookery. Meat is available in a wide variety of forms ranging from assorted cuts found fresh in the meat case to canned, frozen, and cured products. Before making a meat purchase, the consumer should judge the quality, grade, intended use and amount needed, cost, and the time available for preparation. To prevent contamination, meat must be stored properly.

## Vocabulary

Use these vocabulary words to complete the sentences that follow:

anemia
braising
collagen
cured

essential amino
 acids
simmering
stewing
trichinosis

1. The complete protein found in meat is made up of _____, and these are necessary for humans because the body is not able to make them.
2. A protein that appears pearly white, is tough and flexible and makes up the connective tissue that holds the muscle fibers of meat together is called _____.
3. A condition in humans that develops when the iron supply is low, and therefore too few red blood cells exist, is called _____.
4. Because a harmful parasite is sometimes found in pork, all cuts of pork should be completely cooked to avoid risk of the disease called _____.
5. Bacon, ham, and sausage are examples of meats that are _____.
6. A method of cooking meat in a tightly covered pot with the moisture from the meat itself or a small amount of added liquid is called _____.
7. The procedure of cooking meat in enough liquid to almost cover it and for a long time over a low heat is referred to as _____ or _____.

## Chapter Questions

1. Why is it important to eat a variety of foods?
2. What are the six foods that have the essential amino acids and why is eating these foods important?
3. Why is the fat of meat important?
4. What kinds and cuts of meat are in your family's refrigerator and freezer? For each cut of meat, give at least one method of cooking that can be used.
5. What are three kinds of pork that have been cured?
6. What alternatives to meat do vegetarians have? How do these products compare to the nutritional value of meat?

7. What are five different categories of foods that can be made with meat used as an ingredient?
8. What should be considered when meat is purchased?
9. What kinds of fresh, canned, and frozen convenience meat products do you have in your family? What is a way you can use two of the products to create variety in your meals?
10. What are the advantages and disadvantages of using convenience meat items?
11. Compare dry-heat and moist-heat cooking methods.
12. If you were preparing a sirloin steak for a person on a low cholesterol, or low-fat, diet, what would be the best way to prepare it and why?
13. What is the proper way to store cured and ready-to-eat meats?

## Skill Activities

**1. Decision making** In your food journal or card file box, make a collection of meat recipes. Organize the recipes into those for beef, veal, pork, and lamb. For each kind of meat, have sections for appetizers, soups, salads, roasts, stews, casseroles, skillet meals, pies, meat loaves, sandwiches, and low-calorie meals. You can find recipes in books, magazines, newspapers, and on the display board in supermarkets. When you find interesting meat recipes, add them to your collection.

**2. Resource management** Learn the cuts of meat that are available at your local supermarket, and decide which cooking methods are best for each. Use two sheets of lined paper, and write one of these headings at the top of each page: "Beef," "Veal," "Pork," and "Lamb." (Use both sides of the paper.) Now make two columns, and at the top of each column, write one of these headings: "Cut of meat," and "Recommended cooking method." Visit the fresh meat counter of your supermarket. Under the appropriate kind of meat, record the available cuts, and for each cut, tell which cooking method you would recommend.

**3. Math** Visit the fresh meat counter of your local grocery store. Compare the costs for one serving of a boneless beef roast, of ground beef, of a sirloin steak, and of short ribs. What is the cost per serving for each cut of meat? Which cut is the lowest cost per serving? Which cut costs the most per serving?

**4. Resource management** Two of the ways to create flavorful meat meals are to use herbs and marinades. Herbs can be used singularly or in combination with each other. Herbs and marinades can enhance the flavor of meat cooked by dry-heat as well as moist-heat methods. Make a list of the herbs that are especially fine for the different kinds of meat. Make a collection of recipes for herb blends and marinades that season and tenderize meats.

# 19 Poultry

## As you read, think about:

- how to identify, select, use, and store poultry.
- what nutrients poultry provides for you.
- how cooking affects poultry.
- how to prepare poultry.

**Vocabulary**
**giblets**
**truss**
**fricassee**

Poultry refers to all types of fowl served as the main part of a meal. Poultry has been associated with many memorable occasions and is the center of interest for many feasts and holidays. Now this treat is readily available throughout the year. Poultry is a high-quality, relatively low-cost food that can replace meat. Chicken and turkey are most commonly used, although duck, geese, guinea and Cornish hens, squab, and pigeons are other choices. Which ones have you eaten?

## Classes and Forms of Poultry

There are several classes of poultry. Each kind of poultry is classified, or grouped, according to age, weight, and sex. Because poultry becomes less tender with age, the groups are related to tenderness and to the suitable cooking method. The chart on page 387 lists the two common forms of poultry, their weight and age, and some suggested methods for cooking.

Ducklings, Cornish hens, and geese are delicacies. Ducklings are young ducks nine to twelve weeks of age, weighing from 3½–5 pounds (1.59–2.27 kg). They contain more fat than chickens. Cornish hens weigh about 1 pound (454 g) and are usually sold frozen and ready-to-cook. Young geese weigh about 6–12 pounds (2.72–5.45 kg).

Most poultry is sold ready-to-cook, either whole or in parts, and in most markets is sold fresh, frozen, or canned. The class name on poultry suggests the cooking method and helps you make the right choice for the use that you have in mind.

### Fresh Poultry

Dressed and ready-to-cook poultry is sold fresh chilled or as cold storage poultry. Dressed

Poultry of all types was once raised for use as food only by individual farms. Today, entire farms are devoted only to the raising of poultry in order to provide this product to wholesale distributors.

## Kinds of Poultry

| Type | Description | Age | Weight | Cooking Method |
|---|---|---|---|---|
| *Chicken* | | | | |
| Broiler or Fryer | Either sex; smooth, thin skin; tender; small amount of fat | 9–12 wks | 1½–2½ lb (0.68–1.1 kg) | Broil Fry |
| Roaster | Either sex; tender; smooth skin with layer of fat | 3–5 mos (fully developed) | 2½–4½ lb (1.1–2.04 kg) | Roast |
| Capon | Desexed male bird; very meaty; juicy flesh | less than 8 mos | 4–8 lb (1.8–3.6 kg) | Roast |
| Stewing chicken or Fowl | Coarse skin; less tender | more than 10 mos | 4–6 lb (1.8–2.7 kg) | Braise Simmer Stew |
| *Turkey* | | | | |
| Fryer or Roaster | Tender | 15–17 wks | 4–6 lb (1.8–2.7 kg) | Broil Fry Roast |
| Roaster | Tender | 5–6 mos | hen: 6–14 lb (2.7–6.4 kg) tom: 9–24 lb (4–10.9 kg) | Roast |

poultry has been bled, has only the feathers, head, and feet removed, and has been drawn (internal organs removed). The liver, heart, and gizzard, known as **giblets** (JIB-lits), are washed, wrapped, and placed inside the body cavity. The bird can be sold whole, in half, or in pieces such as breasts, legs, and thighs. You will find that the already cooked bird—barbecued, roasted, or fried—is sold in some markets and specialty stores.

## Frozen Poultry

Poultry is frozen for your convenience and for safety during shipment and comes ready-to-cook. Stuffed turkeys and Cornish hens are sold frozen. Some poultry is frozen after it has been cooked, and you need only to heat it for serving.

## Canned Poultry

You can make your selection from a variety of canned poultry. The bird may be whole, cut into pieces, or boned and canned. The canned poultry items include chicken, turkey, and specialty foods such as chicken chow mein or turkey 'ala king. As with meats, there are quality signs or clues which will aid you in making the best choice from among the many classes and forms of poultry.

Many forms of poultry, both common and unusual, can be found in markets. Among these forms are:
1. quail;
2. duck;
3. turkey;
4. chicken;
5. goose;
6. squab;
7. pigeon;
8. pheasant.

## For Review

1. What is dressed poultry?
2. What are giblets?

# Selection and Buying

Look for inspection and grade labels when selecting poultry; they are your clues to quality. Poultry sold in interstate commerce must be government inspected; this will assure you that the poultry comes from healthy birds, is processed in sanitary surroundings, and is labeled accurately. Inspection labels indicate that the poultry is wholesome.

Poultry that has passed the federal inspection for wholesomeness may be graded for quality and assigned a U.S. Grade A, B, or C. Grade A poultry is full-fleshed and meaty. Grade B indicates a good quality poultry which is slightly less meaty, and Grade C poultry has less flesh and fat.

You will recognize the best quality poultry by these characteristics: full-fleshed, meaty breast and legs; well-distributed fat; skin with few blemishes or pinfeathers.

Brand names can be clues to quality, but first you will have to use the brand to decide whether its quality meets with your standards. When selecting frozen poultry, watch for freezer burn (dry, pale, frosty areas) that indicates long and improper storage. The wrapper should not be stained or broken. The package labels on both frozen and canned poultry state that the products passed inspection before processing.

Poultry is classified by age and weight and is named in terms of appropriate use as broilers, fryers, roasters, and stewing birds. When you buy, you should have a specific recipe in mind.

Poultry contains more bone in proportion to muscle than does red meat. The following will help you determine the quantity of ready-to-cook poultry to buy for one serving.

- Fryer 3/4–1 lb (0.35–0.45 kg)
- Roaster 1/2–3/4 lb (0.32–0.35 kg)
- Broiler 1 lb (0.45 kg) or 1/2 chicken
- Stewing 1/2–3/4 lb (0.32–0.35 kg)

When poultry is used as an ingredient, you may need to determine the quantity by cups (milliliters). You can figure on 1 cup (200 mL) cooked poultry meat from 1 pound (.45 kg) of a stewing bird.

## Nutrient Contributions

Like meats, poultry of all kinds contains proteins, fats, minerals, and vitamins. Poultry contains a high-quality (complete) protein and is a good source of iron, phosphorus, and the B-complex vitamins thiamin, riboflavin, and niacin. The fat varies with the kind and age of the bird. Ducks and geese have more fat than do chickens and turkeys. Old birds contain more fat than the young birds. The dark meat of all types of birds is slightly higher in fat content than the white meat.

## Uses of Poultry

Since poultry provides the same nutrient values as meat, it can replace meat in your meals. It can be used as the main dish, with vegetables and salad selected to complement it. It is used both in simple and fancy meals and as a snack or a party food. Cooked poultry can be used as an ingredient in a variety of ways, ranging from salads and sandwiches to casseroles and croquettes. For delicious and attractive poultry dishes, select the bird that is suited for the dish you are planning.

### For Review

1. What does the inspection label on poultry tell you? The grade level?
2. What are the characteristics of quality poultry?
3. Which has more fat, the dark meat of a duck or the white meat of a chicken?

## Principles of Poultry Cookery

Like meat, poultry contains an abundance of protein, and, therefore, you can apply the same general cooking rules. The first rule is the same as for all protein foods: cook at a low temperature. You will recall that high temperatures toughen protein, while low temperatures keep the protein tender. You should not roast poultry in a very hot oven because it will cause shrinkage and toughening as well as the loss of juices and flavor. Nor should you use hot fat for frying or browning poultry because this, too, will toughen the protein. When using moist heat, as in braising and cooking in liquid, a low temperature is maintained by letting the liquid simmer rather than boil.

The second rule to remember is that the tenderness of the poultry determines the suitable cookery method. The tenderness of poultry is influenced by age: young birds are tender; older birds less tender. For young birds, broiling, roasting, and rotisserie cooking are good methods. For older, less tender birds, braising and cooking in liquid are most suitable.

Almost all of the poultry you purchase is ready-to-cook. You should inspect it before cooking to make sure all the pinfeathers and hair have been removed. Rinse the cut pieces in cold water. If the bird is whole, let cold water run into the cavity and remove any internal organs that may remain. Dry the washed poultry, including the interior cavity, with paper toweling. If you use frozen poultry, first thaw it in its wrapping in the refrigerator for 24 hours before cooking.

Many recipes call for boned poultry; that is, poultry with the bones removed. Buying boned poultry can be expensive, so you save money by doing the boning yourself. See the directions to the right for boning chicken breasts.

Break the keel bone.

Run your thumb or a knife between the meat and the keel bone.

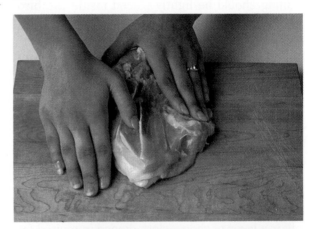

Separate the breast meat from the rib cage.

Remove the skin, and trim away the fat.

## Dry-heat Methods

*Roasting* is the same for poultry as for meats. Tender poultry such as chicken, turkey, and duck can be roasted on a rack in a shallow pan in a 325°F (160°C) oven. Do not cover or add water. Overbrowning the breast of a large bird can be prevented by placing a loose tent of aluminum foil over the breast when the bird is half done. If you wish to stuff poultry, the stuffing should be lightly placed inside the bird just before roasting. The stuffing and the bird may be prepared a day in advance but must be refrigerated separately to avoid the possibility of food poisoning.

You usually **truss** the bird for roasting; that is, you turn back the wing tips on the shoulders and tie the drumsticks to the tail. This prevents the wings and legs from becoming too brown and dry.

If the bird is lacking in fat, you may brush it with soft fat or oil to prevent drying of the skin. You may cover the turkey loosely with a sheet of foil or a layer of cheesecloth dipped in melted fat to avoid overbrowning of the breast.

Before roasting, a bird shoud be properly trussed. The wing tips are turned back and secured, and the drumsticks are tied together. A meat thermometer is an accurate guide to doneness.

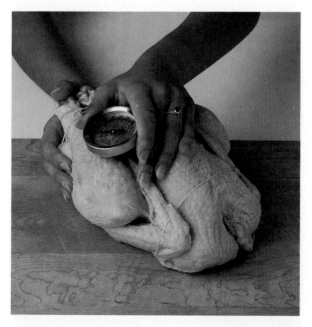

A meat thermometer is your best guide to doneness and should be inserted so that the bulb is ½–1 inch (1.2–2.5 cm) deep in the thickest part of the breast or the center of the inner thigh muscle. The thermometer will register 185–190°F (85–90°C) when a roasting chicken is well done. You may also use this test for doneness: press the thickest part of the drumstick between two fingers (protected with cloth) and move the leg. If the leg moves easily and is soft, the bird has been cooked sufficiently.

Broiler-fryers are used for *broiling*. Depending upon their size, these chickens are split in half lengthwise or quartered. The wing tip is folded back on the shoulder, and the pieces are placed on a broiler rack, skin side down. You may brush the chicken with melted fat. Place the chicken 4–5 inches (10–12.5 cm) from the source of heat for about 15 minutes. Turn the pieces with tongs as they are browned, and cook for another 15 minutes.

Young, tender chicken which has been cut into the desired pieces may be prepared for *frying* in several ways. You may roll it in flour, in egg and bread crumbs, or dip it into a batter. The prepared chicken is browned in about ½ inch (1.2 cm) of fat. The pieces are turned with tongs as they brown. After the chicken is browned, you may continue to cook it slowly until tender in one of three ways: (1) continue the cooking over low heat in the skillet; or (2) continue cooking in the oven; or (3) cover the skillet to complete the cooking. However, if you cover the chicken after browning, the method then becomes braising rather than frying.

## Moist-heat Methods

The term **fricassee** (frick-uh-SEE) is often used in poultry cookery, although it means the same as *braise*. To braise, brown the chicken in fat as if for frying; add 2–3 tablespoons (30–45 mL) of water; cover the pan. The cooking may continue over low heat on top of the range or in the oven at 325°F (160°C) until the chicken is

Chicken that has been braised is called chicken fricassee, which may be cooked on top of the stove or in the oven.

Broiler-fryers are often cut in half lengthwise for broiling. The chicken is sometimes first brushed with melted fat.

Young, tender chicken is suitable for frying. The chicken may be first rolled in flour, egg, and then bread crumbs.

Stewing is most suitable for older, more mature, larger poultry. The broth may be used as a base for a soup or a sauce.

# Tandoori Chicken    Yield: 4 servings

1 frying chicken

½ tsp (2.5 mL) chili powder

¼ tsp (1.2 mL) red pepper

dash of garlic powder

½ tsp (2.5 mL) curry powder

1 tsp (5 mL) lemon juice

½ tsp (2.5 mL) salt

2 tsp (10 mL) melted butter

  or margarine

1. Cut chicken into pieces. Make slits in breasts and thighs to allow seasoning to penetrate the meat.
2. Combine remainder of ingredients, and brush mixture over chicken.
3. Cover and marinate in refrigerator for at least 4 hours, or up to 24 hours.
4. Set oven at 400°F (200°C).
5. Place chicken pieces on a broiler pan, and bake for approximately 1 hour at 400°F (200°C).

Approximate nutrition information per serving: calories–250; protein–41 g; fat–9 g; cholesterol–105 mg; carbohydrates–1 g; sodium–430 mg.

tender (45 minutes to 1 hour). Remove the cover for the last 10 minutes to make the chicken crisp.

Cook old and mature poultry by *simmering* or *stewing*. The water should be below boiling; that is, simmering. Steam will come from the water surface, but the water will not bubble. When tender, the chicken is removed from the bone in large pieces and is used in a variety of chicken dishes such as salads, casseroles, creamed chicken, and sandwiches. You may use the broth for soup, gravy, or white sauce, and as the liquid for prepared chicken dishes.

## Microwaving Poultry

Poultry prepared in the microwave requires less time and attention than red meats, and microwaving enhances the tenderness, flavor and juiciness of poultry.

Both whole chicken and cut parts can be cooked equally well. Use roasting chickens instead of boiling chickens, which are tougher and require long, slow cooking to tenderize them.

Arrange cut pieces with the larger pieces toward the outside, and smaller pieces in the middle. When cooking a whole bird, place the

### Practical Tip

• To save money, bone chicken breasts yourself. You get more chicken for your money, and you can use the bones to make soup.

# Chicken Meals

Chickens are fairly easy to raise in most parts of the world. They provide meat and eggs so that they are a double food source. Perhaps this is why chicken is such a popular dish.

In the United States, we can buy chicken in many cuts and forms. Whole chickens, fryer parts, and boned chicken are available, for example. In addition, particular parts can be purchased separately. This convenience makes it especially easy for us to take advantage of different chicken preparations from around the world.

The dishes below are examples of meals based on chicken from other nations.

## Spain

Paella is a delicious rice-and-chicken stew. It is made in a heavy iron skillet on top of the stove. Although it has many ingredients, it is easy to make. The ingredients include chicken, rice, fresh fish, mussels, pork or sausage, paprika, onion, tomatoes, cayenne pepper, saffron, and thyme. The saffron imparts a yellowish color to the stew, which should be served hot.

## England

Chicken pudding sounds strange to our ears because we think of puddings as sweet. The English, however, prepare a wide variety of puddings, including meat puddings, which are really more like molded pies. A dough for the crust is prepared first, and then is placed inside a cloth-lined bowl. Chicken, ham, parsley, and mushrooms are put onto the dough. A top crust is added and then sealed. The cloth is gathered at the top of the pudding and tied tightly. The pudding cooks in boiling water for about three hours.

## Thailand

A spicy dish from Thailand, chicken khun charoonsri, is served with thick noodles. Strips

Paella is popular in Spain. What foods make up this dish?

of boned chicken and pork are combined with bean sprouts, garlic, soy sauce, and peppers. This mixture is then tossed with the noodles and served with boiled rice.

## Japan

Poached chicken with vegetables includes bamboo shoots, carrots, mushrooms, beans, and peas. It is seasoned with ginger, cayenne pepper, and soy sauce. This dish is served with rice.

## China

Wild mushroom and tree fungus soup with sliced chicken is an unusual soup from the Szechuan region of China. Wood ears, fresh mushrooms, and dried mushrooms are cooked together and added to chicken broth. The small chicken slices look stark white against the dark broth. This soup is served at the beginning of the meal and eaten throughout.

breast side down during the first half of cooking so that the juices will stay in the breast meat.

Poultry may be roasted in one of several ways: in a dish, on a microwave rack, or on an overturned saucer in a baking dish. Always cover poultry with waxed paper to prevent spattering. Poultry can be roasted with stuffing, provided that the stuffing is loosely packed into the cavities. The temperature of the stuffing must be 165°F (74°C) after cooking to prevent bacterial contamination. A microwave thermometer is helpful to test doneness, but if one is not available, look for clear juices when poultry is pierced with a fork or when a cut is made between the thigh and the body. If pink juices appear, continue cooking. The temperature of poultry does not rise much during standing time, so it should be cooked until done.

# Poultry Storage and Convenience

Poultry is a very perishable food. Poultry that has been cut up is more perishable than the whole bird. Some convenience forms, such as canned and frozen poultry, allow you to have poultry on hand at all times, with little concern for spoilage.

## Storage

To store properly, remove fresh poultry from the market wrap, rewrap loosely with waxed paper or a similar wrap, and store in the coldest part of the refrigerator at 35–38°F (2–3°C). The poultry should be used within two or three days.

Poultry may be stored for up to a year if wrapped in freezer wrap to seal out air and then put in the frozen-food compartment. Poultry that you purchase frozen should be stored immediately in the freezer without rewrapping and should not be thawed until you are ready to use it. It will retain its freshness if it is stored at 0°F (−18°C). Frozen poultry is clean and ready for cooking.

Canned poultry is stored in a cool, dry place. Any opened canned or leftover cooked poultry must be stored in the coldest part of the refrigerator in a tightly covered container. If leftover cooked poultry had been stuffed, remove the stuffing before storing. You should use leftover poultry within two or three days. Properly stored, poultry is available for use whenever you need it and, along with other poultry products, can contribute to the convenience of meal preparation.

## Convenience in Poultry

All ready-to-cook poultry is a convenience that allows you to use less time and effort than is usually required to dress and prepare poultry. Ready-to-cook poultry is sold as the whole bird, in halves, in quarters, or cut in pieces such as thighs, legs, breasts, or wings. Buying only the meaty parts such as breasts, thighs, and legs may be more economical in terms of cost per serving.

Most research studies that have compared home-prepared poultry products with similar convenience items indicate a higher cost for the convenience product. The greater the convenience provided for you, the higher the cost. For example, breaded chicken ready for frying and frozen chicken dinners were found to be much higher in cost (double or more) than similar home-prepared products. Canned prepared chicken products were also higher than comparable home-prepared items.

Other studies found that there can be a difference in nutritive values of convenience and home-prepared products. The convenience products tend to contain less poultry meat (which means less protein) than a similar home-prepared food.

A variety of convenience poultry products is available both canned and frozen. Some of the canned poultry items include the canned whole bird, cut pieces, boneless meat, sandwich spreads, soups, and prepared specialties such as turkey àla king. Dehydrated chicken soups are generally available.

Frozen convenience poultry items include birds stuffed with dressing, frozen pieces or parts, breaded cuts, and specialties such as chicken pies, turkey rolls, and complete dinners. Frozen cooked poultry provides an extra convenience, since it only needs to be heated for serving. In some markets and specialty shops, fully cooked items such as barbecued chicken, duck, roasted chicken, and fried chicken are available and require no preparation, not even heating.

There are instances when it is wise to use less time and energy with the help of convenience foods. However, remember that when you buy convenience foods, you are paying for the work involved in its preparation. At times convenience foods may be a good buy, especially if they add to the quality of the meal you serve. How well these and other convenience products serve and meet your needs will be determined by your ability to judge their quality, to fit them into your plans, and to use them creatively for variety in your meals.

### For Review
1. How should fresh poultry be stored?
2. Which is generally higher in nutrients, fresh poultry or a convenience form?

# 19 Chapter Review

## Summary

Chicken, turkey, duck, and Rock Cornish game hen are several examples of popular poultry. The methods of preparing and cooking these and other fowl are influenced by the high content of protein that they possess. Of course, the form and kind of poultry that is purchased for cooking should be based on several factors, including its intended use. Today in most grocery stores, poultry is available in ready-to-cook forms that are fresh, frozen, and canned. Also poultry is an ingredient in many convenience foods. As with all other foods, poultry must be stored properly to prevent rapid spoilage.

## Vocabulary

Match the lettered statements that follow to these vocabulary words:

1. giblets
2. fricassee
3. truss

a. This means the same as braise.
b. This includes the liver.
c. This is the procedure of browning the chicken in fat, then adding a small amount of water, and covering the pan.
d. This is used to prevent the wings and legs from becoming too brown and dry.
e. This includes the heart.
f. This procedure is used to roast poultry.
g. This includes the gizzard.
h. This is a method of cooking with moist heat.
i. This is the method of turning the wing tips back on the shoulders and tying the drumsticks to the tail.

## Chapter Questions

1. What kinds of frozen, canned, and ready-to-eat poultry, and convenience foods containing poultry do you have stored in your family's refrigerator or freezer, or on the canned-goods shelves? Which cooking methods are appropriate for each?
2. List what you think are the characteristics of freezer burn.
3. If you wanted to purchase a turkey roaster to serve eight people, how much should it weigh?
4. What factors should be considered when you purchase poultry?
5. What are five categories of foods in which chicken is an ingredient?
6. How do you thaw a frozen chicken, and why is it necessary to thaw it before cooking?
7. Why is it important to use low temperatures for roasting poultry?
8. What are the two rules to remember for cooking poultry?

9. When you have leftovers of stuffing inside a roasted turkey, how should they be stored and why?

10. What are the three methods of cooking poultry, and when should you use each?

11. Why is poultry that has been cut into parts more perishable than a whole bird?

12. What are the advantages and disadvantages for using ready-to-cook poultry?

## Skill Activities

**1. Decision making** In your food journal or card file box, make a collection of poultry recipes. Organize the recipes into these categories: appetizers, soups, salads, roasts, stews and skillet meals, casseroles, sandwiches, stuffings, and low-calorie meals. You can find recipes in books, magazines, and newspapers and on the display boards in supermarkets. Add to this collection whenever you find interesting recipes for poultry.

**2. Critical thinking** Make a list of the cooking tools and equipment that you would like to have for cooking poultry and give the purpose for each item. Make a star in front of those items that are essential to successful poultry cookery.

**3. Math** Visit the poultry counter at your local grocery store. Calculate the cost per serving (using the serving portions suggested in this chapter) of chicken broilers, fryers, capons, and roasters and stewing chicken. Which form of poultry is least expensive per serving? Which form of poultry would you select for roasting and why? Which form of poultry would you select for frying and why?

**4. Communication** Prepare a guide for carving a roasted chicken or turkey. Write the steps in order and then for each step, draw a diagram to show the proper carving technique. Directions for carving poultry may be found on the display boards in supermarkets and in cookbooks, magazines, and newspapers.

**5. Communication** Write a report that describes a menu for a chicken dinner to serve four people. First, determine how the chicken is going to be prepared, cooked, and served. Next figure out which kind of chicken and how much you should purchase. Then complete the planning by including information about the appetizer, salad, vegetables, dessert, and beverages. Include in your report a time-work plan.

# 20 Fish

## As you read, think about:

- how to identify, select, use, and store fish.
- what nutrients fish provides for you.
- how to prepare fish.
- how cooking affects fish.

**Vocabulary**
seafood
finfish
shellfish
mollusks
crustaceans
iodine
goiter

The products of the sea and inland waters are available without fishing for them. Quick freezing retains the freshness and flavor of **seafood** (edible finfish and shellfish), so you can enjoy clam, crab, lobster, shrimp, a variety of fish, and other seafoods throughout the year. Fish is a unique source of food that is not dependent upon the cultivation of land. It is highly nutritious; the proteins of fish equal those of meat in quantity and quality.

## Kinds and Forms of Fish

About 200 different varieties of fish are sold in markets. Most come from the oceans and some from lakes and rivers. They are classified into two general groups: finfish and shellfish. The **finfish** come from both saltwater and freshwater, and have scales and fins. Some **shellfish,** known as **mollusks,** are enclosed in a hard shell. Common mollusks are oysters, clams, and scallops. **Crustaceans** (kruss-TAY-shunz), the other type of shellfish, have a segmented outer shell. Common examples are lobsters, crabs, and shrimp.

Fish are also classified as lean or fat according to the amount of fat they contain. However, fish contains much less fat than red meats. The flesh of fish with a high fat content is either yellow, pink, or grayish in color, while the flesh of fish with less fat is white. The fat fish include salmon, mackerel, and tuna; the lean fish include haddock, cod, and halibut. Most of the shellfish contain little fat and are lean.

Several forms of fish and seafood are available for your selection. When you visit the market or a fish specialty store, you will find fresh, frozen, canned, cured, and pickled fish. About half of the fish used in the United States is fresh or frozen, and the remainder is canned. A very small amount of cured fish is used in this country, but it is very popular in the Scandinavian countries.

Fishing for all types of fresh fish was once even more difficult work than it is today. Sailing ships were used instead of today's motor-driven fishing boats. Coastline countries especially have developed technological fishing methods.

### Fresh Fish

The common forms of fresh fish which you will see in markets are whole, or round; drawn; dressed; steaks; and fillets. Fish marketed just as it comes from the water is known as *whole,* or *round, fish.* The scales and insides must be removed before the fish is cooked. *Drawn fish* has only the insides removed; the head, fins, and scales remain on the fish. *Dressed fish* comes ready for cooking. The head, tail, fins, scales, and insides are removed. *Fish steaks* are cross-section slices of dressed fish. Large fish such as halibut and salmon are often sold as steaks. The backbone is usually the only bone in a fish steak. A lengthwise cut away from the backbone is a *fish fillet.* A single fillet comes from one side of the fish; a double, or butterfly, fillet comes from

both sides of the fish and is held together by uncut flesh and skin. You will find only a few and sometimes no bones in a fillet.

### Frozen Fish

You may purchase several varieties of frozen fish all year round. Frozen fish can taste like fresh fish because much of the freezing of fish takes place on the boats right after they are caught. Frozen fish is usually sold as fillets and steaks. Fish sticks, which are cut from fillets, may be breaded and partially cooked before freezing. Breaded uncooked fillets and shellfish are also frozen. Frozen fish is ready for cooking without further preparation.

### Canned Fish

Both finfish and shellfish are available canned. Popular canned finfish include salmon, tuna, and sardines. Among the canned shellfish are oysters, clams, lobsters, crab, scallops, and shrimp.

### Cured Fish

Fish may be cured to preserve it and also to give it a distinctive flavor. Fish which has been salted, smoked, or pickled is referred to as cured fish. Examples of cured fish are salted cod, smoked mackerel, finnan haddie, and kippered herring.

Fish such as cod or herring is salted in dry salt or a brine and then dried. Mildly salted fish can be treated with smoke, which gives it a special smoky flavor. Finnan haddie is haddock which has been cured in brine and then smoked. Kippers, salmon, and whitefish may also be cured.

Some of the common forms of fresh fish, as available in specialty markets and grocery stores, are (top to bottom); whole, or round, fish; drawn fish, with the insides removed; dressed fish, with the insides, head, tail, fins, and scales removed; and fish fillets, cut from the backbone of the fish.

Pickled fish is cured in a brine that contains vinegar and pickling spices. After being heat processed, the pickled fish is packed into jars. The many kinds of fresh, frozen, canned, and cured fish can add variety and interest to your eating pleasure.

### For Review

1. What are the two general groups of fish? Describe each one.
2. Describe fat fish and lean fish.
3. What are the five common forms of fresh fish?

## Selection and Uses

Unlike meat inspection, the inspection and grading of fish for wholesomeness is voluntary. The United States Department of Interior supervises the grading program. All inspected fish will be identified with an inspection stamp which indicates its quality. Some of the fish products may show an inspection stamp. The grading standards usually grade fish as U.S. Grade A, U.S. Grade B, and Substandard. When available, these grades will enable you to purchase a wholesome, good-quality, fresh product for a variety of uses. Since inspection is not mandatory, it is important to purchase fish from reliable sources.

## Fish: Seasonal Availability in the United States

| Type of Fish | Best season | Where available |
| --- | --- | --- |
| bluefish | spring, summer, fall | Atlantic, Gulf Coast |
| carp | season varies | throughout U.S. |
| catfish | year-round | East and Gulf Coasts |
| flounder | year-round | Atlantic, Gulf, and Pacific Coasts |
| fluke | spring, summer | North Atlantic |
| haddock | year-round | North Atlantic |
| halibut | year-round | Atlantic, Pacific |
| mackerel | spring, summer | North Atlantic Coast |
| Pacific sole | year-round | West Coast |
| perch | year-round | North Atlantic Coast |
| red snapper | year-round | South Atlantic, Gulf Coast |
| salmon | spring, summer | Pacific Northwest, North Atlantic |
| sea bass | year-round | East Coast |
| swordfish | spring, summer | South Atlantic, Pacific |
| trout | season varies | throughout U.S. |
| tuna | spring, summer, fall | East and West Coasts |

## Shellfish

Shellfish are sold live in the shell, shucked (shell removed), or cooked. The following characteristics will be your clues to the freshness of shellfish: (1) shucked oysters and clams are plump and creamy in color, and the liquid they are in is odorless and clear; (2) shells of live clams and oysters should be tightly closed or should close when touched; (3) the tail of a live lobster snaps back quickly after it is flattened out (both lobster and crab should be kept alive until they are cooked); (4) the fresh deep-sea scallop is white, and the bay scallop is creamy white or pinkish in color; and (5) shrimp should be odorless, and the thin shell should be firmly attached.

## Finfish

The whole, or round, finfish should have bulging, bright, clear eyes, bright-red gills, and scales that cling tightly to the skin. The flesh of the fish should be firm, springy, and leave no dent when pressed. There should be no disagreeable odor.

## Frozen and Canned Fish

Choose only fish that is solidly frozen and is in packages which show no sign of having been thawed and refrozen. Like fresh fish, some frozen and processed fish may not have a government grade. The information on the label and the brand name are your only clues to quality.

## Amount to Buy

The amount you buy is determined by the form of fish. Canned and frozen fish are ready for cooking and therefore will have no waste. Fresh whole or drawn fish will have waste. There is less waste in dressed fish since the insides, head, tail, fins, and scales have been removed.

## Shellfish Buying Guide

| Market Form | Description | Amount to buy per serving |
|---|---|---|
| Live | Clams, Oysters<br>Crabs<br>Lobster | 6<br>3<br>1 lb (454 g) |
| Shucked | Oysters, Clams<br>Scallops | ⅓ pt (167 mL)<br>⅓ lb (151 g) |
| Fresh or Frozen | Shrimp<br>Lobster tails | ¼ lb (117 g)<br>½ lb (227 g) |
| Cooked in the Shell | Crabs<br>Lobster | 3<br>1 lb (454 g) |
| Cooked, Shelled | Shrimp, Crab, Lobster | ¼ lb (117 g) |

## Finfish Buying Guide

| Market Form | Description | Amount to buy per serving |
| --- | --- | --- |
| Whole, or Round | As it comes from the water. Must be scaled, cleaned; head, tail, fins must be removed. | 1 lb (454 g) |
| Drawn | Cleaned only. Scales, head, tail, and fins must be removed. | 1 lb (454 g) |
| Dressed | Scaled, cleaned, usually with head, tail, and fins removed. Ready for cooking. | ½ lb (227 g) |
| Steaks | Cross-section slices of large dressed fish with a section of backbone. | ⅓ lb (151 g) |
| Fillets | Sides of fish cut lengthwise from the backbone. Boneless. | ⅓ lb (151 g) |
| Sticks | Pieces of fish cut from blocks of frozen fillets into portions of uniform dimensions, usually 1 oz (28 g) portions. Usually covered with batter, breaded, and browned in deep fat. | 3 1-oz sticks (75 g) |

Fish steaks will have little waste, and fillets of finfish will have no waste. The table on this page will help you determine how much fish you will need to buy for your intended use.

## Uses of Fish

Like meat, fish may be used as the main dish around which the rest of the meal is planned. It may be combined with other foods to make salads, casseroles, croquettes, and other main dishes around which meals can be planned. Fish chowders or oyster and lobster stews are favorite hearty soups used as lunch or supper main dishes.

Fish can be served as an appetizer. Fresh, frozen, or canned shrimp, lobster, and crab are served as seafood cocktails at the beginning of special meals. Both pickled fish and smoked fish can also be served as part of the appetizer course.

### For Review

1. What must you consider when buying fish that is not graded or inspected?
2. What qualities should you look for when buying fresh shrimp? Fresh finfish?
3. What forms of fish have the least waste? The most waste?

# Nutrient Contributions

In general, the nutrients contributed by fish are similar to those of meat. Fish and meat both contain protein, minerals, vitamins, and fat.

## Protein

The protein of fish is complete and can be used in place of meat or poultry in your meals. An average serving of meat and fish will give you about the same amount of protein.

## Minerals

The mineral content of fish will vary somewhat with the kind of fish. However, fish in general will provide important amounts of *phosphorus* and a fair amount of *iron* and *calcium*. Meat is usually a better source of iron than is fish. Fish makes its most important contribution to your diet through the mineral **iodine,** which is not provided by meat. All foods other than seafoods are poor sources of iodine.

When iodine is lacking, a disease called goiter develops. **Goiter** is an enlargement of the thyroid gland. Some of the early scientists noticed that people who lived near the sea and regularly ate fish did not get goiter, while goiter was common among those who lived inland. Many years later, in 1917, a group of children in Akron, Ohio, who were suffering from goiter, were given 0.2 grams of sodium iodine each day for two weeks at the beginning and end of the school year. The children who received iodine were able to recover from the goiter.

Without iodine, the thyroid gland cannot produce thyroxine, which is needed to control the rate of food oxidation in your body cells. When seafoods are included in your meals regularly, they will supply the needed iodine. Today, iodized salt (salt with iodine added) along with fish help you meet your need for iodine.

## Vitamins

The vitamin content of most fish is comparable to that of meat. The *B vitamins* ($B_1$, $B_2$, niacin) are found in fair amounts in fish. *Vitamins A* and *D* are present in fatty fish, especially in the oil of the fish liver.

## Fats

Fish contains less fat than meat, and lean fish is especially low in fat. Because fish is lower in fat, it will supply fewer calories. This can be an advantage for those who are on low-calorie or low-fat diets.

However, the fat content of cooked fish depends upon the amount of fat added in cooking. Fish is often rolled in bread crumbs, flour, or cornmeal before frying. This enhances flavor, but also increases fat content and calories.

---

### For Review

1. How does fish compare with meat in protein, minerals, vitamins, and fats?
2. What mineral does fish provide that meats do not? Why is this mineral important in your diet?
3. What disease can be prevented by eating seafood?

---

### Practical Tip
- To open fresh clams easily, first place them in the freezer for 30 minutes.

### Practical Tip
- Use tweezers (for kitchen use only) for easily removing bones from fish.

# Marine Biologist

Maureen Myer rises at 5:00 A.M. and looks out the window. "Good," she thinks, "clear weather." She gathers together her equipment and heads out the door. Maureen will spend the next three days on a shrimp boat in the Atlantic Ocean off the coast of Georgia.

Shrimp are an important source of income for the fishermen of Georgia. They are also a good source of protein for consumers. Because the demand for shrimp is high, the fishermen fish the coastal waters as much as they can. The problem is that if too many people fish, the shrimp population can become dangerously low.

For this reason, the state of Georgia employs Maureen, a marine biologist, to keep track of the shrimp population. Marine biologists study life in the seas and marshes. They try to learn the living habits of sea plants and animals.

On the shrimp boat, Maureen fishes—but not to catch food. She also takes samples of the ocean water from various regions. Then she counts the shrimp she has caught. Based on years of record-keeping, she knows how many shrimp to expect in set quantities of water during different times of the year. When the shrimp count is low, she will restrict fishing. When the shrimp count goes up, she gives the fishermen the go-ahead to fish again. In this way, the population of shrimp is never in danger of extinction.

Maureen also conducts research. No one has been successful in "farming" shrimp. Predator fish always seem to decrease the populations. Also, not much is known about the foods that shrimp eat. If they could be farmed, shrimp could provide a good source of protein for the world and a boon to the Georgia economy. Therefore, Maureen spends much time studying the habits of shrimp. She takes water samples from marshes and the ocean, and observes shrimp in various stages of their life cycle. Similar research with different kinds of fish has led to very productive fish farms in this country and around the world.

Fish farming, or aquaculture, has greatly increased the yield of fish from the sea. In Norway this year, fish farmers will harvest more salmon from cages suspended in the sea than fishermen will catch in the whole Atlantic Ocean. Trout can now be grown in tanks. Research into the water quality, food, and oxygen content of the water surrounding fish has led to more efficient ways of farming fish.

Fish and other foods from the sea are extremely rich protein sources. As the world population increases, aquaculture becomes more important. Hope for feeding the world in the future lies beneath the seas. Marine biologists' research helps us to protect the resources of the present and increase the food supply of the future.

This marine biologist conducts research in a laboratory setting as well as doing "field work" at sea.

# Principles of Fish Cookery

Because fish is a food rich in protein, it needs to be cooked at low temperatures to prevent toughening of the protein. Unlike meat, fish contains little connective tissue and cooks quickly. If you cook fish too long, it is apt to break apart. It is sufficiently cooked when it is easily flaked with a fork. Remember that overcooking as well as high temperatures can toughen fish.

You recall that the degree of tenderness of meat depends upon the cooking method. Fish differ from meats in that they are all tender. You may cook fish by moist- and dry-heat methods, but it will be the fat content of the fish rather than tenderness which will be your clue to the best method. Generally, the fatty fish are cooked by dry-heat methods and the lean fish by moist-heat methods.

When you learn which fish are fat and which are lean, you will be able to match the proper cooking method with the fish. The fat fish such as whitefish, mackerel, catfish, salmon, and trout are best broiled or baked. Their fat content keeps them from drying out during cooking. The lean fish include swordfish, red snapper, halibut, haddock, and flounder. They are usually fried, poached, or steamed. The lean fish may be broiled or baked if they are brushed with fat or cooked in a sauce to prevent drying.

Regardless of the cooking method you select, fish should be cooked at a low temperature in order to maintain the best quality. No fish should ever be overcooked.

*Broiling* is the easiest and quickest method of cooking fatty fish. The fish is placed in a single layer on an oiled broiling pan and is brushed with melted butter. The fish is cooked several inches away from the heat source and, if it is thick, is turned to cook the other side.

*Baking* fish helps retain the shape of the fish. Whole fish may be stuffed before baking.

Charcoal-broiled fish is easy to prepare for large groups of people. The fish is placed on grills a few inches away from the flames and is usually brushed with melted butter or barbecue sauce.

The fish is brushed with melted butter, put in an oiled baking dish, and baked uncovered in a 350°F (180°C) oven.

*Poaching* fish is gently simmering it in seasoned water in a covered pan. The fish should be tied in cheesecloth to prevent it from breaking apart.

Some fish may also be pan-fried, deep-fat fried, or cooked in a chowder with your choice of liquid and vegetables. Proper cooking retains the flavor of fish; however, when you do not wish to cook fish immediately, protect its flavor by proper storage.

## Microwaving Fish

Finfish and shellfish are naturally tender and have a high moisture content. The microwave enhances these qualities because there is no hot, dry air to remove the moisture, and the quick cooking time preserves the natural flavors.

# Stuffed Rolled Fish Fillets    Yield: 4 servings

| | |
|---|---|
| 1 lb (454 g) fish fillets | 1 tsp salt |
| 3 Tbs (45 mL) finely chopped onion | ¼ tsp (1.2 mL) ground nutmeg |
| 2 Tbs (30 mL) butter | 1 slightly beaten egg |
| 1 c (250 mL) bread crumbs | 1 Tbs (15 mL) melted butter |
| ¼ c (60 mL) snipped parsley | 1½ tsp (7.5 mL) lemon juice |
| | paprika |

Approximate nutrition information per serving: calories–275; protein–23 g; fat–12 g; cholesterol–115 mg; carbohydrates–18 g; sodium–955 mg.

1. Set oven at 350°F (180°C).
2. Melt butter in skillet; add onions and cook until tender.
3. Stir in the bread crumbs, parsley, salt, nutmeg, and egg.
4. Spread mixture over fish fillets, and roll up, fastening with toothpicks.
5. Place fillets, seam side down, in a baking dish.
6. Combine the melted butter and the lemon juice; drizzle over the fish. Sprinkle with paprika.
7. Cook uncovered at 350°F (180°C) for about 15 minutes, or until fish flakes easily with a fork.

## Tips for Microwaving Fish

- Make sure that frozen whole fish are completely defrosted before cooking in order to insure precise cooking time.
- Since fish produce juices that may dilute sauces during cooking, make sauces extra thick, or use butter for basting.
- Take skin off fillets, and score the membrane to prevent curling.
- Use breaded frozen fish, not batter-dipped, which becomes greasy in the microwave.
- Arrange fish in single layers of even thickness. Tuck thin pieces under to even out the thickness.
- To remove fish odors from the microwave, cook 1 cup (250 mL) water with the juice of one-half lemon in the oven, uncovered, for 6–8 minutes.

Since overcooking will toughen fish, cook it in the microwave only until it has lost its translucent or shiny quality and has begun to turn opaque, or dull. Timing is especially important because fish will continue to cook during standing time.

Cook breaded fish uncovered; cover all other fish dishes during cooking to retain moisture. Fillets and steaks are easy to prepare in the microwave oven, but whole fish can also be successfully prepared. Because of their uneven shape, rotate whole fish one-quarter turn twice during cooking. When stuffing a whole fish, pack the cavity loosely, and use a moist stuffing. Dry stuffings may become tough.

**For Review**
1. Why should fish be cooked at a low temperature and not be overcooked?
2. Why should salmon be broiled and not fried?
3. How would you poach fish?
4. What are two guidelines to follow when cooking fish in the microwave?

## Storage and Convenience

You can preserve the quality, freshness, and flavor of the fish you select by storing it properly. All fish, except the canned convenience form, is very perishable.

### Fresh Fish

To store fresh fish, wrap it tightly in waxed paper or foil, and place it in a covered container in the coldest part of the refrigerator. If you are unable to use it within a day, wrap it tightly in moisture-proof paper and place it in the freezer. Keep in mind that fish odors can easily penetrate other foods.

### Frozen Fish

Commercially frozen fish is stored in its original package and should be placed in the freezer immediately after purchase. It should not be thawed until you are ready to use it. Thin or small pieces of frozen fish can be cooked without thawing. Large pieces of frozen fish are thawed in the original wrappings in the refrigerator. They will cook more evenly when thawed.

### Canned Fish

Canned fish keeps well at room temperature, but once the can is opened, it must be kept in a tightly covered container in the refrigerator. In addition to the fresh, frozen, and canned fish, there are several convenience fish and seafood products that you should know about.

Fresh fish can be prepared into sushi, a Japanese dish consisting of thin strips of raw fish wrapped around rice.

## Convenience

You will find that there is a variety of convenience fish and seafood items. The convenience forms of frozen fish include frozen fillets, steaks, fish sticks, fish pies, chowders, and other processed fish products. These products may be breaded and ready-to-cook, or they may be precooked and require only heating before serving. Frozen steaks, fillets, and whole fish are ready to cook. Shrimp, oysters, scallops, and fillets may be breaded, or breaded and precooked. The breaded seafoods require cooking, while the precooked ones require only heating.

Frozen fish soups are another convenience item. Frozen fish dinners packaged in divided foil plates usually include vegetables and need only to be cooked in their containers before serving.

You may use canned fish as it comes from the can, in salads and sandwiches, or as an ingredient in any recipe that calls for cooked fish. Tuna, salmon, sardines, lobster, crab, and shrimp are popular canned items. In addition, smoked fish such as oysters, herring, and salmon are ready to eat without further cooking. You will also find boil-in-bag fish and seafoods that are vacuum-sealed to preserve their goodness.

The use of these convenience items may permit you to serve more elaborate dishes and menus, to include more variety, to make up for lack of experience and skill, as well as to use less time. But, wherever there are advantages, there

Convenience forms of fish, such as canned tuna, can be used to make salad niçoise. This salad often combines many ingredients such as olives, green beans, potatoes, tomatoes, cucumbers, and anchovies to provide a filling, main-dish meal.

may also be disadvantages. Convenience items may deprive you of eating pleasure because flavor and quality may be inferior or may deprive you of the satisfaction of creating. They can also be a strain on your budget. You should evaluate their contributions in terms of your needs, abilities, and values.

### For Review

1. Why should fresh fish be wrapped tightly for storage in the refrigerator or freezer?
2. What are some uses for canned fish?
3. What are some disadvantages of convenience forms of fish?

## Summary

Fish is a highly nutritious source of food and one that is not dependent upon the cultivation of land. Fresh, frozen, canned, and cured finfish and shellfish are available for consumption. However, to preserve the quality of this perishable food, proper storage and usage is required. As with other foods that have a high concentration of protein content, the principles of cookery are designed to protect that nutrient and make the fish palatable.

## Vocabulary

Use the following vocabulary words to fill in the blanks in the paragraphs below:

crustaceans          mollusks
finfish              seafood
goiter               shellfish
iodine

Fish are found in saltwater and fresh water, and they are categorized into two groups. The general term for the group of fish that have a hard outer shell is __(1)__. This group is further broken down into __(2)__, such as clams and oysters, and __(3)__, such as crabs and lobsters. The other group of fish, which has fins and scales, is referred to as __(4)__. The name that is applied to all fish products from the sea is __(5)__.

Fish supply valuable nutrients, but they make their most important contribution to a person's diet by supplying the mineral __(6)__. Without this mineral, the thyroid gland enlarges, which is a symptom of the disease called __(7)__.

## Chapter Questions

1. Why is it that frozen fish often tastes like fresh fish?
2. Why is it important to purchase fish from reliable sources?
3. What can you use as signs of quality for purchasing frozen fish?
4. For each of the following fish descriptions, what is the term that is used to name its market form? a) cross-section slices from large fish that have been scaled and cleaned; b) uniform pieces of fish, usually breaded or covered with a batter, which have been cut from the frozen sides of fish; c) fish that has been cleaned only; the head, tail, and fins still need to be removed; d) boneless sides of fish that have been cut lengthwise from the backbone; and e) fish ready for cooking that is already scaled, cleaned, and usually the head, tail, and fins are removed as well.
5. If you wanted to purchase haddock fillets to serve six people, how much should the fish weigh?
6. What are ways that you can meet your body's need for iodine?
7. In what ways do finfish differ from shellfish, and how does the preparation of each kind differ?

8. If you were on a low-fat diet, what are two of the best varieties of fish to buy, and what is the best way to cook them?
9. What should you consider when selecting a cooking method for fish?
10. What are four different categories of foods that can be made with fish as an ingredient?
11. Why is it important to brush lean fish with fat or cook them in a sauce if they are baked or broiled?
12. What kinds of fresh, frozen, canned, and cured fish and convenience fish items do you have available to eat in your home? For each item, tell how you would prepare the fish for a meal.

## Skill Activities

**1. Decision making** In your food journal or card file box, make a collection of fish recipes. Organize the recipes into categories for appetizers, salads, stews and chowders, fish in cream sauces, cakes and loaves, casseroles and pies, and stuffings. You can find recipes in books, magazines, newspapers, and on the display board in supermarkets. When you find interesting recipes for fish, add them to your collection.

**2. Science** Research information in books, magazines, and newspapers, and write a report about the uses of fish oil and its value to the human body in helping it stay healthy. Cold-water fish, such as mackerel and salmon, have a fish oil that when consumed by people, helps keep them healthy. In your report, try to include information about Omega-3 and eicosapentanoic acid, known as EPA, which is a factor found in fish oil that is believed to help protect people from heart disease.

**3. Decision making** Go to the frozen foods counter of a supermarket. Look for frozen seafoods, and find those fish products that claim to have fewer calories and those products that do not make that claim. On both types of products look for ingredients labels and nutritional labels. On a sheet of paper, list the product and then the kind of information that is given on the labels. What information is given on the labels? Which products have the fewest calories? Which products have the greatest protein? Which products are coated with a batter? Which ones are breaded? Did you find any seafood packages with government grades? What clues to quality did you find on the products?

**4. Critical thinking** Visit the fish counter at a supermarket, and learn which fresh finfish and shellfish are available. On a sheet of paper, write the name of each finfish, the forms, and the price for each. Also record the names and prices of the shellfish that are available. Compare the cost for a one-serving portion of a finfish with that for a one-serving portion of a shellfish. Which is more economical? Of the fish that is available, which one would you purchase to make a fish dinner? Why?

# 21 Vegetables

## As you read, think about:

- how to identify, select, use, and store vegetables.
- how to prepare vegetables.
- how cooking affects vegetables.
- what nutrients vegetables provide for you.

**Vocabulary**
chlorophyll
cellulose
au gratin

Two million years ago, people roamed the earth and ate fruits, roots, and berries; these were their first foods. People's wanderings became seasonal, according to the growth of plants. They learned what plants to eat and realized that seeds could grow into plants.

The word *vegetable* refers to the plant or its parts that can be eaten. When you eat vegetables, you eat leaves, stems, flowers, fruits, seeds, tubers, and roots. Vegetables can be prepared in a variety of ways to enhance the color, flavor, and texture of meals.

## Classes, Forms, and Uses of Vegetables

It is convenient to think of the many varieties of vegetables in classes or groups. They are often grouped according to the parts of the plant from which they come, their flavor, nutrient content, or color.

### Parts of Plant

Vegetables can be most easily classified according to the parts of the plant from which they come, such as seeds, leaves, tubers, roots, flowers, bulbs, stems, and fruits. You will find some of the vegetables from each group in the photographs on the next two pages.

### Flavor Classification

According to flavor, vegetables are grouped as either mild or strong. The strong-flavored vegetables include those with a cabbagelike flavor, such as brussels sprouts, turnips, and cauliflower, and those with an onionlike flavor, such as leeks and garlic. Most other vegetables are considered mild in flavor.

### Nutrient Classification

Some vegetables have a high water content, while others are high in starch. It is the part of

Corn was a staple crop and important food for the American Indians long before European settlers arrived. The Indians taught the settlers how to grow and prepare it.

the plant from which the vegetable comes that will influence its nutrient value. The fruits, stems, flowers, and leaves are usually high in water content. Vegetables from these plant parts, such as tomato, celery, broccoli, and lettuce, have a high water content and are referred to as the juicy or succulent vegetables. The tubers, bulbs, roots, and seeds are usually high in the carbohydrate starch. Vegetables from these parts of the plant, such as potato, sweet potato, lima beans, and corn, are often referred to as the starchy vegetables.

### Color Classification

The color of a vegetable may also be a clue to its nutrient value. The leafy green and yellow vegetables are grouped together because they contain a yellow substance called carotene. Your body can change carotene into vitamin A. In some vegetables, the deep-green color hides or masks the yellow color of carotene.

1. Leeks
2. Beets
3. Rutabagas and purple-top turnips
4. Celery
5. Asparagus
6. Potatoes
7. Chives
8. Shallots
9. Bamboo
10. Garlic
11. Yellow onions
12. Radishes
13. Sweet potatoes and yams
14. Parsnips
15. Carrots

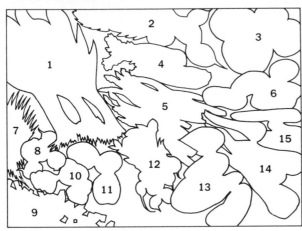

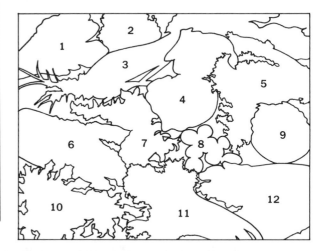

1. Romaine
2. Red leaf lettuce
3. Swiss chard
4. Cabbage
5. Kale
6. Chinese cabbage
7. Spinach
8. Brussels sprouts
9. Iceberg lettuce
10. Dandelion
11. Mustard greens
12. Collards

414

1. Yellow, green, and red bell peppers
2. Broccoli
3. Cauliflower
4. Artichokes
5. Eggplant
6. Okra
7. Tomato
8. Salad and pickle cucumbers
9. Zucchini
10. Summer squash
11. Butternut squash
12. Corn
13. Peas
14. Shell beans
15. String beans

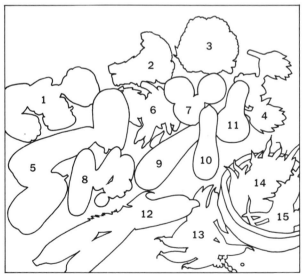

These various classes of vegetables will help you to select a pleasing variety for your meals. A good rule to follow is to select no more than one vegetable from the same group for the same meal. All groups of vegetables usually can be purchased in more than one form.

## Forms of Vegetables

Because of modern transportation and refrigeration, some fresh vegetables are available throughout the year. You may buy fresh carrots, lettuce, potatoes, and onions any time of the year. Other vegetables such as lima beans, corn, peas, and asparagus may be available in the fresh form only part of the year. You may purchase these seasonal vegetables throughout the year in other forms such as canned, frozen, or dried.

## Uses of Vegetables

Vegetables are most commonly served as an accompaniment both to enhance and to complement the main dish. Vegetable accompaniments add contrast in color, texture, flavor, size, and shape. They may even appear at breakfast as a vegetable juice, or as potatoes to be served with eggs. They are served as appetizers, soups, salads, side dishes, casseroles, and even as garnishes.

### For Review

1. What are the ways in which vegetables are classified?
2. Describe and give examples of the starchy vegetables.
3. If fresh vegetables are not available in your area, what other forms could you purchase?

## Vegetables: United States Seasonal Availability and Nutrient Qualities

| Vegetable | Season | Vitamins | Minerals |
|---|---|---|---|
| alfalfa sprouts | year-round | | zinc |
| asparagus | spring, summer | A, C, E, folacin | potassium, zinc |
| beans, green | summer | A, C | potassium, magnesium |
| beans, lima | summer | A, $B_6$, C, folacin | potassium, zinc, iron, phosphorus, magnesium |
| beets | summer, fall | folacin | potassium |
| broccoli | spring, fall | A, C, K, folacin, riboflavin | calcium, potassium |
| brussels sprouts | fall, winter | A, C, $B_6$, folacin | potassium |
| cabbage | year-round | C, K, riboflavin | potassium |
| carrots | year-round | A, $B_6$ | potassium |
| cauliflower | fall, winter | C, $B_6$, K | potassium |
| celery | year-round | | potassium |
| chives | summer | A | iron |
| collard greens | summer, fall, winter | A, C, folacin, riboflavin | calcium, magnesium |
| corn | summer | A, $B_6$ | magnesium |
| cucumber | year-round | E | |
| dandelion greens | spring | A, riboflavin, folacin | magnesium |
| endive | fall, winter | A, riboflavin | |

# Nutrient Contributions

Vegetables are especially rich in vitamins and minerals. For this reason, they should be included in your meals.

## Vitamins

**Chlorophyll** is the green substance of plant cells that gives some vegetables their green color. It is in the green leaves of plants that vitamins are made.

The leafy green and deep-yellow vegetables are excellent sources of *vitamin A*. You will recall that these vegetables contain carotene (a yellow substance) which can be converted into vitamin A. The deeper the yellow and the darker the green of the vegetable, the higher the vitamin A content. Dark-green vegetables such as broccoli and spinach, and deep-yellow vegetables such as carrots and sweet potatoes are abundant sources of carotene. When carotene is converted into vitamin A, it serves the same purpose as the vitamin A found in milk. Do you remember that vitamin A is needed to help your

| Vegetable | Season | Vitamins | Minerals |
|---|---|---|---|
| kale | fall, winter | A, C, E, K, folacin, riboflavin | calcium |
| kohlrabi | summer, fall | C | |
| leeks | fall, spring | C | |
| lettuce (dark leafy types) | summer | A, riboflavin | magnesium |
| mushrooms | year-round | niacin | potassium, zinc |
| mustard greens | early fall | A, C, E, folacin, riboflavin | calcium, magnesium |
| onions | year-round | | potassium |
| parsley | summer | A, E, C, folacin, riboflavin | iron, magnesium, calcium |
| peas | spring, summer | A, C, niacin | magnesium, iron, zinc |
| peppers (red and green) | summer, fall | A, C | |
| potatoes | year-round for most varieties | C, $B_6$, thiamin, riboflavin, niacin, folacin | potassium |
| pumpkins | fall | A | potassium |
| spinach | spring, summer | A, C, K, E, riboflavin, folacin, $B_6$ | iron, magnesium, calcium, potassium, zinc |
| tomatoes | summer | A, C | potassium |
| watercress | summer | A, E, riboflavin folacin | magnesium |

eyes adjust quickly to light or dark, to help you grow, and to add a glow and softness to your hair and skin?

Leafy green vegetables are also good sources of *vitamin C*. Most vegetables contain vitamin C, but some are richer sources of it than others. Broccoli, green peppers, tomatoes, and raw cabbage are important sources of vitamin C.

In addition to vitamins A and C, vegetables contain fair amounts of the *B vitamins*. However, seed vegetables such as lima beans and peas are good sources of vitamin B.

## Minerals

The leafy green vegetables are doubly good since they are not only rich in vitamins, but they are also excellent sources of the minerals *calcium* and *iron*.

## Carbohydrates

*Cellulose, starch,* and *sugar* are the carbohydrates in vegetables. The carbohydrate content of most vegetables is low except in the seeds, such as beans and corn, and in tubers, which are good sources of starch. The skin and pulp of vegetables contribute **cellulose,** a carbohydrate substance that cannot be digested by the body but serves as a natural laxative. The sweet flavor of young corn, peas, and sweet potatoes is due to their sugar content. As these vegetables mature, the sugar is changed into starch and then the vegetables no longer have a sweet flavor.

Vegetables as a rule are low in calories, but vegetables which are rich in starch will also supply more calories than those low in starch. The nutrient content of vegetables can be your clue to their caloric values. Vegetables are considered lower in calories than most other food groups; the vegetables with a high water content supply fewer calories than the vegetables with a high starch content.

## Protein

Most vegetables contain only small amounts of incomplete protein. Dried peas and beans (legumes) contain important amounts of protein even though it is incomplete. The incomplete protein food should be supplemented with a complete protein food to provide the missing amino acids. (See pages 43 and 56.)

The vitamins and minerals which vegetables provide make great contributions to your health, vitality, and appearance. It is important to know how to cook vegetables so that they will keep their bright color and nutrients.

### For Review

1. How do the leafy green and deep-yellow vegetables help your eyes adjust to the light and dark?
2. What kind of vegetable is low in calories? High in calories?
3. Why should vegetables be supplemented with animal protein in your diet?

# Principles of Cookery

Along with valuable nutrients, vegetables will add color, flavor, texture, and a pleasing contrast to other foods of a meal. Careless cooking will make vegetables drab and lifeless, and will destroy their important vitamins and minerals.

Several changes take place when vegetables are cooked. The cellulose structure softens, and the vegetables become less crisp. The starch absorbs water, swells, and becomes more soluble. There are changes in color and flavor, and some nutrients dissolve into the cooking liquid. The principles of vegetable cookery are designed to protect color, flavor, and texture, and to preserve nutrients. The amount of water to be used and the cooking time are important considerations.

## Amount of Water

Some of the nutrients in vegetables are soluble in water, and they therefore seep out into the cooking liquid. The B vitamins, vitamin C, and minerals dissolve in water. When you bake vegetables or cook them in small amounts of water or with no added water, the loss of soluble nutrients is reduced. In order to cook vegetables in small amounts of water, the pan is covered to prevent both scorching and loss of water due to evaporation.

Strong-flavored vegetables, such as onions and cabbage, may be cooked in larger amounts of water, enough to cover the vegetable, so that the flavor will become milder. However, more of the soluble nutrients will be lost in the larger amount of water.

## Length of Cooking Time

There are several ways in which the length of cooking time will influence vegetables. You will recall that some vitamins are destroyed by

Water-soluble nutrients are reduced or lost when vegetables are cooked in large amounts of water. Steaming the vegetables, however, preserves these nutrients. What are some water-soluble vitamins?

Not all vegetables have to boiled or steamed. Charcoal broiling vegetables on skewers provides a break from the plain taste of other cookery methods. Often the vegetables are first slightly boiled before being placed on the grill.

## Methods of Cookery

*Boiling* is suitable for all vegetables and is the method used most often. The vegetable is added to a small amount of boiling water, and then the pan is covered. The water is quickly returned to a boil, and then the heat is reduced so that the water simmers gently. To protect the color of bright-green vegetables, cook them without a cover for the first few minutes. Frozen vegetables are placed directly into boiling water. They will cook in a shorter time than fresh vegetables because they have been scalded in preparation for freezing.

Some vegetables can be *baked* in their skins. Vegetables such as potatoes and squash are washed thoroughly and placed directly on the oven rack or in a shallow pan and baked until tender. Baking is a way to preserve water-soluble nutrients.

Mild-flavored vegetables may be *steamed*. The steamer consists of a pan in which to boil water, and a basket to hold the food. The vegetable is steamed over rapidly boiling water.

Vegetables such as potatoes may be fried. Others, such as eggplant, may first be dipped in batter or crumbs and then fried. With either method, the vegetables are fried in hot but not smoking-hot fat. They may be fried in shallow fat or in deep fat. *French frying* is cooking in fat deep enough to cover the vegetable.

Vegetables cook very quickly when *pressure-cooked*. Carefully follow the directions which come with the pressure cooker. Vegetables cooked in a pressure cooker usually have a good color and flavor because of the short cooking time. Be careful not to overcook them.

To *stir-fry* or *braise* vegetables, place 1–2 tablespoons (15–30 mL) of fat in a skillet or pan. Melt the fat, and add broken or cut vegetables. Cover the pan, and cook the vegetable over low heat for a short time. The cooked vegetable will be slightly crisp.

heat and overcooking. To avoid nutrient loss, vegetables should be cooked only until they are fork tender and still slightly crisp.

Overcooking dulls the bright colors of vegetables and can cause an unpleasant flavor to develop in cabbage-flavored vegetables. The strong flavor of cabbage- and onion-flavored vegetables is influenced more by overcooking than by the quantity of water used. Overcooked vegetables lose their texture and shape and become mushy. Properly cooked vegetables retain their color, flavor, and texture, as well as their nutrients.

# Excitement in the Produce Department

Walk down the aisles of the produce department of a grocery store, and you are likely to find an array of unusual vegetables and fruits. Among the traditional apples and pears, you might see fuzzy brown kiwi fruit or star-shaped yellow carambola. With the carrots and potatoes, you might spy some green squash-shaped chayote. Across the United States, produce departments are undergoing a revolution.

Food producers in the United States have responded to an increased demand for the unusual. Since many of the fruits and vegetables come from tropical climates, California and Florida lead the country in the production of the "new" produce. Where oranges and grapefruit once grew, carambola are now planted. Winged beans from the Philippines replace more traditional crops in Florida.

This change in American tastes can be partly explained by two phenomena: the new wave of immigrants to the United States and improved methods of transporting perishable products.

War, political unrest, and lack of economic opportunity have driven many people from Central and South America, Indochina, the Philippines, and China to immigrate to the United States. Since 1970, our population has increased by 17%. Within that population, the Hispanic population increased by 87% and the Asian population by 127%. Like the immigrants who came before them, these new Americans brought "new" types of food and cooking. The exotic fruits and vegetables of the tropics are working their way into the mainstream diet.

For many years, these fruits and vegetables were unavailable in the United States because shipping the highly perishable products was almost impossible. Today, improved storage and packing methods make transporting perishable products feasible. Foam plastic or insulation is wrapped around fruits that are easily bruised. Shippers can regulate the temperature of refrigerated containers to maintain optimal storage temperature.

So the next time you are in the grocery store, see if you can find any of these "new" fruits and vegetables:

*Winged beans* from the Philippines are beans with four frilly wings that run the length of the bean. They are used in dishes with other vegetables, chicken, or fish.

*Chayote* (called mirliton in Louisiana and vegetable pears in other places) is from Mexico and Central America. A member of the cucumber family, it is green or white and resembles a gourd. It can be served as a vegetable.

*Jicama* is a brown root vegetable that looks somewhat like an oddly-shaped turnip. Peeling its thick skin reveals white flesh that is sweet. Jicama can be cooked with stir-fry dishes or eaten raw with cheeses or fruits.

*Carambola* ranges in color from yellow to a pinkish orange. This unique fruit is sweet and is added to salads, eaten alone, or served in cold drinks. When sliced, the fruit pieces resemble stars; thus, it is also called star fruit.

How many of these unusual produce items can you identify?

To *broil* raw or cooked vegetables, brush them with fat or oil.

Canned vegetables are cooked during canning and require only heating. Some of the water-soluble nutrients are dissolved into the liquid. The amount of liquid in the can is usually more than is served with the vegetable. You will benefit from all of the dissolved nutrients if you first drain the liquid from the vegetable and heat it in an uncovered pan to evaporate the excess water. When only about one-third of the liquid remains, add the vegetable and heat to serving temperature. In this way, the liquid can be served with the vegetable.

Dried vegetables or legumes such as mature beans and peas require soaking before cooking. They may be covered with boiling water, or they may be boiled for two minutes and allowed to soak for about an hour. They also may be soaked in cold water for several hours. Cook dried vegetables in the liquid which remains after soaking to avoid loss of soluble nutrients. For dehydrated or instant dry vegetables, follow the directions on the package.

### Microwaving Vegetables

Vegetables retain their natural color, flavor, texture, and nutrients with microwave cooking. Even microwave reheating does not detract from these qualities because, unlike conventional cooking, heat comes from within.

Most vegetables can be cooked on a high power setting until they are still firm but not soggy. Little or no water is needed—about 2–3 tablespoons (30–45 mL) for 1 pound (454 g). The water produces steam which helps cook the vegetables evenly. Uniform cooking is also assured by choosing whole or cut vegetables of equal size, and by stirring once or twice during cooking. Standing time may be required. Vegetables with skins should be pierced with a fork to allow steam to escape during cooking, and to prevent bursting.

# Selection, Storage, and Convenience

A large variety of vegetables is available in modern food markets. You as a consumer need to know the signs of quality vegetables, as well as how to store vegetables to preserve their quality.

### Selection and Buying

You may purchase fresh, canned, frozen, and dried or dehydrated vegetables. Which to choose often depends on which will best serve your purpose.

**Fresh Vegetables** You can judge the freshness of a vegetable by its crispness, color, firmness, and soundness, or by the absence of bruises and decay. Fresh vegetables have a characteristic bright color, but are not overripe.

The size of the vegetable does not necessarily influence quality. Small carrots and tomatoes can be as fresh as the larger ones. Fresh vegetables are of the best quality when they are in season. Keep in mind that crispness, firmness, soundness, and bright color are good general clues to help you select good-quality, fresh vegetables.

Canned vegetables such as corn may be used as basic ingredients in soups, chowders, stews, and casseroles.

**Canned Vegetables** The information on the labels of canned vegetables will be your best guide to their quality. Vegetables that have been canned according to United States Government standards may have a grade on the label. The grade may be listed as a letter or a descriptive word. The quality grades of canned vegetables set by the United States Department of Agriculture are Grade A, or Fancy; Grade B, or Extra Standard; Grade C, or Standard; and Grade D, or Substandard.

Canned vegetables usually carry a brand name on the label. A manufacturer may pack several grades of a vegetable and use a different brand name for each to indicate its quality. Your experience with brand labels will be your only clue to the selection of brands which are best for your purposes.

When buying canned vegetables, consider the size of the can that is best suited for your purpose. Of the cans listed, the 303 is the principal can size for vegetables.

| 8 oz (227 g) | #303— 1 lb (454 g) | #2½—29 oz (822 g) |
|---|---|---|
| 1 c (250 mL) | 2 c (500 mL) | 3½ c (875 mL) |
| 2 servings | 4 servings | 7 servings |

**Tips for Herbs and Spices**

Herbs and spices to use on vegetables and in vegetable dishes are: basil, caraway, chives, dill, garlic, ginger, marjoram, nutmeg, oregano, parsley, pepper, poppy seed, rosemary, saffron, sage, tarragon, and thyme.

**Frozen Vegetables** Frozen vegetables may or may not be graded. The information on

## Honeyed Carrots  Yield: 4 servings

| | |
|---|---|
| 1 lb (454 g) fresh carrots | ¾ tsp (3.7 mL) lemon juice |
| 1 Tbs (15 mL) vegetable oil | ¼ tsp (2.5 mL) salt |
| 3 Tbs (45 mL) honey | |

1. Peel carrots; slice crosswise.
2. Cook in a small amount of water for about 15 minutes, or until tender; drain.
3. In a skillet, combine remainder of ingredients; cook until mixture bubbles.
4. Add carrots; cook over low heat until carrots are well coated.

Approximate nutrition information per serving: calories–130; protein–1 g; fat–4 g; cholesterol–0; carbohydrates–25 g; sodium–330 mg.

the labels is your best guide to quality. Purchase only solidly frozen vegetables. Vegetables once thawed deteriorate in quality.

**Dried Vegetables**  Again, the information on the labels is your clue to quality of dried or dehydrated vegetables. It is not only important to select good-quality vegetables, but it is also important to preserve their quality during home storage.

### Care and Storage

You probably will not shop daily for your supply of vegetables; therefore, you will need to store vegetables until they are used. It is important to preserve the quality of a vegetable during storage. With improper storage, there will be loss of flavor, crispness, color, and nutrients. Good vegetable products cannot be prepared from poor quality vegetables. The method for storing will vary with the form of vegetable.

**Fresh Vegetables**  Most fresh vegetables are stored in the refrigerator compartment specially designed for this purpose. Before putting vegetables in the refrigerator, examine them carefully, remove any imperfect leaves, and wash them to remove dirt and spray. When storage space in the vegetable crisper is limited, vegetables should be stored in a plastic bag or a covered container in the refrigerator. Several hours of proper refrigeration can restore crispness in vegetables to be eaten raw.

Tubers and root vegetables such as potatoes, onions, and turnips may be stored in a cool (45–50°F (7–10°C)) dry, dark place. Other root vegetables such as carrots and beets maintain their quality best when they are stored in the refrigerator.

During prolonged and improper storage, vitamin C is lost, and the color, flavor, and texture of the vegetable deteriorates. Most vegetables are at their peak of quality at the time they are harvested.

**Canned Vegetables** Canned vegetables are stored at room temperature or in a cool, dry place. They will keep for a long period, but you should plan to use them within a year. There is some loss of nutrients and quality in canned vegetables when they are stored for a longer period of time.

**Frozen Vegetables** Frozen foods keep best when they are stored at 0°F (−18°C) or below. They should be placed in the freezer or frozen-food compartment immediately and kept there until they are cooked. Any vegetable that has thawed should be used immediately.

**Dried Vegetables** Dried and dehydrated vegetables may be kept at room temperature on shelves. Opened packages should be tightly sealed or the contents transferred to a tightly closed container to prevent bugs or insects from reaching the vegetable.

## Convenience in Vegetables

Canned and dried vegetables have been with us for some time. The frozen, dehydrated, and prepared vegetable products are rather recent developments that contribute to the convenience of vegetable use. Convenience vegetables have been partially or completely prepared. They eliminate the washing, peeling, chopping, cutting, shredding, shelling, straining, and simmering often involved in vegetable preparation. Vegetable convenience items include prewashed vegetables and salad greens, shredded cabbage and tossed salad vegetables, washed and bagged carrots and spinach, and cut vegetables.

A large variety of canned vegetable items is available, but the variety of frozen vegetable products is even larger. You can purchase frozen vegetables, vegetable soups, boil-in-bag vegetables, vegetables in a butter or a special sauce, and prepared gourmet vegetable specialties such as spinach soufflé or artichoke hearts in lemon-butter sauce. Frozen potato products include grated potato patties, precooked french fries, hash brown potatoes ready-to-fry, and baked stuffed potatoes that need only to be heated for a relatively short time.

Dried beans and peas have been favorites for many years. Modern processing has added dehydrated vegetables to the large assortment of canned and frozen products. Dehydrated vegetables are used in dried soup mixes; dried processed potatoes, onions, and parsley are also popular. Dehydrated processed potato products include flaked potatoes, scalloped potatoes, hash browns, and **au gratin** (o GRAH-tin) potatoes, potatoes that have been covered with bread crumbs or grated cheese and then browned.

As with other convenience items with which you are familiar, these require less time and energy, and in many cases cost more than a similar home-prepared product. Again, you become the judge as to how good they are. Do their quality, color, flavor, texture, and nutrient values meet with your standards? How important is the time and energy they save? Would you use the same amount of time and energy by simplifying your menu? These questions are yours to answer in terms of your goals and needs.

### For Review

1. What qualities should you look for when selecting fresh vegetables? When selecting canned vegetables?
2. How should fresh vegetables be stored? What happens if fresh vegetables are not stored properly?
3. What are some advantages of using convenience vegetable items?

# *21* Chapter Review

## Summary

Vegetables are most often an accompaniment to a main dish. They come from plants or the parts of plants that are edible, and they are frequently categorized according to the part of the plant they come from. Today, vegetables are not only available fresh, but they also may be purchased as dried, frozen, canned, or dehydrated as well as in a variety of convenience forms. A rich source of vitamins and minerals, vegetables add color, texture, flavor, and shape to a meal. To properly prepare vegetables, the principles of cookery center around preservation of the color, flavor, texture, and nutrients. The procedures for storing vegetables also are influenced by these same considerations.

## Vocabulary

Match the lettered statements that follow to the numbered vocabulary words below:

1. au gratin
2. cellulose
3. chlorophyll

a. A structure that softens during cooking
b. The green substance that is found in plant cells
c. A carbohydrate that is found in vegetables
d. Vegetables that may be covered with bread crumbs
e. A substance that gives some vegetables their green color
f. A substance that cannot be digested but serves as a natural laxative
g. A vegetable dish that may be covered with grated cheese
h. The substance that is found in the skin and pulp of vegetables
i. A substance that is protected by cooking bright-green vegetables uncovered for the first few minutes

## Chapter Questions

1. Describe and give three examples of vegetables that have a high water content.
2. What are the clues to the nutrient value of a vegetable?
3. Why is it a good rule to select no more than one vegetable from the same group for the same meal?
4. What fresh vegetables do you have in your home? First classify them according to the parts of plants and then classify them according to nutrients.
5. What are the principles or rules for cooking vegetables and with what are they concerned?
6. To reduce the loss of water-soluble vitamins, how can you cook the vegetables?
7. Why is it sometimes necessary to boil vegetables in a large amount of water?
8. How can you avoid overcooking vegetables?

9. When you are heating canned vegetables, how can you prevent the loss of soluble nutrients?

10. What methods would you use to cook each of the following vegetables: a) fresh spinach; b) fresh cabbage; c) frozen corn; and d) canned peas.

11. To purchase canned peas to serve 10 people, how many cans and which size or sizes should you purchase? Why?

12. What are three different categories of foods in which vegetables can be used?

13. Describe the proper storage for fresh celery, canned asparagus, frozen broccoli, dried beans, and dehydrated onions.

14. What kinds of frozen convenience vegetable products do you have in your family's freezer or frozen food compartment? For each item, tell why it can be considered a convenience food.

## Skill Activities

**1. Communication** In your food journal or card file box, make a collection of vegetable recipes. Organize these recipes into the following categories: appetizers, beverages, soups, salads, companion dishes, vegetarian main dishes, casseroles, au gratin dishes, pies, and cream sauces. You can find recipes in books, magazines, newspapers, and on the display boards in supermarkets. Add to this collection whenever you find interesting recipes for vegetables.

**2. Resource management** Using dried beans is an excellent way to provide a nutritious, low-cost meal. Although dried beans are a source of protein, they are not a complete protein. To make the protein complete, you must add at the same meal either a small amount of dairy products, rice or pasta products, or corn. Prepare three different menus for a meal in which beans are the main dish. Be sure that the foods included in the menus provide for complete protein. Include with the menus recipes for the three bean main dishes.

**3. Reading** The following 3 organizations have free pamphlets that provide the history and nutritious benefits of dried beans and ways to prepare them as meals and companion dishes: California Dry Bean Advisory Board, 531-D North Alta, Dinuba, CA 93618; Idaho Bean Commission, P.O. Box 9433, Boise, ID 83707; Rocky Mountain Bean Dealers Association, P.O. Box 8775, Denver, CO 80201. Often their publications are available on the display boards or counters where the products are sold in supermarkets. However, if you are unable to find the pamphlets at the store, write to one or more of these organizations to request copies of their literature. Then prepare a report that includes information about the variety of dried beans, the nutritional value of dried beans, the history of one or more of the beans, and several recipes for serving dried beans as a main dish.

# 22 Soups and Casseroles

## As you read, think about:

- how to identify the uses of soups and casseroles in meals.
- what nutrients soups and casseroles provide for you.
- how to prepare stock-base and milk-base soups.
- how to apply the principles of milk, vegetable, and starch cookery in soup and casserole preparation.
- how to prepare casseroles.

Soups and casseroles are mixtures of similar ingredients. Soup making is an art that began when prehistoric people placed liquid and whatever animal flesh they could find into a kettle and cooked it over an open fire. The first casseroles probably originated when combinations of foods were prepared in a crude earthenware pot, and they have evolved to the packaged one-dish meals found in today's supermarkets.

# Soups

Soups may be rich in meats and hearty with vegetables, noodles, rice, or barley. Soups such as shrimp bisque and vichyssoise may be eaten chilled. Others, such as chili and minestrone, are eaten steaming hot. Soups may begin a meal or may be served as the main dish.

### Kinds of Soup

Most soups fall into two groups: stock and milk. **Stock** is the liquid in which meat, poultry, fish, or vegetables were cooked. The soup made with stock may be clear, such as bouillon and consommé, or it may have vegetables, rice, or noodles added. Chicken noodle and French onion are popular meat-stock soups. Cream of tomato, New England clam chowder, and oyster stew are popular milk-base soups.

**Stock Soups** You can make flavorful soup stock from less tender meats, such as the leg and neck sections. Bones and meat from beef and chicken are most commonly used for stock. Veal lacks flavor and is usually combined with other meats. Lamb and fish stocks have distinct flavors and are used only when these flavors are wanted. The meat used for light stock is not browned; it is browned to make brown stock.

When bones and meat trimmings are simmered, the flavorings are extracted into the cooking liquid and stock is produced. The stock may be strained and **clarified** (cleared to remove any solid materials). The clarified broth is known as **bouillon** (BOOL-yon) or **consommé** (kon-suh-MAY). Bouillon is made from meat broth, while consommé is made from meat and vegetables.

The broth or soup in which meats were cooked will gel when cooled. Some of the protein in connective tissues of less tender meats can be converted to gelatin when cooked in moist heat. Meat stock will contain some of this gelatin and will tend to gel when cooled. Concentrated meat broths from beef and chicken are used to form a jellied soup which is served as an appetizer.

**Milk Soups** Cream soups are popular milk-base soups. First, a cream sauce is made

Soups such as consommés were once the starting point for an elegant dinner and were often served from sterling silver tureens. Today, hearty soups and casseroles can be the main course of a meal.

from milk thickened with flour. Vegetables or seafoods are then **puréed** (pyoo-RAYD), forced through a strainer to separate the pulp and juices, and added to the cream sauce to form a cream soup. A **bisque** (BISK), made from thickened milk and pieces of seafood, is a popular cream soup.

**Chowder** and stew are soups made with unthickened milk. Fish, meat, or vegetables in small pieces are added. Some chowders, however, do not use milk; instead they are made with tomato and water. Stews and chowders are similar, except stews have fewer ingredients combined in the milk than chowders.

### Nutrient Contributions

The nutrient values of soups are determined by the foods used to make the soup. Clear soups or broths will contain only dissolved flavoring substances or extractions from the meat; they have little nutrient value. Such soups are valued for their flavor and are used as appetizers. You can increase the nutrient value of a broth by adding vegetables, meats, or noodles. The vegetables would provide vitamins; the meat, protein; and the noodles, carbohydrates. Hearty soups are made from stock to which other foods have been added.

Milk-base soups contribute the nutrients found in milk. The calcium, vitamins, and protein of milk make these soups nutritious. You may get part of your daily milk requirement from the milk in cream soups. The vegetables and seafoods used in milk- and cream-type soups will contribute important nutrients. You will need to know the ingredients or foods used to make the soup before you can judge the nutrients contributed. Soups can be made easily when you follow the principles of soup making.

### Soup Preparation

The foods which you have prepared up to now were treated so that the flavors and nutri-ents remained within the food. When making soup, you will want the food flavors and nutrients to dissolve into the soup.

**Stock-base Soups** Good stock is important to soup making. Meats and vegetables are cut into small pieces for soup, and bones are broken or cracked so that a large surface area of the food comes in contact with the water. The nutrients and flavorings will dissolve in the cooking liquid, giving you a flavorful and nutritious soup. You must protect the dissolved nutrients by allowing the water to simmer but not boil. Here is how to make good soup stock.

1. Use bones and less tender meats from the leg (shin), neck, or oxtail. One-third bone to about two-thirds meat is a good proportion for soup. Crack the bone, and cut any meat and vegetables used. The meat may be browned for brown stock.
2. Use a large kettle with a tight-fitting lid. Add water to cover the meat.
3. Use a long, slow cooking process to extract the flavors. The water should simmer, but it should not boil.

After the simmering is completed, the soup is strained to separate the broth from the solid materials and is stored in the refrigerator in a covered container. The layer of fat which collects on the top may be removed before the soup is used.

### Tips for Herbs and Spices

Herbs and spices to use in soups and casseroles are: allspice, basil, bay leaves, caraway, chives, cinnamon, cloves, cumin, curry powder, dill, garlic, ginger, marjoram, nutmeg, oregano, parsley, pepper, rosemary, saffron, sage, tarragon, thyme, and turmeric.

If you wish to clarify the broth, add a slightly beaten egg white to the broth after it is heated to a boil. The egg protein will coagulate in the hot broth and trap any solid particles. The broth is strained to remove the coagulated egg.

Meat left from making soup is nutritious. It may be cut and served in the soup or used in other dishes calling for cooked meat.

**Milk-base Soups** The milk-base soups may or may not be thickened. Cream soups are made with thickened milk, while chowders or stews call for unthickened milk. The chief ingredients of milk-base soups are milk, other foods such as vegetables or seafoods, and, at times, a thickener such as flour.

The principles of milk, vegetable, and starch cookery apply to cream soups. Remember that: (1) milk requires a low temperature to prevent scorching; (2) vegetables should be cooked in small amounts of water until fork tender to protect their nutrients; and (3) starch grains need to be separated with cold liquid or melted fat to prevent lumping.

The white sauce, which is made with milk, flour, fat, and salt, will determine the quality of a cream soup.

1. Melt the fat over low heat. Butter and margarine are most often used because their flavor is preferred.
2. Next, blend the flour with the melted fat to prevent lumping. Cook the mixture over low heat until bubbly to prevent a raw-starch flavor.

Leftover meat and vegetables are sometimes used to make a flavorful soup stock. They are cut into small pieces and simmered.

# Egg-drop Soup    Yield: 4-6 servings

5 c (1 L + 250 mL) chicken broth    1 tsp (5 mL) sugar
¾ c (185 mL) sliced celery    1 Tbs (15 mL) soy sauce
¼ c (60 mL) chopped onion    ¼ c (60 mL) cold water
½ tsp (2.5 mL) salt    2 Tbs (30 mL) cornstarch
¼ tsp (1.2 mL) pepper    2 eggs

1. Simmer the broth, celery, onion, salt, pepper, sugar, and soy sauce together in a large saucepan or kettle for 15 minutes.
2. Mix together the water and cornstarch; stir the mixture into the soup. Stir and cook until thickened.
3. Beat the eggs slightly and pour into the hot soup while stirring rapidly.

Approximate nutrition information per serving: calories–55; protein–5 g; fat–2 g; cholesterol–60 mg; carbohydrates–4 g; sodium–800 mg.

3. Remove the cooked fat and flour mixture from the range so that the milk can be quickly and easily blended.
4. Finally, cook the milk mixture over low heat with constant stirring until it reaches a boil and is thickened.

**Microwaving Soups**   Soup is a good candidate for the microwave because flavors and seasonings are absorbed more rapidly than with conventional cooking methods. Be sure to cut vegetables into uniform pieces. Soups taste fresher and can be cooked right in the serving bowl to save on clean-up. Cooking times will vary with the density of the soup and with the starting temperature of the liquid. The colder the soup, the longer it will take to cook or reheat. Soups should be covered and stirred several times during cooking.

## Tips for Microwaving Soups

- Milk-base soups will boil over quickly. Fill the heating container for these soups only two-thirds full.
- To adapt conventional recipes to the microwave, count on one-quarter of the cooking time.
- For quick sauces for meat, heat canned convenience soups without diluting. Do not heat the soup in the can, but in nonmetal containers.

# Fortifying Your Soups

Soups do not have to be plain or dull, and they can be a convenient way to use up bits and pieces of vegetables and meat. By improving the nutritional value of homemade and convenience soups, you can also improve the flavor and create some combinations of your own.

*Add barley to beef soups.* This classic combination turns a mere soup into a hearty meal. The barley and beef are complementary proteins. Fiber-rich barley aids your digestion and makes you feel full. It also provides niacin, thiamin, and potassium. Recent evidence suggests that it lowers cholesterol levels.

*Add some oranges to bean soup.* Some amino acids from plant proteins can be absorbed only in the presence of vitamin C. Oranges added to black-bean soup add nutritional value and flavor. You reap the added benefit of resupplying your body with vitamin C.

*Add fresh garlic cloves to any broth.* Whole garlic cloves impart a mild taste to soups. For centuries, people have praised garlic as a medicine. Recent scientific evidence upholds a few of these ancient beliefs. Garlic may lower choles-

Soups can be fortified with potatoes, tofu, and barley.

terol levels and also prevent cholesterol levels from rising after fatty foods are eaten. Recent scientific evidence seems to indicate that garlic prevents blood cells from clumping. It may also stimulate the body's immune system to fight infectious diseases. The Japanese agency that regulates food and drugs recognizes garlic as a treatment for high blood pressure. Garlic is low in sodium, and it serves as a good alternative to salt.

*Add fresh potatoes to cream soups.* Potatoes are a nutritious source of carbohydrates. Contrary to popular belief, they are not fattening. One medium-sized potato contributes about 100 calories. (The toppings put on potatoes—sour cream, butter, and cheese—are fattening.)

*Include tofu in clear broths.* The Chinese and Japanese include tofu in many of their soups. Tofu is a rich source of protein and a good source of B vitamins, vitamin E, iron, and potassium.

*Add pasta.* Adding pasta can turn a light soup into a satisfying meal. Pasta made from durum wheat is especially nutritious, containing more protein and vitamins than regular pasta.

*Add mustard greens.* This relative of the cabbage is rich in vitamin A, supplies good amounts of vitamin C, potassium, and calcium, and contains fair amounts of protein and iron —quite a few nutrients for so few calories. Mustard greens, like cabbage, seem to have cancer-preventing characteristics when eaten in sufficient quantities.

*Skim off excess fat.* When your soup is cooked, let it cool to room temperature. Skim off the fat that rises to the top.

After you have reheated your fat-less soup, ladle it into bowls and sprinkle fresh parsley on it. Parsley is a rich source of vitamins A and C, potassium, and iron, and it contains some protein. Parsley is also a natural breath freshener.

## Uses of Soups

Soups can serve a double purpose. Their flavor and aroma will stimulate your appetite; the variety of foods from which they are made will provide wholesome nourishment. In your meals, you may use soups as an appetizer. At other times, you may use them as the main part of a meal.

Thin, clear soups are used as appetizers and are a good way to begin a meal. Their purpose is to stimulate the appetite for the meal that follows. Stock soups such as broth, bouillon, consommé, or jellied soups are popular appetizers. A hearty stock soup with vegetables, meat, or cereal products such as rice or noodles is used as a main dish. Chowders, stews, and cream soups can be a meal in themselves.

Select a soup appropriate for the rest of your meal. If your meal is rich and heavy, select a thin, clear soup that will rouse your appetite. When you use the soup as a meal in itself or when the foods to follow are light, choose a rich and hearty soup. For soup at its best, serve hot soups very hot, and cold soups very cold.

Cream soups and white sauces are often used as an ingredient in casseroles, creamed foods, croquettes, and scalloped dishes. Clear stock soups can be used as the liquid for a gravy or a casserole.

Soups are served with crackers, **croutons** (toasted bread cubes), bread sticks, or melba

Fruit soups, which are usually tangy and refreshing, are most often served as appetizers, especially during hot weather.

toast. You can add eye appeal and a decorative touch to soups with garnishes such as grated cheese; chopped hard-cooked egg; thinly sliced olives, lemon, or radishes; and crisp bacon curls. Soup as an appetizer or a main dish can make a meal more attractive and enjoyable; as an ingredient, it contributes to the convenience of meal preparation.

## Convenience in Soups

Most canned soups are condensed, which means that part of the water has been removed. You need only to add water and then heat to serving temperature. Some canned soups are not condensed and require no added water; they need only to be heated for serving. The label will indicate the type of soup in the can. Many varieties of canned stock- or milk-base soups are available.

Dehydrated soups are a dry powderlike mixture that remains after all of the water is removed. They are quickly reconstituted with the addition of water or milk. They are then heated to blend the flavors. Both stock-base and milk-base soups keep well on the shelf in their original containers. The instant, dry soup mix may be added as a seasoning to gravies, sauces, vegetables, and meat dishes.

Meat extracts compressed into cubes (bouillon cubes) are another type of dehydrated soup. These cubes come in flavors such as chicken or beef, and they easily dissolve in water to make a broth. In addition to their use as a broth, bouillon cubes can be used as a base for a hearty soup or to add flavor to sauces, gravies, casseroles, and even other soups.

Soup-making convenience is also available if you wish to make homemade soups. Ready-to-use fresh soup vegetables may be purchased in transparent bags. They will save you preparation time and the trouble of buying several different vegetables.

Homemade soups require long, slow cooking and constant supervision. The convenience item can save time and be prepared with a minimum of supervision. You will need to read labels carefully so that you purchase the kind of soup best suited for your purpose. However, a well-prepared homemade soup can have far better flavor and higher nutrient values than the convenience item.

Convenience soups may be used as an ingredient in the preparation of other foods. Condensed soups may be used in sauces, casseroles, or gravies. Undiluted condensed cream soups can replace a cream sauce or a white sauce in a recipe. Canned and convenience soup items can be blended, mixed, or matched to provide a variety of new flavor combinations and a variety of new uses.

---

### Practical Tip

- If a soup or casserole tastes too salty, cook a raw potato in it for several minutes. If it tastes too sweet, add 1 teaspoon (5 mL) cider vinegar.

---

### For Review

1. What is stock and how is it used?
2. How are cream soups made?
3. What determines the nutrient values of vegetable-beef soup? Of cream of tomato soup?
4. Why is it important *not* to boil soup stock?
5. What is the difference between cream soups and chowders?
6. Explain some of the uses of soups.
7. What are the advantages of using convenience forms of soup?

Casseroles can be made from a variety of fresh and leftover foods combined into a tasty meal. Since they can be prepared well in advance, they are a convenient way to serve a complete meal.

# Casseroles

A **casserole** is a baked main dish made with a sauce and a combination of foods. The types of ingredients used to prepare casseroles are similar to those used for soups. However, soups are thinner mixtures than casseroles. Soups often require a relatively long period of range-top cooking, while casseroles are baked.

## Casserole Preparation

You can prepare casseroles from a variety of ingredients such as cereal grains, pastas, meat, poultry, fish, cheese, legumes, and vegetables. A sauce is used to blend flavors. Casseroles can be prepared from cooked, raw, or leftover foods. Rice and pastas are usually cooked before they are combined with other ingredients. The ingredients may be blended together or placed in alternate layers in a baking dish. You can add appropriate herbs and spices to enhance flavor.

When milk is prepared into a white sauce before it is combined with other ingredients for a casserole, you will have a smoother and creamier dish. The starch in the white sauce helps to stabilize the proteins in the milk so that they are less likely to curdle when heated.

## Tips for Microwaving Casseroles

- When heating casseroles, cover them to retain moisture.
- If the casserole cannot be stirred during cooking, rotate the dish one-half turn several times during cooking, and increase standing time, covered, after cooking.
- Cook fresh ground beef for casseroles on HIGH in a colander over a plastic bowl until the pink color is almost gone. If the beef is frozen, thaw on DEFROST or by the cook/rest method for 6–7 minutes per pound. Allow 6–7 minutes of standing time for ground beef.

You may prepare casseroles ahead of time and store them in the refrigerator or freezer until they should be baked. Frozen casseroles prepared with starch-thickened sauce become watery when thawed. Commercially canned sauces and soups contain starches that tolerate freezing and can be used in casseroles to be frozen. For an evenly cooked product, frozen casseroles should be thawed in the refrigerator prior to baking.

As with soups, the nutrient content of casseroles is determined by the ingredients used. Unnecessary calories can be eliminated if you remove the fat from meat or stock and if you replace cream products with nonfat milk. Undiluted canned condensed cream soups can replace cream sauces in many quick casseroles, but they contain more calories than home-prepared cream sauces made with nonfat milk and with little or no added fat. You may need to consider the caloric contribution of condensed soups and high-fat cream sauces when you desire to control or reduce the caloric content of casseroles.

## Microwaving Casseroles

Casseroles are usually a product of complementary cooking; that is, they combine the use of the conventional oven and the microwave oven. They are ideal candidates for do-ahead meal planning, and thus are generally either reheated from the refrigerator or defrosted and reheated straight from the freezer. For a 2-quart (1.9L) frozen casserole, use the DEFROST cycle for about 15 minutes. Stir and use the COOK cycle for about 15 minutes, stirring several times during cooking.

Remember that microwaves heat the outer edges of the food first. Therefore, standing time is necessary because the conduction of heat to the colder center continues even after the power is turned off. You can test the center of casseroles with a microwave thermometer, or you can use a conventional thermometer after the microwave cooking is completed. The optimum temperature, which indicates that the casserole is heated through, is 150° F (65° C).

When preparing casseroles, use uniformly sized slices or pieces of meat. If ingredients are not evenly sized, stir more frequently. Casseroles containing either eggs or large pieces of meat should be reheated on a lower power setting to avoid overcooking.

### For Review

1. What are some differences between soups and casseroles?
2. How do you prevent a curdled sauce in a casserole?
3. How can you control the calories in a casserole?
4. What are two guidelines to follow when microwaving casseroles?

# 22 Chapter Review

## Summary

Soups and casseroles can be prepared easily by using raw, cooked, or leftover foods and by following a few standard cookery procedures. Although soups are served as appetizers or main dishes, casseroles are most often served as entrées. Of course, as with other foods that are a mixture of ingredients, the nutritional values and calories of soups and casseroles are determined by the ingredients that have been added.

## Vocabulary

Use the words below to fill in the blanks in the paragraphs that follow:

bisque          consommé
bouillon        croutons
chowder         puréed
clarified       stock

As an appetizer or main dish, soups are frequently served with crackers, melba toast, bread sticks, or toasted bread cubes, called __(1)__. Most soups are classified into two categories. One kind of soup, known as __(2)__, is made from a liquid in which meat, poultry, fish, or vegetables are cooked. When the liquid in which meat has cooked is strained, the resulting broth is called __(3)__. The term used to refer to the strained broth made from meat and vegetables is __(4)__. Many soups are made from this __(5)__ broth, which has been cleared by removing the solid materials. The other common kind of soup has a milk-base. A __(6)__ is a milk-base soup that is made with unthickened milk and small pieces of fish, meat, or vegetables. Some milk-base soups are made with a thickened cream sauce. A popular cream soup that is made from thickened milk and small pieces of seafood is a __(7)__. When vegetables are added to a cream soup, they are usually __(8)__ by being forced through a strainer to separate the pulp from the juices.

## Chapter Questions

1. In addition to cream of tomato, New England clam chowder, and oyster stew, what are three other kinds of milk-base soups?
2. How can you increase the nutritional values of clear soups?
3. What procedure is used to prepare stock?
4. How do you prepare your favorite soup, and what nutrients does it contribute?
5. What procedure should you use to clarify broth?
6. When you are making cream soups, what are three rules you should follow?
7. Why is it important to cut vegetables in uniform pieces when the soup is going to be microwaved?
8. What kind of container is best to use for microwaving soups?
9. What is the name and what is the base of a soup you would recommend serving as an appetizer for a roast beef dinner?
10. How can soups be used as ingredients to make other foods?

11. What is your favorite casserole, how do you prepare it, and what nutrients does it contribute?
12. What procedures should be used to store casseroles?
13. What cookery techniques should you follow to microwave casseroles and why?

## Skill Activities

**1. Communication** In your food journal or on separate sheets of paper, record the soups and casseroles that you eat during a week. Make four columns and label them as follows: "Kind of soup or casserole," "Major ingredients," "Food groups," and "Nutrients." Now write the day, and then enter the appropriate information in each column. When you finish the chart, look at what you ate, and ask yourself these questions: What were the major ingredients in the soups? Were the same major ingredients used in more than one soup? What were the major ingredients in the casseroles? Were the same major ingredients used in more than one casserole? Which food groups were most often represented by the casseroles and soups? Which nutrients did the soups and casseroles usually provide?

**2. Decision making** In your food journal or card file box, add to the casserole and soup recipes you already have. Look for casserole, meat, vegetables, and gravy recipes that use a convenience soup or sauce as a base or for seasoning. Also, make a collection of soup recipes that have a fruit juice base. You can find recipes in books, magazines, and newspapers.

**3. Human relations** With your classmates, make a chart of the different kinds of pasta that can be used in casseroles. First, write the name of the pasta, make a drawing to show what the pasta looks like or glue an example of it beside the name, and then write how it is used or the kinds of casseroles in which it is usually used.

**4. Decision making** Visit the frozen foods aisle of a supermarket, and find the kinds of convenience casseroles that are available. On a lined sheet of paper, make six columns, and write one of these headings in each column: "Name of casserole," "Price," "Cooking methods," "Number of servings," "Calories for one serving," and "RDA percentage of protein for one serving." Under the heading in each column, write the appropriate information. Use the material on your chart to answer these questions: How many of the convenience foods give directions for microwave oven use? How are the microwave oven procedures similar on the different products? Select two convenience casseroles and determine the cost per serving. Which casserole costs the most per serving? Which casserole has the most calories per serving? Which casserole has the fewest calories per serving? Which casserole provides the highest RDA percentage of protein?

# 23 Salads

## As you read, think about:

- how to select appropriate salads for a variety of uses.
- what nutrients salads provide for you.

- how to prepare a variety of salads.

- how to identify, select, store, and use salad vegetables.
- how to prepare different kinds of salad dressings.

**Vocabulary**
accompaniment
marinade
mayonnaise

Our word *salad* comes from the Latin *sāl*, meaning "salt." The Romans, who are credited with inventing the salad, served greens with only a simple salt dressing. Later, the Italians and Greeks mixed greens with oils and herbs, and this custom spread to Spain and France. The French and Spanish introduced salad to America. The merits of salads were recognized by German doctors who in 1758 prescribed salads for curing illness. In America, salads have gradually gained popularity and have developed into many specialty items. There are salads for every occasion.

Salads, which have been served for centuries, can be a light, nutrient-rich alternative to heavier foods.

## Types of Salads

The salads of the Greeks and Romans were made from leafy green vegetables, similar to our lettuce or cabbage salads. You may also make salads from leafy greens and seasonings. At times, however, you might use the leafy greens as a base upon which to arrange other foods, such as fruits or vegetables. The body of a salad is the food or food combination placed on top of the leafy greens, making up the largest part of the salad. To give additional flavor, you may add a salad dressing. Salads consist of three parts: base, body, and dressing.

Many different greens may be used for the *base.* Lettuce is most often used, but you can use endive, escarole, or watercress. The *body* can be made of fruits, vegetables, meats, fish, poultry, cheese, eggs, and macaroni. The *dressing* may be French, mayonnaise, or cooked dressing.

Salads are made from many different foods, and they can be grouped according to the way they are used—as accompaniments, main dishes, appetizers, desserts, and garnishes.

### Accompaniment Salads

Salads are most frequently used as an **accompaniment,** a food that completes and is served with a main dish such as meat, poultry, fish, or a casserole. Accompaniment salads are light, small salads that stimulate the appetite. Salad greens, tart fruits, and combinations of raw vegetables as a tossed salad are examples.

You may prefer to use raw fruits and vegetables in your salads because of their crisp texture. However, cooked or canned fruits and vegetables offer variety and make suitable accompaniment salads. Gelatin made with fruits or vegetables is another possibility.

### Main-dish Salads

The hearty salads are used as the main dish of a lunch or a dinner. They are usually made from protein foods such as cooked or canned meat, poultry, fish, eggs, or cheese. Cottage, feta, Cheddar, Parmesan, and Swiss cheeses are popular for salads. Hearty salads can also be made with kidney beans, potatoes, macaroni, rice, or other grains.

The freshest fruits and vegetables not only taste the best in a salad, but they are also the most nutritious. Made with slices of cheese and served with bread, a tossed salad can become a main dish.

Main-dish salads are made from protein foods such as shellfish, shown in this shrimp salad. Served during warm weather, main-dish salads make a light, refreshing meal.

Like all appetizers, appetizer salads should complement the main course by being light when a heavy meal is planned.

A less hearty salad, such as tossed salad, can be served as a main dish if thin slices of meat, poultry, or cheese are added. These foods will make your salad substantial and satisfying. Main-dish salads are, as a rule, larger in size than accompaniment salads.

## Appetizer Salads

Appetizer salads are served at the beginning of a meal. Their purpose is to stimulate the appetite. They are light, small salads. You may use tart fruit, salad greens, and seafoods with a tangy sauce for appetizer salads.

## Dessert Salads

Dessert salads are a colorful and attractive ending for meals. Fruits, gelatin, and frozen salads are suitable desserts. Canned, frozen, or fresh fruit attractively arranged and framed by crisp greens can be a picture-pretty dessert. Gelatin and frozen salads with a base of whipped cream make an elaborate dessert salad. Dessert

Colorful fruit salads make eye-pleasing desserts. When served with whipped cream or sherbet, these sometimes-tart salads can be made sweet.

Main dishes also benefit from being attractively garnished. What contrasts to the ham do these garnishes provide?

salads are sweet rather than tart so that they satisfy the appetite.

## Garnish Salads

Small colorful salads are used as a garnish for a meat or a main dish. They add attractiveness or eye appeal to meals. Vegetables in interesting shapes such as wedges, rings, curls, and strips are used as garnishes. Small servings of fresh fruits, spiced or pickled fruits, and vegetables add variety.

### For Review

1. List and describe the parts of a salad.
2. What is the purpose of an accompaniment salad?
3. Describe main-dish salads.

## Waldorf Salad    Yield: 4 servings

2 medium apples
¾ c (185 mL) diced celery
¼ c (60 mL) coarsely
  chopped walnuts

3 Tbs (45 mL) cooked
  salad dressing or
  mayonnaise
4 lettuce cups

1. Wash, quarter, core (do not pare), and cut apples into bite-size cubes.
2. Cut up the celery, and chop the nuts.
3. Place all ingredients, including salad dressing, into salad bowl; toss gently with a fork.
4. Arrange on lettuce cups.

Approximate nutrition information per serving: calories–195; protein–4 g; fat–13 g; cholesterol–10 mg; carbohydrates–16 g; sodium–90 mg.

## Nutrient Contributions

The nutrients contributed by salads are determined by the foods used to make them. The fresh fruits and vegetables are important sources of vitamins, minerals, and cellulose. The dark leafy greens are especially helpful in meeting your needs for iron and vitamins A and C. When you make whole salads from greens, the salad can be counted as one serving of a leafy vegetable. The green leaf that you use as a base for a salad is too small to be counted as one serving of a leafy green.

Other foods used in salads include meat, fish, poultry, cheese, and egg. These foods are rich sources of complete proteins. Nuts and mature beans contribute incomplete proteins and add to your protein needs.

When compared with other foods, the caloric value of salads, in general, is low. The starchy vegetables such as potato and mature beans, and cereal products such as macaroni are higher in caloric values than are fruit and juicy vegetables. Both potato and macaroni salads will contain starch and contribute to your energy needs.

### Practical Tip

- To crisp fresh spinach and lettuce leaves, put them on a clean towel, roll it up, and refrigerate.

The type and quantity of salad dressing will also influence the caloric value of your salads. The fat or the cream in the salad dressing is rich in calories. Some dressings, such as cooked salad dressings, contain very little fat and are lower in calories than mayonnaise, which contains more fat. You will find the nutrient values of other foods used in salads in the food nutrient chart on pages 50 and 51.

### For Review

1. Describe a salad that helps meet your needs for iron and vitamins A and C.
2. Describe a high-protein salad.
3. Describe a high-calorie salad. A low-calorie salad.

# An American Specialty

The immigration of people from many countries to the United States has made American cuisine unique. With each new group of immigrants come new foods and new cooking techniques. Aspects of many cultures' tastes are incorporated into American cooking, creating new versions of old dishes. American salads perhaps best reflect the joining of cultures.

Americans enjoy a reputation as innovative salad makers. With increasing concern about the fat-heavy, fiber-poor American diet, salads have become more popular meals. With a rich ethnic heritage to draw from, American salad makers have adopted salads from many cultures, and have adapted the spices and food ingredients from other dishes to create new salads.

Chicken salad with ginger dressing is influenced by Chinese spices. Cooked chicken is served with lettuce and water chestnuts. The dressing is made from oil and vinegar spiced with fresh ginger.

Baba ghanouj comes from the Middle East and the Mediterranean. It is made of eggplant covered with tahini, a paste made from sesame and lemon juice.

A Mexican salad combines lettuce with pieces of tortillas, cheese, onion, and tomato. The salad can be dressed with sour cream, and garnished with hot peppers.

Many potato salads have been developed. An Italian potato salad combines potatoes, zucchini, carrots, lettuce, and beans dressed with garlic, oil, and vinegar. Several German-influenced potato salads include potatoes and onions with a vinegar and mustard dressing.

Curry spices from India can be used to spice up chicken salads or fish salads. Raisins, nuts, and apples can be added for an unusual taste.

Americans have adopted Greek salads wholeheartedly. The main ingredients include feta cheese, greens, olives, and tomatoes. Many Americans also now make tabouleh, a salad made from bulgar wheat, tomatoes, mint, lemon juice, olive oil, and water.

These are just a few samples of the salads prepared by American cooks. Salads can be a good source of many nutrients. However, make sure that ingredients are fresh whenever possible and be creative—salads with international ingredients are an American specialty.

Potatoes provide a versatile starting point for a variety of salads.

Pieces of cubed chicken can be artistically arranged with fruits and vegetables to create a pleasant contrast in color, texture, form, and shape.

Fresh fruits and vegetables are crisp, have a bright color, and a pleasing flavor. When freshness is lost, they become limp, dull in color, and may become tasteless. You will best protect the freshness of fruits and vegetables by storing them in the covered vegetable compartment of the refrigerator. Salad greens begin to wilt, or lose their crispness, soon after the dressing is added. This is because dressing tends to draw out the juices from the fruits and vegetables. For this reason, you usually add the dressing just before serving the salad. However, the flavor of a few salads, such as potato, meat, or fish salads, will improve if mixed with salad dressing an hour before serving. The salad dressing then serves as a **marinade,** a liquid into which foods are placed to enhance flavor and, often, to tenderize. For gelatin and fruit salads, it is better to pass the dressing at the table so that individuals can help themselves.

### Protecting Salad Nutrients

You can protect the nutrient values of salads through proper storage, preparation, and use. Salad materials, especially salad greens, are perishable and should be used soon after purchase. Some nutrients are lost during storage. When cut surfaces of fruits and vegetables are exposed to air for long periods, there is some loss of vitamin C. Cut fruits and vegetables prepared in advance will retain their nutrients better when stored in a covered container. Vegetables that have wilted have smaller amounts of vitamins than fresh vegetables.

### Protecting Salad Attractiveness

The bright color and crispness of fresh fruits and vegetables contribute to the attractiveness of salads, but you can enhance the beauty of these foods by arranging them attractively to form the salad. You become the artist when you make the best possible use of the natural color and shape of the vegetable, fruit,

# Principles of Salad Making

The principles of salad preparation are designed to help you protect the freshness, the nutrient values, the colorfulness, and the attractiveness of salads.

### Protecting Salad Freshness

The freshness of fruits and vegetables will influence the texture, color, and flavor of salads.

and other salad foods. You can create pleasing salad combinations when you include contrasts in color, texture, form, and shape. The color combination within a salad should be chosen with the same care that you select the colors for your clothes.

Salad ingredients may be cut to a size convenient for eating, but not so small that they cannot be distinguished. Salad materials should be arranged simply. Avoid the fixed look. Simple and natural arrangements are the most attractive and are difficult to improve. You should use a large enough plate so the salad does not extend over the edge. The salad should be framed by the plate.

You will be able to create more attractive salads when all salad materials are well drained. Excessive moisture on salad ingredients will dilute the salad dressing and cause an unattractive watery appearance. For a pleasing blend of flavors, use strong-flavored foods in small amounts. Protect the beauty of your salad by handling the ingredients gently to avoid bruising. Use citrus fruit juices such as lemon juice to prevent the browning of cut fresh fruits such as bananas and apples. Remember, a clean, crisp, cool salad is an attractive salad and is a salad at its best. Well-chosen ingredients become your first step toward making fresh, nutritious, and attractive salads.

## For Review

1. For what types of salads should you add the dressing just before serving? Why?
2. Why is a salad dressing sometimes used as a marinade?
3. Why should cut salad ingredients be stored in covered containers?
4. What are some things you can do to create an attractive salad?

## Tips for Herbs and Spices

Herbs and spices to use on salads and in salad dressings are: allspice, basil, caraway, chives, cinnamon, cloves, curry powder, dill, garlic, ginger, marjoram, oregano, parsley, pepper, poppy seed, rosemary, saffron, sage, tarragon, thyme, and turmeric.

# Selecting and Storing Salad Vegetables

A salad can be only as good as the materials from which it is made. When you shop for salad vegetables, be careful to select only top-quality vegetables that are sound, crisp, and firm. Poor-quality vegetables have lost their crispness, much of their flavor, and most of their nutrient values.

Salad greens are very perishable. Buy them only in quantities that you can use while they are fresh. Many salad greens are prepackaged in transparent wraps. Examine the package carefully, and make sure that you can see the quality of the vegetable. All leafy greens should be crisp and should have a bright-green, rather than a yellow, color.

After you have purchased high-quality, fresh salad vegetables and greens, be sure to preserve their quality by proper storage. The soil in which greens are grown may cling to the leaves and stems. First wash the greens in cold water to remove the soil. Then drain them thoroughly on paper toweling, and place them in a vegetable crisper, a lettuce keeper, or in a transparent bag for storage in the refrigerator. All washed vegetables should be well drained before they are stored in order to avoid spoilage by excess water. Be careful to handle greens and all other vegetables gently to avoid bruising them.

# Salad Dressings

The three basic types of salad dressings are French, mayonnaise, and cooked. The kind of salad dressing you use with a salad is your personal preference. However, some salad dressings seem to blend well with certain kinds of salad materials. Some popular salad and dressing combinations are French dressing with tossed salad, mayonnaise with potato or macaroni salad, and cooked dressing with fruit salad. Any one of these three basic dressings is suitable for most salads.

## French Dressing

French dressing can be made easily at home. You need only to blend the proper proportion of vinegar, salad oil, and seasonings to make a French dressing. You may include the seasonings of your preference when you make French dressing. Homemade French dressing will separate on standing. Blend the ingredients by shaking the dressing before it is used on salads.

## Mayonnaise

**Mayonnaise** is an uncooked dressing prepared from vinegar, salad oil, seasonings, and egg yolk. The yolk will help to form a permanent emulsion (see page 346) so that the dressing will not separate on standing. To make mayonnaise, beat the yolk, seasonings, and vinegar until they are blended. Continue beating as the oil is added very slowly, at first, drop by drop. As the mixture thickens, slowly increase the amount of oil and continue beating until all of the oil is added and the mayonnaise is thick and smooth.

Many salad dressings are easily made at home. Using a variety of them keeps salad an interesting part of a meal.

1. Blend the yolk, seasonings, and vinegar.

2. Add the oil, drop by drop.

3. Beat until all the oil has been added.

4. The mayonnaise will be thick and smooth.

Preparing Mayonnaise

A salad can be made totally from home-prepared ingredients or from a combination of home-prepared and convenience items. The same is true of the salad dressing that will be added.

## Cooked Salad Dressing

Cooked salad dressing resembles mayonnaise. It is thickened with flour or starch, and usually does not contain large amounts of either oil or fat.

1. The flour and seasonings are combined by blending.
2. The egg yolk and milk or water are blended in. Then the vinegar is stirred in gradually.
3. The mixture is cooked slowly over very low heat with constant stirring until it becomes thickened.

Other ingredients may be added to the basic salad dressings to increase variety. For example, chili sauce, catsup, or Roquefort cheese may be added to French dressing; mayonnaise may be blended with relish, horseradish, peanut butter, or tomato paste; cooked dressing may be combined with cream, fruit juice, or crushed fruit such as pineapple. The flavor of the ingredients added to the basic dressing should harmonize with the flavor of the salad. All salad dressings should be stored in a covered container in the refrigerator to keep them fresh and to keep the refrigerator free of odor.

## For Review

1. How does French dressing differ from mayonnaise?
2. How does mayonnaise differ from cooked salad dressing?

# Convenience in Salad Making

Many prepared basic salad dressings and dressings containing special flavors can be purchased ready-to-use. The label on the container will list the ingredients included and is a useful guide for selecting the salad dressing you wish. A mayonnaise dressing is labeled "mayonnaise" to distinguish it from one labeled "salad dressing," a cooked dressing.

If you wish to have only a part in preparing salad dressing, packaged salad dressing mixes are available. The mix usually contains a blend of herbs and seasonings which you combine with oil and vinegar. The prepared mixes permit you to enjoy the flavors of herbs and seasonings which you may not use often and do not wish to purchase individually.

Salad-making convenience items include more than salad dressing. Washed salad greens and shredded cabbage can be purchased in transparent packages. In some food specialty stores, you may purchase prepared salads such as gelatin, macaroni, potato, or fish. These salads need only to be served on a base of salad greens to be ready for use on the table.

The newest of convenience salad items are the freeze-dried salad mixes. These were first developed for use on space flights and are now becoming available to the food-service industry. The ready-made salad mixes require only the addition of water. They are complete salads; the ingredients and dressing are all-in-one. The freeze-dried salad mixes include ham, tuna, seafood, and egg. These salad mixes keep well and do not require refrigeration until after the salads have been prepared for serving.

The prepared salad mixes and other salad convenience items can be kept on hand to meet emergencies or unexpected company. You will need to read labels carefully so that you can select the salad products which will best serve your purpose.

## For Review

1. What is an advantage of using a packaged salad dressing mix?
2. What are two advantages of using freeze-dried salad mixes?

# 23 Chapter Review

## Summary

Salads are versatile and popular food items that may be used for appetizers, accompaniments, main dishes, desserts, and garnishes. All salads consist of a base, a body, and a dressing. However, because of the wide variety of ingredients that can be used for salads, the nutritional values vary depending on the materials. Since salad greens spoil rapidly, proper storage is necessary to protect their flavor, crispness, and nutritional values. Eye-pleasing salads are created by using crisp, fresh ingredients, and arranging them to complement each other for color, texture, form, and shape. To complete the salad, select a dressing that blends well with the kind of salad materials. Salad convenience products are available in grocery stores, and these may be kept on hand for emergencies or used to help the busy food manager prepare salads easily and quickly.

## Vocabulary

Match the lettered statements that follow to the numbered vocabulary words below. Each vocabulary word has more than one match.

1. accompaniment
2. mayonnaise
3. marinade

a. An uncooked dressing prepared from vinegar, salad oil, seasonings, and egg yolk.
b. A salad dressing into which foods are placed to enhance their flavors.
c. A dressing that is made by beating yolk, seasonings, and vinegar until they are blended, and then by adding oil very gradually.
d. A food that is served with a main dish.
e. A liquid that may be used to tenderize foods.
f. The most frequent use for a salad.

## Chapter Questions

1. What are two uses for greens?
2. Besides lettuce, what are four other greens you can use as a base?
3. How many greens should a salad have in order to count it as one serving of a leafy green vegetable?
4. What is your favorite salad, how do you prepare it, and what nutrients does it contribute?
5. What are three reasons why canned fruit should be drained before it is arranged in a salad?
6. If you wanted to make a low-calorie main-dish salad, what ingredients would you use?
7. What are the guidelines you should follow when purchasing salad greens?
8. What are the three basic types of dressings that are used on salads?
9. For each salad dressing you use in your family, list the ingredients, then categorize it according to the three basic types.
10. How should salad dressings be stored, and why is it important?
11. What are the advantages and disadvantages of purchasing prepared salads?

# Skill Activities

**1. Communication** In your food journal or card file box, make a collection of salad and salad dressing recipes. Organize the recipes for salads into all-vegetable salads; rice, pasta, and potato salads; cheese and egg salads; fruit salads; gelatin salads; and frozen salads. On the recipes, note whether they are suitable for appetizers, accompaniments, main dishes, or dessert, and indicate the kinds of dressings that are appropriate for use with each salad. Also add to the salad recipes in your collection of meat, poultry, and fish recipes. Organize your salad dressing recipes into categories of French dressing, mayonnaise, and cooked salad dressing. Under each category include low-calorie dressings, too. You can find recipes in books, magazines, newspapers, and on the display board in supermarkets. When you find interesting salad recipes, add them to your collection.

**2. Math** Visit the salad dressing aisle in your favorite grocery store to learn the variety of convenience dressings that are available. Divide a lined piece of paper into three columns, and write one of these headings above each column: "French Dressing," "Mayonnaise," and "Cooked Salad Dressing." Divide the paper in half, and on the top half write "Prepared Dressings" and on the bottom half write "Dressing Mixes." Under the appropriate headings record the name of the products that you find. Now select one prepared dressing and a mix for the same kind of dressing. Calculate the cost for one quart of the prepared dressing and for preparing one quart of the mix. When calculating the mix, remember to include the cost for the additional ingredients that must be added. What is the difference in cost between the two dressings? Which dressing is lower in total cost?

**3. Human relations** With your classmates, plan a luncheon menu with a salad as the main dish to serve to your class. Select the other foods that are needed to complete the luncheon menu and to supply the other nutrients that you need. Decide which dishes to prepare, the recipes to use, and the order in which to serve the food. Determine the amount of food necessary to purchase. To assist with your management of time, use the time-work plan and the Meal Preparation Plan.

**4. Communication** Molded gelatin salads are not only attractive but they may be used as an appetizer, an accompaniment, or a dessert. Research and write a report on how to prepare molded gelatin salads. Include directions that tell how to hasten the molding process, how to layer ingredients in a gelatin salad, and how to unmold the salads. Information about molded gelatin salads can be found in books and magazines about foods.

# 24 Quick Breads

## As you read, think about:

- what nutrients quick breads provide.
- how to prepare a variety of quick breads.
- how to use and serve quick breads in various ways.

**Vocabulary**
quick breads
batter
dough
gluten
leavening agents
baking powder
carbon dioxide
baking soda
cut in
knead

The story of bread reveals the traditions of many lands. The crude hearth cakes of primitive peoples were carefully fashioned and became the delicious hot breads of our day. The colonists were taught by the Indians to toast corn and to make thin corn cakes which were baked before an open fire. Hunters took the corn cakes on long journeys, and they soon became known as "journey cakes," and then later as "johnny cakes."

The waffle originated in England during the 13th century when a crusader accidentally sat on some freshly baked oat cakes. His armor flattened them and left deep imprints. Later, the Dutch brought waffle irons to America.

When American hunters sat around their camp fires and fried fish, their dogs howled; to keep them quiet, the hunters tossed leftover corn cakes to the dogs. In this way, the cakes became known as "hush puppies."

Crumpets and muffins came to us from England. Hot biscuits and spoon bread were served daily on southern plantations. Waffles, scones, popovers, and muffins have added variety to our daily bread. These delicious hot breads are known as **quick breads** because they are made with fast-acting leavening agents such as baking powder or baking soda rather than with yeast, which is slower acting.

As you read this chapter, you will learn of the various types of quick breads, how to prepare and use them, and their nutrient values.

## Types of Quick Breads

Quick breads are flour mixtures. They include many different kinds of breads which differ greatly in flavor, size and shape, and general appearance. Some are baked in an oven or on a griddle, and others are deep-fat fried. All of them can be made quickly and served piping hot. They are conveniently grouped according to the thickness of the batter used. Quick breads are of

Long ago, corn was ground into meal to make corn cakes, one of the earliest quick breads.

There is a large variety of quick breads. They differ in size, shape, and flavor, and they are made from pour batters, drop batters, or soft dough. Can you spot the fruit muffins, corn bread, biscuits, pancakes, waffles, tortillas, crepes, and gingerbread?

three types: pour batters, drop batters, and soft doughs. A **batter** is a mixture of flour and liquid. A **dough** is a mixture with less liquid than a batter. The thickness or stiffness of either the batter or dough depends upon the amount of liquid used in relation to the flour. Batters and doughs with less liquid are stiffer than those with more liquid.

*Pour batters* are of a thin consistency and can be poured from the mixing bowl. They may contain equal amounts of liquid and flour, or slightly less liquid than flour (1 c (250 mL) flour to 1 or ¾ c (250 or 185 mL) liquid). Waffles, pancakes, and popovers are examples of quick breads made from pour batters.

*Drop batters* are fairly thick and need to be scraped from the bowl into the baking pan. They usually contain about twice as much flour as liquid (1 c (250 mL) flour to ½ c (125 mL) liquid). Muffins, biscuits, and some quick loaf breads and coffee cakes are examples of quick breads made from drop batters.

*Soft dough* is thick enough to roll and shape by hand. It contains about one-third as much liquid as flour (1 c (250 mL) flour to ⅓ or ½ c (80 or 125 mL) liquid). Biscuits, doughnuts, scones, and some quick coffee cakes are quick breads made from soft dough.

### For Review

1. List and give an example of each type of quick bread.
2. What determines the differences among the types of quick breads?

## Ingredients and Nutrients

All quick breads, regardless of type, contain the basic ingredients of flour, leavening, salt, fat, and liquid. In addition to the basic ingredients in

Pancake batter is a pour batter usually made of equal amounts of liquid and flour. The ingredients are put into a bowl (left) and mixed until combined (right).

quick breads, eggs and sugar are frequently used. Each ingredient contributes a particular characteristic, purpose, and nutrient value to the bread.

## Ingredients Used

The flour contains the materials which form the structure or body of the bread. *All-purpose flour* is used most often for making quick breads. When water is mixed with flour, a substance called **gluten** (GLOOT-in) is formed from the protein of the flour. Gluten gives strength and elasticity to the batter or dough and will retain the air, steam, or carbon dioxide so that the bread can increase in volume. Cornmeal, whole wheat, and other flours are used in some recipes for flavor and variety.

*Salt* in small amounts is used to improve the flavor of quick breads.

**Leavening agents** enable the quick bread to rise so that it becomes light and porous. **Baking powder** is the most common chemical leavening agent used in quick breads, but air, steam, and a combination of baking soda and acid are sometimes used.

Commercial bakers make selections from a variety of leavening acids, each designed to meet the special needs of packaged mixes and doughs, frozen batters, and a variety of baked products. Some of these acids are fast-acting (reacting in the mixing bowl); others are slow-acting (reacting in the oven). A double-acting baking powder contains at least one fast-acting and one slow-acting acid ingredient. The double action refers to the release of some carbon dioxide during mixing and the remainder during baking.

All baking powders are made of soda, a dry acidic powder, and cornstarch. The soda of the baking powder will react with the acid ingredient it contains to form **carbon dioxide,** a harmless gas which causes the dough to rise when heated.

Only double-acting baking powder is available for you, as a home baker. It contains two acid-reacting ingredients, a slow- and a fast-acting ingredient. One reacts in the presence of moisture at room temperature in the dough

# Muffins

**Yield: 12 muffins**

2 c (500 mL) sifted all-purpose flour
1/4 c (60 mL) sugar
1 Tbs (15 mL) baking powder

1/2 tsp (2.5 mL) salt
1 beaten egg
1 c (250 mL) milk
1/4 c (60 mL) cooking oil

Approximate nutrition information per serving: calories–145; protein–3 g; fat–6 g; cholesterol–25 mg; carbohydrates–20 g; sodium–190 mg.

1. Set oven at 400°F (200°C).
2. Grease only bottoms of muffin cups, not the sides.
3. Sift flour with sugar, baking powder, and salt into mixing bowl.
4. Stir milk into egg; add cooking oil.
5. Make a well in center of dry ingredients, and add liquid ingredients all at once. Stir only until flour mixture is moist. The batter will be rough-looking.
6. Fill muffin cups two-thirds full.
7. Bake at 400°F (200°C) for 20 to 25 minutes, until golden brown. Serve hot.

(fast-acting); the other reacts during baking (slow-acting). Some carbon dioxide is released during mixing, but most of it is released after the product is placed in the oven. The double-action baking powder requires both moisture and heat to release completely all of its carbon dioxide.

**Baking soda,** another chemical leavening agent used in quick breads, and acid react rapidly at room temperature to produce carbon dioxide. You will need to work quickly when using baking soda and sour milk or buttermilk so that all of the carbon dioxide is not lost before the product is baked.

*Milk* is the liquid most often used in quick breads. However, *sour milk* or *buttermilk* is used in some recipes. The milk will dissolve the dry ingredients, salt, sugar, and chemical leaveners. Milk contributes to the flavor and browning quality of bread. You may replace fresh milk with *evaporated* or *dried milk.* You must reconstitute evaporated milk before using it by adding an equal amount of water to it. You may reconstitute dry milk to a liquid by following the directions on the package, or you may add it to the dry ingredients and then add the same amount of water to substitute for fluid milk.

The fat or shortening gives tenderness to the breads. *Vegetable shortening* and *lard* are bland in flavor, but *margarine* and *butter* contribute a pleasing flavor.

When *eggs* are used in quick breads, they contribute color, texture, and nutritive values.

The kinds and amounts of ingredients you use will not only influence the character of the breads but also will contribute to their nutrient values.

## Nutrient Contributions

The ingredients you use to make quick breads will determine their nutrient contributions. Flour is a basic ingredient of all quick breads and is the ingredient used in the largest

About 10,000 years ago, groups of people began to plant seeds and then to tend to the resulting crops. In this way, the life of the nomadic hunter-gatherer gave way to the life of the farmer.

Archeologists speculate that these prehistoric farmers discovered bread by accident. The farmers depended on porridge for food. One day some of the porridge—a mixture of grain and water cooked over a fire—fell onto the hot hearth. Not only did the result taste good, but also it was easier to carry and to store. Unleavened bread became a staple food.

Around the world, different grains were available to different groups of people. Through the centuries, a variety of techniques have developed for baking unleavened bread using many different kinds of grain. We still enjoy some of these unleavened breads today.

**Tortillas** Throughout Mexico and some parts of Central and South America, corn is a staple grain. Mexicans combine cornmeal and water, and cook this batter on a greased griddle. The result, a tortilla, looks like a thin corn pancake. Tortillas are stuffed with chicken, beef, or beans to create several dishes including enchiladas, burritos, and tacos.

**Pita Bread** Throughout the Middle East, some parts of the Mediterranean, and some parts of Africa, people eat pita bread (sometimes called Syrian bread or pocket bread). Pita bread is made from the staple grain wheat. The bread is round and thin, and it opens like a pocket.

Pita bread can be stuffed with lettuce and meat, and eaten like a sandwich. Sometimes people tear the pita bread into smaller pieces and pick up food with it.

**Injera** In Ethiopia, the staple grain is teff, a grass with small seeds. The seeds are ground, mixed with water, and baked to produce injera, a bread shaped like a large pancake. This unleavened bread is white, soft, and spongy. Ethiopians tear it into small pieces and use it to pick up pieces of spicy foods.

**Chapatis** In India, a coarse wheat flour called atta is used to make chapatis. Chapatis contains atta, water, and salt. The stiff dough is baked on a griddle over an open fire. Another unleavened wheat bread from India is called roti. Indians eat bread with almost every meal. The unleavened bread complements the rich, spicy sauces of Indian cuisine.

Unleavened bread, in the form of pita bread and tortillas, can be used alone or in combination with other foods.

amount. All kinds of flour are rich in starch and will contribute to your energy needs. In addition to starch, whole-grain and enriched flours will provide the B vitamins and iron.

Milk and eggs are rich sources of nutrients and, when used in quick breads, will increase the mineral and vitamin content of the bread and provide some complete protein.

The fat and sugar in the bread add to its caloric value, but the salt and leavening make no nutrient contributions.

Quick breads that are made with whole-grain or enriched flours contribute vitamins and minerals along with their caloric values.

**For Review**

1. What are the basic ingredients of quick breads?
2. What is the difference between baking soda and baking powder?
3. What contributions do eggs make to quick breads?
4. What nutrients are found in most quick breads?

## Uses and Preparation

Quick breads may be used in a variety of ways. No matter what way you choose, you will get the best results when you apply the principles of quick-bread preparation.

### Uses of Quick Breads

Griddle cakes and waffles are often served as the main dish of a breakfast or a dinner. You may serve them with the traditional syrup and butter or topped with creamed meat or poultry. Ingredients such as raisins, nuts, and bananas may be added to make quick loaf breads for lunch or party sandwiches.

Muffins and biscuits are popular hot breads that add a special touch to almost any meal. They may be used as the breadstuff to complement the main course.

Drop biscuits may be used as dumplings for a stew, and rolled biscuits as a pastry for a meat pie. They are often used as a garnish or an accompaniment to a main dish.

You may be surprised to learn that quick breads are also served as desserts. Baked sweetened biscuits are used as shortcake, or the sweetened dough may be used as the pastry for cobblers, fruit turnovers, and deep-dish pies. Waffles or pancakes topped with sweetened fruits are also served as desserts.

### Principles and Preparation

Success in the preparation of quick breads depends upon the kind and proportion of ingredients you use and upon the manner in which you combine them. Flour is the chief ingredient in all quick breads. In addition to a high proportion of starch, flour also contains two proteins: *gliadin* and *glutenin*. When you mix flour with water, gluten is formed from these two proteins. In the

Corn bread, a quick bread made from a drop batter, is an attractive accompaniment to a main dish such as frankfurters and baked beans.

## Tips for Herbs and Spices

Herbs and spices to use in quick breads are: allspice, chives, cinnamon, cloves, dill, garlic, ginger, nutmeg, pepper, poppy seed, saffron, and vanilla.

batter or dough, gluten forms a meshlike structure that surrounds the gases (carbon dioxide, air, or steam) responsible for leavening. As the gas expands, the gluten stretches. Oven heat coagulates the gluten, setting the batter or dough into a fairly firm, porous form.

The principles of quick-bread preparation are concerned with gluten formation. When you overmix and handle quick-bread mixtures too much, a large amount of gluten is developed and the breads become tough. Quick breads require little mixing and careful handling to avoid overproduction of gluten. You will use one of two methods to mix quick breads: the muffin method or the biscuit method (also called the pastry method).

You will use the muffin method of mixing for muffins, waffles, griddle cakes, popovers, and for quick fruit or nut breads.

1. The muffin method consists of first sifting the dry ingredients into a mixing bowl.
2. In another bowl, beat the eggs until blended. Then add room-temperature milk and melted or liquid shortening.
3. Next, pour the liquid ingredients into a well in the center of the dry ingredients. Mix them only enough to dampen the flour but not enough to make a smooth batter. When you overmix muffins, too much gluten will develop, causing toughness and long, narrow tunnels in the muffin.
4. Carefully lift the batter from the bowl and into the muffin pan to avoid extra mixing. Your results will be a perfect muffin, one that is rounded with a golden-brown and pebbly surface.

**Muffin Method of Mixing**

Step 1

Step 2

Step 3

Step 4

## Biscuit Method of Mixing

Step 1

Step 2

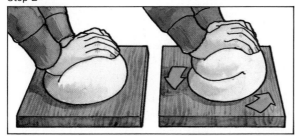

Step 3

Step 4

### Practical Tip

- To make your own baking powder, combine ½ teaspoon (2.5 mL) baking soda with ⅝ teaspoon (3 mL) cream of tartar.

Biscuits can be made quickly and easily. Follow these steps for the biscuit method.

1. Sift together the dry ingredients (flour, salt, leavening) into a bowl, and cut the solid shortening into the flour mixture. To **cut in** the shortening, you divide and distribute it with a pastry blender or two knives.

2. Then add the liquid all at once. Stir the dough with a fork until all the flour is moistened.

3. Form the dough into a ball, and place it on a lightly floured board. You then **knead** the dough 10 to 12 times by folding it toward you and then giving it a light push with the heels of your hands. You then rotate the dough a quarter of a turn and knead it again. During kneading, the ingredients are distributed more evenly, and flakiness is developed. Overkneading will develop too much gluten, and the biscuits will become tough.

4. Next, roll the biscuit dough to ½ inch (1.2 cm) or slightly thicker. If rolled too thin, the baked biscuits will be crusty and dry. Thicker biscuits will be crusty on the outside and breadlike on the inside.

5. Dip the biscuit cutter into flour so that it will not stick when it is used in cutting the dough. Cut as many biscuits as possible from the first rolling. Each rerolling develops more gluten, making the biscuits tougher. Bake the biscuits on an ungreased cookie sheet. Well-made biscuits have a golden-brown crust, a flat top, and are symmetrical.

### Microwaving Quick Breads

Quick breads tend to have an unsatisfactory quality, texture, and taste when baked in the microwave. They are very pale and do not bake evenly, even when rotated during cooking. However, with careful timing (especially for standing time), and the addition of colorful ingredients such as molasses, chocolate, dark spices, and dried fruit, you can prepare some quick breads successfully in the microwave.

## For Review

1. List three uses for quick breads and an example of each.
2. How is gluten formed? What is its function in the preparation of quick breads?
3. What is the major difference between the muffin method and the biscuit method of mixing?
4. What are two disadvantages of baking quick breads in the microwave?

# Storage and Convenience

Muffins, biscuits, and most quick breads are best when they are served soon after baking, but with proper storage their goodness can be retained for some time. There is a wide variety of convenience forms available to keep on hand for emergencies.

## Care and Storage

Since quick breads lose their freshness rapidly, you should store them in a tightly closed container or sealed in moisture-proof wrap. The texture and flavor of quick breads will deteriorate rapidly, even under the most ideal storage conditions.

The freshness of quick breads is better preserved by frozen storage. Breads to be frozen should be packaged in suitable freezer wrap soon after baking. Frozen quick breads are a convenience and need only to be warmed for serving.

## Convenience in Quick Breads

Some forms of convenience quick breads are ready-to-serve, frozen, refrigerated, and mixes. Most mixes require only the addition of milk or water; others may include the addition of eggs. The frozen or refrigerated product may require baking or simply heating.

No standards or means for grading convenience quick-bread products have been established. Your only guide to quality and ingredient content is the information listed on the label. You should be familiar with the usual ingredient content of quick breads so that you will be a better judge of the quality of the convenience item. By using a variety of convenience products, you will discover those which suit you.

Homemade quick breads are generally prepared in a short time. For this reason there may be little difference between the time required to make the homemade item compared with the time required to make the convenience item.

Convenience quick-bread items usually cost more than the homemade product. The frozen quick breads tend to be more expensive than the dry mixes.

Most quick-bread mixes produce a reasonably acceptable product and can be better than many homemade products. However, when you understand the principles involved in quick-bread preparation, you can often prepare products that are superior to a mix.

You can also prepare your own homemade mix by sifting the dry ingredients and cutting in the shortening. This mix will keep for several weeks at room temperature and several months in the refrigerator. It can be used for biscuits, muffins, waffles, pancakes, and coffee cakes.

In deciding which quick bread convenience item to use, you should consider the quality of the mix, the comparative cost, the time involved, and how it will fit into your situation.

## For Review

1. What is the best method of storing quick breads?
2. Explain two advantages and two disadvantages of using quick-bread convenience items.

# 24 Chapter Review

## Summary

While some quick breads are baked and others are fried, they all can be made quickly and are best served piping hot. These delicious breads are made from a mixture of flour, leavening, salt, fat, and liquid, and sometimes eggs and sugar. The measurement of these ingredients plus the way in which they are combined are important for achieving successful results. Of course, the ingredients used determine the nutrient contributions of the bread. To preserve the freshness of quick breads, proper storage is necessary. As a boon to the busy food manager, quick breads are available in a wide range of convenience product forms.

## Vocabulary

Use the vocabulary words below to complete the sentences that follow.

baking powder
baking soda
batter
carbon dioxide
cut in

dough
gluten
knead
leavening agents
quick breads

1. A mixture of flour and liquid is called a _____.
2. Foods made with a mixture of ingredients that includes flour and fast-acting leavening agents instead of yeast are called _____.
3. When water is mixed with flour, the protein in the flour forms _____, which gives strength and elasticity to the mixture.
4. The mixture that is thick enough to shape by hand or to roll and that contains about two-thirds more flour than liquid is called a soft _____.
5. In order for quick breads to rise, _____ are added to the mixture.
6. A harmless gas that causes the dough to rise when it is heated is called _____.
7. To distribute the ingredients evenly when preparing biscuits, _____ the dough by folding it toward you and then giving it a little push with the heels of your hands.
8. To distribute the shortening into the flour mixture, use a pastry blender or two knives to _____ the shortening.
9. Two ingredients that are used in quick bread mixtures to make them rise during cooking are _____ and _____.

## Chapter Questions

1. What are the three types of quick bread?
2. What is the purpose of using flour to make quick breads?
3. What should you remember when you mix baking soda with ingredients such as sour milk or buttermilk?
4. Why is milk often added to the mixture for quick breads?
5. What is your favorite quick bread, how do you prepare it, and what nutrients does it contribute?
6. If you were serving a casserole, what kinds of quick bread could you use and how would you use them?

7. What can you do to insure getting success-ful results when you make quick breads?
8. Why should you stir the quick bread mix-ture only a little?
9. What is the purpose for kneading dough?
10. If you have a loaf of date-nut bread that you will not be able to use for about five days, how should you store it?
11. What is an alternative to buying a quick bread mix to keep on hand?
12. What quick breads do you eat in your family? For each quick bread, describe how they are used.

## Skill Activities

 **1. Decision making** In your food journal or card file box, make a collection of quick bread recipes. Organize your recipes into the three types of quick breads: pour batters, drop batters, and soft doughs. You can find recipes in books, magazines, and newspapers and on the display boards in supermarkets. Add to this collection whenever you find interesting recipes for quick breads.

 **2. Human relations** Pancakes are an international favorite, and just about every country has some form of a pancake, although they may be called by another name, such as crepes, tortillas, hotcakes, and latkes. Pancakes are popular for breakfast and dessert or as an appetizer as well as an entrée. Learn about some of the different kinds of pancake recipes from around the world. Below is a list of countries and the name of some pancakes that are eaten there: Sweden, plattar; Norway, pannekaker; Denmark, aggekage; Germany, pfannkuchen; Poland, racuchy; Holland, flensjestaart; Austria, nockerln; France, Crêpes Suzette; England, dessert pancakes; Israel, latkes; and Mexico, tortillas. Find a recipe for each pancake, and tell how it can be used in a meal. With your classmates, show where your pancake recipes come from by making a map of the world and writing the name of the pancake that is popular in the appropriate country.

 **3. Resource management** Keep a record for a week of the different kinds of quick breads that you use in your home. Tell the name of the quick bread, how it was used, and with which meal or snack. Write the nutrients that were supplied by the quick breads, and if possible the number of calories in a slice. Compare this list with your classmates' lists.

**4. Food science** Carbon dioxide gas is released when baking soda reacts with acid. To demonstrate this reaction, dissolve 2 teaspoons (10 mL) of baking soda in a cup of water. Pour equal amounts of the solution into two large test tubes. Add a few drops of a high-acid substance, such as vinegar or lemon juice, to one tube. Observe if bubbles of gas appear in either one of the tubes.

# 25 Yeast Breads

## As you read, think about:

- what nutrients yeast breads provide for you.
- how to prepare a variety of yeast breads.
- how to use and serve yeast breads in various ways.

**Vocabulary**
fermentation
proofing
punch down

Bread has been known as the "staff of life" throughout history. Excavations of primitive villages of ten thousand years ago show evidence of crude ovens and forms of bread. The first bread was most likely a hard, flat loaf that had been baked on a rock over a fire. The Egyptians were probably the first to make leavened white bread. In England and Europe, bread was a sign of social status.

Over the centuries, every nationality or culture developed its own bread. Examples are Austrian Vienna bread, Swedish limpa, Jewish challah, and French brioche (bree-OHSH). These breads and many others have enriched our American heritage.

## Classes of Yeast Breads

The wide variety of yeast products can be classified according to the flour used to make them, such as whole wheat and rye, or according to their forms or shapes. Yeast products can be conveniently grouped by their basic shape, such as loaf breads, rolls, and doughnuts.

### Loaf Breads

The loaf breads are the most commonly used yeast products and include the plain breads which are known by their flour content as white, whole wheat, cracked wheat, and rye. Some variations of the basic white bread are raisin, cinnamon, and nut breads. Breads made from sweetened yeast doughs may be fashioned into tea rings and coffee cakes.

### Rolls

Small pieces of yeast dough are shaped into rolls. Rolls are made from both plain and sweetened doughs and can be made in a variety of shapes. Rolls made from plain doughs are often used instead of sliced loaf breads.

Because bread is the "staff of life," the oven for its baking has long been a center of the household. Here bread is being baked in a turn-of-the-century Canadian village, which had a bread oven near each house.

Sweet yeast doughs are made into many fancy sweet rolls. Other foods such as raisins and fruits, nuts, and spices are often added to sweet-roll doughs, and the rolls are frequently frosted or iced. Sweet rolls are popular accompaniments to breakfast or to salad lunches.

### Deep-fat Fried Bread

The term *doughnut* refers to dough that has been fried in deep fat. The raised doughnut is made from a yeast dough, and the cakelike

Yeast breads come in a seemingly endless variety of shapes and sizes. What ingredients are in all yeast breads? What yeast breads shown here can you identify?

doughnut is made without yeast. Doughnuts are most often used as desserts or to replace sweet rolls, rather than as substitutes for breads.

Crullers (Dutch for "twisted dough"), Nantucket doughnuts (small irregular pieces of dough), and Bismarcks (jelly-filled balls) are other deep-fat fried yeast doughs. You will find that all of these forms of yeast dough are made of the same basic ingredients.

## For Review

1. Grouped by shape, what are three types of yeast products?
2. What are the two types of dough used for rolls?
3. What is the difference between a raised doughnut and a cakelike doughnut?

# Ingredients and Nutrients

Nothing quite measures up to the satisfaction and pride derived from baking a loaf of fragrant golden-brown bread. This enjoyment and pride can be yours when you begin by selecting the proper ingredients. The basic ingredients of all yeast doughs are flour, yeast, liquid, and salt; sugar and shortening are often used. Crusty, crisp breads, such as French or Italian breads, are made with only the four basic ingredients, while breads with a soft crust use all of them. The ingredients used will determine the characteristics and nutrient value of the bread.

## Ingredients Used

*Flour* is the chief ingredient of yeast breads. You will recall that flour contains two proteins, gliadin and glutenin, which form gluten when liquid is added and the mixture is stirred and kneaded. Gluten gives elasticity to yeast dough and permits it to stretch and retain the leavening gas (carbon dioxide) produced by the yeast. Flours that contain a high percentage of gluten-forming protein are well suited to making yeast breads.

Wheat flour is best for bread making. The two types of wheat flour are made from hard and soft wheat. Hard-wheat flour contains more gluten-forming protein than soft-wheat flour and is best for yeast doughs. Soft-wheat flour is best for quick breads. Hard-wheat flour, or bread flour, is not usually available in local stores. A blend of hard and soft wheat flours, called all-purpose flour, is most often used in yeast breads. All-purpose flour contains enough protein to make good yeast breads and is soft enough for general home baking. Flour gives structure and body to the bread. It is important to buy a flour suitable for yeast doughs and to keep in mind the importance of enriched flour.

*Yeast* is the leavening agent. It is a microscopic plant that can cause sugar to form both carbon dioxide and alcohol—the action known as **fermentation.** The carbon dioxide gas can expand the gluten structure and cause the bread to rise.

Yeast works best at room temperature (80–85° F (27–29° C)) because it is quickly destroyed at high temperatures; low temperatures slow down yeast activity. All liquid must be cooled down to lukewarm (a drop of liquid feels neither hot nor cold when tested on the inner arm). After the dough is mixed, it is allowed to rise in a warm place.

Yeast is purchased in a dry, granular form or as a compressed cake. The compressed yeast requires refrigeration, but the granular yeast keeps well on the shelf. Granular yeast gives the best results when it is used within the date stamped on the back of the envelope. The directions for its use are also included on the envelope. Both granular and compressed yeast give equally good results.

The *liquid* ingredient is usually milk or water or a combination of the two. Breads made with milk have higher nutrient values, brown better, and have a richer flavor. The liquid provides the moisture needed to develop gluten and to dissolve the dry ingredients.

*Salt* improves the flavor of bread and controls the rate of yeast growth. It slows down yeast growth so that fermentation is controlled and the bread texture will be moderately firm. However, too much salt will prevent the growth of yeast and will produce a heavy bread.

*Sugar* is sometimes used in the making of yeast breads; however, breads can be made without it. A small amount of sugar is a ready source of food for yeast, and it speeds up yeast activity. Avoid using too much sugar because this will slow down yeast action. Sugar helps the crust to brown and can contribute to flavor.

A snack of a glass of milk and a piece of whole-wheat bread gives you some important nutrients. What nutrients does whole-wheat flour add to bread?

*Shortening* makes the bread more tender and improves its keeping quality. Shortenings and cooking oils are often used, but they are bland in flavor. Butter or margarine, which may also be used, will add a pleasing flavor to yeast breads.

## Nutrient Contributions

The nutrient values of breads are influenced by the ingredients used to make them. Flour is the chief ingredient of bread and contributes abundantly to its energy value. If you use enriched and whole-wheat flours in yeast breads, they will also provide thiamin, or $B_1$, riboflavin, or $B_2$, niacin, and iron. When milk is used instead of water, it, too, adds to the nutrient value of breads. Since it is a rich source of calcium, riboflavin, and complete protein, milk will make bread an even better food. Whole milk will also supply vitamin A. Some yeast

# Bread That's Safe to Eat

Eating bread is an ancient tradition. However, for some of our ancestors eating bread was not always a safe or healthy activity.

According to archeologists and anthropologists, the ancient Egyptians were probably the first people to add yeast to bread. They used wild yeast that they kept alive in leftover dough. This sourdough bread contained ingredients unfamiliar to us. Because of the grinding process, the bread contained sand and flecks of limestone and mica.

The Greeks learned bread making from the Egyptians and passed this knowledge on to the Romans. Both the Greeks and the Romans improved upon the Egyptians' original recipe. In Rome, bakeries could produce 50,000–100,000 loaves a day. The bread, however, could contain some surprises. Because wealthy people valued the whiteness of bread, some bakers added chalk to their flour.

During the Middle Ages, peasants ate mostly flatbread. In Britain, flatbread, called ashcakes, was so hard that it could not be cut with a knife. People broke the ashcakes with their hands. This bread contained barley, beans, acorns, and sometimes some wheat and rye flours. Bread made from just wheat and rye grains sometimes contained an unwanted ingredient—a fungus that could kill people.

By the early 19th century, a new type of flour mill produced a white flour. People no longer had to endure white bread that contained chalk. In addition, the new mill made white bread available to all people, not just the wealthy.

Almost as soon as the mill was invented, people questioned if the white bread was nutritious. It was discovered that white flour did not contain the vitamins and minerals present in whole grains. As a result, enriched flour was developed.

Through the centuries, yeast bread has been a staple food for many cultures. However, it has taken all those centuries to develop bread that is safe to eat.

The modern technology of bread making assures you a safe-to-eat product. Breads are handled in extremely sanitary surroundings, and bread-making machinery is cleaned thoroughly.

doughs include eggs, which further enrich the nutrient values of breads.

Yeast breads are a rich source of energy and can make important contributions of vitamins and minerals to meet your daily needs. Bread is a nutritious food with a bland flavor that blends well with many other foods. For these reasons, bread continues to be the staff of life and should be included in meals.

### For Review

1. What are the four basic ingredients of yeast doughs?
2. What contributions do sugar and shortening make to yeast products?
3. What contribution does yeast make?
4. What are some things to remember when using yeast?
5. How can you improve the nutrient values of a simple yeast bread?

## Principles and Preparation

The principles of yeast dough preparation are concerned with gluten and carbon dioxide formation. The gluten forms the framework, or structure, of the dough and expands as carbon dioxide is produced by the yeast.

*Gluten formation* begins when liquid is stirred into the flour. The protein particles of the flour absorb water, swell, and stick together to form gluten. The gluten is further developed by kneading. You will recall that kneading is working the dough by folding it over to the edge nearest you and gently pushing it away from you with the heels of your hands. As you develop the gluten by kneading the dough, it will form an elastic network throughout the dough that can entrap, or hold, the leavening gas, which is carbon dioxide.

When you first begin to knead the dough, it may tend to cling to the board; but as you work it, the water will be taken up by the gluten and the dough will become stiffer. The kneading is continued until the dough becomes elastic and satiny smooth with blisters of carbon dioxide showing under the surface. During baking, the gluten network becomes firm and contributes to the shape of the baked bread.

During fermentation, the yeast changes sugar into carbon dioxide and alcohol. Even though yeast plants may begin to grow while you mix the dough, most of the carbon dioxide for leavening is formed during the fermentation period. The dough rises as carbon dioxide is produced during fermentation. This process is called **proofing.** After the dough is kneaded sufficiently, it is placed in a warm spot so that fermentation can occur. Fermentation is continued until the dough has doubled in bulk.

You can help yeast produce carbon dioxide when you measure ingredients accurately and when you are careful to maintain the proper temperature. Too much salt or sugar can interfere with gluten formation; too much flour makes the dough too stiff. Too much heat destroys yeast; too little slows down yeast action.

Kneading the dough sufficiently to develop a strong and elastic gluten will help the dough retain, or keep, carbon dioxide. When the dough is not kneaded enough, the carbon dioxide is not contained and the bread is heavy and small in volume.

Several steps are required to make perfect yeast breads. You need to use the right proportion of ingredients and to combine them in the order listed in the recipe. You must knead the dough sufficiently to develop gluten and permit it to ferment properly so that enough carbon dioxide is produced. The dough must be shaped correctly and baked in the right pan at the proper temperature.

There are several ways to mix yeast dough. You may combine the basic ingredients of flour, yeast, salt, and liquid, and usually sugar and fat, by one of three methods: the straight-dough method, the sponge-dough method, or the batter, or "no-knead," method.

In the *straight-dough method*, all of the ingredients are combined, and the dough is kneaded and set aside to rise (ferment or proof).

1. In the straight-dough method, first add salt, sugar, and shortening to scalded milk. Allow to cool.
2. Then mix one cake of compressed yeast with warm water.
3. Next, add the yeast mixture to the cooled milk-sugar-shortening-salt mixture.
4. In the last step, add flour to the mixture of all other ingredients, and stir until a stiff dough is formed.

In the *sponge-dough method*, the yeast is combined with part of the liquid, flour, and sugar to make a batter. This batter is covered and permitted to rise in a warm place until it becomes light and bubbly. The remaining sugar, salt, shortening, and flour are added to make a stiff dough.

In the *batter*, or *"no-knead," method*, all of the ingredients are combined, but the dough is not kneaded and the texture is not as fine and uniform as in kneaded dough.

The straight-dough method, with a slightly larger quantity of yeast and salt, is sometimes known as the *cool-proofed, cool-rise,* or *quick-action method*. This dough can be held overnight in the refrigerator for baking on the following day. The dough retains enough heat so that fermentation (proofing) continues during refrigeration, and it is doubled in bulk before the dough becomes chilled.

After the ingredients are mixed, place the dough on a lightly floured board, and knead it for 8 to 10 minutes to develop gluten. During kneading, the gluten becomes firmer and more elastic.

1. Grease the kneaded dough or the "no-knead" dough, place it in a large bowl, cover it, and allow it to rise in a warm place (80–85° F (27–29° C)) until doubled in bulk. Test the dough by pressing it with two fingers; a dent should remain in the dough.
2. **Punch down** the dough by pushing your fist into the center of the dough.
3. Briefly knead the fermented dough gently to distribute the bubbles of gas more evenly. Then shape the dough into the form you desire, either loaves or rolls. Place the shaped dough into a suitable pan and allow it to rise until double in bulk.
4. Bake the risen, shaped dough in a hot oven (400° F (200° C)). The high temperature will kill the yeast and coagulate the protein (gluten) to produce a firm, porous structure. The alcohol produced by the yeast is driven off during baking. The bread will become crusty and golden brown with a superb fragrance. The baked bread will have a hollow sound when you tap it on top. Immediately remove the baked bread or rolls from the pan and place the product on a wire rack to cool. If you wish, you may brush the top crust with melted butter or margarine. The crust will be satiny and soft.

## Dough Preparation

Rising and punching down

Kneading after first rising

Kneading and shaping

Shaping for second rising

Shaping for a braided loaf

Sealing the end

Braiding

### Microwaving Yeast Breads

The microwave is not well-suited for baking yeast breads. Because there is no hot air to dry the surface of the bread, no crust will form. The breads will rise, but they will be pale. Recipes written especially for the microwave will therefore call for dark flours and ingredients such as molasses, cinnamon, and other dark spices.

The microwave is useful for freshening stale bread and cakes. Place the food on a paper towel, and reheat on a medium power setting for 15 seconds. Continue reheating, checking often for overheating, up to a total of 45 seconds.

### Tips for Microwaving Yeast Breads

- To defrost frozen bread dough, place 1 cup (250 mL) of water in the back corner of the microwave, and heat to boiling. Leave the water in place. Place the frozen dough in a loaf pan, put it in the microwave, and cook it on a low power setting for up to 5 minutes. Turn the dough and repeat.
- Heat sliced French bread by covering it loosely with waxed paper so that it heats quickly and so that the crust does not become soft.

### For Review

1. How does careful measuring of ingredients help carbon dioxide formation?
2. Why is proper kneading of the dough important?
3. List and briefly describe the three ways to mix yeast dough.
4. How do you know when kneaded dough is ready to be punched down?

Yeast breads form the start of the most basic sandwich and of some of the most elegant tea sandwiches. Adding some garnish makes these sandwiches even more special.

## Uses, Storage, and Convenience

Yeast breads, in the form of sliced breads and rolls, are popular accompaniments to any meal. Proper storage will add to your enjoyment of yeast breads, and the many convenience yeast items will make it even easier to enjoy these breads more often.

### Uses of Bread

Bread is a staple food served as an accompaniment to main dishes or as a base for some main dishes. Toasted slices of bread are used as the base for creamed meats, poultry, or sea-

foods. Rolled yeast dough may be used as a base for pizza, for meat rolls and turnovers served as main dishes, and for fancy rolls and tea rings suitable for desserts.

Bread forms the base for sandwiches, party sandwiches, and canapés (KAN-uh-peez). Hearty sandwiches are often served as the main dish of a meal and consist of a filling between two slices of bread. When you use different breads and fillings, you make possible a variety of sandwiches. Many are served cold, others hot. Sandwich ingredients include bread, spreads, fillings, and garnishes.

White, whole-wheat, French, rye, cracked-wheat, oatmeal, potato, and cornmeal breads are

## Refrigerator Rolls    Yield: 1½ dozen rolls

| | |
|---|---|
| 1 package yeast (128 g cake; 7.5 g dry) | ½ tsp (2.5 mL) salt |
| ¼ c (60 mL) warm water | ¾ c (185 mL) scalded milk |
| ¼ c (60 mL) sugar | 1 egg |
| ¼ c (60 mL) shortening | 3–3½ c (750–875 mL) all-purpose flour |

1. Set oven at 400°F (200°C).
2. Scald milk; add sugar, shortening, and salt; cool to lukewarm.
3. Dissolve yeast in warm water in large bowl.
4. Add cooled milk mixture and egg to yeast.
5. Add one-third of the flour; beat until smooth.
6. Add remaining flour gradually to make a soft dough that leaves the sides of the bowl.
7. Place dough onto floured board and knead about 5 minutes.
8. Place dough into greased bowl, and grease the face of the dough.
9. Cover and place in refrigerator. (dough keeps about 4 days).
10. Shape dough into rolls.
11. Cover rolls and let rise again in warm place until doubled in bulk, about 2 hours.
12. Bake at 400°F (200°C) for 12 to 15 minutes.

suitable for sandwiches. Rolls or buns may be substituted for sliced bread.

Table fat (butter or margarine) or salad dressing are common spreads for bread. Before the filling is added, spreads are put on to seal the bread and prevent moist filling from soaking into it, to add flavor and moistness, and to help hold the filling and bread together. Spreads are usually high in calories.

Sliced meats, cheese, and cold cuts (sandwich meats) are popular fillings for sandwiches. You can prepare many kinds of fillings from chopped, ground, or grated foods, seasonings, and relishes.

To prepare sandwiches, select two bread slices that match each other in shape and size. Put on desired spreads thinly to cover each slice of bread. Place the filling on one slice of bread, and cover the filling with the other slice. Prepared sandwiches may be cut diagonally or horizontally into halves or quarters.

All ingredients in sandwiches should be kept refrigerated, especially the protein foods, until ready for use. Prepared sandwiches should be refrigerated. A well-chilled sandwich keeps for three to four hours after removal from the refrigerator. Sandwiches remain moist when wrapped in plastic wrap. Some sandwiches are served hot. Hot dogs, hamburgers, and grilled cheese are popular hot sandwiches.

Although most sandwiches are served as the main part of a meal, small sandwiches often are served as an accompaniment to another food such as soup or salad. Small, open-faced, and sometimes decorated sandwiches are served as appetizers before a dinner or at a tea or other party.

Whether you use breads as a staple or to add festivity to mealtimes and parties, you will need to store them properly to keep their freshness.

## Storage of Yeast Breads

Yeast breads, like quick breads, should be stored in a covered container or a breadbox to prevent drying and loss of freshness. It is difficult to retain the freshness of breads with prolonged storage. Storing breads in the refrigerator does not protect the freshness of bread, but will retard spoilage by mold. You will find it most satisfying to use bread soon after it is made. When you have an extra supply of yeast breads, it is best to store them in moisture-proof wrap in the freezer.

## Convenience in Yeast Breads

Since the first sliced bread, many new convenience items, including quick- and yeast-bread products, have been added. They include mixes, and frozen, refrigerated, ready-to-serve, and brown-and-serve items. The mix for breads contains all of the measured ingredients except the liquid. Adding the liquid to the mix, stirring, and shaping the dough require little time. The frozen, refrigerated, and brown-and-serve breads need only to be warmed or baked.

The convenience product will help you to save time when the home-prepared product requires many ingredients and several steps for preparation. When the home product requires few ingredients and is simply mixed, there is little saving of time with the use of the convenience item.

Frozen homemade yeast products are also a convenience. Yeast doughs will keep frozen for about six weeks, and frozen baked products for several months. Frozen baked products are more of a convenience than frozen yeast dough, which requires thawing, shaping, rising, and baking.

When it is important to save time and effort, you may wish to select a convenience item. You should check the labels to learn which ingredients were used to make the product. No grades or standards are available to assist you with your selection. You should select products made with enriched flour and those which also contain eggs and milk, in order to add nutrients to your breads.

**For Review**

1. What are the basic parts of a sandwich?
2. What are some of the purposes for spreads in sandwiches?
3. What advantage is there to storing yeast breads in the refrigerator?

# 25 Chapter Review

## Summary

Often referred to as "the staff of life," bread is included with meals because it contributes important carbohydrates, vitamins, and minerals to meet a person's daily needs. It may be served as an appetizer, an accompaniment to a main dish, a base for a main dish, or as a dessert. Considered a staple food, yeast bread products come in a variety of convenience forms. Made from a mixture of yeast, flour, and other ingredients, the breads can be classified by their shapes as loaves, rolls, and doughnuts. The principles for making successful yeast breads are concerned with the formation of gluten and carbon dioxide. Proper storage of yeast breads is necessary to protect freshness and prevent the growth of mold.

## Vocabulary

Match the definitions that follow to the numbered vocabulary words below:

1. fermentation
2. proofing
3. punch down

a. This is the name given to the process of the dough rising.
b. During this period most of the carbon dioxide is formed.
c. This term is used for the action of pushing your fist into the center of the dough.

## Chapter Questions

1. What are the two ways of classifying yeast breads?
2. What are four common flours used to make loaf breads?
3. Besides the basic ingredients, what other foods are often added to sweet rolls?
4. Describe all-purpose flour.
5. What is the purpose of adding yeast to a bread mixture?
6. What steps can you take to make sure your bread dough rises?
7. If you were a busy food manager, which method of mixing yeast dough would you use and why?
8. In the sponge-dough and straight-dough methods, why is the dough kneaded a second time?
9. What are the reasons for using a spread on a sandwich?
10. What is your favorite sandwich made from yeast bread, how do you prepare the sandwich, and what nutrients does it contribute to your diet?
11. Why should sandwich ingredients be kept refrigerated?
12. If you have several loaves of bread, how should you store the extra loaves?
13. What common yeast products do you have in your family, and how are they used?
14. What are at least three guidelines you would recommend that should be used for selecting fresh convenience bread products at the grocery store?

# Skill Activities

**1. Decision making** In your food journal or card file box, make a collection of yeast bread recipes. Organize your recipes into categories for loaf breads, rolls, and deep-fat fried bread. You can find recipes in books, magazines, and newspapers, on packages of flour, and on the display boards in supermarkets. As you find other interesting recipes for yeast breads, add them to your collection.

**2. Communication** Prepare a guide for forming yeast rolls. Find information on how to shape Parker House, cloverleaf, pinwheel, fan-tan, and crescent rolls. For forming each kind of roll, write the steps in order, and then draw a diagram to show the proper technique. Directions for shaping rolls can be found on display boards in supermarkets and in cookbooks, magazines, and newspapers.

**3. Critical thinking** With your classmates make the same kind of bread by three different methods. Use the straight-dough method for one loaf, the sponge-dough method for another loaf, and the batter method for the third loaf. Evaluate the loaves for flavor, texture, and preparation time. Which loaf of bread is the tastiest? Which loaf of bread has the best texture? Which loaf of bread was the quickest to prepare? Which loaf of bread took the most preparation time?

**4. Math** Visit the bakery section of a local grocery store and compare the nutritional information for the serving size of one slice of fresh whole wheat, rye, oatmeal, and white bread. Down the left-hand side of a lined sheet of paper, write the following headings: "Calories," "Protein," "Carbohydrate," "Fat," and "Sodium." Then draw a line and write "Percentage of U.S. RDA." Next, list these nutrients, each on a separate line: "Protein," "Vitamin A," "Vitamin C," "Thiamin," "Riboflavin," "Niacin," "Calcium," and "Iron." Now divide the paper into four columns, and above each column, write one of the kinds of bread and its brand name. For each kind of bread record the information for one slice on your chart. Which kind of bread has the highest calories per slice? Which kind of bread has the most grams of carbohydrate? Which kind of bread has the highest amount of sodium? Which bread provides the highest percentage of B vitamins? Which kind of bread provides the most calcium? Which kind has the most iron? Which loaf would you buy? Why?

**5. Food science** To demonstrate the release of carbon dioxide gas by yeast, prepare a yeast suspension by mixing a packet of yeast in warm water. Pour equal amounts of the yeast suspension into two large test tubes. Add 1 teaspoon (5 mL) of sugar to one test tube, and stir until dissolved. Attach a balloon to the top of each tube, using a string or rubber band to ensure a tight fit. Observe what happens.

# 26 Beverages

## As you read, think about:

- how to select, store, and use beverages.
- what the correct techniques are for preparing and serving beverages.
- what the appropriate uses are for beverages.

**Vocabulary**
caffeine
stimulant
decaffeinated
 coffee
cocoa butter
tannins
brewing
steep

Our most basic beverages—coffee, tea, and cocoa—each emerged from a different part of the world.

Coffee, a popular symbol of hospitality, was discovered centuries ago in Abyssinia. Berries gathered from a shrub and then dried and boiled became a dark beverage called "kaffia," also the name of the shrub. By the 17th century, coffee houses, public rooms where coffee and other beverages are served, were found in England and in the American colonies.

Tea, served with ceremony and glamour for centuries in China and Japan, came to England in the 1660s. At a time when London coffee houses were unable to import coffee, tea shops became popular. Since then, the English have been known for their afternoon tea. Tea also became very popular in America until the Boston Tea Party, after which coffee became the all-American beverage.

In America, the Indians used cacao beans as money, and the explorer Cortez was the first European to taste chocolate. Other explorers —from France, Austria, and the Netherlands —returned the beans to their countries, where people began experimenting with them. Chocolate houses soon became favorite gathering places in Europe; in America, English colonists were serving chocolate.

Today—along with coffee, tea, and cocoa —we have milk, fruit and vegetable juices, soft drinks, and even water on our list of beverages. You can make your selection from a wide variety of beverages to suit your mood, the occasion, and the weather.

## Kinds and Selection

When beverages first appeared in Europe, they were prized foods that only the rich could afford. Today, coffee, tea, and cocoa are staple items in nearly every home. Coffee is our most popular beverage, followed by tea and cocoa. We drink about one-half of the coffee produced in the world. Vegetable and fruit juices, especially

One of the most popular beverages, cocoa has been a favorite drink for many years.

in convenience forms, are also popular beverages, along with a great variety of soft drinks and, of course, the most basic of beverages, water.

## Coffee

Most of our coffee comes from Brazil, although a small amount comes from other countries in Latin America, Asia, Mexico, and the East Indies. Several varieties of coffee beans are blended and roasted to develop a special flavor. You will find that many blends of coffee are available and that they are sold under different brand names. Both the kind of coffee beans used and the degree to which they are roasted influence its flavor.

Even though it is possible to buy coffee in the whole bean, you will notice that most of the coffee offered for sale is ground and sealed in vacuum cans. Vacuum-packed coffee will retain its freshness longer than coffee not vacuum packed. During vacuum packing, air is withdrawn and the container sealed. The coffee that you purchase in paper containers will become stale several days after roasting and grinding. Because ground coffee becomes stale quickly, it is best to purchase it in rather small quantities. Vacuum-packed coffee stays fresh until it is opened, and then, when it is exposed to air, begins to lose some of its freshness.

Coffee comes in several different grinds. The grind to select is determined by the type of coffee maker you use. *Coarse,* or *regular, grind* is used for a percolator; *drip,* or *medium, grind* is used for a drip or a filter coffee maker; *fine grind* is used for a vacuum-type coffee maker. Also available are *ADC grind,* for automatic drip coffee makers, and *electric perc grind,* for electric percolators.

Various types of coffee makers are available. Some are (clockwise from top left) automatic drip, electric percolator, vacuum type, nonautomatic drip, and steep type.

Coffee is produced from coffee beans (top), tea from the dried leaves of an evergreen shrub (middle), and cocoa from cocoa beans (bottom).

All coffee contains **caffeine,** a drug that is a stimulant. A **stimulant** is a substance that increases body activities, such as heart rate and blood pressure. **Decaffeinated coffee,** coffee that does not contain caffeine, has been chemically or naturally treated before roasting in order to remove 95 percent of the caffeine. Many people, especially those with heart disease or high blood pressure, should avoid or restrict the use of caffeine.

Instant coffee, available in either regular or decaffeinated forms, is a powdered, granulated, or flaked form of coffee that dissolves quickly in either hot or cold water. Freeze-dried coffee, which tastes similar to brewed coffee, is also a form of instant coffee.

### Tea

Even though coffee may be a favorite in our country, tea is probably the most popular beverage in the world. Grown in tropical climates, most tea comes from India, Indonesia, Sri Lanka, and Africa.

Tea is the dried leaf of an evergreen shrub. The unopened bud near the end of a shoot produces the best tea, and the first two leaves are used for good quality tea. The quality of tea is determined by the size of the leaves, the variety of the plant, the climate, and the curing of the leaves. Green, black, and oolong are the three teas made from the same type of tea leaves. The fresh tea leaves are steamed and dried to make *green tea.* Green tea is fragrant and has a bitter flavor. For *black tea,* the leaves are permitted to wilt, then are rolled, and spread on trays to ferment. During fermentation, the enzymes of the tea cause a dark color and a mild flavor to develop. Black tea, the tea most popular in the United States, is less fragrant and has a less bitter flavor than green tea. For *oolong* (OO-long) tea, the tea leaves are withered and allowed to ferment slightly. This tea has the combined flavor and color of black and green tea, and is usually imported from Taiwan.

The term *pekoe* (PEE-ko) often appears on the label of a package of black tea. Pekoe (shorter) or orange pekoe (longer) refers only to the size of the tea leaf, not to its quality or flavor.

Tea may be sold in bulk—¼, ½, or 1 pound (114, 227, or 454g)—in tea bags, or as instant tea. Decaffeinated tea and herb tea (made from herbs and usually noncaffeinated) are also available. Some teas may include flavorings such as spices, orange peel, mint, or jasmine. The label will indicate the type of tea, its form, and any flavorings that have been added.

### Cocoa

Both cocoa and chocolate are made from the beans of the cacao tree, which grows near the equator. Most of the cocoa beans come from either Latin America or Africa. The imported cocoa beans are then processed in the United States.

Chocolate and cocoa are made from the meat of the cocoa bean which is passed through rollers to form a "chocolate liquor." Bitter chocolate, or baking chocolate, is made from the chocolate liquor, semisweet chocolate has added sugar, and milk and sugar are added to make milk chocolate. Chocolate is sold in squares or bars, small bits or chips, or premelted in individual envelopes.

Cocoa is made by removing some of the cocoa butter as the chocolate liquor is squeezed by a hydraulic press. Dutch processed cocoa is treated to make it darker in color and less likely to settle in the cup. The label on the product will be your guide when selecting both chocolate and cocoa.

Both cocoa and chocolate tend to lose flavor once the container has been opened. You should purchase both cocoa and chocolate in small quantities which you can use within a reasonable period.

### Fruit and Vegetable Beverages

Fruit and vegetable juices can be prepared at home, or purchased canned or frozen, or sometimes in a powdered form. As you know, the label is your guide in selecting canned, frozen, or powdered juices. Smaller fruits and vegetables and those less perfect in size and shape are usually used to make juices. Fresh, well-ripened fruits and vegetables will give you the most flavorful juices.

### Soft Drinks

Soft drinks are a refreshing, sweet beverage, but they should be consumed infrequently. Made up mostly of sugar and water, they contribute little nutrient value to the diet. In fact, many soft drinks contain high amounts of caffeine and sodium.

Low-calorie soft drinks, sweetened with either saccharine, aspartame, or both, and caffeine-free soft drinks are available. Some soft drinks even have added nutrients.

**Tips for Herbs and Spices**

Herbs and spices to use as ingredients in sweet and savory beverages are: cinnamon, cloves, dill, ginger, nutmeg, and pepper.

## Cocoa      Yield: 4 servings

¼ c (60 mL) cocoa     ½ c (125 mL) boiling water
3 Tbs (45 mL) sugar     3 c (0.75 L) milk
⅛ tsp (0.6 mL) salt

1. Blend cocoa, sugar, and salt in saucepan.
2. Stir in water gradually.
3. Cook over low heat until mixture is thick and syrupy (3-5 minutes).
4. Add milk and continue to heat using low heat, stirring occasionally, until cocoa is steaming hot (do not boil).
5. Remove from heat and beat until frothy to prevent skin from forming on top. Serve immediately.

Approximate nutrition information per serving: calories–170; protein–7 g; fat–7 g; cholesterol–30 mg; carbohydrates–20 g; sodium–170 mg.

## Water

One of the most important nutrients, water is also a beverage that may be consumed either alone or with meals. Water is so important that you cannot survive without it. Involved in all body processes, water carries other nutrients to body cells, and carries waste products away from body cells. Water makes up about two-thirds of your total body weight, it keeps your body temperature regular, and it aids in the digestion process. There is no doubt that water is an important nutrient.

All beverages, such as prepared tea, coffee, fruit, and milk, contain large quantities of water and this important factor makes it easy for you to consume the water that you need each day. Fruits, vegetables, and soups are other food sources of water.

### For Review

1. Why is it best to buy ground coffee in small amounts?
2. List three grinds of coffee.
3. List and describe three types of tea.
4. List three products of "chocolate liquor."
5. Why should you limit the amount of soft drinks in your diet?
6. Why is it important to drink water?

# Nutrient Contributions

Hot tea and coffee have a pleasant flavor and are stimulating and refreshing, but lack nutrient values. You may serve cream or milk and sugar with coffee and tea to increase their caloric value. The quantity of milk added is rather small and cannot be counted as a serving of milk. At times, a small amount of lemon is added to tea to enhance its flavor.

Neither tea nor coffee can replace your need for milk. As a beverage, milk is a superior source of the nutrients which you need for growth and which give vitality and glow to your appearance. Milk is also a more important beverage than soft drinks, which provide only calories and few or no nutrients. When you have too many soft drinks and not enough milk and fruit and vegetable beverages, a poor complexion is the penalty.

Cocoa and chocolate contain small amounts of protein, starch, and minerals, but large amounts of fat. The fat in cocoa and chocolate is called **cocoa butter.** Chocolate is a rich source of energy and gives many calories per pound. Most of the cocoa butter is removed when cocoa is made, leaving it with fewer calories.

The beverages cocoa and chocolate, because of their high milk content, offer you a pleasing way to include a portion of your daily milk. Cocoa and chocolate are considered to be the best hot beverages because of their high milk content. Milk-made beverages are wholesome and can be made in many different flavors. The flavored milk drinks include milkshakes and malted milks which are hearty enough to make a substantial contribution to a meal.

Fruit and vegetable juices, when used as beverages, add contrast to other foods of the meal and are a rich source of vitamins and minerals. If the juices are diluted with water to make ades such as lemonade, the amount of nutrient becomes less concentrated and will contribute little to your nutrient needs. Fruit ades and punches are valued for their refreshing quality and variety of uses rather than their nutrient content.

In general, beverages are stimulating and refreshing and contribute little to nutrient values unless they are undiluted fruit and vegetable juices or ones made with milk. Your greatest enjoyment will come from beverages which you learn to prepare by using the basic principles of beverage preparation.

## For Review

1. What nutrient values do coffee and tea provide?
2. Why does cocoa have fewer calories than chocolate?
3. What beverages contribute the highest nutrient values?

# Principles of Beverage Preparation

The ability to make a good cup of coffee or tea has often been regarded as the sign of a good cook. All beverages that you can prepare contain substances that give a desirable and pleasing flavor, and all, except fruit and vegetable juices, contain stimulants (some in larger amounts than others) which can cause a bitter flavor. The principles of beverage preparation are concerned with developing a pleasing flavor and avoiding the extraction of too much stimulant. The way you will apply the principles of beverage preparation will vary with the nature of the beverage.

# Taking the Jitters out of Beverages

Coffee, tea, and many soft drinks contain caffeine. While caffeine consumed in moderate amounts is probably not harmful, many people are sensitive to its effects. A stimulant, caffeine can make people feel more alert, keep them from falling asleep, or cause jitters.

Caffeine excites the central nervous system, makes the heart beat faster, and speeds up the metabolism. Caffeine causes some blood vessels to expand and others to narrow. It stimulates the stomach to secrete stomach acids.

Individuals react differently to the effects of the caffeine in coffee. Some people feel jittery after two cups; others do not feel nervous until they have consumed four cups. However, drinking more than two cups a day may be harmful. Recent research found that men who drank more than two cups a day had higher cholesterol levels even after diet, age, personality, and weight had been accounted for.

With these reports and a desire to sleep better at night without giving up coffee drinking, Americans have turned to decaffeinated coffee. In recent years, consumption of decaffeinated coffee has doubled.

A variety of caffeine-free beverages is available today.

In the decaffeination process, green coffee beans are softened by steam and water. After softening, they are flushed with a solvent. The first solvent used was methylene chloride, but when that chemical was found to be cancer-causing, the industry switched to ethyl acetate. (This action was taken even though no solvent remains on the bean after processing.)

The solvent soaks through to all parts of the bean. The caffeine is drawn from the bean because it bonds with the solvent. After an hour or so, the solvent is drained. The beans are heated and blown with steam to evaporate the solvent. For 97% caffeine-free beans, this process is repeated 24 times. The caffeine does not go to waste. It is removed, purified, and shipped to beverage companies that use it in soft drinks.

The Food and Drug Administration has approved the decaffeination process. In a study of decaffeinated coffee beans, no traces of the solvent were found on the beans. However, industry, government, and health experts all agree that the process should be very closely monitored.

Decaffeination removes some of the natural oil and waxes from the coffee beans. For this reason, decaffeinated beans are roasted darker. The process also causes the bean to shrink a little over ten percent.

The increased demand for decaffeinated coffee has affected the beverage market nationwide. Now decaffeinated teas and soft drinks are available. In addition, people have turned to herbal teas. These teas, made of herbs and spices such as peppermint, cloves, sage, rose hips, and spearmint, are flavorful alternatives to regular, caffeinated tea. Some of the herbs have an added benefit—they are sources of some vitamins, particularly vitamin C.

**Methods of Coffee Preparation**

Drip Method

Percolator Method

Vacuum Method

Steeping

## Coffee Preparation

Caffeine is the chief stimulant in coffee. The flavor substances of coffee are fatlike compounds called *cafferol*. Other substances called **tannins,** when dissolved, give coffee its bitter flavor. The perfect cup of coffee has a pleasing flavor without bitterness, is sparkling clear with a rich, dark-brown color, and has a pleasing aroma.

The principle of **brewing** coffee requires that the coffee grounds come in contact with water just below the boiling point so that only the soluble flavoring substances can be dissolved without dissolving the tannins. When you allow the water containing the coffee grounds to boil, tannins will also dissolve and give a bitter flavor to the beverage. The length of brewing time will be determined by the method you use to make the coffee. The method or coffee maker may differ due to personal preference or availability, but the principle for brewing coffee is always the same. The methods for making coffee are known by the type of coffee maker as drip, percolator, vacuum, and steeped.

The *drip method* requires a drip coffee maker which consists of three parts: lower section, filter section, and upper section. You may wish to preheat the lower section by rinsing it with hot water. You add the measured drip-grind coffee into the filter section which is then placed into the lower portion of the drip coffee maker. Replace the top section, and pour boiling water into it. Cover and allow to drip. You may remove the filter section with the coffee grounds when dripping is completed. Electric automatic drip makers brew coffee almost immediately.

For the *percolator method,* place the measured amount of cold water into the pot and the regular-grind coffee into the basket. As the water is heated, it will be forced through the tube and into the coffee basket. Allow the coffee to perk slowly for six to eight minutes. Remove the basket before serving the coffee.

When you use the *vacuum method,* you measure cold water into the lower bowl. Assemble the upper part, and place the measured amount of fine-grind coffee into it. Place it over the heat until the water rises into the upper bowl. After one to three minutes, remove the coffee maker from the heat to permit the coffee to return to the lower bowl. Remove the top bowl before serving the beverage.

To **steep** or boil coffee, you may use any pot or pan with a cover. Measure cold water into the pan, and add measured regular-grind coffee. Allow the water to come to a boil, and then let it steep, or soak in the liquid, for two minutes. Add a small amount of cold water to settle the grounds before pouring the beverage.

You can make a perfect cup of coffee by whichever method you use when you: (1) use a clean coffee maker (stains in the pot will ruin the flavor); (2) begin with fresh, cold water for a good-flavored beverage; (3) use fresh coffee (ground coffee loses flavor quickly) of the right grind; (4) measure coffee for desired strength (1 Tbs (15 mL) for each ¾ c (185 mL) water for weak coffee); (2 Tbs (30 mL) for each ¾ c (185 mL) water for strong coffee); and (5) keep coffee warm, and serve as soon as possible.

## Tea Preparation

Tea contains both caffeine and tannins along with other flavoring substances. The principle for brewing tea is the same as for brewing coffee; that is, to take out and dissolve the soluble flavoring substances from the tea leaves without dissolving the tannin that makes the tea bitter. A good cup of tea should be sparkling clear; the color should be amber for black tea, pale greenish yellow for green tea, and light

brownish green for oolong; and the flavor should be brisk without any bitterness.

When you brew tea, you bring freshly drawn water to a full rolling boil. Use a clean china or pottery teapot, and preheat it by filling it with boiling water. Do not put it over direct heat. Pour out the water, and add the measured tea leaves—one teaspoon (5 mL) or one tea bag for each one cup (250 mL) water. Then pour the fresh boiling water over the tea leaves, cover the pot, and let the tea steep for three to five minutes. If you use tea leaves, the beverage should be strained into another preheated pot. The tea bags need only to be removed.

## Cocoa Preparation

Cocoa and chocolate contain starch, cocoa butter, and the stimulant *theobromine* (thee-uh-BRO-meen). Because theobromine is a milder stimulant than caffeine and because only a small

**Tea Preparation**

1. Preheat the teapot.  2. Add tea leaves.  3. Pour in boiling water.  4. Steep for 3-5 minutes.

## Cocoa Preparation

Step 1

Step 2

Step 3

amount of cocoa or chocolate is used to make the beverages, they are considered to be wholesome beverages. Principles for preparing cocoa differ from those used for coffee and tea. When you make coffee or tea, the soluble substances are absorbed into the water; but when you make hot cocoa, the cocoa or chocolate is combined into the milk.

Because both cocoa and chocolate contain starch, you will need to recall the principles of starch cookery when preparing the hot beverages. The starch grains need to be separated with the sugar or cold liquid to prevent lumping, and the starch needs to be cooked to avoid a raw starch flavor.

When you make cocoa, you use milk and sugar in addition to cocoa, and therefore you need to apply the principles of milk cookery. To heat the beverage, use a low temperature to avoid boiling over and scorching.

The perfect cup of cocoa will be smooth and well blended with a pleasing chocolate flavor. When you make cocoa, apply these principles of starch cookery.

1. Blend the sugar and cocoa, and then stir in the cold water to separate the starch grains. When you use chocolate, the starch particles are already separated by the cocoa butter.
2. Cook the cocoa or chocolate mixture so that a raw starch flavor is avoided; as the starch is heated, it will swell and therefore thicken the mixture.
3. Add milk to the cooked chocolate mixture, and warm the beverage to serving temperature. At this point, you will apply the principles of milk cookery by using a low heat to prevent scorching and boiling over.

## Juice Preparation

Most fruit or vegetable juices you consume are probably from a convenience form. However, these nutritious beverages can be prepared easily at home. Juices made from fresh, unstrained fruits and vegetables are higher in nutrient value and flavor than are their convenience forms.

You can juice fresh fruits such as oranges in a juicer, or you can blend and then strain cut-up pieces in an electric blender or food processor. Fresh vegetables such as peppers and cucumbers may also be juiced in the same manner. An advantage to preparing fruit and vegetable beverages at home is that you can easily do so in small amounts, thereby having a fresh, high-nutrient beverage any time you wish. Let creativity be your guide in combining many different fruits and vegetables into wholesome, flavorful beverages.

Electric juicers let you create your own fruit or vegetable drinks quickly and easily at home. Homemade beverages are higher in nutrients than store convenience juices.

## Tips for Microwaving Beverages

- Milk boils over easily. Cook it in a large container, and watch it carefully for signs of foaming.
- Do not use the microwave to heat large volumes; use a conventional range to save time.
- Beverages will be hotter when heated in their serving cups.

## Microwaving Beverages

Heat most beverages on a high power setting in the microwave. Some beverages, such as tea, are first heated on a high setting, and are then put on a low setting to develop flavor. Beverages should be heated uncovered, and then stirred before serving in order to distribute heat evenly.

### For Review

1. When making coffee, why is it important *not* to boil the water containing the coffee grounds?
2. What are the four methods for making coffee?
3. Describe a good cup of tea.
4. Why do you need to follow the cookery principles for starch and milk when making cocoa?

## Uses, Storage, and Convenience

Beverages, like other foods, can serve more than one purpose in our daily eating pattern. Either prepared at home or from a convenience form, beverages must be stored properly to keep their nutrients and/or their distinctive flavor.

### Uses of Beverages

Beverages are most often served as an *accompaniment*. The basic beverages of coffee, tea, cocoa, and fruit and vegetable juices may be served hot or cold along with the main course, with the dessert, or at the end of a meal. On festive and formal occasions, you may choose to serve them in the living room as the conclusion

Attractively served cold beverages, such as iced tea or fruit juice with berries and milk, are pleasing to the eye and thirst quenching.

to a meal. Milk, too, can serve a dual purpose; that is, you may serve it as a beverage and at the same time contribute important nutrient values to your meal. It is an important accompaniment to between-meal snacks. Regardless of the ways in which you choose to serve them, beverages are prized for their stimulating and refreshing qualities.

All beverages may be served as *special refreshments*. On special occasions such as teas and receptions, the beverage is the center of interest, and other foods are chosen to enhance and accompany the beverage. The occasion, whether formal or informal, will help you deter-

mine which beverage to select and how it will be served. The beverage as a special refreshment is very easily included in a simple, friendly gathering or in an elaborate and very formal setting. A good beverage adds something extra to any setting, be it breakfast, an outdoor barbecue, or an elaborate celebration.

Cocoa, chocolate, and coffee are used in a variety of ways as a *flavor ingredient* for cakes, pastry, puddings, fancy frozen desserts, and candies. Fruit juices often add flavor to gelatins, puddings, cakes, cookies, and other beverages. Tea is a base for iced beverages to which fruit juices and other flavorings may be added.

## Care and Storage

The flavor and aroma of coffee, tea, cocoa, and chocolate are best retained when stored in airtight containers; some of the substances that give beverages their flavor and aroma are volatile, or can escape into the air.

Once the coffee bean is ground and exposed to air, it loses its flavor and aroma rapidly. When coffee is purchased in paper bags, its flavor and aroma will be retained best when you place it into a metal or glass container with a tight-fitting lid. Vacuum-packed coffee sold in cans will retain the volatile flavors, but once you open the can, they will gradually be lost. Because it loses its flavor and becomes stale so quickly, ground coffee should be purchased only in amounts that can be used in a week. When you store ground coffee in either the refrigerator or the freezer, the loss of flavor and aroma will be slower.

Tea, cocoa, and chocolate retain more of their original aroma and flavor when kept in a tightly closed container. Cocoa and chocolate contain fat and should be stored in a cool place. When chocolate gets warm, cocoa butter will rise to the surface and produce white spots.

As you know, milk retains its flavor and freshness best when stored in the refrigerator. Once you prepare fruit and vegetable juices, you should store them in the refrigerator in covered containers to retain their flavor and vitamin C value. You will recall that vitamin C is easily destroyed by air.

## Convenience in Beverages

All beverages can be purchased in a convenience form. Instant coffee, tea, and cocoa are available and require only the addition of a liquid.

It may surprise you to know that instant coffee is less expensive per serving than regular coffee. This is due to the fact that less green coffee is needed for the instant coffee than for regular roasted coffee. Because instant coffee is very light and takes up less space than regular coffee, it can be transported for less, and this reduces the cost of the beverage to the consumer. However, you may find the flavor of instant coffee less pleasing than that of regular roasted coffee.

Instant tea is also available. It is widely used for making iced tea because it dissolves quickly in cold water. The flavor of instant tea, like that of instant coffee, is not usually as pleasing and full as the beverage brewed from tea leaves. The tea bag eliminates the need to strain tea and is a convenience used by many. When prepared from tea bags or from instant tea, the beverage is usually more expensive than when prepared from tea leaves. Flavored teas are also more expensive than unflavored teas.

Instant cocoa or hot chocolate requires only the addition of milk or water to prepare the beverage. Powdered fruit-flavored beverages and frozen concentrates require only the addition of water, while canned juices are ready for immediate use. Nonfat dry milk is another example of an instant beverage.

Your guide in the selection of convenience beverages will be the label. You will need to consider the factors of time, effort, and quality of the convenience item in return for its increase in cost over the home-prepared beverage.

### For Review
1. What are three uses of beverages?
2. Why should you store coffee, tea, cocoa, and chocolate in airtight containers?
3. What is one advantage of using instant coffee rather than regular coffee? What is one disadvantage?

# 26 Chapter Review

## Summary

Meals are enhanced with the use of beverages. These may include milk, coffee, tea, cocoa, fruit and vegetable juices, soft drinks, and water. Some of these beverages are so popular that they are staple items in most homes, and they are available in a variety of convenience forms as well. In order for beverages to be a refreshing drink, they need proper storage to protect their flavors and/or nutrients, and they need proper preparation. However, the application of the principles of beverage preparation depends on the particular beverage being made.

## Vocabulary

Use the words below to fill in the blanks in the paragraph that follows.

brewing                 steep
caffeine                stimulant
cocoa butter            tannins
decaffeinated coffee

Tea and coffee have a drug that is called __(1)__. This drug is considered a __(2)__ because it increases body activities, such as heart rate and blood pressure. Because some people can only have reduced amounts of this drug, producers have made __(3)__ and tea available by chemically or naturally treating it to remove almost all of the harmful substance. Other substances found in coffee and tea give it a bitter taste when they are dissolved; these substances are called __(4)__. Because boiling coffee will give it a bitter taste, the principle of __(5)__ is used so that the coffee grounds come in contact with water just below the boiling point. One method of making coffee and tea requires bringing the water to a boil and then letting the coffee or tea soak, or __(6)__, in the liquid for a brief period of time. Tea and coffee lack nutritive values, but cocoa and chocolate do possess a little protein, starch, minerals, and a large amount of fat, known as __(7)__.

## Chapter Questions

1. What is the best kind of grind to purchase for each of the following coffee makers? a) vacuum-type coffee maker; b) automatic drip coffee maker; c) percolator; d) filter coffee maker; and e) electric percolator
2. If you were going to serve a beverage to someone who had a heart problem and was on a low-cholesterol diet, what are two selections you would make?
3. What beverages are available in your family, and when and how are they used?
4. If you planned to serve fresh orange juice, what kind of oranges should you purchase?
5. In addition to beverages, what other foods are sources of water?
6. What are some values other than nutrients that are derived from beverages?
7. Why is cocoa often considered the best hot beverage?

8. What are the characteristics of a perfect cup of coffee?

9. How is the preparation of hot cocoa different from that used for tea and coffee?

10. Should you use a microwave oven or a conventional range to make 20 cups of coffee? Why?

11. If you were planning a dinner menu for a birthday party, what beverages would you serve and with which parts of the meal?

12. What are the qualities you should consider when you decide to purchase a convenience beverage?

## Skill Activities

**1. Decision making** In your food journal or card file box, make a collection of recipes for beverages. Categorize your beverages into categories for coffee and tea, milk, vegetable and fruit juices, cocoa and chocolate, and soft drinks. Also, try to find recipes that have low calories. You can find recipes in books, magazines, and newspapers, and on the display board in supermarkets. Add to this collection, whenever you find interesting recipes.

**2. Communication** Chocolate was first manufactured in the United States in 1765. Research and write a report about the history of chocolate. Also discuss the history of some of the different chocolate products that are manufactured and how chocolate is used in the United States. With the report, include at least three recipes for foods that use chocolate as one of the ingredients.

**3. Critical thinking** Visit a local grocery store to learn the beverage items that are available and how they are packaged. Take two sheets of lined paper and make four columns on each sheet. Then at the top of each column, write one of these headings: "Coffee," "Tea," "Cocoa," "Chocolate," "Fruit juice and drink," "Vegetable juice," "Soft drinks," and "Milk." When you visit the grocery store, try to locate canned, bottled, reconstituted, powdered, dry, instant, fresh, and frozen concentrated beverage products. On your chart, record the different forms for each beverage, its size and price, how the beverages are packaged, and the different kinds of convenience forms available. Notice which products have nutrition labels. When you have completed your chart, ask yourself these questions: Which beverage has the most different convenience items? What kinds of products have nutrition labels? What are the different ways that fruit juices are available? What is the difference in price for one serving of canned orange juice and one serving of frozen orange juice? If you were going to make hot cocoa or hot chocolate, which cocoa or chocolate item would you purchase and why? Look for two different forms of the same kind of beverage that have nutritional labels, and tell how the nutrient values differ.

# 27 Fats and Oils

## As you read, think about:

- what nutrients fats and oils provide.
- how to identify, select, and store fats and oils.
- how to use fats and oils appropriately in food preparation.

Fat may be the chief nutrient in a food, as in butter, margarine, and salad oils; or it may be included in varying amounts with other nutrients, such as in eggs, milk, and lean meats. Fat that is liquid at room temperature is known as **oil,** and fat that is a solid is called **fat.** The terms *fat* and *oil* both refer to the same kind of substance and can be identified by their greasy nature. The entire group of fats and fatlike substance are called *lipids.*

Fats occur naturally in many foods and are often added in the preparation of other foods. As concentrated sources of energy, fats make several valuable contributions to your diet.

## Nutrient Contributions

Fats are the richest source of energy: they provide two and one-fourth times as much energy (calories) as carbohydrates or proteins. Because fats are digested more slowly than carbohydrates and protein, they keep you from getting hungry quickly.

Butter is the most common fat. Produced today in large manufacturing plants, butter was once made at home in devices such as this 19th-century churner.

Some fats are visible; you can easily recognize the fat on bacon. Fats that are less obvious, such as those in nuts, are called invisible. Which of these foods have visible fats? Invisible fats?

Your body can convert the fat that you eat into essential substances it needs. Some of these fat substances are used to build cell walls. Body fat supports and protects the vital organs of your body, and is a reserve supply of energy. The layer of fat under your skin protects your body against excessive heat loss and in this way helps you to maintain a normal body temperature.

Some fats carry with them the fat-soluble vitamins. These vitamins are stable and are not usually lost during cooking. The fats in milk, eggs, butter, and margarine are important sources of vitamins A and D. Other fats contribute vitamin E, found in green leafy vegetables and in fruits, and vitamin K, found in cauliflower, cabbage, and pork liver.

Fats supply another substance called fatty acids. Your body needs them for growth and to prevent skin diseases. Two kinds of fatty acids are found in fats: the saturated and unsaturated. The **saturated fatty acids,** which tend to raise the amount of cholesterol in the blood, have in their structure all of the hydrogen they can hold, while some hydrogen is missing from **unsaturated fatty acids.** One of the unsaturated fatty acids, *linoleic acid,* is called the *essential fatty acid* because your body is unable to make it, and it must be provided by the food you eat. **Polyunsaturated fatty acids** have the least amount of hydrogen, and actually reduce the amount of cholesterol in the blood. The fats that contain a large portion of saturated fatty acids are solid at room temperature, while those that have a large portion of unsaturated fatty acids are liquid at room temperature.

It may be helpful for you to think of fats as being visible and invisible. The visible fats are butter, margarine, meat fats, oils, and cream. The invisible fats make up a part of foods such as eggs, lean meats, cheese, and whole milk. You may not be aware of invisible fats because you do not see them.

## Fat in Food

Fats most often make up a part of other foods, but they may also be in a pure form such as salad or cooking oils. Meats contain fat even after you have trimmed away the fat that you can see. Milk and cheese contain butter fat. The richest sources of fat in your diet are the animal fats (beef fat or suet, lard from pork, and butter), vegetable oils (corn, cottonseed, peanut, olive, soybean), vegetable shortenings, and nuts. The vegetable oils can be hardened by the process of **hydrogenation** (hy-DROJ-uh-NAY-shun) (adding hydrogen) to form both vegetable shortenings and margarines.

Lean pork and beef may have about the same amount of fat, while fish generally contains less fat than beef, pork, or poultry. The fat in eggs is only in the yolk.

Foods prepared with fats and oils (cakes, cookies, pastries, and potato chips, for example) often contain a high proportion of fat. Fruits, except for avocados, and vegetables contain very little fat.

Most of the fats in the diet are *triglycerides* (try-GLISS-uh-rides); that is, are made of glycerol (an alcohol) and three fatty acids. When you fry foods at a high temperature, the glycerol of the fat decomposes to *acrolein,* which has an unpleasant odor and irritates the eyes.

### For Review

1. What is the difference between fats and oils?
2. What is the importance of linoleic acid?
3. What is the difference in the effect of polyunsaturated and saturated fatty acids on the amount of cholesterol in the blood?

# Kinds of Fat

The common fats used in food preparation are butter, margarine, lard, and vegetable shortenings and oils.

*Butter* is the fat of cream which is separated by churning. It is an excellent source of vitamin A and is rich in energy. Butter adds a pleasing flavor to other foods.

*Margarine* was developed as a substitute for butter. It is made of partially hydrogenated vegetable oils. The hardened vegetable oils are churned with milk to produce a product that resembles butter in consistency. Some margarine may be whipped to incorporate air and thus increase its volume. The addition of air and water to margarine reduces the percentage of fat, and thus the calories, in a given amount. Most all margarine is fortified with vitamin A and is artificially colored. Some margarines also have added vitamin D. Margarine, like butter, is a rich source of energy.

*Lard* is the fat separated from the fatty tissues of hogs. The fat that lines the abdominal cavity of the animal makes the best quality lard and is known as "leaf" lard. Lard is soft and is bland in flavor. It is prized for its shortening quality. It is a rich source of energy.

*Vegetable oils* are known by the name of the vegetable from which they are made. The commonly used oils are pressed from seeds or nuts such as corn, cottonseed, safflower, peanut, soybean, olive, and oil palm. Vegetable oils are sometimes referred to as salad oils.

*Vegetable shortenings* are made from vegetable oils by the process of hydrogenation. They are firm, plastic fats with a bland flavor. You will use these types of fat in a variety of ways when you prepare foods.

**For Review**

1. List the five kinds of fat, and briefly describe how each is made.
2. Explain an advantage of using each of the five kinds of fat.

# Uses of Fats and Oils

You can use fats and oils for many purposes in cookery. You can use them to add flavor, to prevent foods from sticking, to make baked products tender, to fry in, and to serve as the chief ingredient of salad dressings. Some fats are suitable for all purposes. Other fats may be used only in a limited number of ways.

### Flavor

Fats add flavor and palatability to foods. You may enjoy the flavor of butter or margarine for seasoning vegetables and sauces and as a spread for breads. Both butter and margarine will contribute a pleasing flavor to cookies, cakes, and pastries. However, if you wish, you may sometimes use bacon and other meat drippings to season vegetables. (The flavor of bacon with green beans is popular.) You may also use meat drippings in cookery where their flavor enhances or blends with the food. When you use olive oil, it will contribute a distinctive flavor to salad dressing. Most other vegetable oils are rather bland and have very little flavor of their own.

# French Sautéed Sandwich  Yield: 1 sandwich

2 slices firm bread
2 thin slices Swiss cheese
1 thin slice ham

2 Tbs (30 mL) butter
or margarine
2 tsp (10 mL) vegetable oil

1. Trim crusts from the bread; put the cheese and ham between the slices.
2. Melt the butter or margarine and the oil in a skillet.
3. Brown the sandwich slowly, about 3 minutes on each side.

Approximate nutrition
information per serving:
calories–665;
protein–25 g; fat–49 g;
cholesterol–65 mg;
carbohydrates–30 g;
sodium–985 mg.

Many people enjoy the taste of butter or margarine on cooked vegetables such as broccoli, squash, and corn. Do butter and margarine contain large or small amounts of saturated fatty acids?

## What Is Cholesterol?

Cholesterol is a chemical that the body needs to build cell membranes, hormones, digestive juices, and vitamin D. The liver manufactures some cholesterol, but most of it comes from the diet. Animal fat in meats and dairy products have high levels of cholesterol. Eggs do, too. Although the body needs cholesterol, too much of this chemical can be deadly, and the typical American diet includes about twice as much cholesterol as needed.

High levels of cholesterol in the bloodstream have been linked to high rates of heart disease. This link was discovered in Europe during World War II. During the war, when some people ate a diet based on rationed food, few of them developed heart disease. After the war, these people once again ate eggs, meat, and butter in abundant quantities, and heart disease among them increased.

In the bloodstream, cholesterol is surrounded by capsules of fat and protein. The capsules cluster along artery walls, damaging the artery. This process can also cause the body, perhaps as a repairing process, to build tissue around the cluster. The build-up, called plaque, can harden over time. The plaque can also clog a blood vessel, causing heart attacks and strokes.

Most of the symptoms of diseases linked to high cholesterol levels do not appear until middle age. Some doctors, however, believe that some diseases related to cholesterol may begin in infancy.

To reduce cholesterol levels in your diet, follow these guidelines:

**Reduce saturated fats**   Saturated fats are found in animal products, such as milk, cheese, butter, and beef. Reducing the amount of these products in the diet has been linked to lower cholesterol levels. You can eat fish and poultry more often, and substitute skim milk for whole milk.

**Exercise**   Recent evidence suggests that regular exercise helps regulate cholesterol levels and has other beneficial effects.

**Do not smoke**   Smoking disturbs the levels of cholesterol and causes damage to blood vessels.

**Eat more fiber**   Fiber from oat bran, beans, and corn seems to lower cholesterol levels.

Which foods shown here would you eat if you were trying to cut down on saturated fats?

For deep-fat frying, use a deep pot and a wire basket.

Use salad oils, vegetable shortenings, or high-quality lard.

Heat the fat, measuring the temperature with a deep-fat thermometer.

Deep-fat fry small amounts of food so the fat will not cool.

Remove the food from the fat, and drain.

## Shortening and Tenderness

In addition to flavor, fats contribute to the shortness, or tenderness, of baked products. The fat forms layers that separate the starch and gluten particles: this helps produce a tender product. Lard has a superior shortening value and is often used in making pies. Vegetable shortenings are also suitable for pastry, but butter and margarine have less shortening value. You will need to use special recipes when you make pastry with oil. Quick breads and yeast breads are made tender with fats and oils.

Vegetable shortenings are important in the aeration of shortened cakes because air beaten into the cake is held in the batter by the fat. Vegetable shortenings, instead of lard, are usually preferred for cakes. Chiffon-type cakes require a special recipe and are made with oil. Cake recipes are delicately balanced formulas, so you will be most satisfied by using a recipe developed for the shortening you prefer.

## Frying

You may also use fat to fry foods. Fat prevents the food from sticking to the pan and helps to distribute the heat. Fried foods become crisp, form an attractive brown crust, and absorb some of the flavor of the fat.

Pan-frying or sautéeing is browning food in a small amount of fat. Deep-fat frying requires a large amount of fat. Fats that have a high smoke point (those that can be heated to a high temperature without smoking) are best suited for frying. When you permit fats to smoke, they break down chemically to form substances that are irritating to the eyes and nose and have an unpleasant flavor. Use vegetable shortening, lard, and oils for frying; margarine and butter have a low smoke point and decompose quickly at high temperatures. Deep-fat frying is cooking foods by immersing them completely in hot fat. You will use deep-fat frying for foods such as doughnuts and fritters, french-fried potatoes and onions, breaded or batter-dipped poultry, fish, and seafoods.

For deep-fat frying, you need a deep pot and a wire basket for holding the food in the hot fat. Automatic deep-fat fryers, with thermostatic temperature controls, provide equally good results.

For deep-fat frying, use salad oils (but not olive oil, which has a low smoke point), vegetable shortenings, and high-quality lard. Fill the pot or fryer one-third to one-half full of fat. The food should be surrounded by fat with room for the fat to bubble over the food.

Heat the fat to the temperature listed in the recipe before adding the food. Check the temperature with a thermometer unless you are using an automatic deep fryer. When the fat becomes too hot, the food turns brown and hard on the surface but may not be cooked in the center. It becomes soggy and grease-soaked when the fat is not hot enough.

Place a small amount of food into the basket, and lower the basket into the fat. Too much food will cool the fat, and the food will absorb more fat and need longer cooking. Once the food is cooked, remove it from the fat and drain it on absorbent paper.

## Salad Dressings

One of the chief uses of oil in cooking is for making salad dressings. You recall from Chapter 23 that the oil forms an emulsion in the salad dressing. Usually, oils with a bland or mild flavor are preferable for salad dressing. The consistency of both mayonnaise and French dressing depends upon how well the salad oil forms an emulsion. The oil is usually dispersed (that is, broken into small droplets by beating) in a small amount of acid and flavoring materials to form an emulsion.

## Microwaving with Fats and Oils

Fats absorb microwaves and therefore cook very quickly. Visible fat should be removed from meat, or the meat next to the fat may overcook. A fat layer is not necessary in the microwave as in a conventional oven because there is no hot air to dry the meat.

*Never* use the microwave for deep-fat frying because temperatures cannot be kept constant. However, you can use the microwave oven for sautéeing foods in a small amount of butter or oil.

### For Review

1. Which fats add the most flavor to foods? The least flavor?
2. Which fats are best for shortening?
3. Explain three guidelines to follow when deep-fat frying.

# Buying and Storage of Fats and Oils

Some fats and oils are suitable for several uses in cookery; others are best suited for a special purpose. You will need to consider the use for which each is best suited when you make your choice.

### Tips for Herbs and Spices

Almost any herb can be used fresh or dried to flavor oils for use in salad dressings. Dried dill and chives can be blended with softened butter or margarine for a fragrant sandwich spread.

## Selecting Fats and Oils

There are many fats and oils from which to choose. Your problem in selection will become a little easier when you consider the particular use of each kind of fat. The label will indicate the kind of fat or oil and the ingredients used to make it, but the label will not give you much information concerning the quality. Your experience with the various kinds will be your best guide. However, grades are indicated for butter and may be used as a guide to quality. Grade AA is the highest, followed by Grades A, B, and C. Good butter has a pleasing flavor and odor, and a smooth, waxy texture. Butter is usually salted unless it is labeled "sweet butter." This indicates that the butter is not salted.

When more than one kind of fat will serve your purpose, you will save money by selecting the least expensive fat. Vegetable shortenings and lard usually cost less than margarine, and butter is the most expensive fat. The cost will vary among the various oils, and olive oil is usually the most expensive. Grade and quality will also influence the cost.

Whenever possible, buy a fat that will serve more than one purpose. For example, select a fat suitable both for frying and shortening purposes. It is also unnecessary to purchase a wide variety of fats and oils. You need only a table spread and perhaps some vegetable oil. Fats and oils must be stored properly in order to preserve quality and to prevent any undesirable changes in flavor.

## Care and Storage

Fats and oils will become **rancid** (develop an undesirable flavor) when they are exposed to air. You must keep them tightly covered to keep

There is a wide variety of fats and oils to select from. To prepare this meal, which fats and/or oils would you need to purchase?

out air and to prevent the absorption of other flavors. All fats can pick up flavors when stored uncovered near fish, onions, and other foods. Vegetable oils and shortenings usually keep well at room temperature. Butter, margarine, and lard require refrigeration.

You will be able to reuse fats that are suited for frying when you handle them properly. Avoid overheating the fat to prevent its decomposition. The use of a thermometer is your only accurate guide to the temperature of the fat. Strain the fat to remove any remaining food particles before storing it. Store the fat in a cold, dark place, in a tightly covered container.

## Convenience in Fats and Oils

Fats are available in several forms, and the convenience comes from the manner in which they are used. Oils can be substituted for melted fat in most recipes unless you prefer the flavor of the melted fat.

Butter and margarine are available in sticks. Four sticks equal 1 pound (.45 kg), and markings on the wrappers often indicate fractional amounts in tablespoons (milliliters) and cups (liters). When precise accuracy in measure-ment is not essential (as in cream sauces, puddings, or seasoned food), you may cut the wrapper at the desired mark for an approximate measurement.

Special butters and margarines, which remain soft and easy to spread after refrigeration, are also an available convenience. Since most shortenings are partly precreamed, making them softer and easier to measure, you do not need to soften them in preparation for blending with other ingredients.

Fats, except for butter and olive oil, tend to be bland in flavor. Flavored fats have increased the variety of available fats. Butter-flavored oils and shortenings and butter spreads with an added flavor, such as honey, are available.

### For Review

1. What are two guidelines to follow when purchasing fats and oils?
2. Why is it important to store fats and oils tightly covered?

# 27 Chapter Review

## Summary

Not only are fats present in many foods, they are also added during the preparation of foods. The fats used in food preparation include butter, margarine, lard, vegetable oil, and vegetable shortening. The flavor, composition, and consistency of fats govern their uses and cooking principles. As with the purchase of many other foods, the selection of a fat should be based on its use. To maintain the flavor and quality of fats, proper storage is required. While fats are an excellent source of energy, some fats are also important providers of vitamins A, D, E, and K.

## Vocabulary

Use the words below to complete the sentences that follow:

fat
hydrogenation
oil
polyunsaturated fatty acids
rancid
saturated fatty acids
unsaturated fatty acids

1. Fats that are solid at room temperature and that tend to raise the amount of cholesterol in the blood contain _____.
2. Fat that is solid is called _____.
3. Fats that hold only some hydrogen and are liquid at room temperature have a large amount of _____.
4. Fat that is liquid at room temperature is known as _____.
5. Fats that contain the least amount of hydrogen and that actually reduce the amount of cholesterol in the blood are called _____.
6. Vegetable shortenings and margarines are made from vegetable oils that have been hardened by the process of _____.
7. It is important to keep fats and oils tightly covered to prevent them from becoming _____, or developing an unpleasant flavor.

## Chapter Questions

1. Why should fats be included in your diet?
2. What foods are the richest sources of fat?
3. What common fats are used to prepare foods?
4. If you were going to make a French dressing, what kind of fat would you use?
5. What happens to the fat when the food is fried at too high a temperature?
6. What fats and oils do you have at home? For each kind, give at least one use.
7. If you want to prepare a cake for a person who has to restrict the amount of cholesterol in the diet, what kind of fat ingredient should you look for in the recipe and why?
8. Give the purpose of the fat for each of the following foods: a) cakes; b) pastry; c) fried potatoes; d) cooked green beans; and e) mayonnaise.
9. Evaluate the storage of fat in your home. For each kind of fat, tell how it is stored and the reasons why it is stored that way.

10. Why is it important when you are deep fat frying to use a thermometer to measure the temperature of the fat?

11. Why is it necessary to remove the layer of fat from meat before you microwave it?

12. What are ways that people can reduce the amount of saturated fat in their diet while cutting down on total fat consumption?

## Skill Activities

 **1. Critical thinking** In your food journal or on a sheet of paper, keep a record of the fat you use during food preparation. Make six equal columns on your paper. At the top of each column, write one of these headings: "Name of food," "Kind of fat," "Amount of fat," "Kind of fatty acids," "Purpose of the fat," "Procedures used to add the fat to the food." Add the appropriate information to each column the next time you prepare a food to which you add fat.

 **2. Science** Research information about margarine. Prepare a report that includes the history of how and why margarine was made, the ingredients commonly used in American margarine, and the different kinds of margarine that are now available.

 **3. Decision making** Down the left-hand side of a sheet of lined paper, write these headings: "Serving size," "Servings per container,"

"Calories," "Protein," "Carbohydrate," "Fat," "Cholesterol," "Sodium," "Ingredients," "Price," and "Cost per serving." Now make two columns, and write "Regular margarine" at the top of one and "Low-cholesterol margarine" at the top of the other column. Visit the dairy counter of a local supermarket and locate a package of regular margarine and one of low-cholesterol margarine. Record the findings on your sheet of paper. Compare the ingredients and nutritional labels and price for each product. How are the ingredients of the margarines alike and different? Which margarine has fewer calories? Which margarine has the highest amount of sodium? Which costs less per serving?

 **4. Resource management** Have your class compare shortenings —margarine, vegetable shortening, and lard—for texture and flavor. Make small batches of sugar cookies. Use a different shortening for each batch. Evaluate the taste and texture of the cookies as a result of the shortening.

**5. Food science** The composition and properties of oils from different sources vary widely. Choose two of these oils to compare: corn oil, peanut oil, cottonseed oil, olive oil, or safflower oil. First, find out the proportion of saturated and unsaturated fats in each oil. Use nutrition guides or write directly to the manufacturers of the oils for this information. Then conduct your own experiments to determine and compare the boiling and freezing points of the two oils.

# 28 Cakes and Frostings

## As you read, think about:

- how to prepare shortened and foam cakes.
- how to prepare frostings and to frost cakes.
- why cakes and frostings are nutrient-poor but calorie-rich.

For centuries cakes have continued to be an important part of celebrations. Have you wondered where and how cakes came into being? About 2800 B.C., a spicy cake similar to our gingerbread was invented in Greece. The Romans served cakes at weddings, as we do today. Until the second century, cakes looked like large puddings.

The pound cake originated in colonial America and was made from a pound each of sugar, butter, and flour. The chiffon cake, a blend of sponge cake and butter cake, is the newest creation. The layer cake has developed into an American specialty and comes in many varieties.

# Types of Cakes and Their Ingredients

Many cake recipes are available, some which include fats and others which do not. On this general basis, cakes can be classified into two broad groups: cakes with shortening and cakes without shortening. However, solid fats, when used in cakes, are combined differently

and give a different cake texture than do liquid fats (oil). Because of this difference in fats, you will find it convenient to classify cakes into three basic types: shortened, or butter; chiffon; and foam, or sponge. The types of cakes differ in their mixing methods and in the proportion of the ingredients used.

## Shortened, or Butter, Cakes

The first cakes were made with butter and, therefore, became known as "butter" cakes. Since then, other fats such as margarine and vegetable shortening have been developed and used in cakes. Cakes made with solid fats continue to be called **butter cakes** whether the fat is butter, margarine, or vegetable shortening.

Shortened, or butter, cakes are made by one of two methods: the conventional method or the quick method. They have a fine texture, and are light, tender, and moist.

## Chiffon Cakes

**Chiffon cakes** differ from butter cakes in that they are made with oil instead of a solid fat. They have some of the qualities of cakes made without fat even though oil is used. They are

Cake making and frosting decorating demand the trained skill of a pastry chef. Here, early 20th-century pastry chefs prepare New Year's cakes.

There are three basic types of cakes: (from left to right) the butter cake, the sponge cake, and chiffon cake. They can be used to create an infinite variety of delicious desserts.

made with a large quantity of eggs, which gives them the lightness characteristic of sponge cakes; the oil gives them the tenderness of shortened cakes.

### Foam, or Sponge, Cakes

**Foam,** or sponge, **cakes** are made without shortening. They are leavened with the air beaten into the eggs and with the steam formed during baking. They have a light, fluffy texture.

### Cake Ingredients

Some cake ingredients, such as flour, sugar, and eggs, are basic and used in all cakes. In addition to these ingredients, shortening, chemical leaveners (baking powder or baking soda), and liquid are required for butter cakes.

**Flour** The flour provides the structure of a cake and is the ingredient used in the largest quantity. Cake flour and all-purpose flour are used for cakes. Cake flour has a lower gluten content than all-purpose flour. It produces larger, more velvety and delicate cakes than all-purpose flour, but either one will produce good cakes. The recipe will often specify which flour you should use. When you want to substitute all-purpose flour in a recipe that calls for cake flour, you must remove 2 tablespoons (30 mL) from each 1 cup (.24 L). It is usually best to use the recipe specially developed for the kind of flour (cake or all-purpose) that you wish to use.

It is possible to make a successful cake without sifting flour when you follow the no-sift directions given for the flour you are using. However, for the most accurate measurements of flour and the lightest and most delicate cakes every time, you should sift the flour.

**Sugar** You will recall that sugar gives flavor, improves texture, and helps flour products to brown. The recipe may call for brown or white (granulated) sugar. The sugar should be free of lumps. You may sift granulated white sugar to remove lumps, or roll brown sugar with a rolling pin on waxed paper.

**Eggs** Eggs will improve the color and texture of a cake. Beaten eggs will help to make the cake light and fluffy.

**Shortening** The term *shortening* refers to any solid fat, and any good-quality solid fat may be used. Most shortenings are bland in flavor except butter and margarine, which have a rich, pleasing flavor. The creaming quality of vegetable shortenings is better (due to the emulsifiers which are added) than that of butter. Shortening improves the texture, tenderness, and keeping quality of cakes.

**Liquid** The liquid provides moisture and helps to blend the ingredients together. Milk is the most often used liquid; however, some recipes may specify sour milk or buttermilk, water, or fruit juice.

**Leavening Agent** A leavening agent causes a cake to rise and become light and porous in texture. Baking powder and baking soda are the leavening agents used in butter cakes. Sponge cakes are leavened by beating air into the eggs and by the steam produced during baking.

**Flavor Ingredients** A variety of ingredients such as spices, extracts, nuts, chocolate, and fruits are used to produce definite flavors. These are not basic ingredients, since their only purpose is to contribute flavor.

You should remember that cake recipes are delicately balanced formulas. To bake a good cake, you must not only begin with the proper ingredients, but you must also measure them accurately. When measurements are not accurate or you fail to use the proper ingredients, it is very likely that your cake will not be a success. Also, it is best to have all cake ingredients at room temperature so that they can be well blended, and air can be easily incorporated.

**For Review**

1. What are the three basic types of cakes?
2. What kind of fat is used in each of the three types of cakes?
3. What basic ingredients are in all cakes?

# Principles of Cake Making

The principles of cake making are concerned with the influence of ingredients on gluten formation, the methods of mixing or of combining ingredients, and the baking of the cake.

## Influence of Ingredients on Gluten Formation

The gluten of flour forms a network or structure which entraps the leavening gases (air, carbon dioxide, and steam). Cake flour is very finely milled and contains less gluten than all-purpose flour. For these reasons, cake flour will produce more tender cakes with a finer and lighter texture. Unlike yeast breads, cake batters are mixed only enough to blend the flour into the other ingredients. Too much mixing will overdevelop the gluten and cause toughness.

Fat and sugar tenderize gluten and help to produce a tender cake. However, too much fat or sugar can excessively weaken the gluten structure and produce a heavy, coarse texture and cause the cake to fall.

The liquid provides the moisture necessary to develop gluten and to produce carbon dioxide from the chemical leavening agent (baking powder or baking soda). Too much liquid causes a heavy, soggy cake.

The protein of the egg adds strength to the gluten framework. In foam cakes, the beaten egg incorporates the air that then becomes

## Conventional Method of Mixing

1.

2.

3.

entrapped in the protein of the gluten-egg structure. This air expands when heated and acts as a leavening agent.

## Methods of Mixing

The way you combine the ingredients is as important to the success of a cake as the kind and proportion of ingredients you use. Even very slight differences made in the method given in the recipe can lead to failure. The cakes may have coarse, heavy textures and sugary or sticky crusts. The method of mixing depends on the type of cake.

The two basic methods for mixing shortened, or butter, cakes are the conventional method and the quick method. You may find recipes that are variations of these two basic methods. The variation is usually in the way the eggs are added. The sugar and shortening are creamed in the conventional method, and many

1.

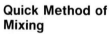

2.

**Quick Method of Mixing**

3.

people think it produces cakes with the lightest and finest texture. To make a cake by the *conventional method,* follow these steps:

1. Gradually add sugar to the softened fat, and cream it until it is as light and fluffy as whipped cream. Remember that thorough creaming incorporates air bubbles into the fat-and-sugar mixture, giving lightness to the cake.
2. Beat the eggs or yolks into the creamed mixture until thoroughly blended.
3. Add the flour, sifted with the baking powder and salt, in four parts. Add it alternately with the milk, which you will add in three parts. You should begin with flour and end with flour. After each addition of flour or milk, stir only until the ingredients are blended.

Cakes made by the quick method are usually made with vegetable shortenings. To make a cake by the *quick method,* follow these steps:

1. Sift together all of the dry ingredients (flour, baking powder, salt, sugar) into a bowl. Be sure the bowl is large enough.

2. Add part of the milk (usually about one-half) and the vegetable shortening (at room temperature) to the sifted dry ingredients. Beat the mixture vigorously for 300 strokes with a spoon or for two minutes with an electric mixer at low speed.
3. Add the remaining liquid and the unbeaten eggs, and continue beating for two more minutes.

The mixing method for foam cakes differs from that for shortened cakes. The beating of the egg and folding in of the flour are techniques used to make foam cakes. Foam cakes are divided into two groups: sponge cake, which contains both the yolk and white, and angel food cake, which uses only the white. To make foam cakes, you usually separate the white from the yolk. To make a foam cake, follow these steps:

1. Sift and measure the flour. For some foam cakes, a part of the sugar is added to the flour and resifted. This makes it easier to blend the flour into the beaten egg whites.
2. Beat the egg whites until foamy, and add the

1.

2. a

2. b

3. a

3. b

**Foam Cake Method
of Mixing**

salt and cream of tartar. Continue beating until the egg whites hold a soft peak. Add the remaining sugar in amounts of 2 tablespoons (30 mL), and beat it into the egg whites.

3. Sprinkle or sift a small amount—3 tablespoons (45 mL)—of the flour-sugar mixture over the beaten egg, and fold in gently. To fold, use a wire whisk in a circular path over the sides of the bowl, across the bottom, and up and over the top of the mixture. Fold carefully so that the air bubbles are not broken. Remember that foam cakes are leavened with air beaten into egg whites and with steam that forms during baking.

Oil and beaten egg whites are among the ingredients used in mixing chiffon cakes. For this reason, chiffon cakes have some of the characteristics of both shortened and foam cakes.

As in the quick method, the dry ingredients, including part of the sugar, are sifted into a bowl. The unbeaten egg yolk, liquid, and flavoring are added to the dry ingredients, and the mixture is beaten until smooth. Then, as with foam cakes, the egg whites and cream of tartar are beaten to form soft peaks. The remaining sugar is added to the whites gradually, and they are beaten until the mixture forms a stiff peak. The egg whites are folded carefully into the yolk-oil-flour mixture. The beaten eggs give lightness to chiffon cakes, and the oil adds tenderness.

## Baking Cakes

Your success in making a cake not only depends upon the ingredients used and the mixing method but also upon the way it is baked. Your recipe will give you the specific directions for the kind and size of pans to use, the oven temperature, and the baking time.

For the best results, select the pan size and shape specified by your recipe. When you bake cake in pans that are too large, the cake will not brown well; and when the pan is too small, the cake batter may flow over the sides of the pan. Cake pans with a light, dull finish, such as aluminum, are used successfully for cakes. Dark pans cause a dark heavy crust to form.

You should prepare the pan for the cake batter before you mix the cake. The pans for shortened cakes are prepared by greasing the bottom of the pan and lightly dusting it with flour, or by lining the bottom of the pan with greased waxed paper cut to fit. To line a pan with waxed paper, place the pan on a piece of waxed paper, and with the point of the scissors trace the outline of the pan before cutting the paper. Do not grease the sides of the pan. Foam cake batter is poured into clean pans.

The cake batter should be divided evenly when a layer cake is to be baked. The pans are usually filled one-half full. After the batter is in the pan, push the batter from the center to the sides of the pan, leaving a slight depression in the center. In this way, the baked cake will have a slightly rounded top rather than a hump in the center.

Cakes should be baked as quickly as possible after being mixed. Your recipe will give you the oven temperature and baking time. You should place the cake into a preheated oven set for the correct temperature. Too hot an oven will cause peaks, and the cake may crack on top. When the oven is too cool, the cake will not rise or brown properly.

Arrange the pans so that the oven heat can circulate freely around them. Place the pans so that there is at least 1 inch (2.5 cm) of space

### Tips for Herbs and Spices

Spices to use in cakes and frostings are: allspice, cinnamon, cloves, ginger, nutmeg, poppy seed, and vanilla.

## Orange-almond Cake      Yield: 1 cake layer

| | |
|---|---|
| 1½ c (375 mL) cake flour | 1 egg |
| 1 c (250 mL) sugar | 2 tsp (10 mL) grated |
| 1½ tsp (7.5 mL) baking powder | orange peel |
| ½ tsp (2.5 mL) salt | ¼ c (60 mL) sliced almonds |
| ¾ c (185 mL) milk | 1 Tbs (15 mL) sugar |
| ⅓ c (80 mL) shortening | 2 Tbs (30 mL) orange juice |

1. Set oven at 350°F (180°C).
2. Grease and flour a 8- or 9-inch (20- or 22.5-cm) round layer pan.
3. In electric mixer bowl, combine all ingredients except the almonds, the 1 Tbs (15 mL) sugar, and the orange juice. Beat on low speed 30 seconds, then on high speed for 3 minutes.
4. Pour batter into pan; sprinkle almonds on top.
5. Bake 40 minutes or until toothpick inserted comes out clean.
6. Sprinkle the 1 Tbs (15 mL) sugar on top; drizzle with the orange juice.
7. Cool 10 minutes; then remove from pan and cool completely.

Approximate nutrition information per serving: calories–65; protein–1 g; fat–3 g; cholesterol–5 mg; carbohydrates–9 g; sodium–70 mg.

between the pans and from the sides of the oven. When you use more than one oven rack, never place the pans directly above or below each other.

At the end of the minimum baking time given in the recipe, check the cake for doneness. Notice if the cake is evenly browned and has begun to pull away from the sides of the pan. Then follow these steps:

1. Lightly touch the center of the cake with your finger tip; if no impression remains, the cake is done. Another way to test for doneness is to insert a toothpick into the center of the cake. If the toothpick comes out clean, the cake is done. Keep in mind that overbaking will cause a dry, toughened cake.
2. After the shortened cake is baked, place it on a wire rack to cool for about ten minutes. Then loosen the edges of the cake with a spatula.

### Practical Tip

• To frost cupcakes quickly and easily, dip each cupcake into soft frosting, twist, and quickly pull out.

Two ways to test for doneness

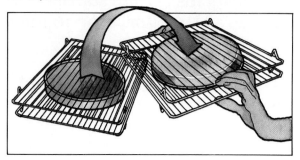

Inverting the cake

Removing and cooling the cake

permitted to remain in an inverted pan until they are cool and firm.

## Microwaving Cakes

Cakes baked in the microwave are very light and airy, but they do not brown. This problem can be disguised by using dark ingredients or by using frostings to disguise the pale color. Pudding-type cakes give a good result, but recipes that call for several eggs should be avoided.

Layer cakes should be cooked one layer at a time, preferably in a ring mold. A turntable helps assure even cooking and a level top. If a turntable is not available, rotate the cake several times during cooking.

### For Review

1. Why is cake flour better than all-purpose flour for cake making?
2. What are the two methods for mixing shortened, or butter, cakes? Briefly describe the differences between the two methods.
3. How does the mixing method for foam cakes differ from that for shortened cakes?
4. Explain three guidelines to follow when baking cakes.
5. Describe two ways to test a cake for doneness.

3. Place the cake pan between two cooling racks and invert it.
4. Carefully remove the cake pan from the cake. Again invert the cake between two racks so that the top of the cake faces up. Remove the top rack, and permit the cake to cool before frosting it.
5. You should allow foam and chiffon cakes to remain in the baking pan until they are completely cooled. These cakes are very delicate and may collapse if they are not

# Frostings

Frostings are concentrated sugar mixtures, either cooked or uncooked. They make cakes attractive and help to keep them moist. Most cakes are frosted, but chiffon and foam cakes are sometimes served without frosting.

## Tips for Microwaving Cakes

- Grease pans—never flour them—for microwave baking. Floured pans leave soggy bits of dough on the cake. Line the bottom of pans with waxed paper.
- Unless it is to be served directly from the baking pan, turn the cake out of the pan after standing time in order to prevent sticking.
- Microwaved cakes get stale quicker than conventionally baked cakes. Be sure to store the cakes in airtight containers.

## Cooked Frostings

Cooked frostings are similar to candy but require a shorter cooking period. The principles of cooked frostings deal with the formation of small sugar crystals so that the frosting will have a smooth texture. The sugar mixture must be cooked to the correct temperature so that the fudge-type or syrup-type frosting will be of the proper consistency for spreading and will remain on the cake. A candy thermometer is your best guide to the temperature of cooked sugar mixtures. When you allow the sugar mixture to cook too long, the frosting becomes hard and sugary; when it is not cooked enough, the frosting remains too soft. You must cool fudge-type frostings before they are beaten in order to avoid the formation of large crystals. After the syrup-type frostings reach the correct temperature and are cooled, beat the cooled syrup into stiffly beaten egg whites.

The seven-minute frosting is a variation of the syrup-type frosting. The sugar, water, and egg whites are beaten over boiling water until the mixture stands up in peaks. This frosting is called the seven-minute frosting because seven minutes of cooking time are usually required to reach the "peak" stage, or be of the right consistency to spread.

## Uncooked Frostings

Uncooked frostings are mixtures of confectioners' (powdered) sugar. The sugar is combined with a liquid (such as milk, cream, or fruit juice) and often with margarine or butter. The thickness of an uncooked frosting is determined by the amount of liquid you use. Uncooked frosting containing fat, such as butter, margarine, or chocolate, remains soft longer than the type made only with liquid. Uncooked frostings will become creamy with vigorous beating. Cake

Frosting can add an extra attractiveness to a cake. This homemade wedding cake has been beautifully frosted, and marzipan roses are added for an even more special look.

1.

2.

These cakes demonstrate the skill and variety of design that go into frosting a cake. Elaborate flowers, attractively arranged cherries, nuts, and colorful designs all enhance the beauty of these cakes.

frostings are not difficult to make when you follow the directions given in the recipe and apply the principles of sugar cookery.

## Frosting the Cake

A beautifully frosted cake can be yours when you follow the suggestions below. Be sure that the cake is cool, and brush the loose crumbs from the sides of the cake before you begin to frost it.

1. Place the first layer upside down on the plate. You may arrange narrow strips of waxed paper under the cake edge to keep the plate clean. Place frosting in the center of the layer, and spread it evenly to the edge.
2. Arrange the top layer, bottom side down, on the frosted layer. Frost the sides with a spatula.
3. Place frosting on the top layer, and make swirls with the spatula or the back of a spoon. Remove the waxed paper strips if you have used them.

3.

## For Review

1. Name and describe the two types of cake frostings.
2. What should you add to make an uncooked frosting thinner?
3. What are two guidelines to follow when frosting a cake?

# Pastry Chef

Tree McCann had wanted to be a chef ever since she graduated from high school. Today, after more than ten years in the business, she is the executive pastry chef for a large hotel in Atlantic City, New Jersey, where she oversees a staff of 25 people. She orders and purchases supplies and ingredients, and she organizes work and production schedules for a pastry shop that can prepare over 380 different items.

To Tree, pastry making requires technical skills and creativity. A pastry chef "has to think of the looks, taste, and feel of a pastry, how it will be seen by someone else . . . Pastry making is an art form that uses all the senses."

To achieve a successful pastry cart or display, pastry chefs have to consider the color and texture combinations, customer preferences, the sizes and shapes, and the flavor combinations of various pastries. They must know how to make a tender crust; what the strengths of different flours are; how to time the mixing, resting, and baking of dough; and what combinations of eggs, fat, and flour are appropriate.

Tree acquired her skills gradually, mastering basic baking skills first and then learning to do more specialized work. Wanting to learn about cooking, she got a job as a waitress and "hung out . . . in the kitchen." She became a pantry attendant, making salads and shrimp cocktails. One chef recognized her interest and motivation. He made her his assistant. For two years, Tree worked one-on-one with this reputable chef. She prepared vegetables, scrubbed floors and steam tables, made soups and sauces, and learned basic butchering and baking. Because she worked in a small restaurant, Tree was able to take on more responsibility as she mastered more skills. By the time she left, she was working as relief chef. She then served as an apprentice in Switzerland for 6 months. In both places, she worked 12- to 14-hour days.

After this initiation period, Tree became the assistant pastry chef at a hotel in Washington, D.C. This led her to another position where she learned "show work." Show work includes making chocolate baskets and flowers, forming chocolate or marzipan figures, and blowing sugar into figures.

Tree has also worked in a wholesale bakery. "I baked danish, rolls, muffins, and bread, and made desserts for twenty major restaurants and hotels. I had contact with major chefs . . . I got experience in volume baking and learned to work fast. The work was fun because I planned and organized everything myself."

Because of the many jobs she has had, Tree advises, "Always try to leave a job on good terms . . . You always run into somebody who knows somebody."

This is one of the reasons that mastering each skill of baking and pastry making is so important. Tree suggests, "The levels of the profession allow you to establish credibility." A pastry chef has to master organizational skills, develop an artistic sense, constantly sharpen technical skills, and learn to work with others.

A pastry chef puts the finishing touch on a festive treat.

# Storage, Nutrients, and Convenience

Careful storage of all types of cakes is important in order to preserve their taste and quality, especially because of the amount of fat in many cakes. These calorie-rich desserts are available in a variety of convenience forms, making it easy for you to bake and/or serve a cake quickly.

## Storage of Cakes

If you plan to use the cake within a short time, store it in a regular cake saver. Should you wish to keep the cake for several days, wrap it gently in foil or transparent wrap and place it in the refrigerator. Cakes with custard or cream fillings should be stored covered in the refrigerator. Cakes may be frozen and stored for later use. Place the cake in the freezer to harden the frosting, and then wrap the entire cake with moisture-proof paper for storage in the freezer.

These two cakes were baked on the same day. The cake on the left is to be served immediately, while the cake on the right is being prepared for freezer storage and use at a later time. What ingredient in cakes calls for their careful storage?

## Nutrient Contributions

Cakes are usually served at the end of a meal since their sweet flavor and high caloric content will satisfy the appetite. The nutrient value of cakes will vary somewhat with the ingredients used. Cakes made with enriched flour and milk have the added nutrients of those ingredients. However, the quantity of milk or egg you get in a piece of cake is very small and cannot be considered an important source of the nutrients in these foods.

Because of the high proportion of sugar, starch, and fat in shortened cakes, the main contribution of cakes is their calories. Foam cakes, with their much higher proportion of egg, are a somewhat better source of nutrients than shortened cakes. Cake frostings are primarily sugar, and contribute only calories. Foam or sponge cakes, because they do not contain fat, will contribute fewer calories than shortened or chiffon cakes.

## Convenience

Among the convenience cake items, you will find dry cake mixes and ready-to-eat and frozen products. Shortened cakes are available in an endless variety of flavors. Foam and chiffon cakes are also available in several forms. Cake frosting comes as a dry mix or in the ready-to-spread form.

Cake mixes are made of the same ingredients basic to all cakes. In addition, many mixes include emulsifiers, which contribute to the soft texture of cakes, and preservatives, which extend the shelf life of the mix. When you use a cake mix, you add the liquid (water or milk) and at times you may add the egg.

Convenience cake items do save time. The ready-to-eat product saves the greatest amount of time, but is usually the most expensive. Some frozen cake products may be more expensive than the ready-to-eat items. A complete cake mix (requiring only the addition of water) and

For the inexperienced cook, a cake mix may be a good way to start learning the pleasures of cake baking.

the home-prepared item may cost about the same, but some cake mixes may be less expensive than the home-prepared product. You should compare the cost of convenience cakes with similar home-prepared cakes, and in this way learn which products best fit your food budget.

The quality of cake mixes and other convenience items varies greatly. The label shows the ingredients used but gives no information regarding quality. Here again, it is only through your use of these convenience items that you will be able to judge their quality. It is possible that a mix could result in a better cake than one made by an inexperienced cook. However, the quality of a home-prepared cake will vary with the experience of the person making the cake. An experienced cook can produce a cake that is superior to a mix.

When you use cake and frosting mixes, you will get the best results when you follow all of the instructions on the package. Remember that all cake recipes are balanced formulas; you should not add extra ingredients to cake mixes, except flavor ingredients such as extracts, spices, coconut, or chopped nuts. The creativity and variation that you provide should come from the frosting or filling, the decoration, or the way in which you serve the cake.

You can provide homemade convenience cake items for yourself. You may freeze shortened cakes either as a batter or after they have been baked. However, the volume may be slightly less when cake is made from a frozen batter. You may freeze angel food cake batter in the baking pan but not sponge cake batter.

After considering time, cost, quality, and personal preferences, you will be ready to select the cake products that best fit your circumstances and your plans. Comparison of the products will be important in making final choices.

## For Review

1. If a frosted cake is to be frozen, why should it be put in the freezer for a while before wrapping it?
2. Which type of cake usually has the most nutrients and the fewest calories? Why?
3. What is one advantage of using a cake mix? One disadvantage?

# 28 Chapter Review

## Summary

For thousands of years, cakes have been an important food. Some cake recipes call for shortening, while others do not. However, ingredients such as flour, sugar, and eggs are used in all cakes. The three basic kinds of cake are shortened or butter, chiffon, and foam or sponge. To create a light, moist, and tender cake, it is important to follow the principles for gluten formation. Making a successful cake also depends on the ingredients used, the mixing and combining of the ingredients, and the way the cake is baked. Frostings are frequently used on cakes to enhance their appearance and taste and to keep them moist. To preserve the taste and quality of cakes, it is essential to store them properly. The nutrient values of cakes depend on their ingredients, but most often, the main contribution of cakes is their calories.

## Vocabulary

Match the lettered statements that follow to the numbered vocabulary words below. Each vocabulary word has more than one match.

1. butter cakes
2. chiffon cakes
3. foam cakes

a. Cakes that are a blend of sponge cakes and butter cakes.
b. Cakes that are made without shortening.
c. The newest kinds of cakes.
d. The oldest kinds of cakes.
e. Cakes that are leavened with the air beaten into the eggs and the steam formed during baking.
f. Cakes made with solid fats.
g. Cakes that can be made by the conventional method or the quick method.
h. Cakes that are made with oil.
i. Cakes that have the most light and fluffy texture.

## Chapter Questions

1. Explain the importance of flour when baking a cake.
2. What is a procedure for removing the lumps from brown sugar before you use it as an ingredient in the cake batter?
3. How are butter and sponge cakes alike and different?
4. What is your favorite cake? How do you prepare it? What type of cake is it?
5. When making a cake, why is it important to use the right amount of fat, liquid, and sugar and not to overmix the ingredients?
6. What is the procedure to use for folding egg whites?
7. What kinds of ingredients do you have available in your home that can be used to flavor cakes?
8. To have a cake that is lightly browned with a slightly rounded top, what should you do?
9. How does the cooling procedure for butter cakes differ from that used for chiffon and foam cakes?

10. If you wanted to prepare a cake to serve to people who were on a low-calorie diet, which kind of cake would you make? Why?

11. What kind of frosting does your favorite frosting recipe make? How do you prepare the frosting?

12. Explain the principles of cooked frostings.

13. What considerations should you make before purchasing a cake mix?

14. How can you prepare homemade convenience cake items?

15. Why are frosted cakes nutrient-poor but calorie-rich?

## Skill Activities

**1. Decision making** In your food journal or file box, collect cake and frosting recipes. Organize the cake recipes into these categories: shortened, or butter, cakes; chiffon cakes; and foam, or sponge, cakes. Include recipes that use puddings as ingredients, and recipes for cakes that may be microwaved. If the cake is frosted, make a note at the bottom of the recipe of an appropriate frosting. Organize the frosting recipes into these categories: cooked and uncooked. You can find recipes in books, magazines, and newspapers.

**2. Resource management** Develop a time-work plan. Find a recipe for a yellow cake, and the directions for a yellow cake from a mix. Make a time-work plan for each. What food supplies do you need to make the cake from the recipe? From the mix? What utensils are needed to make each cake? Which cake takes less time to make?

**3. Social studies** With your classmates make a display to show ways of decorating cakes with and without applicators. Have one group use applicator tips to make flowers, leaves, garlands, piping, and other decorations. Beside each decoration, write the kind of tip used, and the directions for making it. Have a second group demonstrate frosting decorations that can be made without applicators. For each kind of decoration, show a sample or draw a diagram. Tell the utensils needed and the steps to follow to make each. Several common ways to decorate cakes without applicator tips include using knives, spatulas, and confectioners' sugar sprinkled over a doily. Information about ways to decorate cakes may be found in books, magazines, and newspapers.

**4. Mathematics** Visit the bakery and frozen foods counters at a supermarket. Compare the cost per serving of a ready-to-eat cake, a cake made from a mix, and a frozen cake. On a sheet of lined paper, write the name of the cake, the convenience form, and then its price. Next, determine the cost per serving by figuring out the number of servings that can be made from the product. Which convenience form costs the most per serving? Which product costs the least per serving? Give at least one use, one advantage, and one disadvantage for each form.

# 29 Cookies and Pastry

## As you read, think about:

- how to prepare a variety of cookies.
- how to prepare pastry for one-crust and two-crust pies.
- why cookies and pastry provide mostly calories.
- how to store and serve cookies and pastry.

Cookies and pies, like cakes, are served as desserts. Rich in calories, they will satisfy your appetite at the end of a meal. Both desserts originated in other countries.

Cookies came to us from many lands. For instance, Scotland contributed its thick, rich shortbreads, while Finland gave us nut-studded butter strips known as *finska kakor.* In our own country, in colonial times, the early settlers made a large, flat chewy molasses cookie.

Pies, too, came from other countries, notably ancient Greece and Rome, and England, where "pyes" were baked in deep pans called "coffins." An American development was the round, shallow pan, which, by 1790, was lined with pastry, filled, and baked to become one of our most traditional desserts.

## Types of Cookies

The stiffness and the method of handling the dough make it convenient to classify cookies into six basic types: drop, bar, rolled, refrigera- tor, pressed, and molded. The dough for bar cookies and drop cookies is softer than the dough for the other types of cookies.

*Drop cookies* are made from a dough that is pushed from a spoon onto a cookie sheet. You should allow about 2 inches (5 cm) of space between the cookies to keep them from spread- ing into each other. Use the same amount of dough on the spoon each time so that the cookies will be uniform in size. It is best to use a cool cookie sheet so the dough will not spread before it is placed in the oven.

*Bar cookies* are made from a soft dough that is spread evenly in a pan and baked. You may cut them into any shape (square, rectangle, or trian- gle) after they are baked. Brownies are probably the most popular bar cookies.

*Rolled cookies* are made from a stiff dough that has been rolled into a thin sheet. You may cut the rolled dough into various shapes with a cookie cutter. When you roll the dough, use only a small amount of flour on the board so that you will not have a hard cookie. You may find it easier to roll cookie dough that has been chilled.

Baking—and eating—pies has long been a favorite American pastime, hence the expression "as American as apple pie." At left is a recreation of pie making in the early 1800s.

1.

2.

3.

4.

5.

6.

1. Drop cookies
2. Bar cookies
3. Rolled cookies
4. Refrigerator cookies
5. Pressed cookies
6. Molded cookies

Roll only a small amount of cookie dough at a time so that you will avoid overhandling, which causes toughness. Leave a small amount of space between the cookies when you place them on the cookie sheet.

For *refrigerator cookies,* a stiff dough is pressed with the hands into a long, smooth roll and chilled before slicing and baking. The fat in the cookie will harden, making it easy to slice the cookies from the roll. If you slice the cookies thinly, they will be crisp and crunchy. The refrigerator cookie dough may be stored in the refrigerator for several days before baking.

*Pressed cookies* have a rich, stiff dough. The dough is packed into a cookie press and forced out through cookie discs (cutters) onto an un-greased cookie sheet. The dough will stick to the cookie sheet as you lift the cookie press from it. Leave a small amount of space between the cookies as you squeeze them onto the sheet.

*Molded cookies* are made from a stiff dough. A small amount of dough is shaped and molded with the fingers to form the desired shape (such as crescents, rolls, or balls). As you form the

molded cookies, space them evenly in rows on the cookie sheet, allowing a small amount of space between cookies.

## Ingredients and Preparation

Cookie doughs require the same basic in-gredients that are used in cake batters, but the proportion of ingredients is different. You use flour, salt, leavening agents, sugar, shortening, eggs, and liquid to make cookies. Cookies need less liquid and leavening and may need more fat than is used in cakes. Cookies have a crisp texture rather than the light texture of cakes. Each ingredient serves the same purpose in cookies as in cakes.

**Ingredients in Cookies** *All-purpose flour* is suitable for all cookies unless cake flour is specified. Flour provides the structure for cookies.

The *fat* or *shortening* is often used to contribute flavor as well as richness to the cookie. Butter or margarine is used to give a pleasing flavor to the cookie. Margarine can usually replace butter in most cookie recipes. Vegetable shortening is bland, so other ingredients, such as brown sugar, honey, and molasses, are used to provide flavor. Chocolate, spices, coconut, nuts, fruits (usually dried or candied), and **extracts** (natural or artificial flavor essences, usually dissolved in alcohol) are also used for flavor.

Milk is the *liquid* most often used in cookies. It may be sweet milk, sour milk, or buttermilk. Occasionally cream is used for some of the liquid, and at the same time it contributes richness (fat) and a pleasing flavor. Some cookies require no added liquid.

**Mixing Cookies** Cookies are usually mixed by methods similar to those used for cakes. Most cookies are mixed by the conventional method (see page 513) or a slight modification of it. Because a crisp, crunchy, or chewy texture is characteristic of cookies, rather than a light, delicate texture, cookies require less creaming than cakes. The flour may be added all at once, instead of in four parts, as in cakes. Cookies such as macaroons and meringues do not contain fat and are mixed in much the same way as foam cakes.

The following steps will show you how the conventional method can be modified and still produce perfect cookies.

1. Blend the softened shortening, sugar (including molasses or syrup if used), eggs, and melted chocolate (when used) thoroughly.
2. Stir in the liquid and flavoring all at once. (In a few recipes, the liquid and flour may be added alternately.)
3. Sift the flour, salt, and leavening (including spices) together, and stir them into the shortening-sugar-egg mixture.

**Baking Cookies** Baking sheets are best for baking cookies because there are no sides to interfere with the circulation of heat. The shiny and bright cookie sheet will give your

**Mixing Cookies**

Step 1

Step 2

Step 3

cookies a delicately browned crust. You should not use cake pans because their deep sides will interfere with distribution of heat, and the cookies will remain pale. However, you may turn a cake pan upside down and use the bottom of it for baking cookies.

Because most cookies will spread a little as they bake, spacing is necessary to prevent them from running together. You should arrange cookies on cool baking sheets to avoid excessive spreading. Rolled cookies spread less, so spaces between them can be smaller. Drop and refrigerator cookies spread more and require greater space—usually about 2 inches (5 cm)—between them. When you arrange cookies, space them evenly and try to get as many cookies as you can on the sheet.

Bake the cookies in a preheated oven set at the temperature indicated in the recipe. When you bake one sheet of cookies at a time, place it on a rack near the center of the oven. When you want to bake two sheets of cookies at the same time, place the oven racks so that the oven is divided into thirds. During the last few minutes of baking, you may need to change the cookie sheets from one rack to the other so that the cookies will be browned evenly.

You should check for doneness of cookies when the minimum baking time is up. Cookies are done when almost no imprint remains after they are touched lightly. Be careful that you do not underbake or overbake cookies. Overbaking will cause cookies to dry out and become too dark; underbaking will leave the cookies doughy and pale. Properly baked cookies are delicately browned.

You should remove cookies from the sheet as soon as you take them from the oven, unless the recipe instructs otherwise. As the cookie cools, it becomes hardened, sticks to the pan, and may break as you remove it. Use a wide spatula to remove the warm cookies onto a cooling rack.

## Microwaving Cookies

Drop cookies and refrigerator cookies are not suited for baking in the microwave because they bake very unevenly. In addition, there is no savings in time because they must be cooked in very small batches.

Bar cookies and brownies, however, bake well in the microwave. Because of their high sugar content, though, timing is crucial to avoid overcooking. Cookies prepared in rectangular or square pans should have shields over the batter at each corner to keep from overcooking.

## Nutrient Contributions

Flour, sugar, and fat are the ingredients that you will use in the largest amounts in cookies. Their chief contribution is in calories, or energy. Because all other ingredients are used in rather small amounts, you can count on cookies to contribute only to your energy needs. You need to include milk, fruits, cereals, and meats in your daily eating pattern to meet your needs for vitamins, minerals, and protein.

## Storing Cookies

To keep the perfect eating quality of your cookies, store them in covered containers. Bar and drop cookies are made from soft dough and

To bake two sheets of cookies at the same time, position the racks in the oven so that the oven is divided into thirds. Why should you rearrange the sheets during baking?

usually will have a soft texture. Cookies made from stiff dough, such as rolled and refrigerator ones, are crisp. In order that soft cookies remain soft, and crisp cookies remain crisp, store each separately in the proper containers.

Soft cookies keep best in airtight containers. A slice of fresh bread or slices of apple or orange in the jar with the soft cookies will help to keep them moist. The fruit will need to be changed frequently. Crisp cookies should be kept in a can or container with a loose cover.

When you open a package of ready-to-eat cookies, retain their texture and flavor by folding the protective wrap tightly around the remaining cookies, or store the cookies in covered containers, as you do home-baked cookies.

## Convenience in Cookies

Cookie convenience comes in several forms: (1) ready-to-eat, (2) refrigerated or frozen, and (3) as a mix. All of these can be ready to serve on a moment's notice. Cookie mixes come in several varieties and usually require only the addition of the liquid and sometimes an egg. To some cookie mixes, you may add flavor ingredients such as coconut, nuts, and extracts. For best results, follow the directions on the package, and display your creative ability in shaping and decorating the cookies. You can throw cookie formulas out of balance when you add any extra amounts of basic ingredients such as flour, sugar, and shortening.

Cookie doughs from the refrigerated case require only to be shaped (cut or sliced and spread in a pan) and baked. The ready-to-eat cookies are found in all grocery stores and bakeries. They are ready for immediate use without any further preparation.

The advantage in the use of these products may come from the time saved, but you should consider which of these items are really good buys and which are luxury items. You can create your own "cookie convenience" by preparing a double batch of cookies, part for immediate use and the rest to be frozen for later use.

As with most other convenience products, no clue to quality is given on the label. The reputation of the manufacturer and your experience are your best guides in their selection.

### For Review

1. List and describe the six basic types of cookies.
2. List the basic ingredients for cookies.
3. What are three guidelines to follow when baking cookies?
4. How should you store soft cookies? Crisp cookies?

# Kinds of Pastry

The term **pastry** refers to a large variety of baked crusts made from doughs rich in fat. It includes cream puffs, puff pastry, Danish and French pastries, rich yeast and cake-type sweet rolls, as well as pies.

Either plain or puff pastry may be used for pies, but plain pastry is used most often. It has a golden-brown flaky (blistered) surface and is tender. Puff pastry is extra rich and extra flaky and is used for special pies or fancy tarts.

## Ingredients and Preparation

To make good pastry, you need only four ingredients: flour, fat, salt, and liquid. The kind and proportion of ingredients you use and the manner in which you mix and handle the dough will determine the success of your pastry.

**Pastry Ingredients** *All-purpose flour* is usually used for pastry. The gluten of the flour forms the structure of the pastry.

1. Cinnamon rolls
2. Cranberry muffin
3. Cinnamon, fruit-filled coffee roll (raspberry nut roll)
4. Eclairs
5. Danish ring
6. Cinnamon twist sticks
7. Danish
8. French fruit pastries
9. French creme puff

A firm *fat* such as lard or vegetable shortening is most frequently used for pastry. Butter and margarine produce a less tender pastry than other fats, and they are not usually used for pastry. The firm fat will produce flaky pastry, while the oils, which are liquid in nature, will make a mealy pastry. Because lard is a soft fat, it has more shortening power than vegetable fats, and will produce a more tender pastry. Oils will give a very tender, mealy pastry that is not flaky. For each 1 cup (250 mL) of flour, you will use ⅓ cup (80 mL) vegetable shortening and only ¼ cup (60 mL) of lard or oil.

Use only a small amount of *water,* about 2 tablespoons (30 mL), for each 1 cup (250 mL) of flour. Water is an important ingredient because it provides the moisture needed to develop gluten.

## Cocoa Drop Cookies  Yield: 3½ dozen

| | |
|---|---|
| 1¾ c (435 mL) sifted all-purpose flour | 1 egg |
| ½ tsp (2.5 mL) baking soda | ¾ c (185 mL) buttermilk |
| ½ tsp (2.5 mL) salt | 1 tsp (5 mL) vanilla |
| ½ c (125 mL) cocoa | If desired, 1c (250 mL) chopped nuts or 1c |
| ½ c (125 mL) soft shortening | (250 mL) raisins may be |
| 1c (250 mL) sugar | added with the flour. |

1. Set oven at 400°F (200°C).
2. Sift together flour, baking soda, salt, and cocoa.
3. Blend shortening and sugar; add egg; mix thoroughly.
4. Stir in milk and vanilla.
5. Add flour mixture; stir until blended.
6. Drop rounded teaspoonfuls of dough on ungreased cookie sheet about 2 inches (5cm) apart.
7. Bake at 400°F (200°C) for 8 to 10 minutes or until almost no imprint remains when lightly touched with finger.
8. Remove cookies immediately from sheet by sliding spatula completely under cookie, and then lift to wire cooling rack.

Approximate nutrition information per serving: calories–25; protein–3 g; fat–trace; cholesterol–0; carbohydrates–4 g; sodium–85 mg.

*Salt* contributes to the flavor of pastry but has no influence on flakiness or tenderness.

**Gluten Formation**  One of the principles of making pastry is concerned with the influence of ingredients on gluten formation. The gluten in the flour forms a structure in which entrapped air and moisture expand during baking, giving a blistered effect that is characteristic of flaky pastry. Too much flour will produce a tough pastry.

The fat coats the particles of flour, separates the gluten strands, and shortens (makes tender) the pastry. Solid fats are cut into the flour to form many particles so that the gluten strands will be separated. Because oils are liquid, the gluten is separated into very short strands, making the pastry grainy or mealy. For this reason, oil pastry is tender and crumbly or mealy rather than flaky. Too little shortening causes a tough pastry because the gluten is not separated into short strands. Too much shortening weakens gluten strands. The pastry is fragile and crumbly.

The liquid, which is usually water, moistens the flour particles so that gluten can be developed. With too much water, the pastry will be tough; with not enough water, the pastry will be dry, crumbly, and difficult to roll.

## The Conventional Method of Mixing

Step 1                                                              Step 2

**Mixing and Handling** Another principle of pastry making concerns the mixing and handling of the dough. You will have a more tender pastry if you use ingredients at room temperature rather than cold ingredients. You should combine and gently mix the ingredients so that the gluten is not overdeveloped, which results in tough pastry.

You can use several methods to combine pastry ingredients. You will recall that plain pastry is most often used for pies. It can be made by any one of three methods: (1) the conventional method; (2) the hot-water method; or (3) the oil method.

The conventional method will give you a crisp, tender, flaky pastry. You can make a perfect flaky pastry when you learn the techniques of the conventional method.

1. To make pastry by the *conventional method,* measure the sifted flour into a bowl, and stir in the salt. Add the shortening to the flour, and cut it in with a pastry blender until the pieces of shortening are the size of small peas. If you do not have a pastry blender, you may cut in the shortening with two table knives. Make sure that the fat is evenly distributed throughout the flour so that the gluten strands will be shortened and the pastry will be tender.
2. Sprinkle the water, 1 tablespoon (15 mL) at a time, over different parts of the flour

mixture. Mix lightly with a fork. Do not overstir, or you will cause too much gluten to develop. You need only to moisten the flour so that the dough will form a loose ball. You should always remember that too much water makes the pastry tough; too little makes it crumbly.

The *conventional paste method* differs from the method just described only in the way the water is added. First, remove 2 tablespoons (30 mL) of flour from the 1 cup (250 mL) of flour used in the recipe. Mix the flour that you removed with all of the water specified by the recipe in order to make a paste. Add the salt to the remaining flour, and cut in the fat. Pour all of the flour paste over the fat-flour mixture, and stir it in thoroughly.

While the conventional method uses cold water, the *hot-water method* uses boiling water. To make pastry by the hot-water method, follow these steps:

1. Pour a measured amount of boiling water over the shortening, and whip it with a fork. This will form a fluffy, creamed mixture.
2. Add all of the measured flour and salt into the shortening-water mixture, and stir until blended. Do not overmix. Hot-water pastry is tender but tends to be mealy and less flaky than conventional pastry.

*Oil pastry* is mealy rather than flaky. Place the measured flour and salt into the mixing bowl

# Different Tastes for Sweets

All over the United States, people celebrate special occasions with sweets. Cakes for weddings, ice cream and cake for birthdays, chocolate hearts for Valentine's Day, and a variety of specially-shaped cookies for winter holidays adorn our tables at different times of the year. Grocery stores, convenience stores, specialty stores, and department stores cater to our national sweet tooth. It is hard to imagine a greater variety of sweets or that "undiscovered" sweets exist elsewhere in the world.

Our taste in sweets has been most influenced by European immigrants and by the kinds of fruits and berries available to these immigrants. English immigrants brought recipes for what has become an all-American favorite, apple pie. Germans, who pride themselves on their baking skills, contributed sticky buns and layer cakes. From the French, we have pastries and fruit tarts.

In other countries, different types of sweets and different tastes for sweets have developed. Often based on available fruits and other ingredients, some of these sweets may seem strange to Americans. Following is a sampling of sweets from around the world.

## South America

In Colombia and Venezuela, coconuts abound. Candies, puddings, and cakes are made from this fruit. A Venezuelan specialty is a sponge cake covered with coconut cream.

Bananas are a favorite in Ecuador. Brown sugar is added slowly to sautéed bananas, and the sweetened fruit is served with powdered sugar.

Although couscous, a steamed grain dish, probably originated in North Africa or the Middle East, the Brazilians have adapted it. One kind of couscous is a sweet. Tapioca, coconut, coconut milk, and sugar are mixed with boiling water and poured into a mold. After chilling, the couscous is sliced and served.

## The Mediterranean and the Middle East

Many Greek pastries are made out of layers of paper-thin dough called phyllo. Baklava, a Greek specialty, is phyllo dough layered with honey and nuts.

The Turks enjoy halva, a sweet made from grain. Halva combines sugar and farina.

Israel is famous for its Jaffa oranges. Israelis eat these plain or prepare desserts with them. One dessert calls for chocolate cookies soaked in coffee and covered with whipped cream. This concoction is chilled and sliced for serving.

## Asia

The Chinese eat few sweets. Steamed dumplings called dim sum are filled with fruit. Steamed buns called pao tzu are also prepared. These yeast breads are filled with sesame, walnuts, and melon-seed kernels and then steamed.

Indians prefer puddinglike confections made from milk. A mixture of milk and sugar is simmered until it is thick. This thickened mixture is called mawa. A flavoring such as almond is added to the mawa.

A cream puff is only one example of an irresistible sweet.

## The Hot-water Method of Mixing

Step 1

Step 2

as you did for the conventional method. Next, add the measured oil and liquid all at once, and stir gently with a fork until blended. The pastry will be moist but not sticky.

If you prefer a tender, flaky pastry, you should use the conventional method; if you prefer a tender, grainy pastry, use the hot-water or oil method. Regardless of the method you choose, the rolling and handling of the pastry will be the same for one- and two-crust pies.

To roll pastry, roll only enough for one crust at a time. Handle the pastry as little as possible to avoid toughening it. It is easy to work too much flour into pastry when you roll it on a floured board or cloth. You will find it easy to roll pastry without flour between two pieces of waxed paper. Your paper will not slide if you first wipe the counter with a damp cloth and place the paper on that spot. The paper will also

help you to lift the pastry into the pie pan without tearing it. Follow these steps for rolling pastry:

1. After you finish mixing the pastry, gather the dough into a ball with your fingers so that the bowl will be clean. With both hands, press the dough into a firm ball.
2. Place the dough on a piece of waxed paper, and flatten the ball gently with the palm of one hand. Cover the dough with a second piece of waxed paper. So the paper will not slide, use a damp cloth to wipe the area where you will roll the pastry.
3. Begin rolling from the center of the pastry toward the edge, and lift the rolling pin as it comes to the outer edge so your pastry will be of uniform thickness. Repeat rolling from the center in all directions to form a circle.
4. Roll gently so that the waxed paper will not wrinkle. Should your paper wrinkle, gently peel it off and smooth it out. Continue to roll until the pastry is ⅛ inch (3 mm) thick and 1 inch (2.5 cm) larger than the inverted pie pan.
5. Remove the top piece of paper. Lift the pastry by the bottom paper, and center the pastry (paper side up) over the pan. Carefully peel back the waxed paper.
6. With your fingers, carefully fit the pastry into the bottom and sides of the pan so that no air bubbles remain between the pastry and the pan. Be careful that you do not stretch the pastry as this will cause it to shrink during baking.

### Tips for Herbs and Spices

Herbs and spices to use in cookies and pastry are: allspice, cinnamon, cloves, dill, ginger, nutmeg, poppy seed, and vanilla.

## Steps for Rolling Pastry

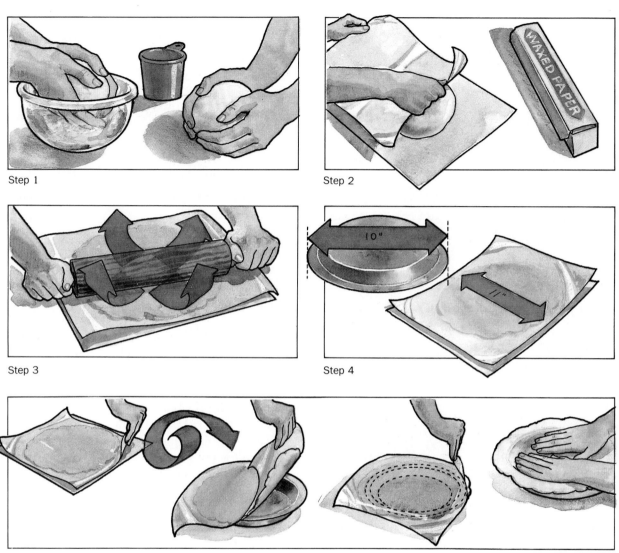

Step 1

Step 2

Step 3

Step 4

Step 5

Step 6

Steps for Rolling Pastry

For a *one-crust pie* in which the filling and pastry are baked together, follow these steps:

1. Trim the overhanging pastry edge so that it is ½ inch (1.3 cm) larger than the pie pan.
2. Fold the extra pastry back and under to form a high edge.
3. **Flute** the edge of the pastry by pinching and shaping it with your fingertips. This will help to retain the filling and give an attractive edge to your pie.
4. Put the filling, such as custard or pumpkin, into the shell.

For making a one-crust pie (such as a chiffon pie) in which the baked pie shell holds a filling that is prepared separately and added later, follow these steps:

## Making a One-crust Pie

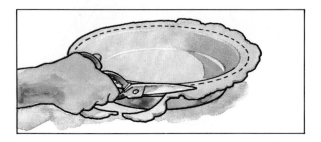

Step 1

Step 2

Step 3

Step 4

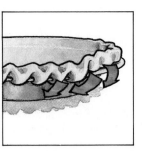

When making a one-crust pie in which the baked shell holds a separately-prepared filling, flute the pastry edge to cut down on shrinkage, and prick the pastry to prevent puffing during baking.

1. After you flute the pastry edge, hook the points of the fluted edge under the pan rim to minimize shrinkage during baking.
2. Prick the bottom and sides of the pastry thoroughly with the tines of a fork to prevent puffing during baking. Should your pastry puff up during baking, prick the pastry again in a few places while it is in the oven to permit the expanding air to escape. Bake the shell until golden brown, following the directions of the recipe.

For a *two-crust pie,* follow these steps:

1. Divide the dough into two balls. Roll out the dough for the bottom crust in the same way as for a one-crust pie. With kitchen scissors, trim the overhanging pastry at the edge of the pan.
2. Roll out the pastry for the top crust so that it is 1 inch (2.5 cm) larger than the inverted pie pan. Add the filling to the pastry-lined pan.
3. Moisten the edge of the bottom pastry with water. This will seal the two crusts so that juices will not escape from the pie during baking.

### Safety Tip
- To prevent fire from fruit pie spills in the oven, sprinkle the spill with salt.

Step 1

Step 2

Step 3

Step 4

Step 5

Step 6

Step 7

Making a
Two-crust
Pie

4. Remove the top piece of waxed paper from the upper crust, turn the crust upside down so that the remaining piece of waxed paper faces up, and center the crust over the pie pan. Remove the paper, and trim the edge ½ inch (1.3 cm) larger than the pan.

5. Fold the extra edge of the top pastry under the edge of the lower pastry. Seal the edge by pressing with your fingers on the edge of the pan. Flute the edge as for a one-crust pie.

6. Cut several slits near the center of the top pastry to allow steam to escape during baking. This will keep the top pastry from rising in the center.

7. Cover the edge with a 1½ inch (3.8 cm) strip of foil to prevent overbrowning.

**Baking Pastry** The third principle of pastry making is the baking of the pie. Pies and pie shells are baked in a preheated oven. If you use only one oven rack, place it near the center of the oven; if you use two racks, arrange them so the oven is divided into thirds (see page 528), and then arrange the pans to allow the heat to circulate. Follow the recipe for oven temperature and baking time.

While you rolled the pastry, the gluten and particles of fat were flattened to form layers of gluten, fat, and entrapped air. The entrapped air and the steam formed during baking force the layers apart and give your pastry a flaky texture. Good pastry is evenly browned with a blistered surface and is crisp and tender.

### Microwaving Pastry

When pastry is baked in the microwave, it is very flaky, although pale. To give the pastry color and to help keep the crust crisp, first brush it with dark corn syrup or a wash of 1 egg yolk beaten with 1 teaspoon (5 mL) of water. Cook the pastry only until brown spots just begin to appear.

### Uses of Pastry

There are three general ways to use pastry: (1) as a dessert; (2) as an accompaniment to other foods; and (3) as an ingredient of main dishes.

**Dessert Pastry**    Pastry in several forms is used as a dessert. Pies, either one-crust or two-crust, are very popular desserts.

*Fruit pies* are often made with two crusts, and sometimes the top crust is a lattice top. For a lattice top, the rolled pastry is cut into strips with a knife and placed across the top of the filling to form square or diamond shapes. Another variation of the fruit pie is the deep-dish pie, in which the fruit filling is placed into a deep dish and covered with a pastry. All kinds of fruit —frozen, fresh, canned, or dried—may be used for pies.

*Custard pies* are made with a filling mixture of milk and egg, which is baked with the pastry. Pumpkin and pecan pies are examples of custard-type pies.

*Cream pies* are filled with a pudding mixture that has been thickened with starch. You

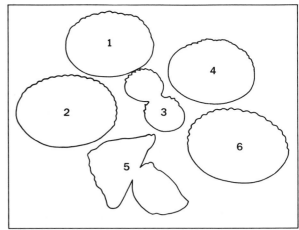

1. Chocolate-cream pie
2. Custard pie
3. Tarts
4. Chiffon pie
5. Turnovers
6. Blueberry pie

can make cream pies in many flavors, and you can add fruits, nuts, and coconut to add interest and variety. Cream pies are topped with a cream topping.

*Chiffon pies* are filled with cooked gelatin mixtures made with beaten egg whites. The filling is poured into a baked pie shell and then chilled until it is set.

*Tarts* are actually miniature, individual pies. They may be filled with any filling used in a regular-size pie.

*Turnovers* are squares of pastry that are folded over a filling to form a triangle.

**Accompaniment Pastry** Pastry may be cut into strips or fancy shapes and sprinkled with cheese and paprika to use as an accompaniment for soups or salads. Pastry pieces may be sprinkled with a sugar-cinnamon mixture or spread lightly with jelly or jam to use as an accompaniment to a fruit or sherbet dessert.

Accompaniment pastry, such as pastry sprinkled with Parmesan cheese and then baked, offers visual appeal along with added nutrients.

Dessert pastry, such as this lemon pie, makes a balanced ending to a less-rich main course. The crust of this pie was peeled back before baking to reveal the fresh lemon slices.

**Pastry as a Main-dish Ingredient** Quiche and meat, poultry, and fish pies are main dishes made with pastry. A quiche is a one-crust pie with a cheese and custard filling. The filling for other main-dish pies is made with meat, poultry, or fish, usually combined with vegetables in a sauce or gravy. This mixture is then baked either in a pastry-lined pan with a top crust or in a casserole dish with only a top crust.

### Nutrient Contributions

All pastries contain a high proportion of fat and therefore are rich in energy and calories. Pastry fillings contain sugar, which adds to their caloric contribution. Pastries make it very easy to overload your meals with more calories than you may need. You should always remember that calories that you do not use up in your work and play will be stored as body fat and thus add to your weight.

There will be some vitamin and mineral values from custard and fruit fillings, but these do not replace your need for milk and fruit. The amount of milk or fruit in a piece of pie is small and cannot be counted as a serving of these foods. The main-dish meat-vegetable pies will offer some protein, B vitamins, and minerals.

A good rule to remember is never to serve more than one calorie-rich food in a meal. Because of their high caloric value, pastry desserts should be served with a light meal. If the starch, fat, or sugar value of your meal is small, pastry may be served. For example, pastries are suitable desserts for most salad or soup lunches. Pastry should be used in moderation and reserved for those times when you may need to increase the caloric value of a meal.

## Storing Pastry

Store unused chiffon, custard, and meat-type pies in the refrigerator to prevent spoilage. Fillings containing milk, eggs, or meats—including poultry and fish—spoil quickly unless they are refrigerated.

Fruit pies, tarts, and turnovers keep satisfactorily for a day, but the quality is best when you eat them the same day they are made. You may freeze both unbaked and baked pies after wrapping them in suitable freezer wrap. Frozen baked pies are best when you reheat them for serving; however, the pastry of the frozen baked pie may not be as crisp as when freshly baked.

Baked and unbaked pie shells can be satisfactorily stored in the refrigerator for several days or in the freezer for future use. You should reheat the baked shells for a few minutes to restore their crispness.

## Convenience in Pastry

You will find that convenience in pastries comes in several forms. You may select from mixes or from frozen, canned, and ready-to-eat convenience items. Pastries come as a dry mix or a compressed stick to which you need only add water. You can also purchase a frozen pie shell in its own pan ready for use. Some dry pie mixes come with both a crust and a filling.

You will find a variety of dry filling mixes for cream or custard pies. Canned fillings are available for pudding and fruit pies. The dry filling mixes require the addition of liquid, and some need to be heated to a boil. The canned pie fillings require no preparation and need only to be put into the pie shell.

You can choose from a variety of frozen fruit and custard pies ready for the oven. Also included are oven-ready frozen turnovers. If you wish, you may select a frozen baked pie that needs only to be warmed, or a frozen cream pie ready to be served. You may make your selection from a host of bakery pies—cream, fruit, and chiffon. In addition to the convenience dessert pies, you will find ready-for-the-oven frozen meat, poultry, and fish pies for the main course.

Without a doubt, convenience pastry items will save you time. The frozen and ready-to-eat ones will save the most time. Convenience pastry items tend to be more expensive than mixes, and complete mixes are more expensive than homemade pies.

The convenience item may not measure up to a well-prepared home product, and the finished convenience product may not give the satisfaction derived from a pie made from individual ingredients. However, the convenience item can guarantee success and an acceptable product.

You need to rely on your own judgment and experience when it comes to selecting convenience pastry items. The list of ingredients on the label and the manufacturer's reputation will be your only guides.

You can create your own homemade convenience with pastry items. You can prepare your own pastry mix from flour, salt, and shortening, and store it in a covered container in a cool place. You then need only to add water when you are ready to bake a pie.

A variety of convenience items for pastry is available. Both crusts and pastry fillings come in many forms. Which convenience items and forms are shown here?

You can freeze homemade pies before or after baking. The quality of the frozen unbaked pie tends to be better because the bottom crust of frozen baked pies may become soggy. You may freeze chiffon pies. Custard pie and cream pie do not freeze well because the filling tends to separate.

You will recall that pastry shells may be frozen either baked or unbaked. Rolled circles of pastry can be separated with paper and then stacked and frozen in a suitable container or freezer wrap. Homemade and purchased convenience pastry items save time and energy, but the homemade ones may cost less than the purchased convenience products.

# 29 Chapter Review

## Summary

The most common uses of cookies are for desserts and snacks. There are drop, bar, rolled, refrigerator, pressed, and molded cookies. Pastry, however, has broader uses than cookies. Probably the most popular uses of pastry are for making pies that are served as a main dish or for dessert and for making accompaniments that are served with soups, salads, and desserts. The main contribution of cookies and pastry is their high caloric value; therefore, they should be consumed sparingly. To preserve quality and prevent spoilage, proper storage of cookies and pastry products is necessary. For the busy food manager, convenience forms of ready-to-eat, frozen, and dry mixes for cookies and pastry save time and effort.

## Vocabulary

Use the vocabulary words below to complete the numbered sentences. Each vocabulary word is used more than once.

extracts
flute
pastry

1. One reason to _____ the edges of pie crusts is to keep the filling from spilling out.
2. Baked crusts that are made from doughs rich in fat are called _____.
3. _____ are used for flavor.
4. Pies may be made with plain or puff _____.

5. Natural or artificial flavor essences, usually dissolved in alcohol, are known as _____.
6. Pies appear more attractive if you use your fingertips to _____ the edge of the _____.
7. _____ are used for flavoring cookie dough, but not pie dough.

## Chapter Questions

1. What is your favorite cookie? How do you prepare it? What type of cookie is it?
2. How are the ingredients, preparation procedures, baking, and convenience forms of butter cakes and most cookies alike and different?
3. Describe the procedure to follow if you bake two or more sheets of cookies at the same time.
4. What characteristics should you look for to tell when cookies are done?
5. Why is it important not to store crisp cookies with moist cookies in the same container?
6. What considerations should be made before purchasing a cookie convenience product?
7. What method do you prefer for making pastry? Why do you prefer that method?
8. How should you roll pastry so as not to toughen it?
9. Why do some people choose oil instead of solid fat for making pastry?
10. Before baking a pie shell, why is it important to prick the sides and bottom of the pastry?

11. What procedures should you follow to make a flaky, tender pie crust?
12. Why is it important not to serve more than one calorie-rich food at any one meal?
13. Why do cookies and pastry provide mostly calories?
14. What kinds of convenience cookie and pastry products do you have available for use in your family? Which product do you consider to be the best? Why?

## Skill Activities

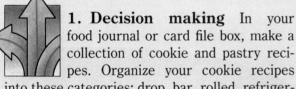

**1. Decision making** In your food journal or card file box, make a collection of cookie and pastry recipes. Organize your cookie recipes into these categories: drop, bar, rolled, refrigerator, pressed, and molded. Continue to add to your collection of recipes for fish, poultry, meat, and cheese and egg pies. Start a collection of pastry recipes for tarts, turnovers, cream puffs, pastry appetizers and accompaniments, Danish and French pastries, as well as dessert pies. Organize the dessert pies into these categories: fruit pies, custard pies, cream pies, and chiffon pies. You can find recipes in books, magazines, newspapers, on the display boards at supermarkets, and on packages of flour, sugar, coconut, chocolate, butter, and margarine.

**2. Communication** One way to trim the edge of pie crust is to flute it. However, there are several other ways to trim the edge. Research at least four other ways. Make a display board that shows what the trimmed edge should look like and provide step-by-step directions for making the decorative edge.

**3. Critical thinking** Plan two dinner menus for four people with pies for desserts. Prepare one menu with a chiffon pie and the other with a deep-dish pie. Include recipes for each dish on your menu. Select one of the menus and include a diagram of the place setting you would have for each person attending the dinner.

**4. Math** Compare the cost and time for making the same sized homemade apple pie and for making one from convenience products. First, find a recipe for an apple pie. On a sheet of lined paper, list the ingredients and the amounts needed for the crust and then the filling. On another sheet of paper, write the words "Convenience crust" and "Convenience filling." Visit a local grocery store to find the costs for the ingredients in the homemade pie and the costs for a crust made from sticks or a dry mix and the canned filling for the pie made from convenience products. Determine the total cost for each kind of pie. Next, prepare a time-work plan for making each pie. Which kind of pie costs more to make? What is the difference in cost between the two pies? Which kind of pie takes more time to make? What is the difference in preparation time between the two pies? When would you make a pie from convenience products? When would you make a homemade pie?

# 30 Food Preservation

## As you read, think about:

- why foods spoil.
- how to preserve food by canning, freezing, and drying.

**Vocabulary**

canning
blanching
hot pack
  method
cold pack
  method
head space
boiling-water
  bath method
steam-pressure
  method
pectin

With the technology of food preservation as it is today, it is possible to preserve the quality of foods from one harvest to the next. A wide variety of food is always available in the marketplace. Centuries ago this was not the case. The first foods to be preserved were grains and nuts. They were dried in the sun and air. Later, meats and fish were preserved by salting, smoking, and drying. It was not until the 19th century that other preservation methods, such as canning, were discovered. The search for new methods resulted from the need for a lasting food supply.

## Food Spoilage

The microorganisms responsible for food spoilage are bacteria, mold, and yeast. You can see them under the microscope. Some microorganisms are considered beneficial because they produce desirable changes in food. For example, bacteria are used in the making of buttermilk and sauerkraut. Molds are used in curing cheeses such as Roquefort and blue cheese. Yeast is used in bread making. Microorganisms, like any other living organisms, need warmth, moisture, and food to grow. When any of these three elements is restricted or absent, microorganisms cannot grow.

Of all the microorganisms, *bacteria* are the most difficult to destroy. There are many kinds of bacteria; some require much higher temperatures to destroy than others. Different kinds of bacteria are found on various foods. A few bacteria can grow at refrigerator temperatures, and some can grow at temperatures well over 100° F (38° C). However, most bacteria grow best at temperatures from 68-100° F (20-38° C).

*Mold* is a fluffy growth that is often white, but some varieties are red, gray, black, orange, or blue-green. Mold grows on many foods, such as fruits, breads, meat, and jellies. Some molds grow at refrigerator temperatures. Most molds

One of the earliest methods of food preservation was drying. In this illustration of an eighteenth-century fishing village, fish are being dried in the sun and air.

are easily destroyed at the boiling temperature. They usually grow on the surface and do not produce a harmful substance. A slight growth of mold on the surface can be removed, and the remaining food eaten. When the mold growth is very heavy, all of the food may be changed in flavor and should be discarded.

*Yeasts* usually have only one cell. They are easily destroyed by boiling, and most yeasts are destroyed at temperatures below boiling—120-140° F (49-60° C)—in about 15 minutes. Yeast is present in the air at all times and can contaminate food.

In addition to microorganisms, certain chemical substances called *enzymes* can cause both desirable and undesirable changes in food. For example, enzymes are responsible for color, flavor, and texture changes that occur as a food grows and ripens. Enzymes can also produce changes in food during storage. Because of enzyme activity, fruits and vegetables will continue to ripen when stored.

Most enzymes act best at room temperature and are easily destroyed by heating foods to the boiling temperature. If you do not destroy the enzymes, they will continue to act and cause, for example, fruits to darken and undesirable changes in the flavor and texture of vegetables. Enzyme activity in meat during storage is considered beneficial because it may tenderize the meat.

As you learn about the principles of food preservation, you will note that they have been designed both to destroy or inactivate microorganisms and enzymes that spoil foods and to protect foods from recontamination.

### For Review

1. What do microorganisms need in order to grow?
2. List and describe three microorganisms that can cause food spoilage.
3. What chemical substances can cause food spoilage?

## Canning Foods

Because of the highly specialized and expensive equipment required, not all methods of food preservation are suitable for home use. However, canning can be done easily and inexpensively in the home.

### The Basics of Canning

**Canning** is preserving foods in sealed containers by using heat to destroy microorganisms and to inactivate enzymes. The heat cooks the food and changes its flavor and appearance. Fruits, vegetables, and meats may be canned.

Canning will not improve the quality of food, but only preserve it. For good canned products, you should select high-quality foods. The crisp, young, tender vegetables and mature, ripe fruits make the best canned products. Because changes occur rapidly in the flavor and texture of foods after they are picked, you should can them as quickly as possible.

Food to be canned should first be thoroughly cleaned. Use a brush to clean large vegetables and fruits. Smaller foods can be cleaned in a sieve under running water. Other foods may be scraped or peeled. Some foods, such as peaches and tomatoes, are dipped into boiling water so that the skin can be removed easily. This slight precooking is known as **blanching.** After fruits and vegetables are cleaned, seeds and cores are often removed, and large pieces of food are cut or sliced.

Certain equipment is needed for canning. Much of this equipment is on hand in your kitchen. You need brushes to clean jars and food, knives for peeling and cutting, measuring cups

There are two types of canning jars. The one on the left has a porcelain-lined zinc cap and a rubber ring. The other has a two-piece metal lid.

and spoons, and some large kettles for blanching foods. You will also need a canner (large kettle with a rack) for processing acid foods, and a pressure cooker or canner for processing non-acid foods such as vegetables and meats.

Glass jars are most often used for home "canning" because they are suitable for all foods and they are reusable until they become cracked or chipped. They are easily sealed with a porcelain-lined zinc cap and a rubber ring or with a two-piece metal lid. Use jars made especially for canning. Do not use jars from commercial products such as mayonnaise or peanut butter.

## Packing Foods

Two methods are used to pack foods into jars for canning. The **hot pack method** requires little precooking and is suitable for all foods, especially firm foods. The **cold pack method** is used for placing raw foods into jars. No matter which method you use, there is a general canning procedure that you should follow.

First, wash all jars, lids, and rubber rings in hot, soapy water, and rinse in hot water. Soak screw band lids in boiling water. Next, sort the food according to size and ripeness, and wash the food thoroughly. Fill the jars, using either the hot pack or cold pack method. For the hot pack method, heat the food for a short time in boiling water; pack the food loosely; and cover the food with the cooking liquid. For the cold pack method, pack the raw food tightly into the jar and cover with boiling water. Leave a ½-1 inch (1.3-2.5 cm) **head space** at the top of the jar. Remove any trapped air bubbles with a table knife or spatula by running it down between the inside of the jar and the food, moving the food to release air. Then seal the jar. If you use the two-piece lid, place the flat lid with the sealing compound next to the top of the jar, and screw the band firmly in place. If you use the porcelain-lined zinc cap, place the rubber ring on the sealing shoulder, and screw on the cap. Then

Before sealing the jar when packing foods for canning, be sure to remove trapped air bubbles by running a spatula down the side of the jar.

loosen the cap about ¼ inch (about 6 mm) to allow some air to escape during processing.

## Processing Foods

The filled and closed jars are processed by either the boiling-water bath method or the steam-pressure method.

The **boiling-water bath method** of processing is used for high-acid foods such as fruits and tomatoes. The boiling-water bath consists of a large kettle, a rack on which to place the jars, and a lid. The kettle should be deep enough to allow at least 1 inch (2.5 cm) of water to cover the tops of the jars. The water is brought to a

The boiling-water bath method is used to process these high-acid peaches. The jars of peaches are placed on a rack in the kettle. When does the processing timing begin?

A pressure canner is used for the steam-pressure method of processing. Why should this method be used for low-acid foods?

Each food has a recommended processing time for either method. Check the recipe or the pressure canner instructions for the processing time. Refer to the chart on page 549 for processing times for popular fruits and vegetables. After processing, tighten the zinc lids completely; the two-piece lids self-seal as they cool and do not need further tightening.

## After Processing

The next day, after the jars have cooled, test the seal. Press the top of the two-piece lid; if it is flat and does not move, it is sealed. Also, if it gives a clear ring when tapped, it is sealed. Place jars with zinc caps on their sides to check for leaks. Should you find a jar not properly sealed, use the contents immediately or recan. Reexamine the container and, if it is defective, you should transfer the food to another container before processing again.

Remove the screw band from the two-piece lids before you store the sealed jars. Wipe the containers to clean them; then label and store them in a cool, dry place. The color of foods in glass containers will be protected when you store them in a dark place.

rolling boil so that the water temperature is 212° F (100° C). Processing timing begins once the water reaches a rolling boil.

The **steam-pressure method** of processing is used for low-acid foods such as vegetables because low-acid foods need higher temperatures to kill the microorganisms, especially clostridium botulinum (see page 128). Because the pressure canner retains steam, temperatures above 212° F (100° C) can be reached. If you use a steam canner, be sure to follow the instructions in the owner's manual.

## Processing Timetable for Fruits and Vegetables

| Fruits | | Vegetables | |
|---|---|---|---|
| Method: Boiling-water bath | | Method: Steam pressure | |
| Quantity: Quart jars | | Quantity: Quart jars | |
| | | Pressure: 10 pounds | |
| Apples | 10 minutes | Asparagus | 40 minutes |
| Apricots | 25 minutes | Beans (string) | 40 minutes |
| Cherries | 15 minutes | Beets | 45 minutes |
| Grapes | 20 minutes | Carrots | 45 minutes |
| Peaches | 20 minutes | Corn | 75 minutes |
| Pears | 20 minutes | Lima beans | 55 minutes |
| Plums | 25 minutes | Mushrooms | 40 minutes |
| Tomatoes | 45 minutes | Peas | 45 minutes |

## For Review

1. What is the purpose of canning?
2. List and describe the two methods for packing foods for canning.
3. List and describe the two methods for processing foods. Which method is used for fruits, and which method is used for vegetables? Why?

Jams and jellies that you make at home or buy in jars at the store are products of food preservation. What fruits, besides the ones shown here, can be used in jelly making?

## Jelly Making

Jelly, made from the juice of fruit, is another form of food preservation. The principles of food preservation apply to jelly making. As the fruit juice and sugar are cooked, microorganisms are destroyed, and the resulting jelly is sealed with paraffin (wax) to protect the jelly from any recontamination.

Another principle of jelly making is the formation of a *gel*. The gelling quality of fruit juices is determined by the amount of **pectin** (a carbohydrate found in all fruits) in the juice. Some fruits, such as grapes, apples, and citrus fruits, are good sources of pectin; others, such as pineapple, peaches, and strawberries, are low in pectin.

In addition to pectin, *acid* and *sugar* are required to make a good gel. Most fruits are somewhat tart and contain acid, but fruits such as bananas and pears are low in acid and are not usually used for jelly. Sugar must be added to all fruit juices to make a good jelly.

The principle of gel formation involves the presence of the right amount of pectin, acid, and

Step 1

Step 2

Step 3

**Jelly Making**

Step 4

Step 5

Step 6

sugar, and the cooking of the juice and sugar mixture to the right stage. As the juice and sugar mixture is cooked, water will evaporate and the juice will thicken. The cooking is continued until the mixture reaches a certain temperature; when the mixture cools, it will form a gel. The gel should be firm enough to retain the shape of the jelly glass but tender enough so that it can be spread easily. To make jelly, follow these steps:

1. First wash the fruit thoroughly, remove stems, and cut large fruits into small pieces. Cook the fruit in water, according to the recipe, until it is soft. Place the cooked fruit into a muslin bag, or into a sieve lined with muslin. Let the juice drip into a bowl.
2. Jelly can be made with or without pectin. When you add pectin, the juice and sugar are cooked until a candy thermometer registers 220-222° F (104-106° C). When no pectin is added, a longer cooking time is required to reach the gel stage.

Commercial pectin is available as a powder or a liquid and can also be extracted from apple or citrus peel. The directions for using the commercial pectins may vary slightly. You must follow the directions given with the pectin for combining the juice with the pectin and the sugar.

3. When the jelly is cooked, remove any scum or foam from the surface.
4. Pour the hot jelly into sterile glasses to within ¼ inch (6.4 mm) of the top.
5. Immediately cover the jelly with melted paraffin, which will make a tight seal as it cools. Add the paraffin gently to make a ¼ inch (6.4 mm) layer on the jelly surface.
6. After the jelly has cooled, wipe the glass to remove any jelly on the surface. Cover the glass with a clean lid or foil, and label it. Store the jelly in a cool, dry place.

You may want to make other spreads such as jams, preserves, conserves, fruit butters, and marmalades. Each of these spreads calls for the

Since 1984, Americans have been eating irradiated herbs and spices. In 1985, the Food and Drug Administration (FDA) approved the practice of irradiating pork to kill trichinosis. Soon irradiated fruits will be stacked in produce departments. The food production and distribution industries consider this process of food preservation a boon, but others are more cautious.

As you read in this chapter, irradiation is a process whereby food is preserved by exposing it to radioactive materials. Cobalt 60, a byproduct of nuclear power plants, is the radioactive material used. When fruits and vegetables are exposed to low levels of radiation, their chemical makeup is altered so that they ripen more slowly. High levels of radiation kill insects and microbes that promote the decay of food. The government has been involved in the testing of irradiation for 30 years.

Despite government testing and FDA approval, some scientists are skeptical about the practice of irradiation.

## The Pros

Supporters of irradiation point out that the process is approved by the FDA and that the government tested the process for 30 years before approving it. They assert that irradiation is safer for the environment than insecticides.

Irradiation is a controversial food-preservation method. Read about it here and in the media. Form your own opinion.

Chemical insecticides can kill needed species and be ingested by other animals including humans. The irradiation process occurs only after food has been harvested, and merely exposes the food to radiation. The food itself does not become radioactive.

In addition, irradiation is less expensive than chemical insecticides and other preservation processes. It lengthens the shelf life of produce, which is good for consumers, distributors, and producers. It does not affect the appearance of the food. Irradiation depletes fewer nutrients from food than cooking does.

## The Cons

Opponents of irradiation worry about the chemicals that irradiation produces. They argue that higher energy chemical reactions, like irradiation, are more likely to be harmful.

According to the FDA, small amounts of hydrogen peroxide are produced in fruits and vegetables when the radiation reacts with water. When radiation reacts with meat, 65 chemicals are produced: about one-third are the same as chemicals caused by cooking, and more than half are found in other foods. The FDA conjectures that approximately ten percent of the chemicals produced are new chemicals about which little is known. Opponents of irradiation challenge the FDA's assumption that these chemicals occur in quantities too small to harm humans. They argue that too many questions have been left unanswered.

Some opponents also object to the potentially dangerous transportation of radioactive materials to irradiation processing centers. They also object to a new Department of Energy research project that will investigate the use of a radioactive by-product of nuclear weapons development to irradiate food.

However, supporters and opponents of irradiation agree on one idea—consumers should know about irradiation and its possible effects.

jelly-making principles and is made from a different form or portion of the fruit. For example, jam is made from mashed fruit, conserves from a mixture of fruits, and fruit butters from the pulp of the fruit.

---

**For Review**

1. What is the importance of pectin for jelly making?
2. Why do low-acid fruits *not* make good jellies?
3. Why is paraffin poured over jelly?

---

# Freezing

Unlike canning, the principles of preserving foods by freezing are based upon the use of very cold temperatures (at least $0°F(-18°C)$) to prevent the growth of microorganisms and to slow down enzyme activity. As soon as the food begins to thaw, microorganisms and enzymes become active, and the food must be used quickly to avoid spoilage.

All foods except the raw, succulent, crisp foods (such as salads or relishes) may be frozen. Freezing causes less change in the color, flavor, and texture of foods than does canning, and the nutrient values of frozen foods are similar to those of the fresh foods.

Use the same care in selecting foods for freezing as you do when you select foods for canning. Freezing cannot improve the quality of the food; it can only preserve the quality present in the food at the time it is frozen. Use only foods that are free of decay, spoilage, or bruises, and those that are at the stage of maturity and ripeness most desirable for eating and cooking.

You may freeze meat, fish, poultry, soups, casseroles, stews, yeast and quick breads, cakes, and pastries.

To freeze foods, you will need a freezer and moisture-vapor-proof packaging materials in addition to the usual kitchen equipment. Containers of aluminum, glass, plastic-coated paper, and transparent freezer wraps are suitable for wrapping irregular shaped foods such as meats and baked products for the freezer.

## Freezing Fruits

You can easily and quickly prepare fruits for freezing. Fruits may be packed dry, with sugar, or with syrup; however, frozen sweetened fruits usually have a better texture than dry-packed fruits. Small whole fruits such as berries may be packed dry. You must keep dry-packed fruits at a constant temperature and sealed tightly to avoid excessive dehydration.

The type of syrup and the proportion of sugar used for sugar and syrup pack will vary with the type of fruit used. In general, prepare enough syrup to cover the fruit. For small or sliced fruits, prepare ⅓ - ½ cup (80-125 mL) syrup for 1½ cups (375 mL) fruit. For halved fruits, prepare about ¾-1 cup (185-250 mL) syrup for 1½ cups (375 mL) fruit. Sugar slows down freezing, so the greater the quantity of sugar used, the lower the freezing temperature must be.

When you prepare fruits for freezing, they need only to be sorted, washed, hulled, peeled, cored, and cut, if desired. When you pack fruits in syrup, you will prepare the syrup in advance and thoroughly chill it.

Some fruits, such as peaches, pears, and apples, may darken during frozen storage unless they are treated with ascorbic or citric acid. You will usually use ½ teaspoon (2.5 mL) of ascorbic acid for each quart (liter) of syrup.

To freeze fruits, follow these steps:

## Food Preparation for Freezing

| Fruits | Preparation—Wash Well | Syrup | Sugar |
|---|---|---|---|
| *Apples | Peel, core, slice. | 40% | ½ c (125 mL) |
| *Apricots | Cut in halves, pit. | 40–50% | ½ c (125 mL) |
| Berries | Sort, wash, drain well. | 30–50% | ¾ c (185 mL) |
| Cherries | Sort, wash, pit or leave whole. | 40–60% | ¾–1 c (185–250 mL) |
| *Peaches | Peel, pit, and slice. | 30–40% | ⅔ c (160 mL) |
| Pineapple | Peel, core, slice or dice. | 40–50% | ⅔ c (160 mL) |
| Plums | Halve and pit. | 40–50% | none |

| Vegetables | Wash, Blanch, Chill in Ice Water | Blanch in Boiling Water |
|---|---|---|
| Asparagus | Cut in desired lengths. | 2–4 minutes |
| Beans, string | Cut, or leave whole. | 3–4 |
|     lima | Shell, sort, wash. | 2–3 |
| Broccoli | Peel stalk, trim, split lengthwise. | 3–5 |
| Carrots | Peel, cut in slices or dice. | 3 |
| Cauliflower | Break into flowerlets (1-inch (2.5-cm) size). | 3–4 |
| Corn | Husk, silk, blanch, cut from cob. | 4 |
| Peas | Shell, sort, wash. | 1–2 |

### Syrups for Freezing

| | | |
|---|---|---|
| 30% | 2 c (500 mL) sugar + 4 c (1 L) water = | 5 c (1.3 L) syrup |
| 40% | 3 c (750 mL) sugar + 4 c (1 L) water = | 5½ c (1.4 L) syrup |
| 50% | 4¾ c (1.18 L) sugar + 4 c (1 L) water = | 6½ c (1.6 L) syrup |
| 60% | 7 c (1.75 L) sugar + 4 c (1 L) water = | 7¾ c (1.9 L) syrup |

*Use ascorbic or citric acid to prevent darkening.

Adapted from "Home Freezing of Fruits and Vegetables," *Home and Garden Bulletin No. 10,* United States Department of Agriculture.

1. Select fresh, ripe fruit free of decay. Gently wash the fruit under running water, and drain on absorbent paper.
2. Slice or cut up the fruit, unless you are using small whole fruits. Put the fruit in a shallow pan, and sprinkle it with the amount of sugar called for in the recipe. Gently turn the fruit until the sugar dissolves and forms a syrup.

### Practical Tip
- The Department of Agriculture has free pamphlets on canning and freezing procedures. Write for them and you will have all the best information available to insure success in canning and freezing.

To pack fruit such as strawberries for freezing, wash, slice, and sprinkle the fruit with sugar (top). Let the sugar form a syrup (bottom left), and then pack it for freezing (bottom right).

3. Carefully pack the fruit and any juice that has formed into a carton suitable for freezing. Gently tap the carton to pack the fruit closely and to remove trapped air. Leave ½ inch (1.3 cm) of head space.
4. If you use syrup instead of dry sugar, slice the fruit directly into the carton, and then add the syrup. Allow 1 inch (2.5 cm) of head space.
5. Wipe the top of the container with a clean, damp cloth. Seal the container tightly, and label and date it.

6. Place the labeled carton into the freezer so that the bottom or sides of the carton are in direct contact with the freezing unit. Foods frozen quickly will have better texture than those frozen slowly.

## Freezing Vegetables

The procedure for preparing vegetables for freezing is similar to that used for canning. Most vegetables are blanched to retard enzyme action, and are then dry packed for freezing. The blanching time will depend on the vegetable (see page 553). Immediately after blanching, the vegetables are cooled in ice water, drained, and packed without any liquid.

## Freezing Meat, Fish, and Poultry

Meat, fish, and poultry require no special preparation for freezing. You may wish to cut them into pieces for serving. Cut pieces, such as several steaks, will be easy to separate after freezing if you place a double layer of wrapping material between them. Do not store meat, fish, and poultry in their original wrappers because they may not be moisture-vapor-proof. Use drugstore or butcher wrap, and follow these steps:
1. Place the food to be frozen in the center of the paper, and bring the opposite edges of the paper together.
2. Fold down the paper in a series of small folds until it is in direct contact with the food.
3. Fold the ends to make points, pressing the paper close to the food to force out air.
4. Turn the folded ends against the package, and seal it with freezer tape.

## Freezing Other Foods

Many other foods can also be frozen. Baked pastry, unfrosted cakes, cookies, breads, and sandwiches may be carefully wrapped for freezing. You will find it easier to wrap frosted cakes

## Preparation of Meat for Freezing

Step 1

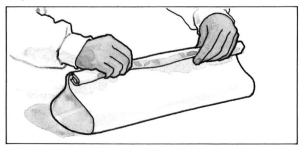

Step 2

Step 3

Step 4

and unbaked pies if you slightly freeze them first. Wrap all foods carefully and closely to exclude as much air as possible. You may freeze foods such as casseroles and stews in special serving dishes that can also be used for baking

or heating. By doing this, there will be one less dish to wash. Be sure to label all packages and containers with the name of the food and the date when frozen.

Some foods will retain their quality for a longer time during frozen storage than others. For example, beef, fish, fruits, vegetables, and cookies can be stored for a year; other foods, such as yeast breads, for six months; and pies and quick breads for only three months.

### Preparing Foods from the Freezer

Frozen foods are prepared by the same methods that are used for fresh foods. Most vegetables, except corn on the cob, are cooked without being thawed first. Frozen fruits are partially thawed, and they do not require cooking. Meat, poultry, and fish may be cooked after thawing, or they may be cooked right from the freezer. Unthawed, these foods will take longer to cook, however.

### For Review

1. How does freezing food keep it from spoiling?
2. Why are fruits usually sweetened before freezing?
3. Why are vegetables usually blanched before freezing?

# Food Drying

The oldest method of food preservation is food drying, which involves removing moisture to prevent the growth of microorganisms. Dried foods, especially dried fruits, are popular because they keep for months and are lightweight and take up little space. These qualities make dried foods popular with campers and hikers.

## Methods of Food Drying

Foods may be dried in the sun, in a conventional oven, in a food dryer, or in a microwave oven. Most foods can be dried. Vegetables should be blanched, and some must be treated with sodium metabisulfite before drying. Fruits are usually treated with ascorbic acid before drying.

**Sun Drying**   Drying food in the sun is the simplest method of food drying. However, weather conditions must be just right (that is; high temperature, low humidity, and direct sunlight), and the food must be protected from dirt and insects. Sun drying can take several hours or up to several days.

Food to be dried in the sun is placed on screen racks, and the food requires occasional turning. The screening lets air circulate around the food for faster drying. You can make your own screen racks at home, but be sure not to use screening made either with fiberglass or with galvanized wire.

**Oven Drying**   A conventional oven can be used for food drying. The food is placed on screen racks or on cheesecloth stretched over

These apricots drying on screens in the California sunshine will "keep" much longer than the fresh fruit. What other fruits are often dried?

Today, fruits and herbs can also be dried in special appliances called food dryers. A fan helps to circulate the warm air which is kept at a consistent temperature.

Approximate nutrition information per serving: calories–25; protein–3 g; fat–trace; cholesterol–0; carbohydrates–4 g; sodium–85 mg.

## Preparing Spinach for Freezing

1 lb (454 g) fresh spinach
1 gal (3.8 L) water for boiling
1 gal (3.8 L) ice water

1. Wash spinach, removing tough stems and damaged leaves.
2. Boil water in a large kettle.
3. Add spinach, cover, and blanch for 1½ minutes.
4. Plunge spinach into ice water; let stand until cold. Drain well.
5. Chop if desired, and then pack in a moisture-vapor-proof container.

oven racks. The oven is set at the lowest possible setting—about 150° F (66° C)—and the food must be stirred or turned occasionally. Drying time varies with the type of food.

Food dryers were created especially for drying food. They not only provide the consistent temperature of a conventional oven, but they also have a fan that circulates the warm air around the food.

Microwave ovens are useful for drying herbs, but not for other foods because microwaves do not cook evenly. The advantage of using a microwave is the fast drying time; for example, several bunches of parsley can be dried in as little as 30 seconds.

### Storing Dried Food

Before storing any dried food, be certain it has cooled completely; otherwise, moisture can build up, and spoilage can occur. Pack the cooled food in airtight containers, and store them in a cool, dry, and dark place, or in the refrigerator.

### For Review

1. What is one advantage and one disadvantage of drying food in the sun?
2. Why are food dryers especially good for drying food?
3. What guidelines should you follow when storing dried food?

# 30 Chapter Review

## Summary

Today people are able to eat a variety of foods even when they are not in season because of the advanced technology of food preservation. Canning is a procedure to preserve fruits, vegetables, and meats by packing them in containers and then subjecting them to extremely high temperatures. Jellies, jams, preserves, conserves, fruit butters, and marmalades are other ways to preserve fruit by following the principle of gel formation. Unlike canning, freezing preserves foods with very cold temperatures. Freezing is a way of preserving not only fruits and vegetables, but also meat, fish, poultry, stews, breads, casseroles, cakes, pastries, and cookies for later use. Food drying is the oldest method of preservation. Originally, people dried food by the sun. Today there are more modern ways to dry food. Whichever method of food preservation is selected, it is especially important to follow directions carefully in order to destroy harmful microorganisms and to inactivate enzymes.

## Vocabulary

Use the vocabulary words below to fill in the blanks in the paragraph that follows.

blanching
boiling-water bath method
canning
cold pack method
head space
hot pack method
pectin
steam-pressure method

During the nineteenth century, a method of preserving food in sealed containers was discovered that used heat to destroy micro-organisms and inactivate enzymes; this process was called __(1)__. There are two ways to pack food into glass jars. When the __(2)__ is used, the raw foods are placed into the jars and then covered with boiling water. However, when another method is selected, known as the __(3)__, the food is heated for a short time in boiling water, packed in the jars, and then covered with the cooking liquid. Whichever method is used, at least 1/2 - 1 inch of __(4)__ should be left at the top of each jar. The containers of food are then processed by either the __(5)__ for low-acid foods such as vegetables or the __(6)__ for high-acid foods such as fruits. The juice of fruits may be preserved as jelly by the formation of a gel. The gelling quality of the juice is determined by __(7)__, which is a carbohydrate that is found in all fruits. Just as with canning, vegetables that are to be frozen or dried are first slightly precooked by a process called __(8)__. After this, the vegetables are packed in containers and then frozen or arranged on racks and then dried.

## Chapter Questions

1. What kinds of fruits and vegetables make the best canned and frozen products?

2. When you are canning foods, why is it important that no air remains trapped in the jar and that the jar is sealed tightly?

3. Why should food that is canned in glass jars be stored in a dark place?

4. For each of the following foods, tell how they should be cleaned, packed, and which method of processing should be used for canning: a) beets; b) peaches; c) carrots; d) pears; and e) string beans.

5. Categorize the kinds of fruit spreads available for use in your family. Besides using the spreads on bread or toast, how else can you use them?

6. When jelly is made, why is the cooked fruit placed in a muslin bag or into a sieve lined with muslin?

7. How is the nutritional value of canned food different from food that is frozen?

8. Take an inventory of the preserved foods you have available for use in your family, and categorize them as canned, frozen, or dried foods.

9. Why should you rewrap fresh meat that you purchase at the store before you freeze it?

10. Which method of food drying would you prefer to dry slices of peach? Why?

## Skill Activities

**1. Decision making** In your food journal or card file box, collect recipes that call for dried fruits and vegetables as ingredients. Dried products can be used to make soups, salads, main dishes, vegetables, casseroles, stews, snacks, breads, and desserts. You can find recipes on the packages of food products, in books, magazines, and newspapers, and on the display boards in supermarkets.

**2. Reading** Compare the percentage of U.S. RDA for one serving of canned beans, fresh beans, and frozen beans and canned peas, fresh peas, and frozen peas. Down the left-hand side of a lined sheet of paper, write these headings: "Protein," "Vitamin A," "Vitamin C," "Thiamin," "Riboflavin," "Niacin," "Calcium," and "Iron." Now make six columns, and write one of these headings at the top of each column: "Canned beans," "Fresh beans," "Frozen beans," "Canned peas," "Fresh peas," and "Frozen peas." Research the information about fresh beans and peas and enter it on your chart. Then visit the canned and frozen goods departments of a local grocery store, and record the information found on the nutritional labels. For each vegetable, what is the difference in nutrients between the fresh, frozen, and canned forms? Which form more closely matches the nutrients contained in the fresh vegetables?

**3. Critical thinking** Most meals are prepared with at least one food that is preserved. Plan a luncheon menu for four people that uses a canned food, a frozen food, and a dried food as a dish or as an ingredient. With your menu, include the recipes for the dishes. Also tell which nutrients your menu provides.

# Unit 5
# Food Around the World

# *31* **Foreign Foods**

## As you read, think about:

- how culture influences food habits and cuisine.
- why you should try foreign foods and the recipes for preparing them.
- how food customs and cuisines are similar and different for countries around the world.

**Vocabulary**
culture
cuisine

Your food habits as well as the food habits of people in other parts of the world have been influenced by cultural beliefs and values, religion, climate, regional location, agriculture, technology, and economic status. Consequently, food habits vary from country to country as well as from region to region within a country.

# Food and Culture

The way of life of a group of people (generally of the same nationality) is identified as **culture.** One culture may think of food only as a way to satisfy hunger, while another culture sees food as a source of pleasure and an opportunity to socialize with family and friends. The family, religious institutions, and schools pass cultural practices and beliefs on from one generation to the next.

### Cuisine

The past history as well as the present environment of a group influence all its habits and customs, including those relating to food.

The style of cooking that develops in a particular culture is called its **cuisine.** Cuisines differ in the kinds of ingredients included in meals as well as in their preparation. One culture's cuisine may be based on beef and potatoes, another's on beans and tortillas, and still another's on rice, fish, or some other combination of foods. Each is capable of providing a nutritional balance. So too are the different ways to prepare food. Quick frying of small pieces of meat and vegetables is a different technique than slow-cooking similar ingredients in a stew, but both can provide nutritious, balanced meals.

### Customs

Through the ages, particular rituals and formalities, or customs, developed in different parts of the world and became accepted as appropriate practices for the consumption of food. In some cultures, for example, good manners require that people sit on the floor, eat food from their fingers, and smack their lips. Other groups of people observe their cultural etiquette by sitting at a table, eating from plates and using utensils, and trying to make as little noise as

In many cultures, customs associated with particular meals or dishes have been passed down for centuries. The beautiful Japanese tea ceremony is one example.

possible. It is not that one way is right and another is wrong. Rather, different cultures have developed different rules, and you should always try to respect the cultural etiquette of your host when you dine in a foreign country, in a foreign restaurant, or in the home of a person whose cultural background is different from your own.

## Preparing Foreign Food

Food preparation methods vary in different cultures. Some cultures tend to prepare elaborate meals; others thrive on one-pot meals. Whether the recipe you choose is elaborate or simple, foreign or familiar, the ingredients (such as leavening, shortening, eggs, meats, vegetables, or fruits) will serve the same function. For example, yeast will always supply the leavening for the flour mixture in which it is used, and shortening will always contribute tenderness to a dough, regardless of the nationality of the recipe.

Foreign-food recipes will give you new and interesting ways to prepare foods, as well as the pleasure and excitement of trying new dishes and learning about the countries and peoples from which they come. Don't hesitate to try recipes from other cultures. The general techniques, such as creaming sugar and shortening, folding in egg foams, and kneading dough, are much the same in all cultures.

## American Food Patterns

We have a variety of cultural food patterns in the United States. The American diet is a blend of foods from other countries. As new foods gain acceptance, an American version of these foods comes to be a part of the American scene. Italian spaghetti, Mexican tacos, and French crepes are now popular parts of the American diet. The blending of cultures has given us a wide variety of main dishes, breads, soups, salads, and desserts from which to choose.

Dinner is the main meal of the day for most Americans. It is usually served early in the evening and is often considered a social occasion. Lunch is a moderate meal, and breakfast the lightest meal for many Americans. In some cultures, however, the noon meal is the main meal of the day. The American breakfast may be considered a heavy meal when compared to the first meal of the day served in some other countries. The European breakfast, called a Continental breakfast, is often light and may consist only of a bread item and a beverage.

It is very interesting to travel abroad and participate in the customs—including the dining customs—of other cultures. English high tea or the Japanese tea ceremony may be a pleasurable experience when visiting another country—or the home of a friend whose cultural background is different from yours. These special meals and the dishes that they include can also be "brought home" by doing some research in the many cookbooks that specialize in foods from particular cultures. As more and more Americans sample and enjoy them, "foreign foods," such as croissants and chili, become part of the American food heritage.

## For Review

1. What factors determine the food habits of different cultures?
2. Name five "foreign foods" that have become so accepted and common in the United States that Americans no longer regard them as foreign.
3. Name one foreign food that you would like to try and why you would like to try it. Name one that you would *not* like to try and explain why.

An elaborate "afternoon tea" has been an important part of British life for generations. What is included besides the beverage itself?

# Foods Around the World

Traditional food customs are promoted from one generation to the next, and they carry with them strong meanings and feelings which bind families and communities into close units. Even as the world has "grown smaller" and people sample and accept many dishes from other cultures, they still tend to have special feelings for their own traditional foods. As you read about the food traditions and cuisines of other countries, think about which dishes and customs have become part of the "American melting pot."

## England

Many of the dishes popular in England seem quite familiar to Americans. After all, it was the original English colonists and settlers who had the first and most important influence on what is thought of as standard American cooking. There are some differences, too, of course. Besides raising beef cattle, the English raise sheep, and therefore mutton is a popular meat. Also, because they live on an island, the English rely more on fish as main course dishes than Americans have traditionally done.

The English prefer roasted and grilled meats, and do not use as many sauces or spices as many other cultures do. The most common meats in the English diet are beef, mutton, and pork. Chicken, game (meat from wild animals hunted for food), and organ meats are also popular. Since fish has long been a major industry for the English, cod, Dover sole, haddock, herring, and plaice are among their favorites. While fresh fish is often prepared simply, kippered, or smoked, fish are also popular.

A traditional English dinner is substantial, consisting of a roast (beef or lamb), a potato dish or *Yorkshire pudding* (a batter of flour, eggs, and milk baked in the drippings of the roasting meat), and a vegetable. Cabbage, cauliflower, brussels sprouts, and grilled tomatoes are commonly served.

The English also like one-dish pies of meat and vegetables, or meat and potatoes. Traditionally, these meat pies have been a good way to make use of dinner leftovers. *Steak and kidney pie* contains beef and kidneys covered with a pastry crust. *Shepherd's pie* is made from ground meat and mashed potatoes, while *bubble and squeak* is a combination of chopped beef, mashed potatoes, and vegetables. Another popular combination of foods is *fish and chips*. This favorite snack can be purchased at small shops. The fish is deep-fried, and the chips are similar to french fries. They are often served in cones of rolled newspaper.

Grains occupy a very prominent place in the English diet. White, whole-wheat, and rye

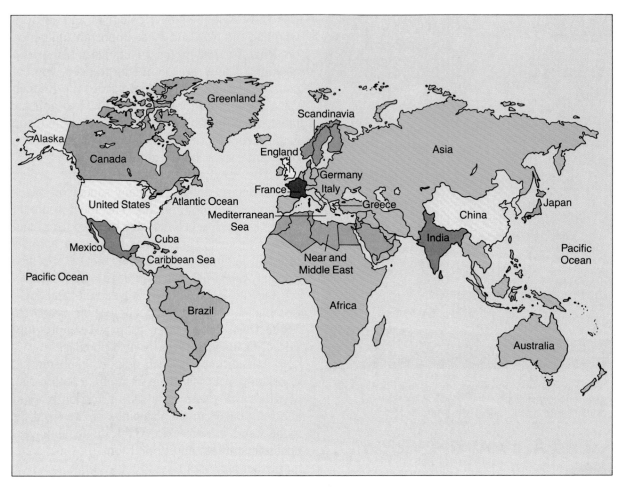

As you read this chapter, use the map to help you compare the cuisines of regions with similar climates as well as inland countries versus coastal areas. Also, see if neighboring countries always share cooking styles.

breads are served with meals. Scones and biscuits are popular accompaniments for afternoon tea. Oatmeal is served at breakfast, in oaten cakes, or in the evening meal as a porridge. Yorkshire pudding, the popular roast-beef accompaniment, is also a grain dish. It is made of flour, eggs, and milk.

Milk, buttermilk, and cheese frequently appear in meals. Hot milk is served with cereal and with tea. Cheddar and soft cheeses are often served in the evening meal with biscuits or bread. Popular desserts include fruit pie topped with hot custard sauce, and trifle, which is a combination of sponge cake, fruit or jam, and whipped cream.

Two English "meals" deserve special mention. The first is the English breakfast, which is more substantial than that served in many other cultures. It often includes hot cereal; broiled ham or bacon, or kippers; eggs; and toast. The other "meal" is afternoon tea, which can range from a cup-of-tea break at work to an elegantly served meal of light sandwiches, breads, and pastries accompanied by brewed tea with milk.

This traditional English Sunday dinner features roast beef with Yorkshire pudding, boiled potatoes, Brussels sprouts and natural gravy.

If an elaborate tea is served late in the afternoon, a light supper usually follows later in the evening.

## France

The French regard cooking as an art, and they consider meals not just for the consumption of food but as leisurely social events as well. Conversation is nearly as important as well-prepared dishes at French tables. French cuisine is famous for flavorful soups and sauces, crisp-crusted breads, tarts, and pastries. While the food of some Parisian restaurants is called *haute cuisine* (classic or gourmet cooking), each region of France also has a distinctive cookery style. The regions of France are called provinces, and French regional fare is called provincial cooking. *Nouvelle cuisine* (translated as "new cooking") is a relatively recent version of classic French cookery. It is lower in flour, sugar, and fat than traditional French cooking and emphasizes the freshness, shape, color, and texture of ingredients, as well as their natural flavors. The portions are also smaller than in classic dishes.

Provincial cooking is sometimes called the food of the ordinary people of France. It is hearty and simple, relying on long-cooking, one-dish casseroles. A flavorful mixture of meat and vegetables, *ragout* (ra-GOO) is a popular French stew; *bouillabaisse* (boo-yuh-BAYSS) (a fish soup containing lobster, fish, eel, mussels, scallops, tomatoes, and herbs) is eaten as a main-course dish. You may also be familiar with *ratatouille* (ra-ta-TOO-ee), a vegetable stew of eggplant, zucchini, and tomatoes all flavored with garlic.

Paris would not be Paris without its sidewalk cafés. There, the French enjoy food and beverages in a relaxing yet entertaining atmosphere.

Classic French cooking requires a great deal of skill and time for its preparation. It emphasizes rich sauces, such as made-from-scratch mayonnaise (served on fish, eggs, or vegetables, rather than on salads) and hollandaise. Elegant desserts and time-consuming dishes such as soufflés, *aspics* (clear jellies made from meat or fish stock), and puff pastries are part of this classic style of cooking. The freshest ingredients are used, and great care is taken in their preparation.

A classic French dinner has many courses, beginning with *hors d'oeuvres* (or-DURVZ), or appetizers. Baked or poached fish is often the second course, followed by the main course, which features veal, lamb, chicken, beef, or pork. Rather than serving a roast, the French often prepare meat in a flavorful sauce. A vegetable, such as artichoke, spinach, eggplant, turnips, green beans, or asparagus, usually accompanies the meat dish. Mushrooms and onions are often used in the preparation of the main course.

The French prefer a green salad *after* the main course. They use a simple dressing based on olive oil and vinegar. Fresh, crusty bread is served at all meals. The long, thin loaf that Americans call French bread is termed a *baguette* in France.

While Americans are familiar with many of the fancier French desserts, such as crepes, mousses, éclairs, soufflés, and caramel custards, the French usually have only fresh fruit and

**Practical Tip**
- To keep frozen crepes from sticking or breaking, separate individual crepes with waxed paper. Then roll groups of six crepes into tube shapes to freeze.

cheese for dessert. Strong coffee is served with this light dessert.

The French breakfast is light, consisting of coffee, served with boiled milk, or hot chocolate and a croissant, bread, or pastry. The largest meal is served in the middle of the day. Most French people take time for a substantial, leisurely noon meal. Schools and offices are usually closed from noon until 2 P.M.

Between meals, the sidewalk café is popular with the French. Located on bustling city streets or in the main squares of small towns, a café is a good place to sip coffee, have a light snack, chat, and watch the world stroll by.

## Germany

The German cookery tradition features hearty meals, a variety of breads, festive desserts, and the use of fruits in main dishes as well as in desserts. *Wursts,* or sausages, come in many varieties and are the ancestors of the American hot dog. Gingerbread people—and their houses—can also be said to "come from" Germany, where shaped pastries are traditional holiday fare.

In Germany, the heavy main meal is customarily eaten at noon. It usually features pork, veal, or another meat, and potatoes or cabbage. One-dish meals are popular in German cooking. So are sweet-sour recipes, many of which were developed as ways to preserve food. To preserve beef, for example, Germans traditionally marinated it in a sweet-sour mixture of vinegar and spices to create *sauerbraten. Sauerkraut* is cabbage preserved by salting and fermentation. Even the famous wursts originated as ways to preserve meats by seasoning and smoking them. Along with the meat dish, Germans frequently have vegetables such as beets, carrots, onions, and turnips, or sauerkraut. They have bread at most meals: dark, seeded, and shaped breads are popular.

An almost endless variety of wursts is popular in German meals. Making meat into these smoked and seasoned sausages is also a good method of preserving it.

A variety of popular dairy products includes milk, buttermilk, sour milk, sour cream, cottage cheese, and brick cheeses. Milk is used more for cooking than as a beverage. Cottage cheese is used in noodle dishes, cake, and *strudel*. Butter is primarily used for cooking; little is eaten on bread. Jams are the preferred spread on bread.

The Germans begin the day with a breakfast of rolls or bread and coffee, and a few hours later they eat a second breakfast. A midmorning snack and a midafternoon coffee are popular. The last meal of the day, supper, is light and is served late in the evening. Cold cuts are often provided along with bread and cheese, salad, eggs, or leftovers. It is not customary to eat dessert at supper.

When they do prepare desserts, Germans take great care to produce attractive sweets. Black Forest cake, apple strudel, Bavarian cream, and coffee cakes are well-known German desserts.

## Italy

While pasta is central to many Italian meals, it is not the only kind of dish you will find on dinner tables in Italy. Seafood is also very popular there. Meats such as chicken and veal are often cooked in flavorful sauces or with cheese and tomato, while beef is ground, seasoned, and made into meatballs. A variety of omelets is popular; and hearty soups, such as *minestrone* (min-uh-STRO-nee), are often served as the main course of a light supper.

Italian foods tend to be highly seasoned, but the style and ingredients of the cookery vary according to the region of the country. In the north, rice and *gnocchi* (NYAW-kee), or dumplings, are as popular as pasta. Butter is used in northern Italian cooking as are many green vegetables.

The Italian cuisine most familiar to Americans is that of the south of Italy. There, pastas made of semolina come in tubes of various shapes and sizes (such as spaghetti, ziti, and macaroni), and tomato sauces are often flavored with garlic, green pepper, onion, and spices. Olive oil, rather than butter, is used in cooking. Because fishing has long been an important industry in the seacoast towns of southern Italy, favorite seafoods there are sea bass, sole, mullet, tuna, anchovies, and sardines as well as squid, octopus, and shellfish.

A complete Italian dinner (usually the midday meal) begins with an antipasto (meaning "before the meal"), an attractive appetizer platter of salads, pickled vegetables, cheeses, and

Pasta is the "heart" of many Italian meals, but its many ingredients, shapes, sizes, and sauces make it the basis for a wide variety of dishes.

cold meat and fish. A pasta or soup course is next. Third comes the main course of meat or fish served with vegetables and crusty bread. Salad follows, and then there may be a light dessert, often cheese and fruit, accompanied by espresso coffee. A variety of Italian ice creams, or *gelati,* are familiar to Americans. *Spumoni* (containing fruits, nuts, or candy) and *Neapolitans* (three ice-cream flavors arranged in layers) are favorites, as are *granita* (grah-NEE-tuh), or fruit ices. They are all a cool complement to spicy Italian dinners.

Breads and cheeses are important parts of Italian meals. Long, broad loaves and crusty round loaves may accompany a salad and a hearty soup to make a complete meal. Cheeses are used in cooking and at the table. Mozzarella and ricotta are ingredients in many Italian dishes, while grated Parmesan and Romano may be sprinkled on food by individual diners.

## Greece

The daily meals in Greek homes are relatively simple, while holidays are festive occasions that call for a variety of delicacies. Bread is the central part of every meal and is eaten without any spread. White bread is preferred. The Greeks also eat noodles, spaghetti, and macaroni, either plain or prepared with tomato-and-meat sauce.

Lamb is the favorite meat in Greece, though mutton, goat, pork, and poultry are well liked and some beef is eaten. The Greeks often cut meat into small pieces, brown it in olive oil, and cook it with rice and vegetables. *Dolmades* (dole-MAH-theez) (grape leaves stuffed with rice and ground meat) and *moussaka* (moo-suh-KAH) (eggplant and ground meat baked in layers) are popular Greek main dishes. In Greece, poultry is often cooked for its broth; *soupa avgolemono* is a popular lemon-flavored soup with a base of chicken broth.

Greece has a long Mediterranean coastline and includes a number of small islands. Since

This popular Greek dessert of honey and nuts between very thin layers of phyllo dough is called baklava. It is often served with very strong, dark Turkish coffee.

ancient times, the Greeks have relied on fishing, so it is not surprising that fish is an important part of their diet. Fresh, smoked, and salted fish are used often, or the seafood may be fried or steamed with vegetables.

The Greeks also use a wide variety of vegetables, including cabbage, cauliflower, eggplant, peppers, and zucchini. When cooked until very soft and seasoned with meat broth or tomato, onion, olive oil, and parsley, vegetables are frequently served as a main dish. What Americans call a Greek salad is also popular. It is a platter of feta cheese, greens, and raw vegetables such as tomatoes, cucumbers, black olives, and green peppers. The Greek salad usually comes with a dressing of olive oil, vinegar, or lemon juice. Feta cheese, made from sheep's or goat's milk, is just one of the cheeses that Greeks enjoy.

Fresh fruits in season are served as dessert in Greece. Melons, dates, and figs are popular as well as the fruits more familiar to Americans. The Greeks make sweet pastries, too. Many feature a thin dough called *phyllo* (FEE-lo). You may be familiar with *baklava* (BAHK-luh-VAH), which contains honey and nuts between layers of phyllo. Strong Turkish coffee is often served with meals and in coffee houses where Greeks meet to socialize. A milder coffee similar to the American beverage is served at breakfast.

## Scandinavia

Scandinavia includes the countries of Norway, Sweden, and Denmark. Fishing has long been a major occupation for these descendents of the seafaring Vikings, and fish is an important part of their diet. Both fresh and saltwater fish are popular, and they are smoked, salted, canned, or used fresh. Fish are broiled, boiled, formed into balls, steamed with vegetables, or prepared in soup.

Scandinavian cookery includes not only fish but also pork, poultry, lamb, and mutton. In the far north, reindeer are still herded for their meat, milk, and hides; and reindeer meat is popular in many parts of Scandinavia. Organ meats and sausages are also used frequently in Scandinavian cooking. Many meats are served smoked or salted. Hearty soups are popular during the long northern winters, but Scandinavians also prepare light fruit soups that can be served hot or cold. Potatoes appear often in Scandinavian meals along with other vegetables such as beets, green beans, cabbage, carrots, leeks, and peas. Scandinavians eat fresh seasonal fruits, and use preserved fruits in sauces, puddings, and soups.

Bread is an important element of the Scandinavian diet since many meals consist of open-faced sandwiches. White breads as well as hearty ryes and dark breads come in an assortment of shapes and sizes. Butter is used as a spread on bread, and so are a variety of cheeses, some made of goat's milk.

Scandinavians are famous for their *smorgasbord*, a buffet of a wide variety of foods, many of which are served cold. It is traditional to select from the smorgasbord in this order: cold fish dishes, including herring, salmon, and shrimp; cold meats, often smoked or in pâtés; hot dishes, including meatballs, sausages, omelets, and fish; and finally desserts of fruit, cheese, and pastry.

Of course, most family meals in Scandinavia are not smorgasbords. In Norway, for example, breakfast is usually cereal (oatmeal porridge is traditional) and bread spread with cheese, jam, or marmalade. Open-faced sandwiches are popular for lunch and supper. Dinner, the hot meal, usually includes soup, meat or fish, vegetables (including potatoes), and dessert. Farm families often have their hot meal at noon, while those who live in cities have dinner as their evening meal. The most common beverages in Scandinavia are coffee and tea. Cocoa is also popular as a midafternoon treat.

## China

The Chinese try to preserve the original flavor, color, and texture of food. They use the freshest possible ingredients, cut them in small pieces, and usually stir-fry them quickly at a high temperature in a small amount of fat. Vegetables are cooked just before serving and so retain their crispness.

Rice is the staple grain, and it appears in almost every meal, particularly in the southern part of China. In the north, wheat is also grown

# The World of Pasta

People from many different nations eat pasta. It takes many different forms and contains different ingredients, depending on what foods are available. Some people suspect that our ancestors made pasta out of ground grain and water, dried it, and then carried it on journeys.

One common myth asserts that Marco Polo introduced pasta to Europe. He allegedly brought the well-loved food from China in the late 13th century. More likely, people in Europe and other world areas developed pasta independently.

Throughout the Middle Ages, pasta was popular in several regions of continental Europe and England. Thomas Jefferson is credited with introducing pasta to the United States. During a trip to Naples, it is reported, he became so attached to pasta that he brought back crates of it. First produced commercially in the United States in the 1800s, pasta did not become part of the everyday diet of Americans until this century. Immigrants from Italy and other pasta-consuming nations at the beginning of the century brought their talent for pasta making, adding an important food to our national diet.

Italians lead the world as pasta consumers. They eat between 60 and 70 pounds of pasta per person each year. The United States is fourth. Americans eat about 10 pounds of pasta per person per year. In the last decade, American demand for pasta has risen steadily.

The ingredients and shape of pasta vary around the world. In the United States, over 300 shapes are available. In Italy, the number is over 1,000. Pasta can be made with enriched flour, durum wheat flour, whole wheat, or a mixture of soy and wheat flours. All these ingredients, except enriched white flour, contain complex carbohydrates. In the United States, pastas that contain at least 5.5% egg solids are called noodles. In China and Japan, pasta is made with seaweed, mung beans, a mixture of wheat and shrimp paste, rice flour, yams and other roots. Several of these ingredients make the pasta a rich source of protein.

Several popular pasta dishes from around the world are described below.

*Kreplach,* Jewish dumplings, resemble ravioli or won tons. The dumplings are stuffed with meat and vegetables, cooked in broth, and served in the broth.

*Szechuan noodles* are a spicy Chinese dish. Thin noodles are served with a sesame sauce seasoned with hot chili oil, garlic, and scallions. Peanut sauce can be substituted for the sesame sauce.

*Pasta primavera* is a creamy dish from Italy. It combines pasta, usually fettucine (flat pasta), with steamed fresh vegetables such as broccoli, carrots, and zucchini. It is served with a creamy sauce flavored with Parmesan cheese.

*Pastitsio* is a Greek casserole. Layers of pasta, cheese, and ground lamb (or beef) are covered with a custard and baked. The result is a filling, hearty main dish.

A colorful dish that is rich in texture, pasta primavera makes an appetizing meal.

What Chinese foods are you familiar with? China is such a large country with many different cuisines that this Chinese shrimp dish may be unfamiliar even in some parts of China.

In general, vegetables are used in greater quantity and variety than meat in Chinese cooking. Pork is the favorite meat, but lamb, goat, and poultry are also popular. Organ meats and eggs also contribute protein to the Chinese diet as do fish and shellfish. *Tofu,* an ingredient in many Chinese meals, is made from soybeans, which are also used to make sauces, a cheese, and a milk for infants. The favorite vegetables in China are water chestnuts, bamboo shoots, bean sprouts, cabbage, and mushrooms.

Fruit is frequently used in Chinese cooking. For example, meat cubes are rolled in batter and fried in oil, and then simmered in a thin sauce made of pineapple, green peppers, brown sugar, vinegar, and seasonings. Fish and shellfish are often prepared as sweet-sour dishes, too. The eggs of chickens, pigeons, and ducks are important in Chinese cookery. They may be combined with mushrooms and bean sprouts and served with soy sauce or made into egg-drop soup. Most Americans are familiar with Chinese egg rolls, which consist of shrimp or meat and chopped vegetables rolled in a thin dough and then fried in deep fat. Peanut oil and lard, not butter, are used in Chinese cooking; and the popular seasonings are soy sauce, sesame seed, salt, garlic, ginger, pepper, and fresh herbs.

Tea is the national beverage of China, and is served at every meal. Sweets are seldom served as dessert, but fresh fruits, such as kumquats, are eaten raw. While daily meals are simple family occasions in China, holiday meals may be very elaborate and consist of many courses. The quantity and quality of the meal is considered important as a sign of hospitality to guests and a reflection of the status of the host.

and made into bread and noodles. China is a very large country, and its different regions have developed different cuisines. The *Shanghai* region is known for hearty one-dish meals that take more cooking time than the stir-frying preferred in other provinces. Soy sauce is the important flavoring in these casseroles. *Cantonese* cooking, on the other hand, uses lighter flavorings in delicate sauces. The natural flavors and textures of ingredients are preserved. By contrast, *Szechuan* and *Hunan* cuisines are hot and spicy. Ginger is an important flavoring in these provinces. *Peking-style* cooking comes from the capital of China (now called Beijing) and was the cuisine of the royal household. Like French haute cuisine, it is time-consuming and relies on exacting recipes. Drying and pickling of foods are important in Peking cookery.

### Practical Tip

- Thin-sliced broccoli stalks are a good substitute for water chestnuts.

## Japan

The staple food of the Japanese diet is rice. It appears at almost every meal. Boiled rice with pickled vegetables is a favorite rice dish. The vegetables popular for pickling are cabbage, cucumbers, eggplant, and radishes.

Fish is the most popular of the meat-group foods in Japan. Chicken, shrimp, and eggs are also used often. Fish is frequently salted and then broiled over an open flame, or it is eaten raw in a popular dish called *sushi (SOO-shee)*, which is a combination of vinegar-flavored rice, a type of horseradish, and the raw fish. Beef is often cooked with vegetables in a wok for a dish called *sukiyaki* (sook-ee-YAH-kee). For *tempura* (tem-POOR-uh), a variety of foods including fish, shrimp, and vegetables are coated with a light batter and deep-fat fried.

Several very important elements of the Japanese diet are made from soybeans. A soybean paste is used in many dishes; so is *tofu*, the soybean cured cake. For flavoring, salty brown soy sauce is very popular.

Like the Chinese, the Japanese value fresh foods. They prefer quick frying as well as other methods of cooking that emphasize the natural flavors of foods rather than the use of many sauces and spices.

Tea is the most popular beverage in Japan. It is often served during elaborate rituals and ceremonies. All food is prepared and served as attractively as possible. The Japanese value the appearance, aroma, and atmosphere of a meal as well as its taste.

## India

Indian food choices have been strongly influenced by their two traditional religions. The Hindus in India do not eat beef, and Muslims do not eat pork. Many Indians are vegetarians. Vegetables, nuts, and fruits are therefore very important to Indian cooking. When meat dishes

Many types of seafood are popular in the Japanese diet. Notice how beautifully this sushi dish is arranged.

Many Indian meals feature spicy dishes like this Indian curry. Rice pilaf often serves as a popular grain accompaniment.

are served, they contain primarily lamb, chicken, and goat; seafood may also be served.

Grain foods are the staples of the Indian diet. Rice is popular and is usually served with sweet spices as a *pilaf*. The breads of India vary. In the northern part of the country, bread is made by grinding grain into flour. Water is added to make the dough, which is cooked into flat cakes. In southern India, rice and vegetable seeds are made into dumplings. The grains or seeds are first soaked and turned into paste. The most popular grains in India, in addition to rice, are barley and wheat. Seed-pod vegetables (such as beans and peas), raisins, coconut, lentils (particularly *dal*), and cashews are also important in Indian cooking.

*Curry* is a popular Indian dish made from eggs, fish, meat, or vegetables. The ingredients are cooked in a sauce made from a combination of spices. A mixture of these spices is called curry powder in the United States. Meat and other foods are often cut into small pieces and marinated before cooking. When these pieces are grilled on skewers, they are called *kabobs*.

Milk and milk products are also important in the Indian diet. Yogurts form a cool, mild contrast to the hot, spicy dishes of Indian meals. A variety of foods is usually served at an Indian meal, ranging from the yogurt salads, crunchy breads, and vegetables to one or more spicy main dishes and fruit.

## The Near and Middle East

The Near East includes the countries next to the eastern end of the Mediterranean, including the countries of Southwest Asia, the Arabian Peninsula, and Northeast Africa. The Middle East includes the area from Afghanistan to Egypt. The traditional eating patterns of both areas have been influenced by several factors. The land and climate are better suited to raising sheep and goats than beef cattle; and Islam, the

Couscous is an extremely versatile food. At left, it appears as part of the main course of a dinner; at right, as a dessert.

most widespread religion, does not permit the eating of pork. Lamb has become the most popular meat, but chicken, goat, and camel are also eaten. Meat is usually roasted when it is available, or it is prepared on skewers as kabobs.

The basic foods of the Near and Middle East are grains and vegetables. Rice, wheat, barley, and oats are all used. The round pocket bread called *pita bread,* which is now popular for American sandwiches, originated in the Middle East. There, it is often filled with chick-peas and eggplant. Another traditional food of the area contains chick-peas. For *falafel* (fuh-LAH-fel), the chick-peas are ground, spiced, and shaped into balls before being deep-fried. Other popular vegetables in Middle Eastern cookery are beans, eggplant, lentils, onions, and squash. Olives, almonds, grapes, figs, and dates are also important in the local diet, and fruit is a favorite dessert. Sweets usually contain dried fruits and nuts, and are sometimes flavored with seasoning made from flower petals. Lemon, parsley, and mint are used to season rice and other foods; and olive oil is important in cooking. *Couscous* (KOOSS-kooss) is a popular food in North Africa. It is made of steamed, ground wheat. When served with a meat sauce, couscous is a main dish; it becomes a dessert when topped with sugar and nuts.

Yogurt and cheese are the important dairy products of the region, while coffee and tea are the most popular beverages.

## Mexico

Mexican food traditions have two origins. One is the cuisine of the Aztec Indians, who used corn, beans, avocados, chili, squash, sweet potatoes, vanilla, and chocolate in their cooking. The Spanish added the use of wheat, rice, chicken, and dairy products to the New World foods when they conquered the Aztecs and gave Mexican cuisine its European influence.

Beans, or *frijoles,* are at the "center" of many meals in Mexico. What other typical Mexican ingredients are part of this dish?

The basic foods of Mexico are still corn and beans. Ground corn flour, or *masa,* forms the basis of many Mexican dishes familiar to Americans. A number of the foods that Mexicans eat daily are based on the *tortilla* (tor-TEE-yuh), a thin, flat masa pancake. When folded and fried, the tortilla can be filled with chopped meat, chicken, cheese, and garnishes to make a *taco* (TAH-ko). When rolled around similar ingredients and covered with hot sauce, the tortilla becomes an *enchilada* (en-chuh-LAH-duh). If the tortilla or pancake is made of flour rather than corn, and rolled around a filling, the result is a *burrito* (buh-REE-to). The tortilla is also eaten as bread by the poorer people of Mexico.

*Frijoles* (free-HO-leez), or beans, are almost always served at Mexican meals. Refried beans, which have been boiled, mashed, and fried, are then fried again just before serving. The rice served with beans is also often boiled and then fried. To balance the spicy flavors of the hot tortilla dish and the hearty rice-and-

beans combination, Mexicans often serve cold sour cream and *guacamole* (gwah-kuh-MO-lee), which is made of mashed avocados.

Mexican cookery is known for spicy dishes. Hot red chili peppers are the best-known of the Mexican seasonings, but chilies come in a variety of colors and strengths, and Mexican cooks also use garlic, onion, and salt. In addition, lemon and lime juices, parsley, saffron, mint, cinnamon, and nutmeg may be added to foods. A favorite holiday dish is turkey served with *mole* (MO-lay), a sauce containing chocolate along with chili, sesame seed, and spices. Mexicans also enjoy tropical fruits such as bananas, mangoes, papayas, and oranges.

While rural Mexican families may rely on a tortilla dish and rice and beans for many of their meals, wealthier Mexicans sometimes eat elaborate midday meals. A light appetizer of fruit is usually the first course of such a meal. Clear broth follows, and then a rice dish. Next is a fish or cooked vegetable dish followed by the main course of meat and salad. Beans are then served separately. Finally, there is dessert and after-dinner coffee. Breakfast and the evening meal in Mexico are generally light and include sweet coffee and tortillas.

## Brazil

Like the other cuisines of Latin America, Brazilian cookery shows the influences of the native Indian population as well as of the Europeans and Africans who came to the area later. Unlike most other Latin American countries, however, Brazil was colonized by Portuguese rather than Spanish settlers, thus giving Brazil's culture a slightly different "flavor." The names of Brazilian dishes are thus usually Portuguese rather than Spanish.

The food that is known as Brazil's national dish is called *feijoada* (fay-ZHWAH-duh). It is a combination of black beans, dried beef, and pork. In southern Brazil, *churrasco* (chu-RAH-sko), which is a preparation of charcoal-broiled meats, is popular. A variety of meats is eaten by the Brazilians who can afford them, but many of the people rely primarily on beans, rice, and *cassava,* a starchy root vegetable. Cassava is served in a variety of forms. It is boiled and ground to make flour, made into breads, added to soups and stews, or served as a side dish.

There is a strong African influence in Brazilian cookery, particularly in Bahia. There, the cuisine features bananas, fish, palm oil, coconuts, and hot peppers. *Dende* (DEN-day) oil, made from palm, was introduced as a cooking ingredient by East Africans; its bright-yellow color is seen in many Brazilian dishes.

The favorite beverage in Brazil is coffee, but sweet fruit drinks are popular, too. *Mate,* (MAH-tay), which is somewhat like tea, is also served in Brazil.

Brazilians, like other Latin Americans, enjoy black-bean dishes. Cassava bread, barbecued chicken, and fresh fruits are also popular.

## Cuba

Located in the Caribbean, Cuba shares the mild climate and rich fishing grounds with many neighboring islands. Like the people of other island nations, Cubans have traditionally turned to the sea for food. Cuban shellfish are known worldwide, particularly the shrimp, lobster, and stone crabs. Fried crab fritters flavored with coconut is a local specialty. Pompano, snapper, and sole are also served frequently. Most Caribbean cuisines also feature *plantains* as a staple food. Although plantains look like bananas, they are starchy and prepared as vegetables. Plantains are usually fried, but they can also be roasted, boiled, baked, or used in combination with meat and cheese. *Flan,* a caramel custard, is a popular Caribbean dessert.

Chicken is the most popular meat in Cuba. Rather than boiling or roasting the fowl, Cubans have traditionally preferred it made into a stew or served with rice. Other meats are also served. Rolled steak with green pepper, tomato, and ham strips is a traditional specialty. A typical meal might consist of pork, yucca, beans, rice, and salad.

Rice is used in or with many dishes in Cuban cookery. Black beans, another favorite, appear often in Cuban meals. *Black-bean soup* is a staple of the Cuban diet, and many families serve it daily. There are special versions of the basic soup; one features ham along with the beans and rice, in addition to a garnish of sliced hard-boiled eggs and lemon. Hearty soups are popular in Cuba, in spite of the hot climate. The climate allows many tropical fruits and vegetables to grow abundantly, and they are used frequently in Cuban cooking. Coconuts, for example, are often made into a cream sauce.

In many Caribbean countries, bananalike vegetables called plantains are a staple food. This Cuban *pollo con plátanos* features chicken and plantains.

## Canada

Like its neighbor the United States, Canada is a large country with a pioneer past. It was settled primarily by the British and French, and so Canadian cuisine has elements of the cookery of both those cultures. The abundance of fish and game also has influenced Canadian eating habits; and bear, buffalo, venison, caribou, and moose are still served. There is even a tree that has influenced Canadian cookery. Products of the maple tree, maple syrup and maple sugar, appear in many Canadian dishes.

Canadians enjoy both fresh and saltwater seafood. Bass, trout, landlocked salmon, pike, and pickerel come from lakes and streams. Coho salmon are fished in the Pacific, and from the Atlantic come lobster, oysters, and Atlantic salmon. In addition to the simpler methods of preparing fish that are familiar to Americans, Canadian seafood specialties include a casserole of oysters and noodles, and hot sardine rolls served as a tea-time snack.

Maple syrup and maple sugar, made from the sap of the maple tree (rear), are used in many Canadian dishes.

Grains are important in the Canadian diet just as they are in the United States. Wheat, maize (corn), oats, and barley are all used frequently. They are prepared differently according to the region of the country and the cultural background of the local population. For example, porridge and oatcakes are popular in Nova Scotia, where people of Scottish descent live, while the French-Canadians prefer their baguettes. Local produce—vegetables and fruits—have also determined the dietary traditions of the different provinces of Canada. As in the United States, now that technology makes most foods available all over the country, some of these regional differences are beginning to blend into one another.

Like the British, Canadians enjoy roast beef and Yorkshire pudding; and many other English-style foods are eaten all over Canada. Quebec, however, is proud of its French heritage and French-Canadian cuisine. Onion soup, hearty pea soup, minced pork pie, and meatball stew are some of their favorites. Canadian bacon is popular in the United States as well as in its native land.

While Canada produces fine apples and a special Canadian apple pie, which can be served hot or cold, many of its desserts owe their distinctive flavor to maple syrup or maple sugar. Canadians use maple syrup instead of sugar in recipes for muffins, biscuits, johnnycake, sweet buns, icing, and baked and steamed custards. It is also found in *tarte au suif* (TART o SWEEF) (meaning "suet pie") which is made of suet and nuts.

## For Review

1. Most people like to snack, and different cultures have developed their own particular snack foods or traditional between-meals breaks. For each of the following, give the country or countries where the snack or custom is popular and a brief description of the dish or activity: fish and chips, afternoon tea, gelati, midafternoon cocoa, falafel, hot sardine rolls.
2. Name two cuisines that emphasize the freshness, shape, color, and texture of ingredients.
3. Describe each of the following soups, and give the country where they are popular: bouillabaisse, minestrone, egg-drop soup, black-bean soup.
4. What do French haute cuisine and Peking cuisine have in common?
5. In what two countries are sweet-sour dishes popular?

# 31 Chapter Review

## Summary

Each country has its own unique style of cooking that has been influenced by history and environment as well as by the habits and customs of the people. Many foods that were once considered foreign have now gained acceptance as part of the typical American diet. For example, many Americans are familiar with spaghetti, pita bread, sausages, quiche, and eclairs, all of which have foreign origins. Although the cuisine of nations varies, the food that is used has many similarities. Depending on each individual country and the preferred styles of cooking, meat, fish, poultry, vegetables, eggs, milk, and cheese are used to make a wide variety of dishes. By following foreign-food recipes, a meal manager can learn different and interesting ways to prepare new dishes as well as to provide a wide variety of exciting meals.

## Vocabulary

Use the vocabulary words below to complete the sentences that follow.

cuisine
culture

1. The way of life of a group of people is known as _____.
2. The style of cooking of a particular group of people is called _____.
3. English high tea and the Japanese tea ceremony are examples of _____.

4. The Italian _____ includes a variety of pastas often covered with tomato sauces that are flavored with garlic, green pepper, onion, and spices.
5. Both the Aztec Indians, who used corn and beans, and the Spanish, who used wheat, rice, and chicken to prepare meals, influenced the Mexican _____.

## Chapter Questions

1. Explain the differences in the kinds of fat used for cooking in Germany, Italy, and China.
2. What are four reasons why the cuisine of different cultures varies?
3. What has influenced your family's food patterns?
4. What ingredients and what preparation techniques remain nearly the same in most of the cultures?
5. What foods are included in a Continental breakfast?
6. How has the environment of the island nations influenced the cuisine?
7. Compare the use of grains in the English and German cuisines.
8. What is the major reason why sweet and sour dishes were developed?
9. For each of the following foreign foods, tell what the food is and the country it is from:
   a. sauerkraut     d. sukiyaki
   b. antipasto     e. ratatouille
   c. dolmades     f. feijoada
10. Which foreign dishes do you particularly

like? Why do you like them? How are the dishes prepared?

11. How does Chinese cuisine differ from Japanese cookery?

12. If you were to open a restaurant specializing in foods from a foreign country, which one would you select and why?

13. Rice is a staple food, used daily, in many countries. Discuss how rice is used as a food in your family.

14. In addition to the contributions by the French and English, what other factors have influenced the development of Canadian cuisine?

## Skill Activities

**1. Resource management** In your food journal or card file box, add to your collection of recipes by starting a section of foreign recipes for each category. For example, under a category such as soups include a section of foreign soups. Beside the name of the dish, write the name of the country from which the recipe comes. You can find recipes in books, magazines, newspapers, and on the display board in supermarkets.

**2. Critical thinking** Discover the convenience forms of foreign foods that are available at your supermarket. On four pages of lined paper, write one of these headings at the top of each page: "Canned," "Frozen," "Dried," and "Ready-to-eat." Take these pages with you when you go to the supermarket. To record your findings, write the name of the country and beside it the name of the food under the appropriate columns. Which country is represented with the most different kinds of meals? Which foods are you familiar with? What are two convenience foods you would like to try and how would you use these foods? Which guidelines would you recommend for purchasing convenience forms of foreign foods?

**3. Social studies** Make a survey of the restaurants in your community that serve foreign foods. Classify the restaurants by country and indicate the variety of food served. Which cuisine is represented with the most restaurants?

**4. Communication** Most countries have cookie recipes for special holidays. Collect holiday cookie recipes, and on a world map, write the name of the cookie beside the name of the country. Although the recipes come from different countries, group similar recipes together. Collect the recipes for a class cookbook.

**5. Resource management** Select one of the foreign countries, and prepare a dinner menu for four. Determine the main dish, accompaniments, dessert, and beverage. If it is appropriate, include an appetizer and salad. With your menu, include recipes for the dishes, a shopping list, and a time-work plan.

# 32 Regional Foods of America

## As you read, think about:

- how and why regional cuisines developed in the United States.
- what factors influenced each regional cuisine.

**Vocabulary**

New England
   boiled dinner
Pennsylvania
   Dutch cooking
Creole cooking
Cajun cooking
potluck dinner

What do you think of when someone says "American cooking"? Your answer probably depends on where you live. American cuisine is really a collection of a number of regional cuisines. Some dishes have remained popular only in their original areas; others have been accepted nationwide. If you were to travel around the country, you would notice regional differences in the way food is prepared and served. You might notice even stronger differences if you "traveled" from neighborhood to neighborhood in many large American cities. Immigrant and ethnic groups who cluster in particular neighborhoods often operate food markets and restaurants that reflect their traditional cuisines. "Immigrants" from other regions of the United States sometimes do the same. You might find a "New York-style deli" advertised next to "Chicago pizza" and "Texas barbecue" in a big-city newspaper. With a little exploration—in this chapter and elsewhere—you will find that shoofly pie and sweet potato pie are just "as American as apple pie"!

# Factors Influencing Regional Cuisine

The United States is largely a nation of immigrants. As settlers came to America, they adapted their food patterns to the foods and conditions they found in their new homeland. This adaptation created a new group of Americanized foods, the basis of American cuisine. Many cultural groups tended to settle together in a specific region of America, and these regions still show their influence. For example, the French influence is strong in the Creole cooking of Louisiana, while German settlers have left their mark on Pennsylvania Dutch cookery. Very often, settlers from a particular country chose areas where the climate or landscape was similar to the one they had left behind. In those cases, they could grow many of the same crops and easily recreate their native cuisines in the new land. The Scandinavians, for example, settled in the cooler northern parts of the Midwest.

The United States is a nation of "immigrants." They came not only in ships from abroad but also in covered wagons from East to West. Each time they moved, they adapted their cuisines to their new homes.

Other settlers, like the original Pilgrims, found survival difficult when they arrived in America. They turned to the native crops and wildlife for food, and to the native Americans, or Indians, for advice on how to grow and prepare food.

### The First American Cookery

The first Americans, the Indians, made contributions to what we call American cuisine through their use and preparation of corn, fowl, and fish. The Indians taught the European settlers how to make pudding and johnnycake from cornmeal. Many vegetables that we consider typically American originated with the Indians; some examples are squash, pumpkin, wild rice, beans, and cranberries. The Indians also introduced the newcomers to cocoa, herbs, and maple sugar to use as flavorings and seasonings.

The Indians made important contributions to American cuisine and to the survival of the first European settlers. What foods did the Indians teach the settlers how to grow and prepare?

### Geographical Differences

Each geographic region of the United States has its special food patterns based on what grows well there. The soft wheat of the South, for example, is well suited for the preparation of the hot breads served with almost every meal. The North Central Plains grow hard wheat from which their flavorful yeast breads are made.

Maine and Idaho are known for their potatoes, Florida and California for citrus fruits, Wisconsin for dairy products, Louisiana for rice, and the coastal states and Alaska for seafoods. From New England come lobsters, codfish cakes, clam chowders, baked beans, pumpkin pies, turkey, and squash. From Hawaii come pineapple and fish. Pennsylvania has its shoofly pie. Texas has its beef and refried beans. Each regional cuisine is a blend of influences, affected by the land and weather, by the native American culture, and by the cuisine of the immigrants who settled the region.

### For Review

1. What three factors influenced the development of American regional cuisines?
2. What staple food was introduced to the early settlers by the Indians? Why was this so important?

## Regional Foods

The regional cuisines of the United States were developed in seven distinct areas: the Northeast, the South, the Midwest, the Southwest, the West Coast, Alaska, and Hawaii.

## The Northeast

From the Northeast comes perhaps the most "American" of all meals, the traditional Thanksgiving dinner. As you know, many of the dishes served at the first Thanksgiving were based on native ingredients. Turkey and cranberries, for example, were both local specialties enjoyed by the Indians long before the European settlers came and renamed the area New England. Other typical New England dishes were derived from American Indian cookery. Using heated rocks and seaweed to steam shellfish led to the traditional *New England clambake. Boston baked beans* owe their distinctive flavor to the advice of the Indians who showed the Pilgrims how to soak and slow-cook dried beans and flavor them with maple syrup. Again, it was the native Americans who taught the settlers to tap maple trees for that syrup.

Other regional favorites in New England are squash, succotash (a combination of corn and lima beans), chowders, and other one-pot meals. In colonial times, many baked goods were made from corn as well as wheat. The *johnnycake,* a cornmeal cake often taken on long trips because it kept well, was originally called a "journey cake." When the settlers were at home, the center of family life was the big open-hearth fireplace. Chowders, made from corn or local seafood and vegetables, were hearty soups that could make a meal. *New England clam chowder* is a favorite to this day, and so is the **New England boiled dinner.** This one-pot meal usually contains corned beef (or another meat), potatoes, onions, carrots, beets, and cabbage. In colonial days, it probably contained whatever the cook had available, and it could simmer on the hearth for hours, leaving the busy settlers time for other necessary tasks.

Berries grow in abundance in New England, and many berry desserts, such as cobblers

The New England clambake has enjoyed many variations since the Indians taught the Pilgrims to steam shellfish on heated rocks.

and puddings, are popular. The local maple syrup still flavors many desserts, including puddings and candies. Pumpkin pie has become a national favorite. New Englanders are justly proud of their local seafood; they like it very fresh and prepare it many different ways. Among the best liked are lobsters and clams as well as fish, the most famous of which is the one from which Cape Cod, Massachusetts, takes its name.

The Dutch, English, and Germans who settled south of New England—in the Middle Atlantic States—found a warmer climate and less rocky soil. They raised fruits and vegetables as well as grain and livestock. Many northern European specialties were easily transplanted to this area. The Dutch, who first settled New York, introduced waffles, griddle cakes, coleslaw, and cottage cheese. They baked cookies, doughnuts, and gingerbread figures; and added molasses flavoring (from maple syrup) to traditional recipes.

**Pennsylvania Dutch cooking** is famous all over the United States, but its origin is not Dutch at all. The name is based on a mispronunciation of "Deutsch," which means "German." The settlers who created the cuisine were German farmers who brought their thrifty, hearty style of food preparation with them. They also made good use of native ingredients and techniques. Today, Pennsylvania Dutch cooking features rich soups, sauerbraten, sauerkraut, pork, noodles, potato pancakes, and dumplings. The meals are substantial and filling; even restaurants often serve them family style. A traditional Pennsylvania Dutch meal contains seven sweets and sours. Relishes; pickled, preserved, and spiced fruits; jams; salads; and apple butter are often served as accompaniments to the main dishes. There is also an ample assortment of desserts. Cakes, pies, crumb cakes, funnel cakes, and *shoofly pie* (imagine how it got its name; it is pastry filled with molasses and brown sugar) are all popular. So is a midmorning coffee-and-pastry break, from which we get our expression "coffee klatch," implying conversation along with refreshment.

Hearty Pennsylvania Dutch meals often feature potato dishes, wursts, and sauerkraut. What other foods are usually part of a typical Pennsylvania Dutch meal?

Southern specialities are popular nationwide. Southern fried chicken and Southern pecan pie tell their origins in their names.

## The South

The colonists who settled in the South found a warm climate and an abundance of wildlife. They took crabs, shrimp, oysters, and crayfish from coastal waters; and fished for bass, catfish, trout, and even turtle in rivers and lakes. Being able to hunt for squirrel, goose, deer, opossum, and turkey for food aided many Southern settlers until they could begin farming. The still popular *Brunswick stew* (usually made with game and vegetables) is a reminder of the importance of hunting in the development of Southern cookery.

Like the New Englanders, Southerners learned from the Indians how to raise corn, but Southern settlers found they could raise crops all year-round in their climate. Many settlers became successful farmers, raising sugar cane, rice, peanuts, and some vegetables. While they did not usually graze many beef cattle on their plantations, pigs and chickens were raised frequently. Thus, pork and poultry dishes became the most popular meats in Southern cookery.

Some foods, like some clothing, go in and out of fashion. Many food fads, however, have a lasting effect on the food industry. New styles of cooking, adapted and adopted by American households, become a permanent part of American cuisine.

Many regional foods of the United States become "in" foods and then part of our everyday diet. Foods from around the world also follow this process. In the last 15 years, American regional foods and lighter styles of cooking have become very popular. Natural foods and Cajun and Creole cooking are two examples of food styles that have affected our national diet.

## Natural Foods

This type of food preparation is sometimes called California Cuisine, probably because many of the ingredients are grown in that state and the natural-foods movement had many followers there. Natural foods refer to foods grown without harmful chemicals. The movement was a response to increasing concern about the American diet and the hazards of chemical pesticides. The natural-foods movement advocates avoiding red meat by substituting poultry, fish, and plant protein. Canned, frozen, and processed foods are replaced with fresh fruits and vegetables; enriched flour with whole-grain flour.

Health-food stores were the center of this movement, which peaked in the 1970s. Many health-food stores remain today. Grocery chains keep a careful eye on health-food stores because the latter are good measures of new buying patterns. In effect, grocery stores allow health-food stores to create the market for a particular product, and then the grocery chains start carrying the product. Some foods made popular by the natural-foods movement are avocados, sprouts, whole-grain breads and rolls, protein-enriched pasta, granola, and tofu.

Chicken gumbo is a hearty Cajun dish made with okra.

## Cajun and Creole Cooking

Cajun and Creole cooking come from Louisiana. Outside of Louisiana, little distinction is made between the two. Cajun has its roots in French country cooking adapted to the available food in Louisiana. Creole cooking combines cooking traditions of the French, Spanish, American Indian, African, and other groups present in New Orleans throughout its history.

Louisiana cooking was discovered by the rest of the nation in the 1980s. The number of Cajun restaurants and cookbooks has increased to meet the demand. Spicy sauces and spicy preparations are characteristic of this cooking style. Long cooking times are also emphasized. Shrimp, catfish, and crayfish are often the main course. Okra, a vegetable known mainly to the South, is now becoming familiar to the rest of the country. Gumbos, thick stewlike soups made with vegetables, seafood, and/or meat, and jambalaya, a hearty rice stew with almost any kind of meat, have also been popularized.

*Southern fried chicken* is now a favorite all over the United States. Cured ham and spareribs became popular dishes, too.

Like their Northern neighbors, Southern settlers and farmers used corn in many dishes. A variety of corn breads, such as *corn pone* (small, oval loaves) and *spoon bread* (which is more like a pudding cooked crisp on the outside but soft enough on the inside to be eaten with a spoon), are Southern favorites. *Hominy grits,* made from white corn, is still served as a breakfast side dish in the South. Other breads, such as baking-powder biscuits, were made from wheat flour. Rice and nuts also became important in Southern cookery. Rice was prepared in combination with seafood, meat, or beans. Pecans found their way into the famous *Southern pecan pie* and the sweet *praline* candies.

The slaves of the large plantations had a significant influence on Southern cookery. They made hog's intestines into *chitterlings,* and used other parts of the pig in soups and stews. Greens and other vegetables were also important in their diet. Spinach, mustard, collard, turnip, and dandelion greens were readily available; and okra had been brought from Africa. Yams, sweet potatoes, squash, rice, and black-eyed peas were also used by slaves. They made corn-bread dishes such as *hush puppies* (fried spoonfuls of cornmeal batter) and *hoecake* (said to be cooked on the back of a hoe in the fields). Many of these foods eventually found their way into the mainstream of Southern cookery.

**Creole cooking** is a distinctive Southern cuisine that developed in Louisiana where there were many French as well as English settlers. There are also Indian, Spanish, and African influences in this cookery. The French influence is seen in many of the cooking techniques as well as in the popularity of such dishes as bouillabaisse and delicate "French pastries." The French tradition of the sidewalk café is also popular in New Orleans. In the French Quarter of that city, the cafés serve *beignets* (bayn-YAYZ)

(hot doughnuts sprinkled with powdered sugar) along with chicory-flavored coffee. From the Spanish came the use of tomatoes, red and green peppers, and the combination of rice with meat, poultry, and seafood. *Filé* (powdered sassafras leaves for thickening and flavoring soups and stews) had long been used by the native Indians. The popularity of okra as a vegetable and as a thickening agent was contributed by the Africans, who called it "kingumbo." The famous stew of okra, meat, poultry, seafood, hot peppers, and filé eventually came to be called *gumbo.* This dish represents another influence on the cooking of the area: **Cajun cooking.**

The Cajuns are descended from people of French origin who settled in Acadia, a part of Canada. When they had to flee Acadia in the 1700s, many Acadians (or Cajuns, as the word came to be pronounced) brought their hearty, southern French provincial cooking with them to Louisiana. They adapted their cooking techniques to the available ingredients and, like the French of New Orleans, were influenced by the

A number of cooking styles combined to create Creole and Cajun cookery. What cuisines influenced the famous jambalaya and gumbo?

local Indians. Another Cajun dish is *jambalaya,* (jam-buh-LY-uh), which contains shellfish, sausage, poultry, and spicy tomato sauce, and is served over rice. While there is a difference in background between Cajun and Creole cookery, the two terms are often used interchangeably.

## The Midwest

The Midwest was settled not only by European immigrants but also by Americans moving westward from eastern parts of the United States. The open prairie lands encouraged the development of large farms, and many Midwestern farm families cooked primarily what they raised. Corn was an early staple, and wheat became more important later. The Midwest is often called "the breadbasket of the nation" because of the large quantity of grain raised there. Midwestern farmers also raised beef, pork, and sheep. The "kitchen garden" provided vegetables for the household, and most families raised chickens for meat and eggs. In the Great Lakes region, dairy farming led to the production and consumption of a wide variety of cheeses, and fish also became an important part of the local diet.

Midwesterners often had to travel considerable distances to their neighbors, and were usually asked to share whatever was "in the pot" when they got there. This is said to be the origin of the **potluck dinner.** When large numbers of people gathered for a social event, the potluck tradition was extended to mean a cooked dish contributed by each family.

Home cooking as well as canning and preserving became important skills on Midwestern farms. Hearty, substantial meals were needed by those who worked in the fields all day. A big breakfast became popular, consisting of hot cereals, pancakes, ham, bacon, eggs, breads, milk, and coffee. Buffet or family-style dinners of many home-cooked dishes and baked goods often welcomed the farmers at dinner, particularly at harvest time when extra "hands" were needed in the fields and there were thus extra mouths to feed as well. The dishes tended to be nutritious, substantial, and uncomplicated. Broiled steak; roast beef, lamb, pork, or chicken; corn on the cob; hash brown or baked potatoes; salad and vegetables from the garden; and homemade breads and fruit pies became standard Midwestern fare.

In addition to preparing food for the family and for neighbors who came to help with the harvest, Midwestern cooks enjoyed the custom of bringing their specialties to county fairs where jams and jellies as well as baked desserts and breads were judged. This competition led to the development of variations and new recipes for these dishes. Overall, however, Midwestern food is typical of what people mean when they call American cooking a simple "meat-and-potatoes" cuisine.

## The Southwest

While the Midwest is known for grain, the Southwest is known for beef. Besides the

"Dinner for the Threshers" by Grant Wood shows the Midwestern tradition of serving substantial meals to those who help harvest.

"chuck-wagon cookery" developed on the trail as cowboys drove cattle to market, Spanish, Mexican, and Indian cuisines had their influence on the cookery of the Southwest.

Much of the Southwest was settled by people of Spanish descent and was ruled by Spain and then Mexico. The Spanish settlers learned from the local Indians to raise corn, chilies, beans, and squash, as well as to hunt wild game. Cattle, sheep, and goats were brought to the area by the Spanish; the settlers also added coriander and oregano to the Indian greens and spices. This combination of influences became Mexican cuisine, and its influence is part of Southwestern tradition. Tortillas, tostados, tacos, and tamales are all popular in the Southwest to this day.

The other major influence came from the cattle ranch and the cattle drive. Beef is by far the most popular meat, and barbecued beef is a specialty of the area. Southwesterners baste the meat with tomato-based sauces; the spices and flavorings for these barbecue sauces are often

The Southwest is the origin of an all-American favorite: the Texas-style barbecue. What sauces are traditional here?

well-guarded family secrets. Cowboys on the trail did not have time to roast whole steers, nor could they afford to. They relied on "son-of-a-gun stew" which was made from the "leftovers" of the expensive beef. Tongue, liver, and sweetbreads were used in this stew, which was usually served with beans and biscuits. Another popular "beef stew" was *chili con carne.* Texans claim to have invented the original version, which was made from beef, red peppers, and marjoram—but contained no beans.

Because of ample rainfall, fruits and vegetables can be grown year-round in parts of the Southwest. Melons are a local treat. In parts of the Southwest, sheep are raised in addition to cattle, and lamb is important in the local diet. The overriding influences, though, are the beef-raising tradition and the Mexican flavoring of Southwestern cuisine.

## The West Coast

While the Pacific Northwest and California are neighbors, their climate, landscape, and style of life are quite different, and so are their cuisines.

California's warm climate encourages the raising of a wide variety of fruits and vegetables. It has also encouraged people from the colder parts of the United States, from the Far East, and from Mexico to settle there in great numbers. Locally grown papayas, pomegranates, grapes, dates, oranges, and grapefruits are popular in fruit salads and desserts, while avocados, kale, and okra, along with lettuce and tomato, are used in salads or main dishes. California's long coastline provides harbors for an important fishing industry. Crab, shrimp, lobster, oysters, and abalone are important in the local diet as are shad, tuna, and salmon. With so many fresh, high-quality ingredients at hand, many California cooks like to let the natural flavors "speak for themselves." Raw salads and simple preparation methods, such as broiling, are popular. There is also a spirit of experimentation in

California cookery, however; and interesting combinations, such as crab with artichoke hearts, are served frequently.

Perhaps one reason that Californians like to experiment is the variety of foreign influences on their cuisine. Spanish settlers were among the first to come to California, and many Mexicans have arrived since, bringing their cookery traditions with them. Chili, gaucamole, refried beans, tacos, enchiladas, and tamales have all found a place in California cuisine. *Cocido* (ko-SEE-do), a Spanish stew made of beef, lamb, ham, fowl, sausage, and vegetables, is also popular in the state.

Another strong influence on California cooking comes from the Far East. West Coast sailors traveled to the Far East to trade, and many immigrants from China, Japan, Korea, and Polynesia came to settle in California. These

Salads made with fresh fruits and vegetables—and often with seafood as well—are popular as main dishes in California. What factors helped create this preference?

immigrants not only kept their cookery traditions in their own families, but many worked as cooks for wealthy families, thus influencing the cuisines of their employers as well.

A third influence came from another group of "immigrants"—the forty-niners or gold-rush prospectors. These miners came from all over America as well as from many foreign lands to try to strike it rich in California. One thing they had in common was the use of sourdough starter to make the now famous San Francisco *sourdough bread*. This bread was a staple food of the prospectors, who always kept their starter, which contained yeast, on hand. The fermented mixture could be used to make bread whenever needed, and the starter itself was easily replenished with flour and water. Tangy sourdough bread is still a popular California specialty.

The Pacific Northwest has a cooler climate, a rockier coast, and more timberland than California. Wild game as well as crab, clams, and salmon are popular there. Fruits and vegetables are served frequently in salads and desserts. Washington and Oregon grow many varieties of berries, and import other fresh produce from nearby California. Cookery techniques in the Pacific Northwest are usually simple. Steaks and chops as well as fish and shellfish are often broiled. Baked seafood dishes are also popular. Vegetables are preferred raw or cooked only briefly to preserve their crisp texture and natural flavors.

## Alaska

While Alaska and California are very different in climate and lifestyle, they do have one important thing in common: the gold rush. When gold was discovered in Alaska, prospectors flocked to that territory, bringing their sourdough with them. Alaskan prospectors even came to be known as "sourdoughs." Sourdough breads and pancakes continue to be popular in Alaska along with all kinds of other breads, pastries, cakes, and doughnuts.

Alaska king crab is enjoyed at home and worldwide. Their ample seafood resources also provide a major industry for Alaskans.

While "American-style" cooking is beginning to be accepted by native Alaskans, or Eskimos, many of them still follow their own cookery customs. The traditional Eskimo diet consists of raw fish, seal meat, and hot tea. A unique ice cream is a favorite of the Eskimo. Reindeer fat is finely grated and blended with seal oil and a small amount of water. The foamy, pale mixture is often flavored with wild berries. This Eskimo specialty is considered a delicacy, especially by the children.

## Hawaii

Many groups of immigrants to the Hawaiian Islands have contributed to what we now think of as Hawaiian cuisine. Even the Polynesians are thought to have come to Hawaii from other Polynesian islands, bringing with them a cuisine that included coconuts, breadfruit, and taro root. Polynesians traditionally favor sweet-sour sauces and cooking with tropical fruits.

The European influence on Hawaiian cookery includes the introduction of chicken and pork by traders and early settlers. Missionaries from New England added stews, chowders, and dishes made from corn. From the Far East came

Alaska has retained its wilderness longer than the other states, and Alaskans are proud of the natural abundance and beauty of their land and of their pioneer spirit. They still enjoy many kinds of fish and game. Local fish include cod, halibut, herring, and salmon. Salmon is especially liked and is often baked or broiled. A variety of wild game is still available in Alaska, including wild duck, geese, ptarmigan, mountain goats, rabbits, and beaver. Other relatively large animals such as bears, moose, and reindeer contribute to the variety of meat available. The meats from these animals are prepared in much the same way as beef is prepared.

In the southern part of the state, there is dairy farming as well as the raising of vegetables and grains. Cranberries, blueberries, strawberries, and gooseberries grow wild; and many are made into relishes, pies, puddings, and catsup. Seaweed pickles and jellies made of Balb kelp, which grows along the shore, are considered Alaskan specialties.

The Hawaiian luau, when it is still prepared in the traditional manner, has become a popular tourist attraction on the islands.

Chinese immigrants who introduced the stir-fry method of cooking as well as such ingredients as rice, bean sprouts, Chinese cabbage, bamboo shoots, snow peas, and soybeans. Japanese settlers brought with them the *hibachi* grill, which added another method to Hawaiian cookery. The Japanese also introduced *teriyaki,* a soy-sauce marinade, and pickled dishes. It was Korean immigrants, though, who introduced *kimchi,* a pickled cabbage.

The Hawaiian Islands themselves and the waters surrounding them provide many high-quality foods. Fish, as you would expect, is important in the cookery. Shellfish, squid, and cuttlefish are popular. Many tropical fruits such as pineapples, mangoes, papayas, and coconuts are also used frequently in Hawaiian dishes.

Probably the most famous Hawaiian food custom is the *luau,* a feast which features a whole pig roasted in a leaf-lined pit. Other foods, such as bananas, sweet potatoes, meats, and fish, are wrapped in leaves and roasted with the pig. The luau can also include many other dishes. Among the local favorites are *poi* (POY) (a paste made from taro root), *lomilomi salmon* (a combination of tomatoes, green onion, and salted salmon), fresh fruits, and macadamia, kukui, and lichee nuts. *Haupie,* a coconut pudding, is also popular.

Poi is the staple food of Hawaii. Traditionally, poi is eaten with the fingers. The consistency is often described as two-finger or three-finger poi, which indicates the number of fingers required to carry it to the mouth. The native daily diet is relatively simple and is based on locally grown foods. Breakfast usually consists of fresh fruit, while the afternoon or evening meal is substantial.

**For Review**

1. What foods and techniques did the Indians contribute to New England cookery?
2. What is the typical New England boiled dinner?
3. What is the origin of Pennsylvania Dutch cookery?
4. What is a coffee klatch?
5. Describe at least three corn dishes popular in the South.
6. What are the four major influences on the Creole cuisine of Louisiana? Name one food contributed by each group.
7. How did the potluck dinner develop in the Midwest?
8. What are three general characteristics of Midwestern cookery?
9. What are the three main influences on Southwestern cookery?
10. What was the original version of chili con carne like?
11. What did the gold-rush prospectors contribute to West Coast cuisine? What did the Spanish contribute?
12. What kinds of meat are more popular in Alaska than in other parts of the United States? Why?
13. What foods grow wild in Alaska? How do Alaskans prepare them?
14. What are three traditional Polynesian foods or dishes?
15. What cookery methods were introduced to Hawaii by the Chinese? By the Japanese?

# 32 Chapter Review

## Summary

The American cooking style is really a collection of regional cuisines: the Northeast, the South, the Midwest, the Southwest, the West Coast, Alaska, and Hawaii. As people came to this nation and settled in a region, they brought the cuisine from their homeland and shared it with other inhabitants of the area. Of course, the native American culture and the conditions of the region, such as the weather and kinds of crops that could be grown, influenced the foods that were prepared, too. Although some dishes are still strictly regional, many are now popular nationwide.

## Vocabulary

Match the statements that follow to the vocabulary words below.

1. Cajun cooking
2. Creole cooking
3. New England boiled dinner
4. Pennsylvania Dutch cooking
5. potluck dinner

a. This cuisine, created by German farmers, features rich soups, sauerbraten, sauerkraut, potato pancakes, pork, noodles, and dumplings.
b. This distinctive southern cuisine, influenced by French, Indian, Spanish, and African cooking styles, features dishes such as gumbo.
c. This tradition, popular throughout the United States, means that each family attending a social event should bring a cooked dish to share with the others.
d. This one-pot meal usually contains corned beef, or some other kind of meat, potatoes, onions, carrots, beets, and cabbage.
e. This hearty southern French provincial cuisine, adapted by the Arcadians and influenced by the Indians in Louisiana, features dishes such as jambalaya.

## Chapter Questions

1. What are the seven regional cuisines of the United States?
2. Why did regional cuisines develop in the United States?
3. Which dishes served in your family are examples of a Northeast regional cuisine? Select two of the dishes and tell how you prepare them.
4. Which native crops and wildlife did the early settlers of New England use that influenced their cuisine?
5. What conditions made it possible for the early settlers of the South to create a dish called Brunswick stew?
6. What contributions did the slaves of the plantations make to Southern cookery?
7. Why did canning and preserving become important skills on Midwestern farms?
8. What is meant by a "meat and potatoes" cuisine?
9. What contributions to the overall American cuisine were developed by the settlers in the Southwest?

10. Which dishes served in your family are examples of a California cuisine? Select two and tell how you prepare them.

11. What are two foods that the cuisines of California and Alaska have in common? Why do these states have these foods in common?

12. How did the Europeans and New Englanders influence Hawaiian cookery?

13. Describe the characteristics of the Hawaiian cuisine and how it developed.

14. If you were to open a restaurant featuring regional cuisine, which one would you choose and why?

## Skill Activities

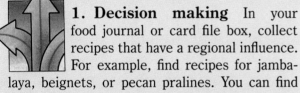

**1. Decision making** In your food journal or card file box, collect recipes that have a regional influence. For example, find recipes for jambalaya, beignets, or pecan pralines. You can find recipes in books, magazines, newspapers, and on the display boards in supermarkets.

**2. Reading** Squash was an important vegetable used by the Indians for thousands of years before the European settlers came to this country. Find information about the history of squash on this continent. Write a report that tells the age and history of squash, its importance and use by the Indians, and the importance of squash to the early settlers and the ways they used it. Also discuss the different winter and summer varieties, and include four recipes for squash dishes with your report.

**3. Critical thinking** Discover the convenience regional foods available at your local supermarket. Before visiting the store, divide seven pages of lined paper into 3 columns. Above the columns, write: "Canned," "Frozen," "Ready-to-eat." Take your pages with you and record your findings. Which region is represented with the most kinds of convenience products at your supermarket? Select two products and tell when and how you would use them. What guidelines would you recommend to be followed for purchasing regional convenience products?

**4. Decision making** Select one of the regions and prepare a dinner menu for four people. Include in your menu an appetizer, main dish, vegetables, salad, and other main dish accompaniments, dessert, and beverage. With your menu include recipes for your dishes. You can find additional information about typical regional cuisine in books and magazines.

**5. Communication** Invite a chef from a local restaurant that features regional cuisine to speak to your class. Prepare a list of questions that you would like her/him to talk about. Include in your list, questions about how the chef determines the menu, what foods are the most popular, and what kind of training the chef had.

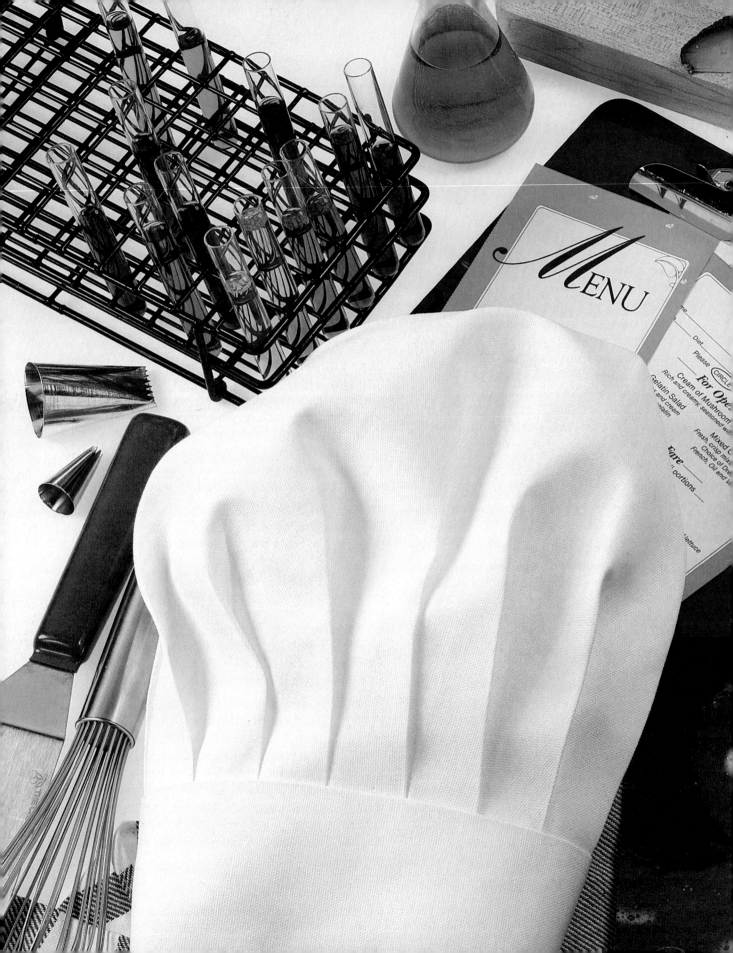

# Unit 6
# Looking Ahead

33 Opportunities

# 33 Opportunities

## As you read, think about:

- your achievements and opportunities in the world of food.
- what the characteristics and requirements are for food-related careers.
- how to find a job in the world of food.

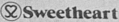

You have just begun to explore the world of food and the art of cookery. Your study of food has introduced you to the many principles involved in the preparation of the foods basic to your needs. It has also started you on the road to a career in a food-related field, should you decide that this is the path you wish to take.

## Is a Food-related Career for You?

A review of what you have learned in this course and a look at the world of food-related jobs will help you decide if you wish to pursue a career in the world of food. As you read this chapter, think about your other interests and skills as well. What do you enjoy doing most? What are you best at? What would you like to

Master chefs are often justly proud of their accomplishments. This 1874 oil portrait, "Jules Harder, First Chef of the Palace Hotel," hangs in the Oakland Museum in California.

learn to do better? First, look at your achievements. Then you will be better able to evaluate your opportunities.

### Your Achievements

If you stop to think about it, you will realize that you have been introduced to a great many ideas, principles, and techniques as you worked your way through THE WORLD OF FOOD. Take some time to review your achievements.

You have learned how the American food culture began and how to use foods in a variety of ways. In addition to methods of food preparation and the principles upon which they are based, you have learned to recognize many of the signs of quality in foods and the standards or guides to use in their selection. You have learned to consider your goals, values, and needs when you make your choices among the various forms of food. You have learned that foods must be stored properly to retain their attractiveness, eating quality, color, texture, flavor, and nutrient values.

You have learned which tools are best suited for the various cookery procedures, and to understand cookery terms and abbreviations, which enable you to use recipes as your guides in food preparation. You have learned to measure ingredients accurately and how to prepare a great variety of food products successfully.

You have learned how to plan, prepare, and serve meals graciously, and how to leave the kitchen and dining areas clean and in order.

You have learned that most foods are available in convenience forms, and are partly or completely prepared, and that while these forms use time and effort to good advantage, they often cost more than the original food or the ingredients necessary to prepare the food. To use them intelligently, you must consider their quality, cost, and nutrient values as well as the time that is saved through their use. When you buy convenience foods, you are aware that you are also paying for the labor and special packaging used to produce the food. You are aware that convenience items can be a good investment when you want to save time and energy or make up for your lack of knowledge or skill in preparing a food, but you also know that too frequent use of the same convenience products can result in uninteresting or monotonous meals. However, when you use convenience foods creatively, you can produce successful meals.

You learned that foods are made of nutrients and that your body has several uses for them. These needs can be classified into three general groups: for growth and repair, you need protein; for energy, you need carbohydrates and fats; and for protection and regulation of your body processes, you need vitamins, minerals, and water. You know that proper storage and preparation techniques are required to retain the nutrient values of the foods you serve.

Because "practice makes perfect," you will want to continue to practice everything you have learned so the principles of cookery will become habits before you forget them. In this way, you can prepare the foods that can bring you self-satisfaction and that will be enjoyed by all.

Your experience with food study can lead the way to greater opportunities in the world of food, and give you a foundation upon which you can increase your knowledge about food.

Culinary students learn more than cooking and baking. They also learn how to run a safe, sanitary, efficient kitchen.

## Your Opportunities

There are many ways to get future satisfaction from what you have learned in this course. Preparing tasty, nutritious, and economic family meals is one way. Knowing that your kitchen is safe, clean, and efficient is another.

Cooking can also be a very satisfying hobby. Many people enjoy cooking for company or preparing specialties for friends and neighbors. Sometimes these home-cooks begin to market their products or to write cookbooks reflecting their cookery styles. At that point, food preparation becomes a career.

Food-related careers cover a wide spectrum. Food columnists and writers, home-economics teachers and food photographers, television chefs and media food editors, master chefs in fine restaurants and therapeutic dieticians in hospitals, caterers and waiters—all are in food-related careers. Perhaps you can combine your interest and skills in food preparation with your abilities and inclinations in order to find a satisfying career in the world of food. Many food careers can be scheduled to coordinate with family responsibilities. A food-service job, for example, can be scheduled during evening hours, and food writing jobs can often be done at home.

### For Review

1. What are two important things to remember about convenience foods?
2. In addition to proper preparation, what else must you do to retain the nutrient value of foods?
3. Which of your interests and abilities could you combine with your knowledge of food to create a food-related career? What career would that be?

# The World of Food-related Careers

The world of food is exciting, and it offers many opportunities. In some food-related careers, you can work directly with food preparation or with the general public. Others are more research-oriented: you study the nutritional requirements of the public at large or of particular individuals with special needs. You could work for food or appliance manufacturers, developing or promoting their products; or you could work for one of the government agencies or consumer-protection groups, testing and advising on the benefits or dangers of particular foods. In some food-related jobs, you might work alone —as a free-lance food writer, for example; or you could supervise large numbers of people —perhaps as food-services director of a school cafeteria. Some food-related jobs require extensive education or training; for others, you can begin "at the bottom" and then work your way "up the ladder" as you gain experience.

Food is frequently in the news because people are becoming more interested in the relationship between diet and health. The constantly changing fashions in food preparation also fill the media as trendy cookbooks and television chefs gain the spotlight. Somewhere in this expanding world of food-related careers, there are sure to be opportunities for you.

### The Food-service Industry

When you think of careers in the world of food, the first area that comes to mind is probably the food-service industry. Restaurants of all types, as well as hotels and caterers, are food-service employers, as are institutions such as hospitals, prisons, nursing homes, and the cafeterias run for businesses and schools. While the **food-service industry** includes all the places where people eat away from home, you can

Which of the many food-related careers are represented above?

see that a hospital kitchen would be run differently than one in a fancy restaurant, and that a job in a hotel snack bar would require different food-preparation skills and personal qualities than a job in a nursing home.

Each year an increasing number of meals are served away from home. All of this food must be prepared and served, and this means many career opportunities for those with an interest in food. If you like good food, have an appreciation of high standards of food production and service, and like people and are interested in their health and welfare, you may enjoy a career in food service.

For the most part, food-service jobs can be divided into two general categories: (1) planning and preparing the meals, and (2) delivering the food to those for whom it is intended. In small food-service businesses, one person often "wears many hats"—from the chef's hat to the bookkeeper's. The manager of a small food-service facility is responsible for the entire food-service operation and the supervision of employees. In a large facility, the responsibility may be divided among several persons. The general manager supervises the entire operation. The food-production manager plans menus, orders food, selects equipment, and keeps records. The purchasing agent buys the food, equipment, and other supplies needed by the various divisions of the operation. The food-cost supervisor studies the menus, estimates the cost per serving, and determines the price for which the food must sell. The food supervisor in each department makes sure that menus are strictly followed, that a good quality food is produced, and that food is ready for service when needed, as well as supervising the production workers in the unit.

The food industry offers a wide variety of jobs that require different skills and training. You can have a successful career in the field of food without a college degree; however, advancement depends upon ability, experience or in-service training, and education. Summer jobs are available at restaurants, hotels, hospitals, lunch counters, and other establishments. You might find it worthwhile to get a part-time job that will give you experience and the opportunity to learn about the food-service industry.

## Chefs, Cooks, and Their Assistants

Although the words *chef* and *cook* are often used interchangeably, the "top of the ladder" in the cooking profession is usually called master chef or executive chef. This is a position that requires great skill, talent, and experience; and usually calls for on-the-job training as well. While some chefs have begun in unskilled food-service jobs and then have worked their way up to their positions, more and more are getting high-school and post-high-school training in vocational programs and two- or four-year colleges.

About forty percent of chefs and cooks work in restaurants. Thirty percent work in educational institutions, and the remainder work part-time in various establishments. In a fine

Preparing the elaborate meals that diners on the S.S. *France* expect takes a well-coordinated staff under the direction of an efficient and creative master chef.

restaurant, the chef is largely responsible for the style and quality of the food and for the reputation of the restaurant. Smaller or less ambitious restaurants usually feature a limited number of easily prepared items; some of the preparation may already have been done even before the food reaches the restaurant. One cook or chef is usually in charge and does most of the preparation with the aid of several less-experienced helpers.

Larger restaurants or those specializing in complicated and exacting recipes often have a more varied menu, and more of their dishes are prepared from scratch in their own kitchen. The head chef supervises a staff, coordinates the work, directs the preparation of specialties, decides the serving size, plans the menus, and even purchases the food supplies. The staff may include one or more *sous-chefs* ("under," or assistant, chefs), apprentices, specialists in different aspects of food preparation (such as pastry chefs or sauce chefs), kitchen helpers (such as salad assemblers), and sanitary workers (such as dishwashers). Chefs and cooks who work in institutional settings, particularly hospitals or nursing homes, are often supervised by a professional dietician.

**Practical Tip**
• To help you relax before going to a job interview, try exercising, taking a warm bath or shower, and/or taking several deep breaths.

Of course, when you enter a cooking career, you don't begin at the top as chef. Entry-level positions include assistants to the various special chefs or to the single cook in a small establishment. The more education and training you bring to your entry-level job, the faster you will probably advance. There are apprenticeship programs offered by professional culinary institutes, industry associations, and trade unions. Often, you can combine the practical experience of an apprenticeship with course work in an educational institution. One example is a three-year apprenticeship program given by local chapters of the American Culinary Federation in cooperation with local employers and junior colleges or vocational institutions. There are also large hotels and restaurants with their own training programs.

Cooperation is the key in a two-chef kitchen such as this one in a resort lodge.

The Culinary Institute of America. People from all over the country and from other nations come to Hyde Park, New York, to attend this renowned cooking school. Drawn by its reputation, its experienced faculty, and the professional facilities, students at the Culinary Institute learn the basic skills of cooking and baking.

Started in 1946 in New Haven, Connecticut, the Institute's first class had only 16 members and a faculty of 3. Today it boasts 1,850 students a year and a nationally and internationally known faculty of 90 chefs, *maitres d'hotel,* and other food-service professionals. Originally a 10-week program, the Institute's course of study for an associate's degree now takes 21 months to complete.

As soon as a student enters the program, he or she immediately assumes the habits of the profession. A school day is over six hours long. During that time, students must adhere to a Personal Hygiene Code. Students with long hair must pull it back, pin it up, and wear a net. Male students cannot have beards. All students wear a traditional cook's uniform—black-and-white checked pants, a white double-breasted jacket, a white apron, a side towel, and a chef's paper hat. Students taking table service classes must wear the Institute's table-service uniform.

Immersion in the food-service professions continues in classroom instruction. The Institute's students learn by doing. Eighty percent of all classes are hands-on. All students take the same classes. The nineteen production kitchens, five bake shops, the food and sanitation laboratory, commercial storeroom, meat room, fish kitchen, experimental kitchen, and demonstration auditoriums provide the settings for practice and learning.

Most of the lecture-style courses are taken in the first of the five required semesters. Students learn sanitation, nutrition, culinary French, storeroom inventory systems, and food-service business law. In this way, they begin developing good work habits and understanding the principles of cooking and baking. At the end of the semester, students begin actual cooking skills—basic butchering, preparation of stocks and soups, sautéeing, braising, and frying.

In the remaining four semesters, students learn about organizing both kitchens and pantries and about managing personnel. They take special courses on seafood cookery, American cuisine, Oriental cookery, baking, and patisserie. All students work for some time in the experimental kitchen developing and testing new uses of ingredients.

Opportunities to work in real-life workplaces enhance the Institute experience. Every student spends the third semester in an "externship." For twenty-one weeks, a student works in a restaurant, a hotel, an industrial catering service or in another food-service workplace. The student applies for the position and gets paid. Fifth semester is spent working in the four restaurants on the Institute's campus.

When students graduate, they have a wealth of jobs to choose from. In fact, the school has a 100% job placement rate.

Cooks learn the proper use of a large mixer.

If you plan to work in a large food-service establishment, courses in **commercial food preparation** (which emphasize planning and cooking for large numbers of people at one time) would be a good idea. These can range from a few months in length to two years, and are offered by trade schools, vocational centers, colleges, professional associations, and trade unions. They often require a high-school diploma. For further information about cooking careers, contact:

National Institute for the Foodservice
    Industry
20 North Wacker Drive, Suite 2620
Chicago, Illinois 60606

Council on Hotel, Restaurant, and
    Institutional Education
Room S-208, Henderson Building
University Park, Pennsylvania 16802

American Culinary Federation
P.O. Box 3466
St. Augustine, Florida 32084

**Food Servers and Their Assistants and Supervisors** The most common job involving serving food is that of waiter or waitress. Counter workers and cafeteria workers are also in this category. In fine restaurants, you will often find an entire staff, including a maitre d', captain or head waiter, waiters and/or waitresses, and buspersons. Even more casual restaurants frequently employ someone to greet patrons and show them to their seats. Sometimes that person is in charge of the food-serving staff, but not always.

There are not usually educational requirements to wait tables, and experience can be gained on the job in many establishments. In more formal restaurants, a knowledge of correct table service techniques (as described in Chapter 11), of the particular cuisine, or even of a

Although they are called "servers," waiters and waitresses do more than just bring food to the table. They often describe items on the menu and make suggestions.

foreign language may be required. Even in these restaurants, however, you might begin as a busperson and work up to waiter or head waiter.

All those who serve food deal with the public. Having a neat appearance, an even disposition, and a well-spoken manner are important for waiting table. Good arithmetic skills are also an advantage. Almost all waiters and waitresses take orders, serve, and write out checks. Some also take payment, make menu suggestions to patrons, and explain how dishes are prepared. In smaller restaurants, they may also set up and clear tables as well as serve as cashiers. Even though some waiters and waitresses work part-time, they are the people who represent their employers to the customers. They are important to customer satisfaction and to the success of the particular restaurant.

**Caterers and Their Staffs** The business of **catering** is something like a traveling restaurant. Most often, food is prepared to order (although the order is placed in advance) and then transported to the customer's home or to the place where the food is to be consumed. Occasionally, it is there that some of the food preparation is done; more often, it is prepared in advance. Many caterers provide full meals, arrange and staff a buffet table, serve sit-down dinners, or provide trays of hors d'oeuvres or desserts, and the personnel to walk among guests and serve. Other caterers are specialists, and provide only one type of food. They may or may not deliver. Like restaurants, complete-meal caterers employ many food-service workers such as chefs, specialist chefs, assistants, waiters and waitresses, and clean-up help. In addition, the caterers transport and keep hot or cold the foods they have prepared. Many catering operations are run like big businesses; some are services provided by restaurants and hotels, using their kitchens and kitchen staffs. Others are small enterprises, sometimes begun as home-based businesses by a skilled and enterprising home-cook.

### The Prepared-food Industry

The prepared-food industry touches just about everyone's daily life. It includes the preparation of all processed foods brought into the home, from the canned soup, cake mix, frozen dinner, and packaged bread found in the supermarket to the fresh rolls or birthday cake picked up at the corner bakery to the fortified milk purchased in the local convenience store. Jobs in the prepared-food industry include those of the unskilled assembly-line workers who peel and sort foods as well as those of food technologists and food scientists who develop new processing techniques. There are also many positions in marketing the finished food products. Small food-preparation businesses employ inexperienced helpers and sanitary workers as well as highly skilled and trained workers such as bakers and cake decorators.

**Food Technologists** Those who study the scientific properties of food and develop methods for its safe processing, preservation, packaging, storage, and transportation are **food technologists.** They look for ways to improve the flavor, appearance, and nutritional value of food as well as ways to make it more convenient to use. They also design and conduct tests to make sure that food products meet industry and government standards.

Many food technologists are specialists. They may concentrate on one type of food (such as milk or seafood) or one technical process (such as canning or dehydration). Others are involved in market research, advertising, or technical sales. Some food technologists do research or teach.

A career in food technology calls for rigorous educational requirements. A bachelor's degree in food technology or in a relevant science is required. Graduate degrees are necessary for advancement. For further information about careers in this field, contact:

Institute of Food Technologists
221 North LaSalle Street
Chicago, Illinois 60601

**Bakers** There are many employment opportunities for bakers in both large and small

Bakers can work in a variety of settings, from large commercial baking companies to restaurants. Some bakers even specialize in catering private parties.

baked goods are made. The most inexperienced personnel often begin as helpers or assistants to a head baker or to a specialty baker. Those with previous training can work in more skilled positions. Vocational schools, culinary institutes, and colleges offer courses in baking. The baking industry even runs its own school. For further information about this school, contact:

American Institute of Baking
1213 Bakers Way
Manhattan, Kansas 66502

## The Home Economics Professions

There are a number of professions open to those with a college degree in home economics. The food-related careers include being a nutritionist or a dietician, or teaching nutrition or cooking. In addition, there are paraprofessional positions that do not require as much education, but they do require an interest in food and/or nutrition and some training beyond high school. Related careers include writing about, illustrating, or filming food-preparation or food-marketing material. Consumer affairs is also a growing field; specialists in nutrition and food safety as well as experts in cooking and marketing keep the public informed about beneficial new developments and possible dangers of particular products or substances in food.

### Dieticians and Their Assistants

Health professionals who apply the principles of sound nutrition to particular circumstances are **dieticians.** *Administrative dieticians* supervise the meal planning and preparation of large-scale food-service operations, such as cafeterias in schools, factories, office buildings, and prisons. They make sure that meals are nutritionally balanced as well as safely and economically prepared. They may hire, train, and direct cooks and other workers; budget and purchase food, equipment, and supplies; and enforce health

businesses. Large commercial baking companies employ skilled bakers as well as food technologists and chemists for research and product development. The companies often operate laboratories or "pilot bakeries," which develop new products. Marketing, sales, and inspection also provide jobs for people with a thorough knowledge of baking.

There is a daily demand for fresh-baked breads, cakes, pastries, and other bakery goods. These can be made in small private bakeries, in the kitchens of supermarkets, or in larger bakeries for local or even national distribution. Bakers and their assistants are employed wherever

Dieticians are health professionals. They must understand the nutritional and health needs of average people as well as of special groups, such as children or those with medical problems.

and dental schools. *Community dieticians* counsel individuals and groups. They work for public-service organizations such as health associations or programs for the elderly.

Dieticians must have a bachelor's degree in dietetics, food and nutrition, or a similar subject. A *registered dietician* (RD) has passed an exam given by the American Dietetic Association, and has completed an internship program. For more information, contact:

American Dietetic Association
430 North Michigan Avenue
Chicago, Illinois 60611

**Dietetic technicians** often assist the dietician in the daily operation of food services. They are the link between the professional dietician and those who actually prepare the food for food-service operations. For example, dietetic technicians might prepare work schedules and supervise the day-to-day ordering, preparing, and delivery of food in order to comply with the dietician's overall plan. In health-care facilities, dietetic technicians often work directly with patients, helping to plan their diets. They observe and record the patients' eating habits as well as work with the food-service personnel to make sure meals are prepared according to each patient's particular needs. In addition, some dietetic technicians work for public health departments, visiting nurse associations, and neighborhood health centers. They help families learn to prepare more nutritious meals. Other dietetic technicians aid in nutritional research.

While dietetic technicians do not need a bachelor's degree, they must have education beyond high school. An associate's degree from a junior or community college or from a vocational school is required.

**Nutritionists** In contrast to dieticians, **nutritionists** are not usually directly involved in food preparation and delivery. They deal with

regulations. *Clinical* or *therapeutic dieticians* do similar work in health-related facilities such as hospitals, nursing homes, and clinics. They adapt general nutritional principles to the special needs of an individual or of groups of patients. They may determine a patient's nutritional needs, develop a diet for that patient, and evaluate the patient's progress. Clinical dieticians confer with doctors and nurses as well as instruct patients and their families. *Research dieticians* do nutritional studies for hospitals, research centers, educational facilities, and community health programs. *Educational dieticians* teach in colleges and in medical, nursing, the broad principles of nutrition, and often engage in research or teaching. Many are consultants to people in related fields, such as the food-processing industry or health organizations. They also instruct and inform by giving interviews and lectures, by appearing on radio and television, and by writing for newspapers and magazines.

Many nutritionists are also registered dieticians, but a master's degree is usually required in order to work as a professional nutritionist.

## Other Home Economics Careers

Professional home economists (those with at least a bachelor's degree in the field) work in a variety of settings. *Business home economists* work for food, utility, and appliance manufacturers. They help the companies to understand and produce what consumers want and need, and sometimes they work on product development. Home economists also help teach consumers about the company's products and how to use them safely and economically, and how to produce the best results. For example, a home economist may create a recipe to highlight a new food product, and give demonstrations at schools, clubs, or trade shows. For a job of this type, a home economist's title might be marketing specialist or director of consumer education. In addition to giving demonstrations, home economists write pamphlets and other materials for businesses.

*Extension home economists* distribute information about all aspects of home economics —including nutrition and food preparation— through the Cooperative Extension Service of the government. *Home economics teachers* do the same in the classroom, from the junior-high level on up through doctoral degree programs. *Home economics writers* work for the media, advertising agencies, public relations firms, government agencies, and consumer-affairs groups.

Business home economists can work in marketing. They often demonstrate their company's appliances, food products, or recipes to consumers or to retailers.

Finally, *research home economists,* like nutritionists and dieticians, conduct research in food-related areas as well as other aspects of home economics. For further information about careers in home economics, contact:

American Home Economics Association
1555 King Street
Alexandria, Virginia 22314

## Related Careers

For many of the professional careers (requiring college degrees) already described, there are related careers that do not require a degree in home economics. Think for a moment about two food-related "products" that you are already familiar with: a cookbook and a televised cooking show. For the cookbook, what other specialists in addition to the author do you think contributed? Technical drawings and photographs are extremely important to the success of a cookbook, and so are the people who produce them. Some *illustrators* specialize in food or in instructional drawings. There are also *photographers* who specialize in food, and *food stylists* who make sure that the food products look their best, just the way make-up and wardrobe artists make sure that actors look their best. TV cooking shows employ similar specialists: food stylists, *directors, camera operators,* and *cooking assistants*—all to make sure that the steps of a televised recipe run smoothly and turn out successfully. Settings, too, must be just right: they must be homey and appealing as well as efficient to use and convenient to film. Specialists who do these kinds of jobs are employed not only by book publishers and television stations, but also by advertisers, periodical publishers, and businesses.

## A Growing Field: Consumer Affairs

While many professional home economists, food technologists, and nutritionists work for food companies, many others are employed by the "watchdog" organizations that regulate or closely watch those companies. You have already read about some of the government agencies, such as the Food and Drug Administration (FDA), that establish safety and nutrition standards and make sure that they are followed. As you know, the Department of Agriculture inspects meat and poultry, and the Federal Trade Commission checks for truth in advertising. These and other federal agencies, as well as health and consumer-protection agencies of local and state governments, all employ people in food-related careers.

A food photographer takes pictures for advertisements, cookbooks, and magazines. In some cases, the photographer may employ a food stylist to "set up" the arrangements.

A career in the world of food can be satisfying as well as rewarding. Wouldn't you be proud to have created these beautiful dishes?

There are also independent consumer-affairs or consumer-protection groups. They do their own research and testing of food products, and then try to influence the food companies and/or government agencies to ban or limit products they think are dangerous or to place information or warnings on product labels. Equally important is their consumer-information function. Through books, speeches, and the media, consumer-protection groups present their findings to the public. Public pressure can then influence the government to look again at a particular product. Public buying patterns can be even more effective: if many people switch to low-salt or whole-grain foods, for example, food companies start producing more of those items to satisfy consumer demand. Consumer-affairs groups employ specialists in food and nutrition as well as people skilled in the communication skills of writing, speaking to groups and to the media, and lobbying or testifying at government hearings. The more that is learned about the relationship between food and health, the more the consumer-affairs field will grow.

## Which Career for You?

Which food-related career appeals to you most? Why? All jobs have their advantages and disadvantages, of course. Some that are not too appealing in themselves are good entry-level positions that can lead to better jobs as you gain experience. Others require substantial training or a degree before you can even begin, but then provide a very satisfying career. In addition, what may be a disadvantage for one person may prove advantageous to another. Some people, for example, like to travel or to make their own schedules. Others look for security and regular hours. Keep in mind that many jobs require mathematical skills and/or the ability to use a computer for purchasing, planning, and book-keeping. Interpersonal and communication skills are important for any positions in which you deal with the public—whether patients, students, or customers—and for which you supervise or consult with other workers.

## For Review

1. In a large food-service facility, what positions make up the staff? Briefly describe each position.
2. To become a master or executive chef, what kind of education or training is desirable?
3. What personal qualities are important for those who serve food? Why?
4. What are the educational requirements for a food technologist?
5. List four types of dieticians. Briefly describe the job of each.
6. What are the educational requirements for a dietetic technician?
7. What kinds of companies employ business home economists? What types of jobs do these people do?
8. What do the independent consumer-protection groups do?

# Finding a Job

With the whole world of food-related careers before you, where should you begin? How can you find your first job? Even if you plan to go on to further education after high school, you may want to find a summer or part-time food-related job to get a first-hand look at what it's like. A job of this type or volunteer work can also provide you with valuable background and experience when you apply for a higher or more permanent position. If you plan to begin your career in an entry-level position right after high school, you will be glad to know that there are job-placement resources within your school.

## How to Look for a Job

When you begin your job search, start with your school placement or guidance counselor or home-economics teacher. They are often contacted by employers interested in hiring high-school students with no or little paid-work experience. Your placement or guidance counselor has probably helped many students find jobs and can give you valuable advice. Ask particularly about programs such as Home Economics Related Occupations (HERO). Jobs in these programs offer not only pay but also school credit.

You can also do some job-availability research on your own. Check the "Help Wanted" section of your local newspaper. The Sunday edition usually has the most ads. Read the ads carefully. Make sure that you are reasonably qualified and can find transportation to a job before you invest time in writing or calling about it. Also look for help-wanted signs in the windows of restaurants or other food-related businesses. You might want to contact seasonal employers, such as country clubs, summer resorts, or camps, well in advance of their season to inquire about application procedures.

## Applying for a Job

There are several ways to apply for a job; the one you use often depends on how you found out about the job. If you are answering a newspaper ad, for example, do exactly what the ad says. If it says, "No calls," don't call. If it gives particular times when you may call, call only during those times. If a letter is required, send one. First impressions are very important. The ability and willingness to follow directions are traits employers look for.

If you are responding to a sign that says "Inquire within," make sure you are properly dressed and prepared to be interviewed when you ask to see the manager or owner. Again, first impressions are important. Any time you go to an *interview,* you should be well-groomed, well-prepared, and agreeable.

For some jobs, you may need to write a *letter of application.* Your letter is your first impression, and it should be neat, absolutely correct, and to the point. Sloppiness or carelessness in a letter implies that you will not care about the quality of your work either. If you are answering an ad, give the date and source of the ad as well as the title or description of the job for which you are applying. Try to find out who is in charge of hiring, and address that person by name and title. Include any information that has been requested in the ad. If no résumé is requested, summarize your qualifications.

A high-school student does not usually have to include a **résumé** (a brief history of education, job experience, and interests), but if it is requested, make sure that it is neat, brief, and in the accepted form. Study your language-arts text for correct letter form and résumé form, or

The impression you make at a job interview is important. Be well-groomed and suitably dressed, agreeable and polite, and prepared to talk about yourself as well as the job.

ask your guidance counselor or teacher to help you with these written materials.

If you *call* to respond to an ad or to make a first contact, be patient and polite. First try to find out whom you should contact, and address that person by name. Have the necessary information about yourself in front of you so that you can answer questions about your background quickly and efficiently. Also have a pen or pencil handy so you can jot down the time of an interview, directions, or other information.

### Personal Information You Will Need

Whichever way you make contact with a prospective employer, you should be prepared to provide the following information about yourself:

- Social Security Number. If you do not already have a Social Security card, get one from your local Social Security Office. You cannot work without one.
- Work Permit. Ask your guidance counselor if your state requires a work permit for persons under 18. If so, be sure you have one when you apply for a job.
- Health Certificate. Jobs that involve handling food often require a certificate to show that you are in good health and do not have any communicable diseases. Again, have this certificate before you meet with a prospective employer.
- References. Most prospective employers ask for **references,** or people they can contact to ask about your character, work habits, and accomplishments. Teachers and former employers are most often used, but be sure to get the permission of anyone you expect to use as a reference; have their names, addresses, phone numbers, and titles (if relevant) available at the interview.
- Work and Education History. Employers may ask for this information in several ways: on a résumé, on a job application, or orally. Be sure

you have dates of attendance and addresses of your schools and previous jobs.
- Other Information. A job application or an interviewer may ask you some questions about yourself, your goals, and your interests. Be prepared to answer them completely but briefly. Think about these topics beforehand, and prepare possible answers: why you want this particular job; how you heard about the job; what qualifies you for the job; and what your long-term goals are. Be prepared to point out what school courses, hobbies, trips, jobs, or other experiences are particularly relevant to the job you are seeking.

If you write a résumé and fill out a job application at home, be sure they are neat and complete. If you have not been asked to fill out an application before the interview, bring the above information to the interview, along with a pen or pencil. Fill out all forms carefully and neatly. Check to be sure you haven't left anything out. Also be sure you can comfortably and easily give this background information orally to an interviewer. Approach any interview with a positive attitude, and be courteous, pleasant, and brief. After all, you have a lot to offer.

### For Review

1. What are three sources you can use to find job openings?
2. What information should you include in a letter of application?
3. What specific information should you be prepared to give a prospective employer, either on an application or in an interview?
4. How should you prepare for an interview? How should you conduct yourself at the interview? Why?

# 33 Chapter Review

## Summary

Within the food-service industry, prepared-food industry, home economics profession, consumer affairs organizations, and other related fields, there are many opportunities for a food-related career. To make an informed decision about the career that is appropriate for you, consider your skills, interests, achievements, and your goals. As you read this book, you were presented with a variety of principles, techniques, procedures, and guidelines that are important to planning, preparing, and serving attractive, wholesome meals. The skills you have developed are a foundation upon which you can increase your knowledge about food.

## Vocabulary

Use the vocabulary words below to fill in the blanks in the paragraphs that follow.

catering
commercial food
  preparation
dietetic
  technicians
dieticians

food-service
  industry
food technologists
nutritionists
references
résumé

When you consider a food-related career, you may decide to become one of the __(1)__, who are registered dieticians who work with the broad principles of nutrition and are often researchers and teachers. There are also health professionals, known as __(2)__, who apply the principles of sound nutrition to particular circumstances, such as supervising meal planning and food preparation in school cafeterias and hospitals. Other food-service professionals, called __(3)__, assist the dietician in the daily operation of food services, or they may work for public health departments or aid in nutritional research. You may also look at career positions in places where people eat away from home. These places include restaurants, hotels, caterers, cafeterias, as well as institutions, and they are all part of the __(4)__. In the __(5)__ business, food is prepared in advance and then carried to the customer's location, where it is eaten. If you decide to work for a large food-service business, enroll in __(6)__ courses that emphasize planning and cooking for large numbers of people at one time. If you like to look for ways to improve the flavor, appearance, and nutritional value of food, consider becoming one of the __(7)__, who specialize in such areas as the scientific properties of food and methods for its safe processing and preservation.

When you apply for a job, provide the employer with __(8)__ of people who know your character, work habits, and accomplishments. You may also consider preparing a brief history of your education, job experience, and interest, which is called a __(9)__.

## Chapter Questions

1. What important considerations should you make when you choose among the various forms of food?

2. What are ways within your home that you can practice what you have learned about food management and the principles of cookery?

3. How do people in food-related careers perform valuable service to all people?

4. What are the two general categories of food-service jobs?

5. What kinds of entry-level positions are available in the food-service industry?

6. How does the prepared-food industry touch just about everyone's life?

7. Which industry was involved with the meal you ate last night? What are the names of the professions for the people who were responsible for the food you were served?

8. Why are food-related careers in consumer affairs organizations a growing field?

9. Which food-related career appeals to you most? Why?

10. Even if a person plans to receive additional education in foods, why would it be important to find a part-time or summer food-related job?

## Skill Activities

**1. Decision making** In your food journal or on four pages of notebook paper, write one of these headings at the top of each page: "Skills," "Achievements," "Interests," and "Goals." Then under each heading, list the appropriate information. Refer to these lists as you make decisions about your future and prepare an application for further education, a career, or an interview.

**2. Human relations** With your classmates, plan a foods-related career and education day. First plan the kind of information you want the day to provide for you and your classmates. One way to do this is to prepare a list of questions that you want your career and education day to answer. Include in your list questions, such as what colleges and institutes offer degrees or certificates in culinary arts, nutrition, food management, and food technology; what is the process for applying to the colleges and institutes; what entry level positions are open in businesses in the community; what is needed to apply for those positions. Collect catalogs from colleges and institutes that provide certificates and degrees, and invite admissions officers from these institutions to speak to your class if possible. Provide listings of businesses in the area that have food-related employment opportunities, and invite those employers to talk with your class. Invite people with food-related careers to discuss with your class the work they do and what they like and dislike about their jobs.

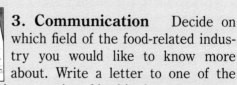

**3. Communication** Decide on which field of the food-related industry you would like to know more about. Write a letter to one of the organizations mentioned in this chapter requesting information. When you have received the material, prepare a brief report to share with the class what you have learned.

# Appendix

## Table of Equivalents

| Food | Quantity | Yield |
|---|---|---|
| Apples | 1 medium (150 g) | 1 c (250 mL) sliced |
| Bread crumbs | 3-4 slices bread | 1 c (250 mL) dry crumbs |
| | 1 slice bread | ¾ c (185 mL) soft crumbs |
| Cabbage | 1 lb (454 g) | 4 c (1 L) shredded |
| Cheese | ¼ lb (113.5 g) | 1 c (250 mL) shredded |
| Cherries | 1 qt (947 mL) | 2 c (500 mL) |
| Crackers, graham | 15 | 1 c (250 mL) fine crumbs |
| Crackers, soda | 16 | 1 c (250 mL) coarse crumbs |
| | 22 | 1 c (250 mL) fine crumbs |
| Cranberries | 1 lb (454 g) | 3-3½ c (750-875 mL) sauce |
| Cream, whipping | 1 c (250 mL) | 2 c (500 mL) whipped |
| Dried raisins, currants | 1 lb (454 g) | 3 c (750 mL) seedless |
| | | 2½ c (625 mL) seeded |
| Dates | 1 lb (454 g) | 2½ c (625 mL) chopped |
| Dry beans | 1 c (190 g) | 2½ c (625 mL) cooked |
| Eggs | 5 medium | 1 c (250 mL) |
| | 8 medium egg whites | 1 c (250 mL) |
| | 12-14 medium egg yolks | 1 c (250 mL) |
| Flour | 1 lb (454 g) | 4 c (1 L) |
| Lemon | 1 | 2-3 T (30-45 mL) |
| Macaroni, spaghetti, noodles | ½ lb (227 g) | 4 c (1 L) cooked |
| Nuts, peanuts | 5 oz (141.75 g) | 1 c (250 mL) |
| Pecans, chopped | 4¼ oz (121 g) | 1 c (250 mL) |
| Pecans, halves | 3¾ oz (106.32 g) | 1 c (250 mL) |
| Walnuts, chopped | 4¼ oz (127.58 g) | 1 c (250 mL) |
| Walnuts, halves | 3½ oz (99.23 g) | 1 c (250 mL) |
| Onion | 1 medium | ½ c (125 mL) |
| Orange | 1 | ⅓-½ c (80-125 mL) juice |
| Rice | 1 c (250 mL) | 3½ c (875 mL) cooked |
| Rice, precooked | 1 c (250 mL) | 2 c (500 mL) cooked |
| Sugar, brown | 1 lb (454 g) | 2¼ c (560 mL) firmly packed |
| Sugar, confectioners' | 1 lb (454 g) | 3½ c (875 mL) sifted |
| Sugar, granulated | 1 lb (454 g) | 2¼ c (560 mL) |

## Table of Substitutions

| Ingredient | Quantity | Substitute |
|---|---|---|
| Baking powder | 1 t (5 mL) double-acting | 1½ t (7.5 mL) phosphate or tartrate; 1¼ t (1.2 mL) baking soda plus 1½ c (125 mL) buttermilk or sour milk |
| Butter | 1 c (250 mL) | 1 c (250 mL) margarine; ⅞–1 c (215-250 mL) hydrogenated fat plus ½ t (2.5 mL) salt; ⅞ c (215 mL) lard plus ½ t (2.5 mL) salt |
| Chocolate | 1 square (28.35 g) unsweetened | 3 T (45 mL) cocoa plus 1 T (15 mL) shortening |
| Cream | coffee cream: 1 c (250 mL) | 3 T (45 mL) butter plus ⅞ c (215 mL) milk |
| | heavy cream: 1 c (250 mL) | ⅓ c (80 mL) butter plus ¾ c (185 mL) milk |
| Eggs | 1 whole egg | 2 egg yolks |
| Flour (for thickening) | 1 T (15 mL) | ½ T (7.5 mL) cornstarch or 2 t (10 mL) quick-cooking tapioca |
| Flour | all-purpose flour: 1 c (250 mL) | 1 c plus 2 T (280 mL) cake flour |
| | cake flour: 1 c (250 mL) | ⅞ c (215 mL) all-purpose flour |
| | self-rising flour: 1 c (250 mL) | 1 c (250 mL) flour: omit baking powder and salt |
| Herbs | 1 T (15 mL) fresh | 1 t (5 mL) dried |
| Honey | 1 c (250 mL) | 1-1¼ c (250-310 mL) sugar plus ¼ c (60 mL) liquid |
| Milk | fresh whole milk: 1 c (250 mL) | 1 c (250 mL) reconstituted nonfat dry milk plus 2 t (10 mL) butter |
| | whole milk: 1 c (250 mL) | ½ c (125 mL) evaporated milk plus ½ c (125 mL) water |
| | sour milk: 1 c (250 mL) | 1 T (15 mL) lemon juice or vinegar plus sweet milk to make 1 c (250 mL) |
| Yeast | 1 cake compressed | 1 package or 2 T (10 mL) active dry yeast |

# Glossary

**absorption** The process of taking up or drinking in; the process that transfers usable nutrients from the digestive system to the bloodstream or lymphatic system.

**accompaniment** Anything that goes with or supplements something else; a food that completes and is served with a main dish.

**aerobic exercise** Any exercise that causes the body to take in more oxygen; intense exercise that requires oxygen to produce physical energy. Aerobic exercise strengthens the cardiovascular system.

**à la carte** With a separate price for each item on the menu.

**albumen** The white of an egg.

**American Gas Association (AGA) blue star** A seal on gas appliances indicating that the appliance meets safety standards of the American Gas Association.

**amino acids** Chemical compounds that contain carbon, hydrogen, oxygen, and nitrogen. Proteins are made up of amino acids, some of which can be produced by the body (nonessential amino acids) and some of which must be supplied by diet (essential amino acids).

**anemia** A lack of red blood cells resulting in fatigue and a lowered resistance to infection. Anemia is often caused by a lack of iron.

**anorexia nervosa** An eating disorder characterized by extreme dieting, even to the point of starvation. Anorexics have a distorted body image; they think they are fat even when they are painfully and unhealthfully thin.

**antidotes** Remedies to counteract a poison.

**antiseptic** A substance that kills germs and prevents infection.

**appetite** The psychological desire to eat.

**ascorbic acid** Vitamin C.

**au gratin** Made with a lightly browned crust of grated cheese and bread crumbs.

**bakeware** The objects that hold food while it is being cooked in the oven.

**baking powder** A common chemical leavening agent.

**baking soda** A chemical leavening agent; bicarbonate of soda.

**basal metabolic rate (BMR)** The rate at which heat is given off by the body when it is at rest; a measurement of a person's particular basal metabolism.

**basal metabolism** The amount of energy needed by an organism at rest in order to sustain life processes.

**batter** A mixture of flour and liquid that is thin enough to be poured.

**beriberi** A disease characterized by nervous disorders and swelling of the body. It is caused by the lack of vitamin $B_1$, or thiamin.

**bisque** A cream soup made from thickened milk and pieces of seafood or vegetables.

**blanching** Bleaching or taking color away; scalding; dipping foods quickly into boiling water so that the skin may be removed easily or so that the foods are ready for freezing.

**bloom** A flower or blossom; the thin film on the outside of an eggshell which helps to seal the pores and protect the egg from contamination.

**boiling-water bath method** A method of processing used for high-acid foods. It involves bringing water to a rolling boil in a large kettle in which the canning jars have been placed.

**botulism** The most deadly form of food poisoning. It is caused by the bacteria clostridium botulinum. The toxin of this bacteria is so strong that only a tiny bit can be fatal. Canned goods that are improperly processed are the most common source of botulism.

**bouillon**   Clarified broth made from meat stock.

**braising**   Cooking in a tightly covered pan by using moisture (steam) from the meat itself or from a small amount of added liquid.

**brewing**   The method of making tea or coffee in which the tea leaves or coffee grounds come in contact with water just below the boiling point.

**buffet service**   An arrangement of food and table appointments on a table so that diners can help themselves.

**bulimia**   An eating disorder characterized by binging (eating to excess) and purging (vomiting). Bulimics want to lose weight but they also want to eat, and they carry both to extremes. Eventually, bulimics become unable to digest foods, and they can starve to death.

**butter cakes**   Cakes made with solid fats.

**caffeine**   A stimulant found in coffee and tea.

**Cajun cooking**   A cuisine that developed from the influence of local Louisiana ingredients and Indian cookery on the French provincial cooking style of the Acadians (Cajuns). Jambalaya is a famous Cajun dish.

**calcium**   A mineral used by the body to build strong bones and teeth, to give firmness to body cells, to aid in the clotting of blood, to regulate muscle action, and to maintain normal nerve function. Calcium is also important in preventing osteoporosis.

**candling**   A method of grading the freshness of an egg. It is done by holding the egg before a bright light, thus making the interior visible without breaking the shell.

**canning**   The process of putting foods in sealed containers for preservation. The foods are first exposed to high temperatures to destroy enzymes and organisms that can cause spoilage.

**carbohydrates**   Nutrients made up of carbon, hydrogen, and oxygen. They include sugars, starches, and cellulose. Carbohydrates are the major suppliers of energy and help the body make the best use of protein and fats.

**carbon dioxide**   A colorless, odorless gas.

**carotene**   A yellow pigment found in some plants. It can be converted into vitamin A by the body.

**casein**   The milk protein that settles out, or coagulates, to form curd.

**catering**   Providing food; preparing food and then transporting it to the customer's home or other designated place. Very often caterers also serve the meal.

**cellulose**   A complex carbohydrate found in the skin and pulp of vegetables. Also called fiber, cellulose cannot be digested by the body but serves as a natural laxative.

**cereal**   Any grain used for food; breakfast food specially prepared from grain.

**chiffon cakes**   Cakes made with oil instead of solid fats.

**chlorophyll**   The green substance in plants that is involved in photosynthesis.

**cholesterol**   A fatlike substance found naturally in the body and in some foods. An excess of blood cholesterol has been linked to heart disease.

**chowder**   A soup made with unthickened milk and small pieces of fish, meat, or vegetables. Occasionally, tomato and water are used in place of the milk.

**circulatory system**   The heart, lungs, and blood vessels; the flow of blood to all parts of the body.

**clarified**   Made clear or free of impurities; cleared to remove any solid materials.

**cocoa butter**   The fat found in cocoa and chocolate.

**cold pack method**   A method of packing foods into jars for canning. It involves packing the raw food tightly into the jar and covering it with boiling water.

**collagen**   The tough, flexible protein material that forms connective tissue and holds muscle fibers together.

**commercial food preparation**   Planning and cooking for large numbers at one time.

**comparison shopping**   Comparing stores and items for sale as to value, including quality and cost per unit or cost per serving.

**complete proteins**   Foods that contain adequate amounts of all the essential amino acids; also called high-quality proteins.

**compromise service** A combination of English and formal meal service. The main dish is served at the table while other foods are served in individual portions from the kitchen.

**condiments** Seasonings used to enhance the flavor of foods. They include herbs and spices as well as combinations such as prepared mustard, catsup, and relish.

**conduction** A transmission of energy, such as heat, from particle to particle of a substance.

**consommé** Clarified broth made from meat-and-vegetable stock.

**contaminants** Substances that infect or make another substance impure; dangerous foreign substances in food.

**convenience foods** Food products that have been prepared or partially prepared to make home preparation easier or faster.

**cookware** The objects that hold food while it is being cooked on the cook-top.

**cover** Anything that conceals, protects, or closes; the place setting for a single person.

**credit** Belief or trust; a method of payment in which the buyer pays small amounts of the purchase price of an item over a period of time. For the benefit of having extra time to pay, interest or a finance charge is also paid.

**Creole cooking** A cuisine that developed in Louisiana from French, Indian, Spanish, and African influences. Gumbo is a famous Creole dish.

**croutons** Small toasted cubes of bread used as a garnish.

**crustaceans** Shellfish with segmented shells.

**cuisine** The style of cooking of a particular culture, area, or restaurant.

**culture** The way of life (including the ideas, customs, skills, and arts) of a group of people (generally of the same nationality).

**curd** The solid part of milk; the white clumps of milk protein that settle out during curdling. They are used to make cheese.

**curdling** Coagulating or congealing; having protein in milk settle out in white clumps, or curds, leaving a greenish-yellow liquid called whey.

**cured** Healed; preserved by treatment with a mixture of salt, sugar, spices, and chemicals and/or wood smoke.

**custard** A sweetened milk mixture thickened with egg.

**cut in** To distribute a solid ingredient into a dry ingredient or mixture by using a pastry blender or two knives.

**decaffeinated coffee** Coffee that has been chemically or naturally treated to remove 95 percent of the caffeine.

**deficiency** A shortage; an absence of something essential.

**dietetic technicians** Assistants to dieticians.

**dieticians** Health professionals who apply the principles of sound nutrition to food service or to special medical or financial circumstances.

**digestion** The process by which the body breaks down food into the nutrients it can use.

**dough** A mixture of flour and liquid that forms a soft, thick mass.

**dovetailing** Interlocking; fitting several tasks together so they are done at the same time.

**dry storage** Storage in any cool, dry, dark place such as kitchen cabinets.

**emulsion** A mixture of oil and another liquid in which the oil is spread evenly through the mixture.

**EnergyGuide labels** Labels found on appliances giving the estimated yearly cost of running the appliance and how that cost compares with other models.

**enrichment** Improvement in the wealth, value, importance, or effectiveness of something; the addition of nutrients to foods to replace, at least in part, those removed by refining or other manufacturing techniques.

**entrée** The main course of a meal.

**enzyme** A protein substance that causes chemical reactions.

**essential amino acids** The amino acids that the body cannot make and must therefore be supplied by diet.

**extracts** Concentrated forms of foods or flavorings; flavorful blends of alcohol and the oils pressed from aromatic plants.

**fad diets**   Weight-loss programs that are very popular for a short time.

**family service**   A form of meal service in which serving dishes are placed on the table and individual diners serve themselves.

**fat**   Any of the solid or semisolid oily or greasy substances composed of fatty acids and found in animal products and some plants. Fats are the most energy-rich nutrients, and help the body use fat-soluble vitamins.

**fermentation**   The breakdown of complex molecules by bacteria; the formation of carbon dioxide and alcohol from sugar, caused by a leavening agent such as yeast; the production of lactic acid from lactose as a result of bacterial action.

**finfish**   Fish with scales and fins.

**flatware**   Eating implements, including knives, forks, spoons, and serving utensils; sometimes called "silverware."

**flute**   To play on the flute; to create an ornamental groove in cloth; to scallop the edge of pastry by pinching and shaping it with the fingertips.

**foam**   A froth, or whitish mass of bubbles; a mixture formed when air is beaten into egg whites.

**foam cakes**   Sponge cakes; cakes made without shortening.

**food additives**   Substances added to foods to improve or protect their flavor, color, and texture or to retain their nutritional qualities.

**food-borne illness**   An illness caused by eating spoiled or contaminated food.

**food poisoning**   The discomfort or sickness caused by eating contaminated food.

**food-service industry**   All of the businesses that provide away-from-the-home dining, such as restaurants, hotels, caterers, hospital kitchens, prison kitchens, and the cafeterias in schools and in factories.

**food technologists**   Scientists who study the scientific properties of food and develop methods for its safe processing, preservation, packaging, storage, and transportation.

**formal service**   A form of meal service requiring someone to wait table and serve each course; it is sometimes called Continental or Russian service.

**fortified**   Strengthened; with nutrients added to foods that otherwise lack these substances; with vitamin D added, as in fortified milk.

**fricassee**   To braise poultry; to brown in fat and then cook, covered, in a small amount of water.

**fruits**   Seed plants used for food.

**full warranty**   A warranty that completely covers parts, labor, and shipping costs over a stated time period.

**garnishes**   Decorations. Garnishes on food also add flavor, texture, color, and interest to a dish.

**generic brands**   Plain-label, "no-name" brands. These wholesome products cost less than national or store brands. They do have the labelling information required by law.

**giblets**   The liver, heart, and gizzard of poultry.

**gluten**   A gray, sticky, nutritious protein substance formed when water is mixed with flour. Gluten gives strength and elasticity to dough or batter.

**goiter**   An enlargement of the thyroid gland caused by a lack of iodine.

**grains**   The edible seeds of certain grasses; cereal seeds.

**GRAS list**   Items on this Generally Recognized As Safe list can be used in food products without special permission of the FDA.

**grounded**   Set on or touching the ground; for an electrical conductor, connected with the ground which thus becomes part of the electrical circuit. Then, if there is a problem with the circuit, the electricity will flow safely to the ground and not to a person touching a wire or appliance.

**head space**   Space left at the top of a canning jar to allow for expansion.

**Heimlich Maneuver**   A quick, simple method to save someone who is choking on a small piece of food. It involves applying sudden, sharp pressure to the abdomen, just below the rib cage.

**hemoglobin**   The red pigment of the blood. It carries oxygen to body cells and carries away carbon dioxide.

**herbs**   The aromatic leaves or flowers of plants used for seasoning foods.

**holloware**  Serving dishes and table accessories, especially those with a concave or hollow shape.

**homogenization**  The process of breaking up the fat particles in milk so that they will remain evenly distributed throughout the milk and not rise to the top.

**hot pack method**  A method of packing food into jars for canning, suitable for all foods but especially for firm foods. It involves heating the food for a short time in boiling water, packing it loosely, and covering it with cooking liquid.

**hunger**  The physiological need to eat.

**hydrogenation**  The process of adding hydrogen to the chemical structure of a substance.

**iodine**  A mineral, found primarily in seafood, that prevents goiter.

**imitation food**  A product, such as imitation butter, that is not as nutritious as the one it is a substitute for.

**insomnia**  The inability to get enough sleep, especially over an abnormally prolonged period of time.

**kilocalorie**  The unit used to measure the energy value of food. Also known as kcalorie or Calorie, a kilocalorie equals 1,000 calories. One kilocalorie is the amount of heat needed to raise the temperature of one kilogram of water one degree Celsius.

**knead**  To mix and work into a pliable mass by folding over, pressing, and squeezing.

**lactose**  Milk sugar, or the carbohydrate found in milk.

**leavening agents**  Substances used to make baked goods rise.

**limited warranty**  A warranty that covers only certain parts or services. It may require the purchaser to pay certain fees, such as shipping or labor costs.

**liquid displacement method**  A method of measuring solid shortening based upon how much water it displaces, or moves out of the way, in a liquid measuring cup.

**malnutrition**  Poor nourishment resulting from insufficient food or improper diet.

**management**  The act, art, or manner of controlling or directing something; all of the decision making and planning of work activities to complete a task.

**marinade**  A liquid into which foods are placed to enhance flavor and, often, to tenderize.

**mayonnaise**  An uncooked dressing of vinegar, salad oil, seasonings, and egg yolk in emulsion.

**meal service**  The way in which foods are served at the table.

**menu**  The foods served at a meal or a list of the foods available at a restaurant.

**meringue**  Egg-white foam to which sugar has been added.

**metric system of measurement**  A system of measurement that uses the decimal system (multiples of ten) and is based on the meter, the gram, and the liter.

**microorganisms**  Living things that are too small to be seen with the naked eye. They include bacteria and viruses.

**microwaves**  A form of electromagnetic energy that can cook food by penetrating it and causing the molecules of the food to vibrate rapidly, thus creating heat.

**minerals**  Inorganic (neither vegetable nor animal) substances occurring naturally in the earth; essential nutrients that help regulate body processes and become part of bones, teeth, tissues, and blood.

**modified English service**  A form of meal service in which food is served at the table. One person serves the main dish, and then plates are passed. Side dishes may be served the same way or previously placed on the plate at each cover.

**molecule**  The smallest particle of a substance that retains the properties of the substance. Molecules are too small to be seen by the naked eye.

**mollusks**  Shellfish enclosed in nonsegmented shells.

**name brands**   Well-known brands that are widely advertised and usually available nationally. The name represents the manufacturer.

**New England boiled dinner**   A one-pot meal usually containing corned beef (or another meat), potatoes, onions, carrots, beets, and cabbage. It derives its name from the one-pot meals of early New England settlers, who used whatever foods were available and allowed the mixture to simmer on the hearth while they were busy with other tasks.

**nutrient density**   The amount of nutrients per calorie provided by a food. Nutrient-dense foods have a high proportion of nutrients for each kilocalorie.

**nutrients**   The chemical substances the body needs for health.

**nutritionists**   Specialists who deal with the broad principles of nutrition. They often do research, teach, or work as consultants in related fields such as food-processing or health care. Nutritionists are not usually directly involved in food preparation and delivery.

**nutrition label**   The particular format required by law when food products list their nutritional qualities. They must include: serving size; number of servings; calories per serving; amounts of protein, carbohydrate, and fat per serving; and percentage of U.S. RDA for protein, vitamin A, vitamin C, thiamin, riboflavin, niacin, calcium, and iron.

**obese**   Describing people who are at least 20 percent above normal weight for their height and frame.

**oil**   Fat that is liquid at room temperature

**omelet**   An egg dish prepared of beaten eggs cooked like a pancake and often folded over a filling.

**open dating**   Dates on food products that help consumers judge how fresh a product is and how long it may be safely and successfully used.

**overweight**   Describing people who are up to 10 percent above normal weight for their height and frame.

**pasteurization**   The process of heating milk to destroy harmful organisms.

**pastry**   Any of a large variety of baked crusts made from doughs rich in fat, including puff pastry, pie, and sweet rolls.

**pectin**   A carbohydrate found in all fruits, but in larger amounts in grapes, apples, and citrus fruits. Pectin is necessary to form a gel in making jam or jelly.

**Pennsylvania Dutch cooking**   The cuisine of the German farmers who settled in Pennsylvania (from *Deutsch,* the German word for "German"). It features hearty, substantial meals of many courses.

**peristalsis**   The wavelike muscular contractions of the digestive organs that move the food along. Peristalsis is an involuntary reflex.

**personal hygiene**   Individual cleanliness.

**phosphorus**   A mineral used by the body to help oxidize foods and, with calcium, to make bones and teeth.

**physiological**   Reflecting or promoting the normal, healthy functioning of the body.

**place setting**   All the pieces of tableware needed by one person at one meal; the number of pieces of dinnerware or flatware sold together as the single setting for a person.

**plate service**   A form of meal service in which plates are filled in the kitchen. They may then be placed on the table by one person or by individual diners.

**poached**   Cooked in water or another liquid near, but below, the boiling point.

**polyunsaturated fatty acids**   Fatty acids with the least amount of hydrogen in their chemical structure.

**potluck dinner**   A meal in which each guest contributes a cooked dish. It is said to have originated in the custom of offering "whatever was in the pot" to visitors in the Midwest.

**pretreatment**   Any process that is done before another process in order to make the second process more effective; rinsing or soaking dishes or pots and pans before washing.

**process cheeses**   Cheeses that are produced from a blend of cheeses.

**processing**   Treatment by a special method; the

intentional treatment given to food to prevent spoilage or deterioration.

**proofing** The process by which carbon dioxide is produced in a yeast dough and the dough rises to double its original size.

**protective foods** Foods that contribute vitamins, minerals, and cellulose and thus prevent deficiency diseases.

**proteins** The basic nutrients used by the body to build and repair cells, to make antibodies, and to form hormones. Proteins can also be burned by the body for energy.

**punchdown** To punch the fist into the center of fermented dough after it has doubled in size.

**puréed** Forced through a strainer to separate the pulp and juices.

**quick breads** Breads that are made with fast-acting leavening agents such as baking powder or baking soda.

**rancid** Having an undesirable aroma and/or flavor, as in fats and oils that have been exposed to air.

**RDA** Recommended Dietary Allowances, or recommendations for the amount of nutrients that should be eaten each day.

**recipe** A blueprint or pattern to follow in preparing food, including the ingredients to use and how to put them together.

**references** Indications of other sources to be consulted; people who can be contacted to provide information about a person's character, work habits, and accomplishments.

**restored** Brought back to a former or normal condition; enriched, or having vital nutrients replaced after their loss during the refining process.

**résumé** Summary; a brief history of education, job experience, and interests often used when applying for a job.

**riboflavin** Vitamin B$_2$.

**salad bar** A buffet offering of the ingredients of salads of all kinds, including vegetables, garnishes, and dressings. Some salad bars also offer soup, bread, cheese, and fruit and can provide an entire light meal.

**salmonella poisoning** A type of severe food poisoning caused by salmonella bacteria, which can contaminate food left at room temperature.

**sanitation** The science or practice of keeping healthful and hygenic conditions; keeping the kitchen, all equipment, food, and workers clean and as free as possible from bacteria.

**saturated fatty acids** Fatty acids that have in their chemical structure all of the hydrogen they can hold.

**scurvy** A disease of the joints, teeth, and blood vessels caused by a severe lack of vitamin C.

**seafood** Edible finfish and shellfish.

**sequential cooking** Cooking one food item after another.

**shelf life** The length of time a food product remains fresh.

**shellfish** Aquatic animals with hard shells.

**shirred** Baked in a greased baking cup, as eggs.

**simmering** Remaining at, or just below, the boiling point; cooking large pieces of meat in enough liquid to cover them.

**spices** Aromatic flavorings of plant origin. They are derived from the seeds, buds, fruit or flower parts, or the bark or roots of tropical plants.

**spoilage** An undesirable change in food caused by enzymes or by microorganisms.

**standards of identity** Standards set by the FDA for the ingredients of certain combination foods, such as mayonnaise or ice cream. Foods must meet these standards in order to be called by the "standard" names.

**standard system of measurement** The system of measurement that is customary in the United States. It includes inches, feet, and miles; gallons, quarts, and pints; and ounces and pounds.

**staple foods** The main or basic foods of the people of a particular region or culture; the foods and/or ingredients most frequently used in a household and kept in large amounts. Household staples include flour and sugar.

**steam-pressure method** A method of processing used for low-acid foods. It involves the use of a steam canner to reach temperatures above the boiling point.

**steep** To soak in liquid; to make coffee or tea using boiling water.

**stewing** Cooking small pieces of food in enough liquid to almost cover them.

**stimulant** A substance that increases body activities, such as heart rate and blood pressure.

**stock** The liquid in which meat, poultry, fish, or vegetables have been cooked. Stock is used to make many kinds of soup.

**storage** The putting aside of items for later use.

**store brands** Products carrying the name of the store or chain that sells them, rather than the name of the manufacturer.

**synthetic foods** Substitute foods; foods containing one or more ingredients made from nonconventional sources.

**table etiquette** Table manners or the rules of table courtesy.

**tableware** Flatware and holloware; the metal utensils, serving pieces, and decorative accessories for dining.

**tannins** Substances that, when dissolved, give coffee its bitter flavor.

**technology** The study or use of the practical or industrial arts, automation, and applied science.

**texture** The arrangement of the particles or parts of any material as it affects the appearance or feel of the surface; the way a food feels when chewed (smooth or crunchy, for example).

**thiamin** Vitamin $B_1$.

**time-work plan** A step-by-step guide to preparing a recipe, including all the necessary activities and how long they take.

**toxins** Poisonous substances that are produced by microorganisms.

**trace elements** Minerals needed by the body in very small amounts.

**trichinosis** A disease caused by a harmful parasite sometimes found in pork. Thorough cooking kills this parasite.

**truss** To tie in a bundle; to turn back the wing tips on the shoulders and tie the drumsticks on the tail of poultry, usually done before roasting.

**Underwriters Laboratories (UL) seal** A seal on electrical appliances indicating that the appliance meets safety standards.

**unit price** The cost for each standard unit of measurement, such as ounce (gram) or quart (liter), of a product rather than for the container size (small box or giant-size bottle).

**unsaturated fatty acids** Fatty acids that have some hydrogen missing from their chemical structure.

**UPC** The Universal Product Code, which is a grid of lines on a food product package. The grid can be read by an electronic scanner at the checkout, and a computer posts the price on the register tape and keeps track of inventory.

**vitamins** Complex chemicals that help regulate the chemical reactions necessary for the body's growth and health. They are needed in small amounts.

**warranty** A guarantee; a promise by the seller or manufacturer that a product will work properly for a certain length of time or the seller/manufacturer will repair or replace it.

**whey** The liquid part of milk that remains when the curd had been removed.

**work centers** Particular areas equipped for particular tasks. The kitchen has three work centers, one for each of the three major activities: the refrigerator center, the sink center, and the range center.

**work flow** The order in which tasks of a particular procedure are done.

**work triangle** An arrangement in which the three kitchen work centers form the points of an imaginary triangle.

**yield** The amount produced; the number of servings a particular recipe will make.

**yolk** The yellow portion of an egg.

# Index

*c* indicates a chart or table
*r* indicates a recipe

## A

Abbreviations, in cookery, 212
Absorption, 67, 69–70
Accidents, kitchen, 135–141
Accompaniment beverages, 491–492
Accompaniment salads, 441
Acetylcholine, 79
Acne, 82
Acrolein, 498
Additives, 10, 24–25
  coloring, 25, 192, 275
  federal regulation of, 192
  in fruit, 275
  vitamins, 25
Adolescence, 58, 80–82
Adrenalin, 71, 80
Advertisements, food store, 90, 186–187
Aerobic exercise, 75
Afghanistan, foods of, 317
Africa, foods of, 247, 317, 459
Agricultural technology, 15
À la carte, 107
Alaska, foods of, 586, 593–594
Albumen (egg), 341
Allergy to foods, 7, 86
  to MSG, 25
Allspice, 259
Aluminum cookware, 133, 165–166
American Culinary Federation, 606, 608
American Dietetic Association, 611

American foods, 317, 445, 585–595
  cultural differences in, 585–586
  foreign influence on, 481, 533, 564, 565, 573, 585
  geographical differences, 586
  by region, 586–595
American Gas Association (AGA) blue star, 161, 162
American Home Economics Association, 613
  American Indians' influence on, 586, 587, 588
American Indians, foods of, 481, 586, 587, 588
American Institute of Baking, 610
American Standard Association Institute, 205
Amino acids, 43, 70, 77, 295, 357
  essential, 357–358
Anemia, 45, 48, 92, 343, 358
Angel food cakes, 513, 521
Anorexia nervosa, 92, 93
Antibodies, 43
Antidotes, 138
Antioxidants, 25
Antipasto, 570
Antiseptic, 141
Appetite, 7–8
Appetizers
  salads as, 442
  soups as, 429, 430, 434
Apples, 279
Applesauce, *r*281
Appliances, 145

buying, 146, 148–149, 159–163, 179
cleaning, 136, 158
comparing, 161–163
electric, 158
energy efficient, 163, 179
for the handicapped, 123–124
location of, 150–151, 160
major, 118, 146–152, 160, 163
repair and care of, 146, 148, 158
researching 161–163
small, 118, 121, 153–158, 160
storage of, 118
time-saving, 177
warranties, 163
wiring and plumbing of, 121
*see also names of appliances*
Ascorbic acid, 25, 44, 273. *See also* Vitamin C
Aspics, 568
Athletes, food for, 84
ATP (adenosine triphosphate), 72
Au gratin potatoes, 425
Austria, foods of, 467

## B

Baba ghanouj, 445
Bacon, 359, 365, 499
Bacteria
  growth of, temperature and, 111, 128, 129, 545
  in yogurt, 317
Baked custard, *r*320

# Acknowledgments

## WORLD OF FOOD - CREDITS/PHOTOGRAPHY

**TITLE PAGE:** John Curtis Studio, Boston. Styled by Laurel Anderson/Photosynthesis.

**UNIT OPENING PHOTOGRAPHS:** Bob Schlowsky Studio, Boston. Inset photos for Units One & Six: Grant Heilman Photography. Unit Three inset: G. Peet/"The Acorn". Kitchen design by S. Lebovitz, Boston.

**CHAPTER ONE Opener:** John Curtis Studio. **Page 3L:** North Wind Picture Archive. **Pg. 3R:** H. Morgan/Rainbow. **Pg. 4T:** David Dempster/Curtis Studio. **Pg. 4C:** V. Weinland/PRI. **Pg. 4B:** A. Lax/PRI. **Pg. 5:** G. Palmer/The Stock Market. **Pg. 6T:** J. Goell/The Picture Cube. **Pg. 6B:** D. Dempster/Curtis Studio. **Pg. 7L, R:** R. Morsch/The Stock Market. **Pg. 8T;** G. Mancuso/Stock, Boston. **Pg. 8C:** A. Hagen/OPC. **Pg. 8B:** M. Manheim/Gartman Agency. **Pg. 9TL:** M. Manheim/The Stock Market. **Pg. 9BL:** D. McCoy/Rainbow. **Pg. 9TR:** M. Reichenthal/The Stock Market. **Pg. 9BR:** B. Cole/The Picture Cube. **Pg. 10:** R. Frerck/Odyssey Productions. **Pg. 11TL:** North Wind Picture Archive. **Pg. 11TR:** M. Ferri/The Stock Market. **Pg. 11B:** G. Gardner. **Pg. 12:** D. Dempster/Curtis Studio. **Pg. 13:** G. Gardner. **Pg. 14:** D. McCoy/Rainbow. **Pg. 15:** L. Enkelis/Stock, Boston. **Pg. 16L, R:** D. Dempster/Curtis Studio. **Pg. 17L:** P. Chapman. **Pg. 17R:** W. Campbell/Sygma.

**CHAPTER TWO Opener:** Barry Runk/Grant Heilman Photography. **Page 21-T:** Brown Bros. **Pg. 21-B:** G. Robinson/F-Stop Pictures. **Pg. 22:** E. Momativk/The Image Works. **Pg. 23,24:** D. Dempster/Curtis Studio. **Pg. 26T:** D. Dempster/Curtis Studio. **Pg. 26B:** E. Herwig/The Picture Cube. **Pg. 27:** D. Dempster/Curtis Studio. **Pg. 28,29T:** D. Dempster/Curtis Studio. **Pg. 29B:** Bettmann Archive. **Pg. 31-T:** J. Curtis/Studio. **Pg. 31B:** G. Gardner. **Pg. 33:** P. Chandoha.

**CHAPTER THREE Opener:** Karen Leeds/The Stock Market. **Page 39T:** The Bettmann Archive. **Pg. 39BL, R:** J. Curtis/Studio. **Pg. 40:** J. Running/Stock, Boston. **Pg. 41:** J. Curtis/Studio. **Pg. 42:** S. Rowin/The Picture Cube. **Pg. 43:** P. Chapman. **Pg. 44, 45:** J. Curtis/Studio. **Pg. 46:** E. Herwig/Stock, Boston. **Pg. 47:** A. Sirdofsky/Medichrome. **Pg. 48:** L. Enkells/Stock, Boston. **Pg. 49:** D. Dempster. **Pg. 52:** Camerique. **Pg. 54:** D. Dempster/Curtis Studio. **Pg. 55:** S. Lapides. **Pg. 56, 57:** J. Curtis/Studio. **Pg. 58L, R:** J. Curtis/Studio. **Pg. 59:** D. Dempster/Curtis Studio. **Pg. 60:** J. Curtis/Studio. **Pg. 62T:** R. Morsch/The Stock Mkt. **Pg. 62C:** Courtesy, The Rice Council. **Pg. 62B:** Courtesy, The American Lamb Council.

**CHAPTER FOUR Opener:** Robert Kaufman. **Page 67L:** Courtesy, The National Library of Medicine. **Pg. 68:** J. Clark/PRI. **Pg. 70:** B. Alper/Stock, Boston. **Pg. 71:** P. Kaplan/Stock Shop. **Pg. 72:** E. Degginger. **Pg. 73:** Mauritius/The Stock Shop. **Pg. 75T, B:** C. Wolinsky/Stock, Boston. **Pg. 76:** B. Gallery/Stock, Boston. **Pg. 77:** R. Nettis/PRI. **Pg. 81:** C. Hammell/The Stock Market. **Pg. 82:** A. Glauberman/PRI. **Pg. 83:** P. Chandoha. **Pg. 84:** G. Gardner. **Pg. 85:** F. Siteman/Stock, Boston. **Pg. 86:** P. Chandoha. **Pg. 89L:** B. Zaunders/The Stock Mkt. **Pg. 89R:** L. Lawfer. **Pg. 90:** P. Chandoha. **Pg. 91:** J. Curtis/Studio. **Pg. 92:** Vega.

**CHAPTER FIVE Opener:** John Curtis/Studio. **Page 97:** Popperfoto, London. **Pg. 98:** P. Chandoha. **Pg. 99:** D. Dempster/Studio. **Pg. 101:** P. Chandoha. **Pg. 102:** D. Fraizer/The Stock Mkt. **Pg. 103:** J. Curtis/Studio. **Pg. 104:** D. Dempster/Curtis Studio. **Pg. 105TL:** Keller & Peet. **Pg. 105C:** E. Sparks/The Stock Mkt. **Pg. 105B:** C. Collins/PRI. **Pg. 106:** L. Jones. **Pg. 107:** J. Feingersh/The Stock Mkt. **Pg. 108L:** S. Stokes/The Stock Mkt. **Pg. 108R:** K. Straiton/The Stock Mkt. **Pg. 110:** C. Wolinsky/Stock, Boston. **Pg. 111:** L. Jones.

**CHAPTER SIX Opener:** John Curtis/Studio. **Page 117:** The Bettmann Archive. **Pg. 118, 119:** D. Dempster. **Pg. 122T:** B. Rourke/The Stock Mkt. **Pg. 122B:** B. Olman/Bruce Coleman. **Pg. 123:** Courtesy, Merrillat Ind. **Pg. 125T, B:** S. Lapides. **Pg. 126T, B:** Science Source/PRI. **Pg. 127:** D. Dempster. **Pg. 129:** J. Curtis/Studio. **Pg. 130T, B:** Curtis/Studio. **Pg. 131T:** M. Grimes/PRI. **Pg. 131B:** D. Dempster/Studio. **Pg. 132:** G. Gardner **Pg. 135T, B:** D. Dempster/Studio. **Pg. 136, 137:** Curtis & Dempster/Studio. **Pg. 138:** R. Hutchings/The Picture Cube. **Pg. 139B:** T. Cordingley.

**CHAPTER SEVEN Opener:** John Curtis/Studio. **Page 145:** The Bettmann Archive. **Pg. 147:** T. Cordingley. **Pg. 148:** Curtis Studio. **Pg. 149L, R:** T. Cordingley. **Pg. 150:** P. Chapman. **Pg. 151:** T. Cordingley. **Pg. 152:** Courtesy, of Westinghouse. **Pg. 153:** D. Frazier/The Stock Mkt. **Pg. 154:** J. Curtis/Studio. **Pg. 155:** J. Curtis/Studio. **Pg. 156, 157:** D. Dempster/Curtis Studio. **Pg. 159:** P. Chandoha. **Pg. 160:** Curtis & Dempster/Studio. **Pg. 161:** P. Chapman. **Pg. 166, 167:** D. Dempster. **Pg. 168:** T. Cordingley.

**CHAPTER EIGHT Opener:** J. Myers/H. Armstrong Roberts. **Page 177:** The Bettmann Archive. **Pg. 178:** P. Chapman. **Pg. 179:** P. Chandoha **Pg. 180:** F. Bodin. **Pg. 182T:** Curtis Studio. **Pg. 184T:** B. O'Rourke/The Stock Mkt. **Pg. 184B:** M. Ferri/The Stock Mkt. **Pg. 185:** P. Chapman. **Pg. 186:** T. Cordingley. **Pg. 188:** Curtis Studio. **Pg. 189:** F. Bodin. **Pg. 191:** T. Cordingley. **Pg. 193:** Curtis Studio. **Pg. 195:** T. Cordingley.

**CHAPTER NINE Opener:** David Hundley/The Stock Mkt. **Page 199T:** Courtesy, Olde Sturbridge Village. **Pg. 199B:** D. Dempster/Curtis Studio. **Pg. 203:** F. Bodin. **Pg. 205:** J. Curtis/Studio. **Pg. 213:** D. Dempster. **Pg. 214:** P. Chapman. **Pg. 217:** D. Dempster.

**CHAPTER TEN Opener:** John Curtis/Studio. **Page 221:** North Wind Picture Archive. **Pg. 222-226:** P. Chapman. **Pg. 227, 228:** Curtis Studio. **Pg. 230, 231:** P. Chapman. **Pg. 232:** Curtis Studio. **Pg. 233:** P. Chapman.

**CHAPTER ELEVEN Opener:** John Curtis/Studio. **Page 239:** D. Dempster. **Pg. 241:** Keller & Peet. **Pg. 242, 243:** J. Curtis/Studio. **Pg. 245:** G. Gardner. **Pg. 247:** J. Lei/Stock, Boston.

**CHAPTER TWELVE Opener:** John Curtis/Studio. **Page 259:** North Wind Picture Archive. **Pg. 260:** D. Dempster/Studio. **Pg. 260R:** J. Anderson/The Stock Market. **Pg. 261:** D. Dempster. **Pg. 262:** Namuth/PRI. **Pg. 263:** Keller & Peet. **Pg. 264:** D. Dempster/Studio. **Pg. 265T:** S. Van Etten/The Picture Cube. **Pg. 265B:** R. Marcialis/P.R.I. **Pg. 266:** J. Curtis/Studio. **Pg. 267:** T. Cordingley. **Pg. 268:** J. Curtis/Studio. **Pg. 269L,C,R:** Marcialis/P.R.I. **Pg. 274:** J. Curtis/Studio.

**CHAPTER THIRTEEN Opener:** John Curtis/Studio. **Page 276:** Brown Bros. **Pg. 277:** D. Dempster/Studio. **Pg. 280:** D.

Dempster/Studio. **Pg. 281:** J. Curtis/Studio. **Pg. 282:** D. Dietz/ Stock, Boston. **Pg. 284,285:** J. Curtis/Studio.

**CHAPTER FOURTEEN Opener:** John Curtis/Studio. **Page 295T:** G. Holton/PRI. **Pg. 295B:** W. Ferguson. **Pg. 297:** J. Curtis/Studio. **Pg. 298:** Marcialis/PRI. **Pg. 299:** D. Dempster/ Studio. **Pg. 302:** J. Curtis/Studio. **Pg. 305:** D. Dempster/ Studio.

**CHAPTER FIFTEEN Opener:** John Curtis/Studio. **Page 311:** Brown Bros. **Pg. 312:** J. Curtis/Studio. **Pg. 313:** Courtesy, American Dairy Assoc. **Pg. 315,316:** D. Dempster/Studio. **Pg. 317:** J. Curtis/Studio. **Pg. 320-322:** J. Curtis/Studio.

**CHAPTER SIXTEEN Opener:** John Curtis/Studio. **Page 327:** Old Sturbridge Village. **Pg. 328:** J. Curtis/Studio. **Pg. 331:** J. Curtis/Studio. **Pg. 332:** R. Jaques/PRI. **Pg. 334, 335:** J. Curtis/Studio. **Pg. 336T:** Courtesy, American Egg Counci. **Pg. 336B:** Courtesy American Dairy Assoc.

**CHAPTER SEVENTEEN Opener:** John Curtis/Studio. **Page 341:** The Bettmann Archive. **Pg. 342:** H. Levart/PRI. **Pg. 345-350:** J. Curtis/Studio.

**CHAPTER EIGHTEEN Opener:** John Curtis/Studio. **Page 359:** The Bettmann Archive. **Pg. 364:** J. Curtis/Studio. **Pg. 366:** D. Dempster. **Pg. 370-371:** J. Curtis/Studio. **Pg. 373-379:** J. Curtis/Studio.

**CHAPTER NINETEEN Opener:** David Dempster/Studio. **Page 387:** North Wind Picture Archive. **Pg. 389-391:** D. Dempster/Studio. **Pg. 392, 393:** J. Curtis/Studio.

**CHAPTER TWENTY Opener:** David Dempster/Studio. **Page 399:** North Wind Picture Archive. **Pg. 400:** Keller & Peet. **Pg. 405:** P. Chandoha. **Pg. 406:** D. Hundli. **Pg. 407:** D. Dempster/ Studio. **Pg. 408:** Keller & Peet. **Pg. 409:** J. Curtis/Studio.

**CHAPTER TWENTY-ONE Opener:** Robert Kaufman. **Page 414, 415:** J. Curtis/Studio. **Pg. 419:** D. Dempster/Studio. **Pg. 420:** R. Dias/H. Armstrong Roberts. **Pg. 421:** J. Curtis/Studio. **Pg. 423:** J. Curtis/Studio. **Pg. 424:** J. Curtis/Studio.

**CHAPTER TWENTY-TWO Opener:** John Curtis/Studio. **Page 429:** North Wind Picture Archive. **Pg. 431:** D. Dempster/ Studio. **Pg. 432-433:** J. Curtis/Studio. **Pg. 434:** Keller & Peet. **Page 436:** T. Firak/Gartman Agency.

**CHAPTER TWENTY-THREE Opener:** R. Morsch/The Stock Market. **Page 441:** North Wind Historic Picture Archive & John Curtis/Studio. **Page 442TL:** T. Firak/Gartmen. **TR:** Keller & Peet. **BL:** T. Firak/Gartman Agency. **Pg. 443T:** Keller & Peet. **Pg. 443B:** Laszlo/The Stock Market. **Pg. 444-445:** J. Curtis/ Studio. **Pg. 446:** T. Firak/Gartman Agency. **Pg. 448:** J. Curtis/ Studio. **Pg. 449:** D. Dempster/Studio. **Pg. 450:** T. Firak/ Gartman Agency.

**CHAPTER TWENTY-FOUR Opener:** American Egg Board. **Page 455:** The Peabody Museum of Salem, Mass. **Pg. 456-460:** J. Curtis-D. Dempster/Studio.

**CHAPTER TWENTY-FIVE Opener:** John Curtis/Studio. **Page 467:** North Wind Picture Archive. **Pg. 468:** J. Curtis/Studio. **Pg. 470:** J. Curtis/Studio. **Pg. 471:** Amer. Inst. of Baking. **Pg. 475-476:** J. Curtis/Studio.

**CHAPTER TWENTY-SIX Opener:** Courtesy The Lipton Co. **Page 481:** North Wind Picture Archive. **Pg. 483:** R. Frerck/ Odyssey Productions. **Pg. 483C:** PRI. **Pg. 483B:** Wm. Ferguson. **Pg. 485:** D. Dempster/Studio. **Pg. 487:** J. Curtis/ Studio. **Pg. 491:** D. Dempster. **Pg. 492:** Courtesy The Lipton Co.

**CHAPTER TWENTY-SEVEN Opener:** John Curtis/Studio. **Page 497T:** North Wind Picture Archive. **Pg. 497B:** D. Dempster/Studio. **Pg. 500T:** D. Dempster/Studio. **Pg. 500B:** J. Curtis/Studio. **Pg. 501:** J. Curtis/Studio. **Pg. 504:** G. Gardner.

**CHAPTER TWENTY-EIGHT Opener:** David Dempster/Studio. **Page 509:** North Wind Picture Archive. **Pg. 510:** Curtis Studio. **Pg. 515:** D. Dempster/Studio. **Pg. 517:** J. Sullivan/PRI. **Pg. 518:** J. Curtis/Studio. **Pg. 519:** E. Herwig/Stock, Boston. **Pg. 520-521:** P. Chapman.

**CHAPTER TWENTY-NINE Opener:** John Curtis/Studio. **Page 525T:** P. Arnold/Old Sturbridge Village. **Pg. 530-531:** J. Curtis/Studio. **Pg. 533:** D. Dempster/Studio. **Pg. 538:** J. Curtis/Studio. **Pg. 539:** D. Dempster.

**CHAPTER THIRTY Opener:** John Curtis/Studio. **Page 541:** North Wind Picture Archive. **Pg. 546-547:** D. Dempster. **Pg. 548:** B. Runk/Grant Heilman Photography. **Pg. 551:** Courtesy the USDA. **Pg. 554:** Keller & Peet. **Pg. 556:** T. Eltroth/Rodale Press. **Pg. 557:** J. Curtis/Studio.

**CHAPTER THIRTY-ONE Opener:** John Curtis/Studio. **Page 565:** North Wind Picture Archive. **Pg. 567:** Keller & Peet. **Pg. 568:** S. Pashko/The Stock Market. **Pg. 569:** R. Frerck/Odyssey Productions. **Pg. 570:** Marcialis/PRI. **Pg. 571, 573:** Keller & Peet. **Pg. 574:** Marcialis/PRI. **Pg. 575:** Keller & Peet. **Pg. 576:** J. Curtis/Studio. **Pg. 577L, R:** Keller & Peet. **Pg. 578:** G. Smith/PRI. **Pg. 579, 580:** Marcialis/PRI. **Pg. 581:** Courtesy, Canadian Tourist Information Board.

**CHAPTER THIRTY-TWO Opener:** John Curtis/Studio. **Page 585-586:** North Wind Picture Archive. **Pg. 587:** E. Harris/PRI. **Pg. 588T, B:** Keller & Peet. **Pg. 589:** T. Firak/Gartman Agency. **Pg. 590:** B. O'Rourke/The Stock Market. **Pg. 590:** R. Duchaine/The Stock Market. **Pg. 591:** Permission of Laurie Winfrey/Carousel. **Pg. 593:** N. Wheeler/Black Star. **Pg. 594T:** Vautier de Nanxe/Click Chicago.

**CHAPTER THIRTY-THREE Opener:** John Curtis/Studio. **Page 601:** Permission of Laurie Winfrey/Carousel. **Pg. 602:** R. Hutchings/PRI. **Pg. 604:** J. Curtis/Studio. **Pg. 605:** R. Jaques/ PRI. **Pg. 606:** D. Madison/Bruce Coleman. **Pg. 607:** D. Madison/Bruce Coleman. **Pg. 608:** T. Cordingley. **Pg. 610:** D. Hyde/PRI. **Pg. 611:** K. Williamson. **Pg. 613:** J. Apoian/ Nawrocki/Stock.

Picture Research and Styling by Laurel Anderson/PHOTO-SYNTHESIS.

Prentice Hall would like to extend its thanks to those corporations providing transparencies and to the Lechmere Corp. for their cooperation in providing props.

## CREDITS/ILLUSTRATION

**Susan Avishai:** pages 54, 69, 87, 98, 119, 120, 121, 158, 164-165, 170-171, 172, 190, 238, 244, 292, 241, 353, 368, 482, 488, 502, 528, 548, 550.

**Susan Banta:** pages 67, 206, 209, 369, 387, 461, 462, 474, 490, 512, 513, 516, 518, 526, 527, 532, 534, 535, 536, 537, 555.

**Anne Bissette:** pages 228, 300, 301, 328, 364, 373, 374, 375, 377, 378, 414, 415, 530, 538.

**Boston Graphics:** map page 566, logos; Human Resources, Food Science, Communications.

**Michael Burggren:** pages 129, 192, 274.

**Nancy Edwards** pages 201, 266, 281, 299, 320, 334, 346, 379, 392, 407, 424, 432, 444, 458, 476, 485, 500, 515, 531, 558.

**Graphics Etcetera:** charts pages 109, 140, 311.

**Lane Gregory:** pages 139, 248, 249, 250, 252, 253, 489.

**William Ogden:** logos; Decision Making, Reading, Critical Thinking, Social Studies, Human Relations, Recource Management, Math.

**Sheaff Design:** Special Feature logos.

**Terry Presnal:** etching page 441.